Merchant Marine Deck
Examination Reference Material ·

REPRINTS FROM THE

LIGHT LISTS
AND
COAST PILOTS

THIS PUBLICATION CONTAINS INFORMATION TO BE USED IN
EXAMINATIONS FOR MERCHANT MARINE LICENSES AND DOCUMENTS

NOT TO BE USED FOR NAVIGATION

COMDTPUB P16721.38

U.S. Department
of Transportation
**United States
Coast Guard**

Commandant   (G-MVP)
United States Coast Guard

Mailing Address:
2100 SECOND STREET SW
WASHINGTON DC 20593-0001
(202) 267-2705

COMDTPUB   P16721.38

COMMANDANT PUBLICATION P16721.38

5 Aug 1993

Subj: MERCHANT MARINE DECK EXAMINATION REFERENCE MATERIAL,
        <u>REPRINTS FROM THE LIGHT LISTS AND COAST PILOTS</u>.

1. <u>PURPOSE</u>. This publication contains reference material for use
    during an examination for a merchant marine deck license. It
    contains excerpts from Light Lists, Volumes 1 and 2, and Coast
    Pilots 2 and 3. This manual is current with the training
    charts used in the examinations.

2. <u>DISCUSSION</u>. Applicants for merchant marine deck licenses are
    tested to ensure their professional qualification. Some
    practical navigation questions are based on material in this
    publication, and applicants must refer to this publication to
    develop the correct answer.

3. <u>PROCEDURE</u>. This publication is available to applicants taking
    a deck merchant marine examination. The covers available for
    sale from the the Government Printing Office (GPO) are printed
    with red ink. The covers used in the Regional Examination
    Centers are printed with green ink. Applicants who purchase
    copies of this publication from the GPO may not use their
    personal copies during examinations.

4. <u>ORDERING INFORMATION</u>.

    a. Regional Examination Centers will be provided with an
        intial supply of this publication. Replacement and
        additional copies are available through standard
        distribution sources.

DISTRIBUTION - SDL No. 131

	a	b	c	d	e	f	g	h	i	j	k	!	m	n	o	p	q	r	s	t	u	v	w	x	y	z
A																										
B		1	1		1		1	1						1				1								
C					*								*													
D																										
E																										
F																										
G																										
H																										

NON-STANDARD DISTRIBUTION (See page 2.)

b. The public and other Coast Guard units may order copies
of this publication from the GPO at the following
address:

> Superintendent of Documents
> U.S. Government Printing Office
> Washington, D.C. 20402

This book may also be ordered by telephone and charged to
a national credit card by calling (202) 783-3238.

R. C. NORTH
Captain, U.S. Coast Guard
Acting Chief, Office of Marine Safety,
Security and Environmental Protection

NON-STANDARD DISTRIBUTION:

C:e Toledo (350); Boston, Miami (225); New Orleans (150);
Baltimore, San Francisco, Honolulu (125), Charleston, San
Juan, Long Beach, Anchorage, Houston (75); Portland OR,
Memphis, St. Louis, Puget Sound (50); Juneau, Norfolk, Guam,
Ketchikan (25) (only)

C:m New York (250) (only).

For sale by the U.S. Government Printing Office
Superintendent of Documents, Mail Stop: SSOP, Washington, DC 20402-9328
ISBN 0-16-041958-1

INSTRUCTIONS

1. This reference contains extracts of the LIGHT LISTS and COAST PILOTS. Some practical navigation questions in the deck examination booklets require plotting on Training Charts to determine the answer. Navigational information necessary to aid in plotting these problems is contained in this manual.

2. Applicants may also refer to this manual when testing with any module except Rules of the Road. For example, if the question in a Navigation General module is, "You lose sight of Orient Point Light, on the eastern end of Long Island, at a distance of 9.0 miles. What is the approximate meteorological visibility?", then you must use the "Luminous Range Diagram" on page xxxiv of the LIGHT LIST found in PART 1, SECTION A.

3. This manual is in 2 parts to correspond with the Training Charts. Each part has a section A (Light List) and a section B (Coast Pilot). Each section has its own index and three sections are printed on colored paper. The other section is printed on white paper.
Part 1, Section A - Blue pages
Part 1, Section B - White pages
Part 2, Section A - Yellow pages
Part 2, Section B - Green pages

4. Applicants who wish to comment on any material in this publication should complete a Comment/Protest form for the question involved and give it to the examiner.

5. Individuals not taking an examination who wish to make a comment about this publication should send a written comment, citing this publication and the appropriate page and paragraph to:

Commandant (G-MVP-5)
U.S. Coast Guard
REPRINTS from LIGHT LISTS & COAST PILOTS
2100 Second Street SW
Washington, D.C. 20593-0001

All comments are welcomed and will be acknowledged. Valid comments will be incorporated into this publication.

MERCHANT MARINE DECK EXAMINATION
REFERENCE MATERIAL

Reprints from

LIGHT LISTS and COAST PILOTS

TABLE OF CONTENTS

PART 1. BLOCK ISLAND and EASTERN LONG ISLAND SOUNDS

PART 2. CHESAPEAKE BAY ENTRANCE and approaches

NOTE: For general information, regulations, and appendix refer to appropriate section in PART 1. This general information has been deleted from PART 2.

PART 1 - SECTION A

LIGHT LIST

Volume I - Atlantic Coast

covering

BLOCK ISLAND SOUND and EASTERN LONG ISLAND SOUND

including

general information on pages i to xxxiv

contents found on page iv

DEPARTMENT OF TRANSPORTATION, U.S. COAST GUARD

LIGHT LIST

Volume I

ATLANTIC COAST

St. Croix River, Maine to
Toms River, New Jersey

IMPORTANT

THIS PUBLICATION SHOULD BE CORRECTED
EACH WEEK FROM THE LOCAL NOTICES TO MARINERS
OR NOTICE TO MARINERS AS APPROPRIATE.

COMDTPUB P16502.1

U.S. GOVERNMENT PRINTING OFFICE
WASHINGTON, DC:

For sale by Superintendent of Documents, U.S. Government Printing Office, Washington, DC 20402
Stock number: 050-012-00314-9

PREFACE

Lights and other marine aids to navigation, maintained by or under authority of the United States Coast Guard, on the Atlantic coast of the United States from St. Croix River, ME to Toms River, NJ are listed in this volume.

Included are all Coast Guard aids to navigation used for general navigation. Not included are Coast Guard mooring buoys and some buoys having no lateral significance such as special purpose, anchorage, fish net, and dredging.

PRIVATE AIDS TO NAVIGATION

Included–Class I: Aids to navigation on marine structures or other works which the owners are legally obligated to establish, maintain, and operate as prescribed by the Coast Guard.

Included–Class II: Aids to navigation exclusive of Class I, located in waters used by general navigation.

Not included–Class III: Aids to navigation exclusive of Class I and Class II, located in waters not ordinarily used by general navigation.

This list, published annually, is intended to furnish more complete information concerning aids to navigation then can be conveniently shown on charts. It is not intended to be used during navigation in place of charts or Coast Pilots and should not be so used. The charts should be consulted for the location of all aids to navigation. It may be dangerous to use aids to navigation without reference to charts.

This list is corrected to the date of the Notices to Mariners shown on the title page. Changes made to aids to navigation during the year are published in the Local Notice to Mariners and the Notice to Mariners. Important changes to aids to navigation are also broadcast by the U.S. Coast Guard through Coast Guard or Naval radio stations. Mariners should keep their Light List, as well as charts and other nautical publications, corrected from these notices and should consult all notices issued after the date of publication of the Light List.

IMPORTANT: A summary of corrections for this publication, which includes corrections from the dates shown on the title page to the date of availability, is published in the Local Notices to Mariners and the Notice to Mariners. These corrections must be applied, in order to bring the Light List up-to-date. Additionally, this publication should be corrected weekly from the Local Notice to Mariners or the Notice to Mariners as appropriate.

Mariners and others are requested to bring to the attention of the District Commander (see p. iii) or Commandant (G-NSR-3/14), U.S. Coast Guard, 2100 Second St., S.W., Washington, DC 20593-0001, any apparent errors or omissions in these lists.

RECORD OF CORRECTIONS PUBLISHED IN LOCAL/WEEKLY NOTICES TO MARINERS

YEAR 19___

1............	14...........	27............	40...........
2............	15...........	28............	41...........
3............	16...........	29............	42...........
4............	17...........	30............	43...........
5............	18...........	31............	44...........
6............	19...........	32............	45...........
7............	20...........	33............	46...........
8............	21...........	34............	47...........
9............	22...........	35............	48...........
10............	23...........	36............	49...........
11............	24...........	37............	50...........
12............	25...........	38............	51...........
13............	26...........	39............	52...........

YEAR 19___

1............	14...........	27............	40...........
2............	15...........	28............	41...........
3............	16...........	29............	42...........
4............	17...........	30............	43...........
5............	18...........	31............	44...........
6............	19...........	32............	45...........
7............	20...........	33............	46...........
8............	21...........	34............	47...........
9............	22...........	35............	48...........
10............	23...........	36............	49...........
11............	24...........	37............	50...........
12............	25...........	38............	51...........
13............	26...........	39............	52...........

North American Datum of 1983: Through the use of satellites and other modern surveying techniques, it is now possible to establish global reference systems which provide more accurate geographic positions. Currently, several datums such as the North American Datum of 1927, U.S. Standard Datum, Old Hawaiian Datum, Puerto Rican Datum, Local Astronomic Datum, and others are in use. The National Oceanic and Atmospheric Administration (NOAA) has identified the North American Datum of 1983 (NAD 83) to replace the various datums in use on charts.

NOTE: The geographic positions listed in the Light List are referenced to the horizontal datum of the current edition of the chart identified in the heading preceding an entry. Corrections to the geographic positions listed will appear in the Local Notices to Mariners and the Notice to Mariners as new charts referencing NAD 83 are issued.

COAST GUARD DISTRICTS AND ADDRESSES OF DISTRICT COMMANDERS

DISTRICT	ADDRESS	WATERS OF JURISDICTION
FIRST	408 Atlantic Avenue Boston, MA 02110–3350 PHONE: DAY 617–223–8338 PHONE: NIGHT 617–223–8558	Maine, New Hampshire, Massachusetts, Vermont (Lake Champlain), Rhode Island, Connecticut, New York, to Toms River, New Jersey.
SECOND	1222 Spruce Street St. Louis, MO 63103–2835 PHONE: DAY 314–539–3714 PHONE: NIGHT 314–539–3709	Mississippi River System, except that portion of the Mississippi River south of Baton Rouge, Louisiana and the Illinois River north of Joliet, Illinois and the Tennessee–Tombigbee Waterway below Mile 411.9.
FIFTH	Federal Building 431 Crawford Street Portsmouth, VA 23704–5004 PHONE: DAY 804–398–6486 PHONE: NIGHT 804–398–6231	Toms River, New Jersey to Delaware, Maryland, Virginia, District of Columbia and North Carolina.
SEVENTH	Brickell Plaza Building 909 SE 1st Avenue Miami, FL 33131–3050 PHONE: DAY 305–536–5621 PHONE: NIGHT 305–536–5611	South Carolina, Georgia, Florida to 83°50'W, and Puerto Rico and adjacent islands of the United States.
	Commander Greater Antilles Section U.S. Coast Guard P.O. Box S–2029 San Juan, PR 00903–2029 PHONE: 809–729–6870	Immediate jurisdiction of waters of Puerto Rico and adjacent islands of the United States.
EIGHTH	Hale Boggs Federal Building 501 Magazine Street New Orleans, LA 70130–3396 PHONE: DAY 504–589–6234 PHONE: NIGHT 504–589–6225	Florida from 83°50'W, thence westward, Alabama, Mississippi, Louisiana and Texas.
NINTH	1240 East 9th Street Cleveland, OH 44199–2060 PHONE: DAY 216–522–3991 PHONE: NIGHT 216–522–3984	Great Lakes and St. Lawrence River above St. Regis River.
ELEVENTH	Union Bank Building 400 Oceangate Blvd. Long Beach, CA 90822–5399 PHONE: DAY 310–499–5410 PHONE: NIGHT 310–499–5380	California.
THIRTEENTH	Federal Building 915 Second Avenue Seattle, WA 98174–1067 PHONE: DAY 206–553–5864 PHONE: NIGHT 206–553–5886	Oregon, Washington, Idaho, and Montana.
FOURTEENTH	Prince Kalanianaole Federal Bldg. 9th Floor, Room 9139 300 Ala Moana Blvd. Honolulu, HI 96850–4982 PHONE: DAY 808–541–2320 PHONE: NIGHT 808–541–2500	Hawaii, American Samoa, Marshall, Marianas, and Caroline Islands, and Subic Bay, Philippines.
SEVENTEENTH	P.O. Box 25517 Juneau, AK 99802–5517 PHONE: DAY 907–463–2245 PHONE: NIGHT 907–463–2000	Alaska.

CONTENTS

INTRODUCTION

Arrangement. Aids to navigation on the Atlantic coast from St. Croix River, ME to Toms River, NJ are listed in this volume.

Aids to navigation are arranged in geographic order from north to south along the Atlantic coast. Seacoast aids to navigation are listed first, followed by entrance and harbor aids to navigation listed from seaward to the head of navigation.

Names of aids to navigation are printed as follows to help distinguish at a glance the type of aid to navigation listed:

**Seacoast Lights, Secondary Lights, and Large
  Navigational Buoys**
Radiobeacons
Fog Signals
RIVER, HARBOR, AND OTHER LIGHTS
Lighted Buoys
Daybeacons and Unlighted Buoys

Light List numbers are assigned to all aids to navigation in order to facilitate reference in the Light List and to resolve ambiguity when referencing aids to navigation. Aids to navigation are numbered by fives in accordance with their order of appreance in each volume of the Light List. Other numbers and decimal fractions are assigned where newly established aids to navigation are listed between previously numbered aids to navigation. The Light Lists are renumbered periodically to assign whole numbers to all aids to navigation.

International numbers are assigned to certain aids to navigation in cooperation with the International Hydrographic Organization. They consist of an alphabetic character followed by three or four numeric characters. A cross reference listing appears after the index.

Description of Columns

Column (1)	Light List number.
Column (2)	Name of the aid to navigation. A dash (–) is used to indicate the bold heading is part of the name of the aid. When reporting defects or making reference to such aids to navigation in correspondence, the full name of the aid to navigation, including the geographic heading, should be given. Bearings are in degrees true, read clock wise from 000° through 359°. Bearings on rangelines are given in degrees and minutes.
Column (3)	Geographic position in latitude and longitude. *NOTE:* Latitude and longitude is approximate, to the nearest tenth of a minute, and is intended only to facilitate locating the aid to navigation on the chart.
Column (4)	Light characteristic for lighted aids to navigation. Morse characteristic for radiobeacons.
Column (5)	Height above water from the focal plane of the fixed light to mean high water, listed in feet. For metric conversion, see table inside rear cover.

Column (6)	The nominal range of lighted aids to navigation is listed in nautical miles, except for Lake Champlain which is listed in statute miles. Nominal range is further listed by color for alternating lights. The nominal range is not listed for ranges, directional lights or private aids to navigation. Effective range for radiobeacons is listed in nautical miles.
Column (7)	Structural characteristic of the aid to navigation, including; daymark (if any), description of fixed structure, color and type of buoy, height of structure above ground.
Column (8)	General remarks, including; fog signal characteristic, RACON characteristic, light sector's arc of visibility, radar reflector if installed on fixed structure, emergency lights, seasonal remarks, and private aid to navigation identification.

Abbreviations used in the Light Lists.

Al	– Alternating	lt	– Light
bl	– blast	LNB	– Large Navigational Buoy
C	– Canadian	MHz	– Megahertz
ec	– Eclipse	Mo	– Morse Code
ev	– Every	Oc	– Occulting
F	– Fixed	ODAS	– Anchored Oceangraphic Data Buoy
fl	– flash		
Fl	– Flashing	Q	– Quick (Flashing)
FS	– Fog Signal	Ra ref	– Radar reflector
Fl(2)	– Group flashing	R	– Red
G	– Green	RBN	– Radiobeacon
I	– Interrupted	s	– seconds
Iso	– Isophase (Equal interval)	si	– Silent
		SPM	– Single Point Mooring Buoy
kHz	– Kilohertz	W	– White
LFl	– Long Flash	Y	– Yellow

RELATED PUBLICATIONS

Other Light Lists published by the Coast Guard

VOLUME II, ATLANTIC COAST, describes aids to navigation from Toms River, New Jersey to Little River, South Carolina.

VOLUME III, ATLANTIC AND GULF COASTS, describes aids to navigation from Little River, South Carolina to Econfina River, Florida.

VOLUME IV, GULF OF MEXICO, describes aids to navigation from Econfina River, Florida to the Rio Grande, Texas

VOLUME V, MISSISSIPPI RIVER SYSTEM, describes aids to navigation on the Mississippi River and its navigable tributaries.

VOLUME VI, PACIFIC COAST AND PACIFIC ISLANDS, describes aids to navigation on the Pacific coast and outlying Pacific islands.

VOLUME VII, GREAT LAKES, describes aids to navigation on the Great Lakes and the St. Lawrence River above the St. Regis River.

Coast Guard Light Lists are sold by the Superintendent of Documents, U.S. Government Printing Office (GPO), Washington, DC 20402, by GPO Bookstores, and by GPO Sales Agents.

Charts, Coast Pilots, Tide Tables, and Tidal Current Tables covering the United States and its territories are published by the National Ocean Service (NOS), Rockville, MD 20852, and are for sale by NOS and authorized NOS Sales Agents.

Maps for the Mississippi River System are published by the various District Engineers, U.S. Army Corps of Engineers.

Sailing Directions covering the waters outside of the U.S. and its territories are published by the Defense Mapping Agency Hydrographic/Topographic Center.

Radio Navigational Aids (RAPUB 117) is published by the Defense Mapping Agency Hydrographic/Topographic Center. This publication lists selected radio stations (worldwide) that provide services to mariners. Included are stations transmitting radio navigation warnings, radio time signals, medical advice; chapters on distress, emergency and safety traffic; AMVER, and miscellaneous navigational instructions and procedures. Also included are descriptions of long range aids to navigation such as Loran and Omega. Discussions and instructions for use of radio navigational aids are also provided.

Sailing Directions and Radio Navigational Aids can be purchased from Defense Mapping Agency (DMA) Combat Support Center, Washington, DC 20315-0010, or authorized DMA Sales Agents.

NOTICES TO MARINERS

Broadcast Notices to Mariners are made by the Coast Guard through Coast Guard and Navy radio stations. These broadcast notices, which are broadcast on VHF-FM, NAVTEX, and other frequencies, are navigational warnings containing information of importance to the safety of navigation. Included are reports of deficiencies and changes to aids to navigation, the positions of ice and derelicts, and other important hydrographic information.

Radio stations broadcasting Notices to Mariners are listed in the National Ocean Service Coast Pilots and in the Defense Mapping Agency publication Radio Navigational Aids (RAPUB 117).

Local Notices to Mariners (U.S. regional coverage) are another means by which the Coast Guard disseminates navigation information for the United States, its territories, and possessions. A Local Notice to Mariners is issued by each Coast Guard district. It reports changes to, and deficiencies in, aids to navigation maintained by and under the authority of the Coast Guard. It contains other marine information such as channel depths, naval operations, regattas, etc., which may affect vessels and waterways within the jurisdiction of each Coast Guard district. Reports of channel conditions, obstructions, menaces to navigation, danger areas, new chart editions, etc., are also included in the Local Notice to Mariners.

These notices are essential to all navigators for the purposes of keeping their charts, Lights Lists, Coast Pilots and other nautical publications up-to-date. These notices are published as often as required, but usually weekly. They may be obtained, free of charge, by making application to the appropriate Coast Guard district commander (see pg. iii). Vessels operating in ports and waterways in several districts will have to obtain the Local Notice to Mariners from each district in order to be fully informed.

Weekly Notices to Mariners (worldwide coverage) are prepared jointly by the Defense Mapping Agency Hydrographic/Topographic Center, the U.S. Coast Guard, and the National Ocean Service, and are published weekly by Defense Mapping Hydrographic/Topographic Center. The Weekly Notice to Mariners advises mariners of important matters affecting navigational safety including new hydrographic discoveries, changes in channels and aids to navigation. Also included are corrections to Light Lists, Coast Pilots, and Sailing Directions. Foreign marine information is also included. This notice is intended for mariners and others who have a need for information related to ocean-going operations. Because it is intended for use by ocean-going vessels, many corrections that affect small craft navigation and waters are not included. Information concerning small craft is contained in the Coast Guard Local Notices to Mariners only. The Weekly Notice to Mariners may be obtained, free of charge, upon request to: Director, Defense Mapping Agency, Combat Support Center, Code PMSA, Washington, DC 20315-0010.

Change of Address. Persons receiving the Local Notice to Mariners or the Weekly Notice to Mariners are requested to notify the appropriate agency of a change of address, or when the Notice to Mariners is no longer needed. Both the old and new address should be given in the case of an address change.

Notices to Mariners may be consulted at Coast Guard District Offices, National Ocean Service Field Offices, Defense Mapping Agency Hydrographic/Topographic Center offices and depots, local marine facilities, and chart sales agents.

REPORTING DEFECTS IN AIDS TO NAVIGATION

Mariners should realize the Coast Guard cannot keep the thousands of aids to navigation comprising the U.S. Aids to Navigation System under simultaneous and continuous observation and that it is impossible to maintain every aid to navigation operating properly and on its assigned position at all times. Therefore, for the safety of all mariners, any person who discovers an aid to navigation that is either off station or exhibiting characteristics other than those listed in the Light Lists should promptly notify the nearest Coast Guard unit. Radio messages should be prefixed "COAST GUARD" and transmitted directly to one of the U.S. Government radio stations listed in Chapter 4, Section 400B, Radio Navigational Aids (RAPUB 117).

Recommendations and requests pertaining to aids to navigation and to report aids to navigation that are no longer needed should be mailed to the Coast Guard district concerned (see pg. iii).

U.S. AIDS TO NAVIGATION SYSTEM

The waters of the United States and its territories are marked to assist navigation by the U.S. Aids to Navigation System. This system encompasses buoys and beacons, conforming to the

International Association of Lighthouse Authorities (IALA) buoyage guidelines, and other short range aids to navigation.

The U.S. Aids to Navigation System is intended for use with nautical charts. The exact meaning of a particular aid to navigation may not be clear to the mariner unless the appropriate nautical chart is consulted. Additional, important information supplementing that shown on charts is contained in the Light List, Coast Pilots, and Sailing Directions.

TYPES OF MARKS

Lateral marks are buoys or beacons that indicate the port and starboard sides of a route to be followed, and are used in conjunction with a "conventional direction of buoyage".

Generally, lateral aids to navigation indicate on which side of the aid to navigation a vessel should pass, when navigable channels are entered from seaward and a vessel proceeds in the conventional direction of buoyage. Since all channels do not lead from seaward, certain assumptions must be made so the system can be consistently applied. In the absence of a route leading from seaward, the conventional direction of buoyage generally follows a clockwise direction around land masses.

Virtually all U.S. lateral marks are located in IALA Region B and follow the traditional 3R rule of "red, right, returning". In U.S. waters, returning from seaward and proceeding toward the head of navigation is generally considered as moving southerly along the Atlantic coast, westerly along the Gulf coast and northerly along the Pacific coast. In the Great Lakes, the conventional direction of buoyage is generally considered westerly and northerly, except on Lake Michigan, where southerly movement is considered as returning from sea.

A summary of the port and starboard hand lateral mark characteristics is contained in the following table.

Characteristic	Port Hand Marks	Starboard Hand Marks
Color	Green	Red
Shape (buoys)	Cylindrical (can) or pillar	Conical (nun) or pillar
Dayboard or Topmark (when fitted)	Green square or cylinder	Red triangle or cone, point upward
Light Color (when fitted)	Green	Red
Reflector Color	Green	Red
Numbers	Odd	Even

Preferred channel marks are aids to navigation which mark channel **junctions** or **bifurcations** and often mark wrecks or obstructions. Preferred channel marks may normally be passed on either side by a vessel, but indicate to the mariner the preferred channel. Preferred channel marks are colored with red and green bands.

At a point where a channel divides, when proceeding in the "conventional direction of buoyage", a preferred channel in IALA Region B may be indicated by a modified port or starboard lateral mark as follows:

Characteristic	Preferred channel to starboard	Preferred channel to port
Color	Green with one broad red band	Red with one broad green band
Shape (buoys)	Cylindrical (can) or pillar	Conical (nun) or pillar
Dayboard	Green square, lower half red	Red triangle, lower half green
Topmark (when fitted)	Green square or cylinder	Red triangular cone, point upward
Light (when fitted)		
Color	Green	Red
Rhythm	Composite group flashing (2+1)	Composite group flashing (2+1)
Reflector color	Green	Red

NOTE: U.S. lateral aids to navigation at certain Pacific islands are located within Region A and thus exhibit opposite color significance. Port hand marks are red with square or cylindrical shapes while starboard hand marks are green with triangular or conical shapes.

CAUTION: It may not always be possible to pass on either side of preferred channel aids to navigation. The appropriate nautical chart should always be consulted.

Non-lateral marks have no lateral significance but may be used to supplement the lateral aids to navigation specified above. Occasionally, daybeacons or minor lights outside of the normal channel will not have lateral significance since they do not define limits to navigable waters. These aids to navigation will utilize diamond-shaped dayboards and are divided into four diamond-shaped sectors. The side sectors of these dayboards are colored white, and the top and bottom sectors are colored black, red, or green as the situation dictates.

Safe water marks are used to mark fairways, mid-channels, and offshore approach points, and have unobstructed water on all sides. They can also be used by the mariner transiting offshore waters to identify the proximity of intended landfall. Safe water marks are red and white striped and have a red spherical topmark to further aid in identification. If lighted, they display a white light with the characteristic Morse code "A".

Isolated danger marks are erected on, or moored above or near, an isolated danger, which has navigable water all around it. These marks should not be approached closely without special caution. These marks were introduced in 1991.

Isolated danger marks are colored with black and red bands, and if lighted, display a group flashing (2) white light. A topmark consisting of two black spheres, one above the other, is fitted for both lighted and unlighted marks.

Special marks are not intended to assist in navigation, but rather to alert the mariner to a special feature or area. The feature should be described in a nautical document such as a chart, Light List, Coast Pilot or Notice to Mariner. Some areas which may be marked by these aids to navigation are spoil areas, pipelines, traffic separation schemes, jetties, or military exercise areas. Special marks are yellow in color and, if lighted, display a yellow light.

Information and regulatory marks are used to alert the mariner to various warnings or regulatory matters. These marks have orange geometric shapes against a white background. The meanings associated with the orange shapes are as follows:

1) An open-faced diamond signifies danger.

2) A diamond shape having a cross centered within indicates that vessels are excluded from the marked area.

3) A circular shape indicates that certain operating restrictions are in effect within the marked area.

4) A square or rectangular shape will contain directions or instructions lettered within the shape.

BUOYS AND BEACONS

The IALA maritime buoyage guidelines apply to buoys and beacons that indicate the lateral limits of navigable channels, obstructions and other dangers such as wrecks, and other areas or features of importance to the mariner. This system provides five types of marks: lateral marks, safe water marks, special marks, isolated danger marks and cardinal marks. (Cardinal marks are not presently used in the United States.) Each type of mark is differentiated from other types by distinctive colors, shapes and light rhythms. Examples are provided on the enclosed color illustrations.

Buoys are floating aids to navigation used extensively throughout U.S. waters. They are moored to the seabed by concrete sinkers with chain or synthetic rope moorings of various lengths connected to the buoy body.

Buoy positions represented on nautical charts are approximate positions only, due to the practical limitations of positioning and maintaining buoys and their sinkers in precise geographical locations. Buoy positions are normally verified during periodic maintenance visits. Between visits, atmospheric and sea conditions, seabed slope and composition, and collisions or other accidents may cause buoys to shift from their charted locations, or cause buoys to be sunk or capsized.

Buoy moorings vary in length. The mooring lengths define a "watch circle", and buoys can be expected to move within this circle. Actual watch circles do not coincide with the symbols representing them on charts.

CAUTION: Mariners attempting to pass a buoy close aboard risk collision with a yawing buoy or with the obstruction which the buoy marks. Mariners must not rely on buoys alone for determining their positions due to factors limiting buoy reliability. Prudent mariners will use bearings or angles from fixed aids to navigation and shore objects, soundings and various methods of electronic navigation to positively fix their position.

Beacons are aids to navigation which are permanently fixed to the earth's surface. These structures range from lighthouses to small unlighted daybeacons, and exhibit a daymark to make these aids to navigation readily visible and easily identifiable against background conditions. The daymark conveys to the mariner, during daylight hours, the same significance as does the aid to navigation's light at night.

CAUTION: Vessels should not pass fixed aids to navigation close aboard due to the danger of collision with rip-rap or structure foundations, or with the obstruction or danger being marked.

LIGHTED AIDS TO NAVIGATION

Most lighted aids to navigation are equipped with controls which automatically cause the light to operate during darkness and to be extinguished during daylight. These devices are not of equal sensitivity, therefore all lights do not come on or go off at the same time. (Mariners should ensure correct identification of aids to navigation during twilight periods when some lighted aids to navigation are lit while others are not.)

The lighting apparatus is serviced at periodic intervals to assure reliable operation, but there is always the possibility of a light being extinguished or operating improperly.

The condition of the atmosphere has a considerable effect upon the distance at which lights can be seen. Sometimes lights are obscured by fog, haze, dust, smoke, or precipitation which may be present at the light, or between the light and the observer, and which is possibly unknown by the observer. Atmospheric refraction may cause a light to be seen farther than under ordinary circumstances. A light of low intensity will be easily obscured by unfavorable conditions of the atmosphere and little dependence can be placed on it being seen. For this reason, the intensity of a light should always be considered when expecting to sight it in thick weather. Haze and distance may reduce the apparent duration of the flash of a light. In some conditions of the atmosphere, white lights may have a reddish hue.

Lights placed at high elevations are more frequently obscured by clouds, mist, and fog than those lights located at or near sea level.

In regions where ice conditions prevail in the winter, the lantern panes of unattended lights may become covered with ice or snow, which will greatly reduce the visibility of the lights and may also cause colored lights to appear white.

The increasing use of brilliant shore lights for advertising, illuminating bridges, and other purposes, may cause marine navigational lights, particularly those in densely inhabited areas, to be outshone and difficult to distinguish from the background lighting. Mariners are requested to report such cases in order that steps may be taken to improve the conditions.

The "loom" (glow) of a powerful light is often seen beyond the limit of visibility of the actual rays of the light. The loom may sometimes appear sufficiently sharp enough to obtain a bearing.

At short distances, some flashing lights may show a faint continuous light between flashes.

The distance of an observer from a light cannot be estimated by its apparent intensity. Always check the characteristics of lights so powerful lights, visible in the distance, are not mistaken for nearby lights (such as those on lighted buoys) showing similar characteristics of low intensity.

If lights are not sighted within a reasonable time after prediction, a dangerous situation may exist requiring prompt resolution or action in order to ensure the safety of the vessel.

The apparent characteristic of a complex light may change with the distance of the observer. For example, a light which actually displays a characteristic of fixed white varied by flashes of alternating white and red (the rhythms having a decreasing range of visibility in the order: flashing white, flashing red, fixed white) may, when first sighted in clear weather, show as a simple flashing white light. As the vessel draws nearer, the red flash will become visible and the characteristics will apparently be alternating flashing white and red. Later, the fixed white light will be seen between the flashes and the true characteristic of the light will finally be recognized – fixed white, alternating flashing white and red (F W Al WR).

If a vessel has considerable vertical motion due to pitching in heavy seas, a light sighted on the horizon may alternately appear and disappear. This may lead the unwary to assign a false characteristic and hence, to err in its identification. The true characteristic will be evident after the distance has been sufficiently decreased or by increasing the height of eye of the observer.

Similarly, the effects of wave motion on lighted buoys may produce the appearance of incorrect light phase characteristics when certain flashes occur, but are not viewed by the mariner. In addition, buoy motion can reduce the distance at which buoy lights are detected.

Sectors of colored glass are placed in the lanterns of some lights in order to produce a system of light sectors of different colors. In general, red sectors are used to mark shoals or to warn the mariner of other obstructions to navigation or of nearby land. Such lights provide approximate bearing information since observers may note the change of color as they cross the boundary between sectors. These boundaries are indicated in the Light List (Col. 8) and by dotted lines on charts. These bearings, as all bearings referring to lights, are given in true

degrees from 000° to 359°, as observed from a vessel toward the light. Altering course on the changing sectors of a light or using the boundaries between light sectors to determine the bearing for any purpose is not recommended. Be guided instead by the correct compass bearing to the light and do not rely on being able to accurately observe the point at which the color changes. This is difficult to determine because the edges of a colored sector cannot be cut off sharply. On either side of the line of demarcation between white, red, or green sectors, there is always a small arc of uncertain color. Moreover, when haze or smoke are present in the intervening atmosphere, a white sector might have a reddish hue.

The area in which a light can be observed is normally an arc with the light as the center and the range of visibility as the radius. However, on some bearings the range may be reduced by obstructions. In such cases, the obstructed arc might differ with height of eye and distance. When a light is cut off by adjoining land and the arc of visibility is given, the bearing on which the light disappears may vary with the distance of the vessel from which observed and with the height of eye. When the light is cut off by a sloping hill or point of land, the light may be seen over a wider arc by a vessel farther away than by one closer to the light.

The arc drawn on charts around a light is not intended to give information as to the distance at which it can be seen, but solely to indicate, in the case of lights which do not show equally in all directions, the bearings between which the variation of visibility or obstruction of the light occurs.

OIL WELL STRUCTURES

Oil well structures in navigable waters are not listed in the Light List. The structures are shown on the appropriate nautical charts. Information concerning the location and characteristics of those structures which display lights and sound signals not located in obstruction areas are published in Local and/or Weekly Notices to Mariners.

In general, during the nighttime, a series of white lights are displayed extending from the platform to the top of the derrick when drilling operations are in progress. At other times, structures are usually marked with one or more fixed or quick flashing white or red lights, visible for at least one nautical mile during clear weather. Obstructions which are a part of the appurtenances to the main structure, such as mooring piles, anchor and mooring buoys, etc., normally are not lighted. In addition, some of the structures are equipped with sound signals (bell, siren, whistle, or horn). When operating, bells sound one stroke every 15 seconds, while sirens, whistles, or horns sound a single two–second blast every 20 seconds.

CHARACTERISTICS OF AIDS TO NAVIGATION

LIGHT COLORS

Only aids to navigation with green or red lights have lateral significance. When proceeding in the conventional direction of buoyage, the mariner in Region B, may see the following lighted aids to navigation:

Green lights on aids to navigation mark port sides of channels and locations of wrecks or obstructions which must be passed by keeping these lighted aids to navigation on the port hand of a vessel. Green lights are also used on preferred channel marks where the preferred channel is to starboard (i.e., aid to navigation left to port when proceeding in the conventional direction of buoyage).

Red lights on aids to navigation mark starboard sides of channels and locations of wrecks or obstructions which must be passed by keeping these lighted aids to navigation on the starboard hand of a vessel. Red lights are also used on preferred channel marks where the preferred channel is to port (i.e., aid to navigation left to starboard when proceeding in the conventional direction of buoyage).

White and yellow lights have no lateral significance. The purpose of aids to navigation exhibiting white or yellow lights may be determined by the shapes, colors, letters, and light rhythms.

Most aids to navigation are fitted with retroreflective material to increase their visibility in darkness. Red or green retroreflective material is used on lateral aids to navigation which, if lighted, will display lights of the same color.

LIGHT RHYTHMS

Light rhythms have no lateral significance. Aids to navigation with lateral significance exhibit flashing, quick, occulting or isophase light rhythms. Ordinarily, flashing lights (frequency not exceeding 30 flashes per minute) will be used.

Preferred channel marks exhibit a composite group–flashing light rhythm of two flashes followed by a single flash. Through 1989, some preferred channel marks may display the former interrupted quick flashing rhythm.

Safe water marks show a white Morse code "A" rhythm (a short flash followed by a long flash).

Isolated danger marks show a white flashing (2) rhythm (two flashes repeated regularly).

Special marks show yellow lights and exhibit a flashing or fixed rhythm; however, a flashing rhythm is preferred.

Information and regulatory marks, when lighted, display a white light with any light rhythm except quick flashing, flashing (2) and Morse code "A".

For situations where lights require a distinct cautionary significance, as at sharp turns, sudden channel constrictions, wrecks or obstructions, a quick flashing light rhythm will be used.

CHARACTERISTICS OF LIGHTS

1. FIXED.
A light showing continuously and steadily.

F

2. OCCULTING.
A light in which the total duration of light in a period is longer than the total duration of darkness and the intervals of darkness (eclipses) are usually of equal duration.

2.1 Single-occulting.
An occulting light in which an eclipse is regularly repeated.

Oc

2.2 Group-occulting.
An occulting light in which a group of eclipses, specified in numbers, is regularly repeated.

Oc(2)

2.3 Composite group-occulting.
A light, similar to a group-occulting light, except that successive groups in a period have different numbers of eclipses.

Oc(2+1)

3. ISOPHASE.
A light in which all durations of light and darkness are equal.

Iso

4. FLASHING.
A light in which the total duration of light in a period is shorter than the total duration of darkness and the appearances of light (flashes) are usually of equal duration.

4.1 Single-flashing.
A flashing light in which a flash is regularly repeated (frequency not exceeding 30 flashes per minute).

Fl

CHARACTERISTICS OF LIGHTS (cont.)

Illustration	_Type Description_	_Abbreviation_

4.2 Group-flashing.
A flashing light in which a group of flashes, specified in number, is regularly repeated.

Fl (2)

4.3 Composite group-flashing.
A light similar to a group flashing light except that successive groups in the period have different numbers of flashes.

Fl (2+1)

5. QUICK.
A light in which flashes are produced at a rate of 60 flashes per minute.

5.1 Continuous quick.
A quick light in which a flash is regularly repeated.

Q

5.2 Interrupted quick.
A quick light in which the sequence of flashes is interrupted by regularly repeated eclipses of constant and long duration.

IQ

6. MORSE CODE.
A light in which appearances of light of two clearly different durations (dots and dashes) are grouped to represent a character or characters in the Morse code.

Mo (A)

7. FIXED AND FLASHING.
A light in which a fixed light is combined with a flashing light of higher luminous intensity.

FFI

8. ALTERNATING.
A light showing different colors alternately.

Al RW

SHAPES

In order to provide easy identification, certain unlighted buoys and dayboards on beacons are differentiated by shape. These shapes are laterally significant only when associated with laterally significant colors.

Cylindrical buoys (referred to as "can buoys") and square dayboards mark the left side of a channel when proceeding from seaward. These aids to navigation are associated with solid green or green and red banded marks where the topmost band is green.

Conical buoys (referred to as "nun buoys") and triangular dayboards mark the right side of the channel when proceeding from seaward. These aids to navigation are associated with solid red or red and green banded marks where the topmost band is red.

Unless fitted with topmarks; lighted, sound, pillar, and spar buoys have no shape significance. Their meanings are conveyed by their numbers, colors, and light characteristics.

NUMBERS

All solid red and solid green aids to navigation are numbered, with red aids to navigation bearing even numbers and green aids to navigation bearing odd numbers. The numbers for each increase from seaward, proceeding in the conventional direction of buoyage. Numbers are kept in approximate sequence on both sides of the channel by omitting numbers where necessary.

Letters may be used to augment numbers when lateral aids to navigation are added to channels with previously completed numerical sequences. Letters will increase in alphabetical order from seaward, proceeding in the conventional direction of buoyage and are added to numbers as suffixes.

No other aids to navigation are numbered. Preferred channel, safe water, isolated danger, special marks, and information and regulatory aids to navigation may be lettered, but not numbered.

DAYBOARDS

In order to describe the appearance and purpose of each dayboard used in the U.S. System, standard designations have been formulated. A brief explanation of the designations and of the purpose of each type of dayboard in the system is given below, followed by a word description of the appearance of each dayboard type.

Designations:

1. First Letter – Shape or Purpose

    S   Square used to mark the port (left) side of channels when proceeding from seaward.

    T   Triangle used to mark the starboard (right) side of channels when proceeding from seaward.

    J   Junction (square or triangle) used to mark (preferred channel) junctions or bifurcations in the channel, or wrecks or obstructions which may be passed on either side; color of top band has lateral significance for the preferred channel.

    M   Safe water (octagonal) used to mark the fairway or middle of the channel.

    C   Crossing (western rivers only) diamond-shaped, used to indicate the points at which the channel crosses the river.

    K   Range (rectangular) when both the front and rear range dayboards are aligned on the same bearing, the observer is on the azimuth of the range, usually used to mark the center of the channel.

    N   No lateral significance (diamond or rectangular-shaped) used for special purpose, warning, distance, or location markers.

2. Second letter – Key color

    G – Green   R – Red

    B – Black   W – White

    Y – Yellow

3. Third letter (color of center stripe; range dayboards only)

4. Additional information after a (–)

    –I   Intracoastal Waterway; a yellow reflective horizontal strip on a dayboard; indicates the aid to navigation marks the Intracoastal Waterway.

    –SY   Intracoastal Waterway; a yellow reflective square on a dayboard; indicates the aid to navigation is a port hand mark for vessels traversing the Intracoastal Waterway. May appear on a triangular daymark where the Intracoastal Waterway coincides with a waterway having opposite conventional direction of buoyage.

    –TY   Intracoastal Waterway; a yellow reflective triangle on a dayboard; indicates the aid to navigation is a starboard hand mark for vessels traversing the Intracoastal Waterway. May appear on a square daymark where the Intracoastal Waterway coincides with a waterway having opposite conventional direction of buoyage.

Example: The designation KRW–I indicates a range dayboard (K); key color red (R); with a white stripe (W); in the Intracoastal Waterway (–I).

Descriptions:

SG   Square green dayboard with a green reflective border.

SG–I   Square green dayboard with a green reflective border and a yellow reflective horizontal strip.

SG–SY   Square green dayboard with a green reflective border and a yellow reflective square.

SG–TY   Square green dayboard with a green reflective border and a yellow reflective triangle.

SR   Square red dayboard with a red reflective border. (IALA Region "A")

TG   Triangular green dayboard with a green reflective

border. (IALA Region "A")

TR — Triangular red dayboard with a red reflective border.

TR-I — Triangular red dayboard with a red reflective border and a yellow reflective horizontal strip.

TR-SY — Triangular red dayboard with a red reflective border and a yellow reflective square.

TR-TY — Triangular red dayboard with a red reflective border and a yellow reflective triangle.

JG — Dayboard bearing horizontal bands of green and red, green band topmost, with a green reflective border.

JG-I — Square dayboard bearing horizontal bands of green and red, green band topmost, with a green reflective border and a yellow reflective horizontal strip.

JG-SY — Square dayboard bearing horizontal bands of green and red, green band topmost, with a green reflective border and a yellow reflective square.

JG-TY — Square dayboard bearing horizontal bands of green and red, green band topmost, with a green reflective border and a yellow reflective triangle.

JR — Dayboard bearing horizontal bands of red and green, red band topmost, with a red reflective border.

JR-I — Triangular dayboard bearing horizontal bands of red and green, red band topmost, with a red reflective border and a yellow horizontal strip.

JR-SY — Triangular dayboard bearing horizontal bands of red and green, red band topmost, with a red reflective border and a yellow reflective square.

JR-TY — Triangular dayboard bearing horizontal bands of red and green, red band topmost, with a red reflective border and a yellow reflective triangle.

MR — Octagonal dayboard bearing stripes of white and red, with a white reflective border.

MR-I — Octagonal dayboard bearing stripes of white and red, with a white reflective border and a yellow reflective horizontal strip.

CG — Diamond-shaped green dayboard bearing small green diamond shaped reflectors at each corner.

CR — Diamond-shaped red dayboard bearing small red diamond shaped reflectors at each corner.

KBG — Rectangular black dayboard bearing a central green stripe.

KBG-I — Rectangular black dayboard bearing a central green stripe and a yellow reflective horizontal strip.

KBR — Rectangular black dayboard bearing a central red stripe.

KBR-I — Rectangular black dayboard bearing a central red stripe and a yellow reflective horizontal strip.

KBW — Rectangular black dayboard bearing a central white stripe.

KBW-I — Rectangular black dayboard bearing a central white stripe and a yellow reflective horizontal strip.

KGB — Rectangular green dayboard bearing a central black stripe.

KGB-I — Rectangular green dayboard bearing a central black stripe and a yellow reflective horizontal strip.

KGR — Rectangular green dayboard bearing a central red stripe.

KGR-I — Rectangular green dayboard bearing a central red stripe and a yellow reflective horizontal strip.

KGW — Rectangular green dayboard bearing a central white stripe.

KGW-I — Rectangular green dayboard bearing a central white stripe and a yellow reflective horizontal strip.

KRB — Rectangular red dayboard bearing a central black stripe.

KRB-I — Rectangular red dayboard bearing a central black stripe and a yellow reflective horizontal strip.

KRG — Rectangular red dayboard bearing a central green stripe.

KRG-I — Rectangular red dayboard bearing a central green stripe and a yellow reflective horizontal strip.

KRW — Rectangular red dayboard bearing a central white stripe.

KRW-I — Rectangular red dayboard bearing a central white stripe and a yellow reflective horizontal strip.

KWB — Rectangular white dayboard bearing a central black stripe.

KWB-I — Rectangular white dayboard bearing a central black stripe and a yellow reflective horizontal strip.

KWG — Rectangular white dayboard bearing a central green stripe.

KWG-I — Rectangular white dayboard bearing a central green stripe and a yellow reflective horizontal strip.

KWR — Rectangular white dayboard bearing a central red stripe.

KWR-I — Rectangular white dayboard bearing a central red stripe and a yellow reflective horizontal strip.

NB — Diamond-shaped dayboard divided into four diamond-shaped colored sectors with the sectors at the side corners white and the sectors at the top and bottom corners black, with a white reflective border.

NG	Diamond-shaped dayboard divided into four diamond-shaped colored sectors with the sectors at the side corners white and the sectors at the top and bottom corners green, with a white reflective border.
NR	Diamond-shaped dayboard divided into four diamond-shaped colored sectors with the sectors at the side corners white and the sectors at the top and bottom corners red, with a white reflective border.
NW	Diamond-shaped white dayboard with an orange reflective border and black letters describing the information or regulatory nature of the mark.
ND	Rectangular white mileage marker with black numerals indicating the mile number (western rivers only).
NL	Rectangular white location marker with an orange reflective border and black letters indicating the location.
NY	Diamond-shaped yellow dayboard with a yellow reflective border.

These abbreviated descriptions are used in column (7) and may also be found on the illustration of U.S. Aids to Navigation System.

OTHER SHORT RANGE AIDS TO NAVIGATION

Lighthouses are placed on shore or on marine sites and most often do not show lateral markings. They assist the mariner in determining his position or safe course, or warn of obstructions or dangers to navigation. Lighthouses with no lateral significance usually exhibit a white light.

Occasionally, lighthouses use sectored lights to mark shoals or warn mariners of other dangers. Lights so equipped show one color from most directions and a different color or colors over definite arcs of the horizon as indicated on the appropriate nautical chart. These sectors provide approximate bearing information and the observer should note a change of color as the boundary between the sectors is crossed. Since sector bearings are not precise, they should be considered as a warning only, and used in conjunction with a nautical chart.

Large navigational buoys (LNBs) were developed to replace lightships and are placed at points where it is impractical to build lighthouses. The unmanned LNBs are 40 feet in diameter with light towers approximately 40 feet above the water. LNBs are equipped with lights, sound signals, radiobeacons, and racons. The traditional red color of LNBs has no lateral significance, but is intended to improve visibility.

Seasonal aids to navigation are placed into service or changed at specified times of the year. The dates shown in the Light List (Col. 8) are approximate and may vary due to adverse weather or other conditions.

Ranges are non-lateral aids to navigation systems employing dual beacons which when the structures appear to be in line, assist the mariner in maintaining a safe course. The appropriate nautical chart must be consulted when using ranges to determine whether the range marks the centerline of the navigable channel and also what section of the range may be safely traversed. Ranges display rectangular dayboards of various colors and are generally, but not always lighted. When lighted, ranges may display lights of any color.

Sound signal is a generic term used to describe aids to navigation that produce an audible signal designed to assist the mariner in fog or other periods of reduced visibility. These aids to navigation can be activated by several means (i.e., manually, remotely, or fog detector). In cases where a fog detector is in use, there may be a delay in the automatic activation of the signal. Additionally, fog detectors may not be capable of detecting patchy fog conditions. Sound signals are distinguished by their tone and phase characteristics.

Tones are determined by the devices producing the sound, e.g., diaphones, diaphragm horns, sirens, whistles, bells, and gongs.

Phase characteristics are defined by the signal's sound pattern, i.e., the number of blasts and silent periods per minute and their durations. Sound signals sounded from fixed structures generally produce a specific number of blasts and silent periods each minute when operating. Buoy sound signals are generally activated by the motion of the sea and therefore do not emit a regular signal characteristic. It is common, in fact, for a buoy to produce no sound signal when seas are calm. Mariners are reminded that buoy positions are not always reliable.

The characteristic of a sound signal can be located in column (8) of the Light List. Unless it is specifically stated that a sound signal "Operates continuously", or the signal is a bell, gong, or whistle on a buoy, it can be assumed that the sound signal only operates during times of fog, reduced visibility, or adverse weather.

An emergency sound signal is sounded at some locations when the main and stand-by signals are inoperative. If the emergency signal is of a different type or characteristic than the main signal, its characteristic is listed in column (8) of this publication.

CAUTION: Mariners should not rely on sound signals to determine their position. Distance cannot be accurately determined by sound intensity. Occasionally, sound signals may not be heard in areas close to their location. Signals may not sound in cases where fog exists close to, but not at, the location of the sound signal.

VARIATIONS TO THE U.S. SYSTEM

Intracoastal Waterway aids to navigation: The Intracoastal Waterway runs parallel to the Atlantic and Gulf coasts from Manasquan Inlet, New Jersey to the Mexican border. Aids to navigation marking these waters have some portion of them marked with yellow. Otherwise, the coloring and numbering of the aids to navigation follow the same system as that in other U.S. waterways.

In order that vessels may readily follow the Intracoastal Waterway route, special markings are employed. These marks consist of a yellow square and yellow triangle and indicate which side the aid to navigation should be passed when following the conventional direction of buoyage. The yellow square indicates that the aid to navigation should be kept on the left side and the yellow triangle indicates that the aid to navigation should be kept on the right side.

NOTE: The conventional direction of buoyage in the Intracoastal Waterway is generally southerly along the Atlantic coast and generally westerly along the Gulf coast.

The **Western Rivers System**, a variation of the standard U.S. Aids to Navigation System described in the preceding sections, is employed on the Mississippi River and its tributaries above Baton Rouge, LA and on certain other rivers which flow toward the Gulf of Mexico.

The Western Rivers System varies from the standard U.S. system as follows:

1) Aids to navigation are not numbered.

2) Numbers on aids to navigation do not have lateral significance but, rather, indicate mileage from a fixed point (normally the river mouth).

3) Diamond shaped crossing dayboards, red or green as appropriate, are used to indicate where the river channel crosses from one bank to the other.

4) Lights on green aids to navigation show a single-flash characteristic which may be green or white.

5) Lights on red aids to navigation show a group-flash characteristic which may be red or white.

6) Isolated danger marks are not used.

Uniform State Waterway Marking System (USWMS): This system was developed in 1966 to provide an easily understood system for operators of small boats. While designed for use on lakes and other inland waterways that are not portrayed on nautical charts, the USWMS was authorized for use on other waters as well. It supplements the existing federal marking system and is generally compatible with it.

The conventional direction of buoyage is considered upstream or towards the head of navigation.

The USWMS varies from the standard U.S. system as follows:

1) The color black is used instead of green.

2) There are three aids to navigation which reflect cardinal significance:

    a. A white buoy with red top represents an obstruction and the buoy should be passed to the south or west.

    b. A white buoy with black top represents an obstruction and the buoy should be passed to the north or east.

    c. A red and white vertically striped buoy indicates that an obstruction exists between that buoy and the nearest shore.

3) Mooring buoys are white buoys with a horizontal blue band midway between the waterline and the top of the buoy. This buoy may be lighted and will generally show a slow flashing white light.

BRIDGE MARKINGS

Bridges across navigable waters are generally marked with red, green and/or white lights for nighttime navigation. Red lights mark piers and other parts of the bridge. Red lights are also used on drawbridges to show when they are in the closed position.

Green lights are used on drawbridges to show when they are in the open position. The location of these lights will vary according to the bridge structure. Green lights are also used to mark the centerline of navigable channels through fixed bridges. If there are two or more channels through the bridge, the preferred channel is also marked by three white lights in a vertical line above the green light.

Red and green retro-reflective panels may be used to mark bridge piers and may also be used on bridges not required to display lights.

Main channels through bridges may be marked by lateral red and green lights and dayboards. Adjacent piers should be marked with fixed yellow lights when the main channel is marked with lateral aids to navigation.

Centerlines of channels through fixed bridges may be marked with a safe water mark and an occulting white light when lateral marks are used to mark main channels. The centerline of the navigable channel through the draw span of floating bridges may be marked with a special mark. The mark will be a yellow diamond with yellow retro-reflective panels and may exhibit a yellow light that displays a Morse code "B"(−...).

Clearance gauges may be installed to enhance navigation safety. The gauges are located on the right channel pier or pier protective structure facing approaching vessels. They indicate the vertical clearance available under the span.

Drawbridges equipped with radiotelephones display a blue and white sign which indicates what VHF radiotelephone channels should be used to request bridge openings.

U.S. AIDS TO NAVIGATION SYSTEM
on the Western River System

AS SEEN ENTERING FROM SEAWARD

PORT SIDE
OR RIGHT DESCENDING BANK
GREEN OR ☐ WHITE LIGHTS (CROSSING)
FLASHING
ISO

LIGHTED BUOY

CAN

SG

JG

CG

PASSING DAYMARK

CROSSING DAYMARK

176.9
MILE BOARD

PREFERRED CHANNEL

PREFERRED CHANNEL TO STARBOARD
TOPMOST BAND GREEN
Fl (2+1) G

PREFERRED CHANNEL TO PORT
TOPMOST BAND RED
Fl (2+1) R

JR

bifercation either side

MARK JUNCTIONS AND OBSTRUCTIONS
COMPOSITE GROUP FLASHING (2+1)

RANGE DAYMARKS—MAY BE LETTERED

INFORMATION AND REGULATORY MARKERS
WHEN LIGHTED, INFORMATION AND REGULATORY MARKS MAY DISPLAY ANY LIGHT RHYTHM EXCEPT QUICK FLASHING AND FLASHING (2).

EXCLUSION AREA

RESTRICTED OPERATIONS

DANGER

DAYMARKS HAVING NO LATERAL SIGNIFICANCE

MAY BE LETTERED

NR

NG ☐ WHITE LIGHT ONLY

NB

☐ YELLOW LIGHT ONLY
FIXED   FLASHING

NY

A

UNLIGHTED

C

B LIGHTED

A

NW ☐ WHITE LIGHT ONLY

DANGER

STARBOARD SIDE
OR LEFT DESCENDING BANK
RED OR ☐ WHITE LIGHTS (CROSSING)
FLASHING (2)
ISO

LIGHT

NUN

LIGHTED BUOY   TR

CR

CROSSING DAYMARK

PASSING DAYMARK

123.5
MILE BOARD

UNIFORM STATE WATERWAY MARKING SYSTEM

STATE WATERS AND DESIGNATED STATE WATERS FOR PRIVATE AIDS TO NAVIGATION

REGULATORY MARKERS

BOAT EXCLUSION AREA

SWIM AREA

ROCK   DANGER

CONTROLLED AREA

SLOW   NO WAKE

THE NATURE OF DANGER MAY BE INDICATED INSIDE THE DIAMOND SHAPE, SUCH AS ROCK, WRECK, SHOAL, DAM, ETC.

TYPE OF CONTROL IS INDICATED IN THE CIRCLE, SUCH AS SLOW, NO WAKE, ANCHORING, ETC.

EXPLANATION MAY BE PLACED OUTSIDE THE CROSSED DIAMOND SHAPE, SUCH AS DAM, RAPIDS, SWIM AREA, ETC.

BUOY USED TO DISPLAY REGULATORY MARKERS
MAY SHOW WHITE LIGHT
MAY BE LETTERED

MULLET LAKE
↑
BLACK RIVER

INFORMATION
FOR DISPLAYING INFORMATION SUCH AS DIRECTIONS, DISTANCES, LOCATIONS, ETC.

AIDS TO NAVIGATION

MAY SHOW GREEN REFLECTOR OR LIGHT

3
PORT SIDE

MAY SHOW RED REFLECTOR OR LIGHT

4
— LOOKING UPSTREAM —   STARBOARD SIDE

SOLID RED AND SOLID BLACK BUOYS
USUALLY FOUND IN PAIRS
PASS BETWEEN THESE BUOYS

LATERAL SYSTEM

MAY SHOW WHITE REFLECTOR OR LIGHT

RED-STRIPED WHITE BUOY
MAY BE LETTERED
DO NOT PASS BETWEEN BUOY AND NEAREST SHORE

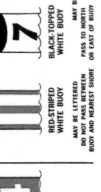
BLACK-TOPPED WHITE BUOY
MAY BE NUMBERED
PASS TO NORTH OR EAST OF BUOY

RED-TOPPED WHITE BUOY
PASS TO SOUTH OR WEST OF BUOY

CARDINAL SYSTEM

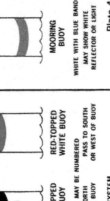
MOORING BUOY
WHITE WITH BLUE BAND
MAY SHOW WHITE REFLECTOR OR LIGHT

Plate 4

FICTITIOUS NAUTICAL CHART

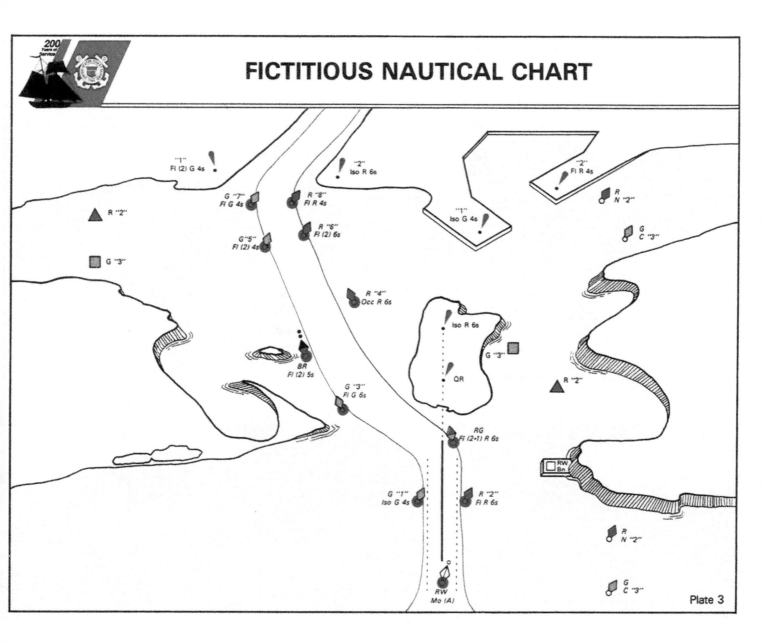

"1"
Fl (2) G 4s

"2"
Iso R 6s

"2"
Fl R 4s

R "2"

G "7"
Fl G 4s

R "8"
Fl R 4s

"1"
Iso G 4s

R
N "2"

R "6"
Fl (2) 6s

G "5"
Fl (2) 4s

G
C "3"

G "3"

R "4"
Occ R 6s

Iso R 6s

G "3"

BR
Fl (2) 5s

QR

R "2"

G "3"
Fl G 6s

RG
Fl (2+1) R 6s

RW
Bn

G "1"
Iso G 4s

R "2"
Fl R 6s

R
N "2"

G
C "3"

RW
Mo (A)

Plate 3

VISUAL BUOYAGE GUIDE

REGION B — by day

Preferred Channel →

Secondary Channel ⇢

REGION B — by night

Preferred Channel →

Secondary Channel ⇢

Plate 2

U.S. AIDS TO NAVIGATION SYSTEM
on navigable waters except Western Rivers

odd green even red
cans , nuns

LATERAL SYSTEM AS SEEN ENTERING FROM SEAWARD

PORT SIDE ODD NUMBERED AIDS

GREEN LIGHT ONLY
FLASHING (2)
FLASHING
OCCULTING
QUICK FLASHING
ISO

STARBOARD SIDE EVEN NUMBERED AIDS

RED LIGHT ONLY
FLASHING (2)
FLASHING
OCCULTING
QUICK FLASHING
ISO

SAFE WATER — NO NUMBERS—MAY BE LETTERED
WHITE LIGHT ONLY   MORSE CODE

PREFERRED CHANNEL — NO NUMBERS—MAY BE LETTERED

COMPOSITE GROUP FLASHING (2 + 1)

PREFERRED CHANNEL TO STARBOARD — TOPMOST BAND GREEN — GREEN LIGHT ONLY

PREFERRED CHANNEL TO PORT — TOPMOST BAND RED — RED LIGHT ONLY

ISOLATED DANGER — NO NUMBERS—MAY BE LETTERED
WHITE LIGHT ONLY

RANGE DAYMARKS—MAY BE LETTERED

KGW   KWG   KWB   KBW   KWR   KRW   KRB   KBR   KGB   KBG   KGR   KGR   KRG

DAYMARKS HAVING NO LATERAL SIGNIFICANCE

MAY BE LETTERED   WHITE LIGHT ONLY

NR   NG   NW   NB

RW Bn   GW Bn   RG Bn   BW Bn

SPECIAL MARKS—MAY BE LETTERED

YELLOW LIGHT ONLY
FIXED
FLASHING

SHAPE: OPTIONAL—BUT SELECTED TO BE APPROPRIATE FOR THE POSITION OF THE MARK IN RELATION TO THE NAVIGABLE WATERWAY AND THE DIRECTION OF BUOYAGE.

TYPICAL INFORMATION AND REGULATORY MARKS

WHITE LIGHT ONLY

INFORMATION AND REGULATORY MARKERS WHEN LIGHTED, INFORMATION AND REGULATORY MARKS MAY DISPLAY ANY LIGHT RHYTHM EXCEPT QUICK FLASHING AND FLASHING (2).

EXCLUSION AREA

RESTRICTED OPERATIONS

DANGER

Aids to navigation marking the Intracoastal Waterway (ICW) display unique yellow symbols to distinguish them from aids marking other waters. Yellow triangles △ indicate aids should be passed by keeping them on the starboard (right) hand of the vessel. Yellow squares □ indicate aids should be passed by keeping them on the port (left) hand of the vessel. A yellow horizontal band provides no lateral information, but simply identifies aids as marking the ICW.

Plate 1

ELECTRONIC AIDS TO NAVIGATION

Racons

Aids to navigation may be enhanced by the use of radar beacons (racons). Racons, when triggered by pulses from a vessel's radar, will transmit a coded reply to the vessel's radar. This reply serves to identify the racon station by exhibiting a series of dots and dashes which appear on the radar display emanating radially from the racon. This display will represent the approximate range and bearing to the racon. Although racons may be used on both laterally significant and non-laterally significant aids to navigation, the racon signal itself is for identification purposes only, and therefore carries no lateral significance. Racons are also used as bridge marks to mark the point of best passage.

All racons operate in the marine radar X-band from 9,300 to 9,500 MHz. Some frequency-agile racons also operate in the 2,900 to 3,000 MHz marine radar S-band.

Racons have a typical output of 100 to 300 milliwatts and are considered a short range aid to navigation. Reception varies from a nominal range of 6 to 8 nautical miles when mounted on a buoy to as much as 17 nautical miles for a racon with a directional antenna mounted at a height of 50 feet on a fixed structure. It must be understood that these are nominal ranges and are dependent upon many factors.

The beginning of the racon presentation occurs about 50 yards beyond the racon position and will persist for a number of revolutions of the radar antenna (depending on its rotation rate). Distance to the racon can be measured to the point at which the racon flash begins, but the figure obtained will be greater than the ship's distance from the racon. This is due to the slight response delay in the racon apparatus.

Radar operators may notice some broadening or spoking of the racon presentation when their vessel approaches closely to the source of the racon. This effect can be minimized by adjustment of the IF gain or sweep gain control of the radar. If desired, the racon presentation can be virtually eliminated by operation of the FTC (fast time constant) controls of the radar.

Radar Reflectors

Many aids to navigation incorporate special fixtures designed to enhance the reflection of radar energy. These fixtures, called radar reflectors, help radar equipped vessels to detect buoys and beacons which are so equipped. They do not however, positively identify a radar target as an aid to navigation.

Radiobeacons

As the first electronic system of navigation, radiobeacons provided offshore coverage and also became the first all-weather electronic aid to navigation. The Coast Guard operates about 200 radiobeacons located on the Atlantic, Gulf, and Pacific coasts, and on the Great Lakes. These radiobeacons are located at lighthouses, on large buoys and along the coasts. All positions are charted.

In order to use this system, the mariner needs a radio direction finder, which is a specifically designed radio receiver with a directional antenna. This antenna is used to determine the direction of the signal being emitted by the shore station, relative to the vessel.

The basic value of the radiobeacon system lies in its simplicity of operation and its relatively low user costs, even though the results obtained may be somewhat limited. The general problems and practices of navigation when using radiobeacons are very similar to those encountered when using visual bearings of lighthouses or other charted objects.

A radiobeacon is basically a short range navigational aid, with ranges from 10 to 175 nautical miles. Although bearings can be obtained at greater ranges, they will be of doubtful accuracy and should be used with caution. When the distance to a radiobeacon is greater than 50 miles, a correction is usually applied to the bearing before plotting on a Mercator chart. These corrections, as well as information on accuracy of bearings, plotting, and other matters are contained in the Defense Mapping Agency Hydrographic/Topographic Center publication, Radio Navigational Aids (RAPUB 117).

All radiobeacons operated and maintained by the U.S. Coast Guard are classified as either Sequenced or Continuous radiobeacons, and are usually organized into groups of six stations transmitting on a single frequency. Typically, one station in each group transmits for one minute out of six and is silent for the remaining five minutes. Continuous radiobeacons operate continuously through every minute of the hour. All Coast Guard-operated radiobeacons are assigned Morse code characteristics for ease in station identification.

The accuracy to be expected from radiobeacons depends to a large extent on the skill of the operator, the condition and type of equipment being used, the range from the stations, and the accuracy of the ship's calibration curve. The Coast Guard operates special calibration radiobeacons for use by the mariner. A comparison of visual bearings with radio bearings, will determine what, if any errors exist in the shipboard direction-finder installation. These calibration beacons transmit either continuously during scheduled hours or upon request.

The range at which a particular marine radiobeacon will be heard depends on atmospheric conditions and on the sensitivity of the receiver being used. The advertised service range of marine radiobeacons is expressed in miles: nautical miles for the Atlantic, Gulf, and Pacific coasts and statute miles for the Great Lakes.

In general, the better the sensitivity of a receiver (i.e., the lower the signal strength required to obtain satisfactory bearings) the better the receiver is for direction-finding purposes. Unless the receiver and antenna combination being used by the mariner is capable of obtaining a radio bearing on a signal as low as 50 microvolts per meter, full benefit will not be obtained from the system.

For example, a mariner using a direction-finder with a sensitivity of 50 microvolts per meter could obtain a bearing on a 50-mile radiobeacon located near New York at the advertised service range of 50 miles. However, using a direction-finder with a sensitivity of only 100 microvolts per meter, the mariner would not be able to obtain a bearing on the same 50-mile New York radiobeacon until approached to within approximately 25 miles of the radiobeacon station.

The selectivity of a receiver is important because it allows the direction finder to receive a desired signal on a particular frequency, while rejecting any undesired signals which may be present on adjacent frequencies.

Since the bandwidth of the transmitted radiobeacon signal is relatively narrow, being only 2.1 kilohertz, a narrow-band receiver, having good selectivity is well suited for direction-finding purposes. The narrow-band receiver should extract all of the useful information from the transmitted marine radiobeacon signal.

Although a wider-band receiver may also extract all of the useful information from the transmitted signal, it will also admit more noise and more undesired signals, if these signals are present on adjacent frequencies. The additional noise and undesired signal interference may reduce the usefulness of the desired signal and effectively reduce the service range of the radiobeacon below its advertised value. This is a receiver defect, not a system error.

Information regarding the location, and operation of marine radiobeacons is given on pages xxx - xxxii. Radiobeacons are individually listed in the Light List.

LORAN-C

LORAN, an acronym for LOng RAnge Navigation, is an electronic aid to navigation consisting of shore-based radio transmitters. The LORAN system enables users equipped with a LORAN receiver to determine their position quickly and accurately, day or night, in practically any weather.

A LORAN-C chain consists of three to five transmitting stations separated by several hundred miles. Within a chain, one station is designated as master while the other stations are designated as secondaries. Each secondary station is identified as either whiskey (W), x-ray (X), yankee (Y), or zulu (Z).

The master station is always the first station to transmit. It transmits a series of nine pulses. The secondary stations then follow in turn, transmitting eight pulses each, at precisely timed intervals. This cycle repeats itself endlessly. The length of the cycle is measured in microseconds and is called a Group Repetition Interval (GRI).

LORAN-C chains are designated by the four most significant digits of their GRI. For example, a chain with a GRI of 89,700 microseconds is referred to as 8970. A different GRI is used for each chain because all LORAN-C stations broadcast in the same 90 to 110 kilohertz frequency band and would otherwise interfere with one another.

The LORAN-C system can be used in either a hyperbolic or range mode. In the widely used hyperbolic mode, a LORAN-C line of position is determined by measuring the time difference between sychronized pulses received from two separate transmitting stations. In the range mode, a line of position is determined by measuring the time required for LORAN-C pulses to travel from a transmitting station to the user's receiver.

A user's position is determined by locating the crossing point of two lines of position on a LORAN-C chart. Many receivers have built-in coordinate converters which will automatically display the receiver's latitude and longitude. With a coordinate converter, a position can be determined using a chart that is not overprinted with LORAN-C lines of position.

CAUTION: The latitude/longitude computation on some models is based upon an all seawater propagation path. This may lead to error if the LORAN-C signals from the various stations involve appreciable overland propagation paths. These errors may put the mariner at risk in areas requiring precise positioning if the proper correctors (ASF) are not applied. *Therefore, it is recommended that mariners using Coordinate Converters check the manufacturer's operating manual to determine if and how corrections are to be applied to compensate for the discontinuity caused by the overland paths.*

There are two types of LORAN-C accuracy; absolute and repeatable. Absolute accuracy is a measure of the navigator's ability to determine latitude and longitude position from the LORAN-C time differences measured. Repeatable accuracy is a measure of the LORAN-C navigator's ability to return to a position where readings have been taken before.

The absolute accuracy of LORAN-C is 0.25 nautical miles, 95% confidence within the published coverage area using standard LORAN-C charts and tables. Repeatable accuracy depends on many factors, so measurements must be taken to determine the repeatable accuracy in any given area. Coast Guard surveys have found repeatable accuracies between 30 and 170 meters in most ground wave coverage areas. LORAN-C position determination on or near the baseline extensions are subject to significant errors and, therefore, should be avoided whenever possible. The use of skywaves is not recommended within 250 miles of a station being used, and corrections for these areas are not usually tabulated.

If the timing or pulse shape of a master-secondary pair deviates from specified tolerances, the first two pulses of the secondary station's pulse train will blink on and off. The LORAN-C receiver sees this blinking signal and indicates a warning to the user. This warning will continue until the signals are once again in tolerance. A blinking signal is not exhibited during off-air periods, so a separate receiver alarm indicates any loss of signal. Never use a blinking secondary signal for navigation.

In coastal waters, LORAN-C should not be relied upon as the only aid to navigation. A prudent navigator will use radar, radio direction finder, fathometer and any other aid to navigation, in addition to the LORAN-C receiver.

LORAN-C interference

Interference to LORAN-C may result from radio transmissions by public or private sources operating near the LORAN-C band of 90-110 kHz. Anyone using the LORAN-C system, who observes interference to LORAN-C, should promptly report it to one of the Coast Guard commands listed below. Include in such reports information regarding the date, time, identifying characteristics, strength of the interfering signals and your own vessel's position. These interference reports are very important and cooperation from users of LORAN-C will assist the Coast Guard in improving LORAN-C service.

Atlantic Ocean and Gulf of Mexico
Commander (Atl)
Atlantic Area, U.S. Coast Guard
Governors Island
New York, NY 10004-5000

Pacific Ocean
Commander (Ptl)
Pacific Area, U.S. Coast Guard
Coast Guard Island
Alameda, CA 94501-5100

All areas

Commandant (G-NRN)
U.S. Coast Guard
Washington, DC 20593-0001

LORAN-C Charts and Publications

Navigational charts overprinted with LORAN-C lines of position are published by the National Ocean Service (NOS), Distribution Branch (N/CG33), 6501 Lafayette Avenue, Riverdale, MD 207371199 and the Defense Mapping Agency (DMA), Combat Support Center, Code: PMSR, Washington, DC 20315-0010, and may be purchased directly from NOS or DMA, or through local chart sales agents.

A general source of LORAN-C information is the LORAN-C User Handbook written by the U.S. Coast Guard. This publication can be purchased from the Superintendent of Documents, Order Section, U.S. Government Printing Office, Washington, DC 20402.

GLOBAL POSITIONING SYSTEM (GPS)

The Global Positioning System (GPS) is a satellite-based Radionavigation System providing continuous worldwide coverage. It provides navigation, position, and timing information to air, marine, and land users. Current plans call for GPS to be fully operational in late 1993. The GPS is being developed and will be operated and controlled by the Department of Defense (DOD) under U.S. Air Force management. Although originally intended for military use only, federal radionavigation policy has established that GPS will be available for civil use. Due to the orbiting nature of the incomplete satellite constellation, GPS coverage currently varies in quality throughout the day from place to place. Computer programs are available from commercial sources so that interested users can determine the quantity and quality of GPS coverage at their particular location.

The USCG is the government interface for civil users of GPS and has established a GPS Information Center (GPSIC) to meet the needs of the civil user. The GPSIC is a Coast Guard facility located in Alexandria, Virginia. It provides voice broadcasts, data broadcasts, and on-line computer-based information services, which are all available 24 hours a day. Personal telephone service is currently available Monday-Friday from 08:00 AM to 4:00 PM, excluding holidays. The information provided includes present or future satellite outages and constellation changes, user instructions and tutorials, lists of service and receiver provider/users, and other GPS-related information.

Users are cautioned that, per DOD policy:

The GPS system is not yet fully operational. Signal availability and accuracy are subject to change due to an incomplete satellite constellation and operational test activities.

However, whenever possible, advance notice of when the GPS satellites should not be used will be provided by the DOD and made available by the U.S Coast Guard.

Information concerning the GPS constellation is provided on a "test and evaluation" basis only. GPS advisory services are updated only during the time 8:00 AM and 4:00 PM, Monday through Friday (except Federal holidays). GPSIC services are described below.

The GPSIC 24 hour voice recording is a 3-line telephone answering machine. Up to 3 callers can listen to the 90 second recording at the same time.

The Department of Commerce transmits recorded time information on WWV/WWVH 5, 10, 15, and 20 MHz frequencies. During the 40 second interval between time ticks, atmospheric and navigation information is announced by voice. Listen at minute 14 & 15 on WWV and minute 43 & 44 on WWVH for GPS status information.

The computer bulletin board system (BBS) is capable of handling 16 simultaneous callers and provides GPS information such as GPS Status Messages, Satellite Almanacs, Notice Advisories to Navstar Users and post-mission ephemeris data. Also included is status information on the OMEGA navigation System and the Coast Guard's Differential GPS System.

The GPSIC disseminates safety GPS advisories broadcast messages through USCG broadcast stations utilizing VHF-FM voice, HF-SSB voice, and NAVTEX broadcasts. The broadcasts provide the GPS user in the marine environment with the current status of the GPS satellite constellation, as well as any planned/unplanned system outages that could affect GPS navigational accuracy.

To comment on any of these services or ask questions about GPS status, contact the GPSIC at:

Commanding Officer   Phone: (703) 866-3806
U.S. Coast Guard ONSCEN   FAX: (703) 866-3825
7323 Telegraph Road
Alexandria, VA 22310-3393

GLOSSARY OF AIDS TO NAVIGATION TERMS

Adrift: Afloat and unattached in any way to the shore or seabed.

Aid to navigation: Any device external to a vessel or aircraft specifically intended to assist navigators in determining their position or safe course, or to warn them of dangers or obstructions to navigation.

Alternating light: A rhythmic light showing light of alternating colors.

Arc of visibility: The portion of the horizon over which a lighted aid to navigation is visible from seaward.

Articulated beacon: A beacon-like buoyant structure, tethered directly to the seabed and having no watch circle. Called articulated light or articulated daybeacon, as appropriate.

Assigned position: The latitude and longitude position for an aid to navigation.

Beacon: A lighted or unlighted fixed aid to navigation attached directly to the earth's surface. (Lights and daybeacons both constitute "beacons".)

Bearing: The horizontal direction of a line of sight between two objects on the surface of the earth.

Bell: A sound signal producing bell tones by means of a hammer actuated by electricity or, on buoys, by sea motion.

Bifurcation: The point where a channel divides when proceeding from seaward. The place where two tributaries meet.

Broadcast Notice to Mariners: A radio broadcast designed to provide important marine information.

Buoy: A floating object of defined shape and color, which is anchored at a given position and serves as an aid to navigation.

Characteristic: The audible, visual, or electronic signal displayed by an aid to navigation to assist in the identification of an aid to navigation. Characteristic refers to lights, sound signals, racons, radiobeacons, and daybeacons.

Commissioned: The action of placing a previously discontinued aid to navigation back in operation.

Composite group-flashing light: A group-flashing light in which the flashes are combined in successive groups of different numbers of flashes.

Composite group-occulting light: A light similar to a group-occulting light except that the successive groups in a period have different numbers of eclipses.

Conventional direction of buoyage: The general direction taken by the mariner when approaching a harbor, river, estuary, or other waterway from seaward, or proceeding upstream or in the direction of the main stream of flood tide, or in the direction indicated in appropriate nautical documents (normally, following a clockwise direction around land masses).

Daybeacon: An unlighted fixed structure which is equipped with a dayboard for daytime identification.

Dayboard: The daytime identifier of an aid to navigation presenting one of several standard shapes (square, triangle, rectangle) and colors (red, green, white, orange, yellow, or black.)

Daymark: The daytime identifier of an aid to navigation. (See column 7 of the Light List.)

Diaphone: A sound signal which produces sound by means of a slotted piston moved back and forth by compressed air. A "two-tone" diaphone produces two sequential tones with the second tone of lower pitch.

Directional light: A light illuminating a sector or very narrow angle and intended to mark a direction to be followed.

Discontinued: To remove from operation (permanently or temporarily) a previously authorized aid to navigation.

Discrepancy: Failure of an aid to navigation to maintain its position or function as prescribed in the Light List.

Discrepancy buoy: An easily transportable buoy used to temporarily replace an aid to navigation not watching properly.

Dolphin: A minor aid to navigation structure consisting of a number of piles driven into the seabed or riverbed in a circular pattern and drawn together with wire rope.

Eclipse: An interval of darkness between appearances of a light.

Emergency light: A light of reduced intensity displayed by certain aids to navigation when the main light is extinguished.

Establish: To place an authorized aid to navigation in operation for the first time.

Extinguished: A lighted aid to navigation which fails to show a light characteristic.

Fixed light: A light showing continuously and steadily, as opposed to a rhythmic light. (Do not confuse with "fixed" as used to differentiate from "floating.")

Flash: A relatively brief appearance of a light, in comparison with the longest interval of darkness in the same character.

Flash tube: An electronically controlled high-intensity discharge lamp with a very brief flash duration.

Flashing light: A light in which the total duration of light in each period is clearly shorter than the total duration of darkness and in which the flashes of light are all of equal duration. (Commonly used for a single-flashing light which exhibits only single flashes which are repeated at regular intervals.)

Floating aid to navigation: A buoy, secured in its assigned position by a mooring.

Fog detector: An electronic device used to automatically determine conditions of visibility which warrant the turning on and off of a sound signal or additional light signals.

Fog signal: See sound signal.

Geographic range: The greatest distance the curvature of the earth permits an object of a given height to be seen from a particular height of eye without regard to luminous intensity or visibility conditions.

Gong: A wave actuated sound signal on buoys which uses a group of saucer-shaped bells to produce different tones.

Group-flashing light: A flashing light in which a group of flashes, specified in number, is regularly repeated.

Group-occulting light: An occulting light in which a group of eclipses, specified in number, is regularly repeated.

Horn: A sound signal which uses electricity or compressed air to vibrate a disc diaphragm.

Inoperative: Sound signal or electronic aid to navigation out of service due to a malfunction.

Interrupted quick light: A quick flashing light in which the rapid alternations are interrupted at regular intervals by eclipses of long duration.

Isolated danger mark: A mark erected on, or moored above or very near, an isolated danger which has navigable water all around it.

Isophase light: A rhythmic light in which all durations of light and darkness are equal. (Formerly called equal interval light.)

Junction: The point where a channel divides when proceeding seaward. The place where a distributary departs from the main stream.

Large navigation buoy (LNB): A 40-foot diameter, automated disc-shaped buoy used to replace lightships. Most LNB's are used in conjunction with major Traffic Separation Schemes. All LNB's are equipped with Emergency lights.

Lateral system: A system of aids to navigation in which characteristics of buoys and beacons indicate the sides of the channel or route relative to a conventional direction of buoyage (usually upstream).

Light: The signal emitted by a lighted aid to navigation. The illuminating apparatus used to emit the light signal. A lighted aid to navigation on a fixed structure.

Light sector: The arc over which a light is visible, described in degrees true, as observed from seaward towards the light. May be used to define distinctive color difference of two adjoining sectors, or an obscured sector.

Lighted ice buoy (LIB): A lighted buoy without sound signal, and designed to withstand the forces of shifting and flowing ice. Used to replace a conventional buoy when that aid to navigation is endangered by ice.

Lighthouse: A lighted beacon of major importance.

Local Notice to Mariners: A written document issued by each U.S. Coast Guard district to disseminate important information affecting aids to navigation, dredging, marine construction, special marine activities, and bridge construction on the waterways within that district.

Luminous range: The greatest distance a light can be expected to be seen given its nominal range and the prevailing meteorological visibility (see page xxviii).

Mark: A visual aid to navigation. Often called navigation mark, includes floating marks (buoys) and fixed marks (beacons).

Meteorological visibility: The greatest distance at which a black object of suitable dimension could be seen and recognized against the horizon sky by day, or, in the case of night observations, could be seen and recognized if the general illumination were raised to the normal daylight level.

Mileage number: A number assigned to aids to navigation which gives the distance in sailing miles along the river from a reference point to the aid to navigation. The number is used principally in the Mississippi River System.

Nominal range: The maximum distance a light can be seen in clear weather (meteorological visibility of 10 nautical miles). Listed for all lighted aids to navigation except range lights, directional lights, and private aids to navigation.

Occulting light: A light in which the total duration of light in each period is clearly longer than the total duration of darkness and in which the intervals of darkness (occultations) are all of equal duration. (Commonly used for single-occulting light which exhibits only single occultations which are repeated at regular intervals.)

Ocean Data Aquisition System (ODAS): Certain very large buoys in deep water for the collection of oceanographic and meteorlogical information. All ODAS buoys are yellow in color and display a yellow light.

Off shore tower: Monitored light stations built on exposed marine sites to replace lightships.

Off station: A floating aid to navigation not on its assigned position.

Passing light: A low intensity light which may be mounted on the

structure of another light to enable the mariner to keep the latter light in sight when passing out of its beam during transit.

Period: The interval of time between the commencement of two identical successive cycles of the characteristic of the light or sound signal.

Pile: A long, heavy timber driven into the seabed or riverbed to serve as a support for an aid to navigation.

Port hand mark: A buoy or beacon which is left to the port hand when proceeding in the "conventional direction of buoyage".

Preferred channel mark: A lateral mark indicating a channel junction or bifurcation, or a wreck or other obstruction which, after consulting a chart, may be passed on either side.

Primary aid to navigation: An aid to navigation established for the purpose of making landfalls and coastwise passages from headland to headland.

Quick light: A light exhibiting very rapid regular alternations of light and darkness, normally 60 flashes per minute. (Formerly called quick flashing light.)

RACON: A radar beacon which produces a coded response, or radar paint, when triggered by a radar signal.

Radar: An electronic system designed to transmit radio signals and receive reflected images of those signals from a "target" in order to determine the bearing and distance to the "target".

Radar reflector: A special fixture fitted to or incorporated into the design of certain aids to navigation to enhance their ability to reflect radar energy. In general, these fixtures will materially improve the aid to navigation for use by vessels with radar.

Radiobeacon: Electronic apparatus which transmits a radio signal for use in providing a mariner a line of position.

Range: A line formed by the extension of a line connecting two charted points.

Range lights: Two lights associated to form a range which often, but not necessarily, indicates a channel centerline. The front range light is the lower of the two, and nearer to the mariner using the range. The rear range light is higher and further from the mariner.

Rebuilt: A fixed aid to navigation, previously destroyed, which has been restored as an aid to navigation.

Regulatory marks: A white and orange aid to navigation with no lateral significance. Used to indicate a special meaning to the mariner, such as danger, restricted operations, or exclusion area.

Relighted: An extinguished aid to navigation returned to its advertised light characteristics.

Replaced: An aid to navigation previously off station, adrift, or missing, restored by another aid to navigation of the same type and characteristics.

Replaced (temporarily): An aid to navigation previously off station, adrift, or missing, restored by another aid to navigation of different type and/or characteristic.

Reset: A floating aid to navigation previously off station, adrift, or missing, returned to its assigned position (station).

Rhythmic light: A light showing intermittently with a regular periodicity.

Setting a buoy: The act of placing a buoy on assigned position in the water.

Sector: See light sector.

Siren: A sound signal which uses electricity or compressed air to actuate either a disc or a cup-shaped rotor.

Skeleton tower: A tower, usually of steel, constructed of heavy corner members and various horizontal and diagonal bracing members.

Sound signal: A device which transmits sound, intended to provide information to mariners during periods of restricted visibility and foul weather.

Starboard hand mark: A buoy or beacon which is left to the starboard hand when proceeding in the "conventional direction of buoyage."

Station buoy: An unlighted buoy set near a Large Navigation Buoy or an important buoy as a reference point should the primary aid to navigation be moved from its assigned position.

Topmark: One or more relatively small objects of characteristic shape and color placed on an aid to identify its purpose.

Traffic Separation Scheme: Shipping corridors marked by buoys which separate incoming from outgoing vessels. Improperly called SEA LANES.

Watching properly: An aid to navigation on its assigned position exhibiting the advertised characteristics in all respects.

Whistle: A wave actuated sound signal on buoys which produces sound by emitting compressed air through a circumferential slot into a cylindrical bell chamber.

Winter marker: An unlighted buoy without sound signal, used to replace a conventional buoy when that aid to navigation is endangered by ice.

Winter light: A light which is maintained during those winter months when the regular light is extinguished. It is of lower candlepower than the regular light but usually of the same characteristic.

Withdrawn: The discontinuance of a floating aid to navigation during severe ice conditions or for the winter season.

ABBREVIATIONS USED IN COAST GUARD BROADCAST NOTICES TO MARINERS

Word/phrase	Abbrev
Light characteristics	
Fixed	F
Occulting	OC
Group–Occulting	OC(2)
Composite Group–Occulting	OC(2+1)
Isophase	ISO
Single–Flashing	FL
Group–Flashing	FL(3)
Composite Group–Flashing	FL(2+1)
Continuous Quick–Flashing	Q
Interrupted Quick–Flashing	IQ
Morse Code	MO(A)
Fixed and Flashing	FFL
Alternating	AL
Characteristic	CHAR
Colors	
Black	B
Blue	BU
Green	G
Orange	OR
Red	R
White	W
Yellow	Y
Aids to Navigation	
Aeronautical Radiobeacon	AERO RBN
Articulated Daybeacon	ART DBN
Articulated Light	ART LT
Destroyed	DESTR
Discontinued	DISCONTD
Established	ESTAB
Exposed Location Buoy	ELB
Fog signal station	FOG SIG
Large Navigation Buoy	LNB
Light	LT
Light List Number	LLNR
Lighted Bell Buoy	LBB
Lighted Buoy	LB
Lighted Gong Buoy	LGB
Lighted Horn Buoy	LHB
Lighted Whistle Buoy	LWB
Ocean Data Acquisition System	ODAS
Privately Maintained	PRIV MAINTD
Radar responder beacon	RACON
Radar Reflector	RA REF
Radiobeacon	RBN
Temporarily replaced by unlighted buoy	TRUB

Word/phrase	Abbrev
Temporarily replaced by lighted buoy	TRLB
Whistle	WHIS
Organizations	
Coast Guard	CG
Commander, Coast Guard District (#)	CCGD(#)
U.S. Army Corps of Engineers	COE
Defense Mapping Agency Hydro./Topo. Center	DMAHTC
National Ocean Service	NOS
National Weather Service	NWS
Vessels	
Aircraft	A/C
Fishing Vessel	F/V
Liquified Natural Gas Carrier	LNG
Motor Vessel	M/V[1]
Pleasure Craft	P/C
Research Vessel	R/V
Sailing Vessel	S/V
Compass Directions	
East	E
North	N
Northeast	NE
Northwest	NW
South	S
Southeast	SE
Southwest	SW
West	W
Months	
January	JAN
February	FEB
March	MAR
April	APR
May	MAY
June	JUN
July	JUL
August	AUG
September	SEP
October	OCT
November	NOV
December	DEC
Days of the Week	
Monday	MON
Tuesday	TUE
Wednesday	WED
Thursday	THU
Friday	FRI
Saturday	SAT
Sunday	SUN

---

[1] M/V includes: Steam Ship, Container Vessel, Cargo Vessel, etc.

ABBREVIATIONS USED IN COAST GUARD BROADCAST NOTICES TO MARINERS

Word/phrase	Abbrev	Word/phrase	Abbrev
Various		Prohibited	PROHIB
Anchorage	ANCH	Publication	PUB
Anchorage prohibited	ANCH PROHIB	Range	RGE
Approximate	APPROX	Reported	REP
Atlantic	ATLC	Restricted	RESTR
Authorized	AUTH	Rock	RK
Average	AVG	Saint	ST
Bearing	BRG	Second (time; geo pos)	SEC
Breakwater	BKW	Signal station	SIG STA
Broadcast Notice to Mariners	BNM	Station	STA
Channel	CHAN	Statute Mile(s)	SM
Code of Federal Regulations	CFR	Storm signal station	S SIG STA
Continue	CONT	Temporary	TEMP
Degrees (temperature; geo pos)	DEG	Through	THRU
Diameter	DIA	Thunderstorm	TSTM
Edition	ED	True	T
Effect/Effective	EFF	Uncovers; Dries	UNCOV
Entrance	ENTR	Universal Coordinate Time	UTC
Explosive Anchorage	EXPLOS ANCH	Urgent Marine	UMIB
Fathom(s)	FM(S)	Information Broadcast	
Foot/Feet	FT	Velocity	VLCTY
Harbor	HBR	Vertical clearance	VERT CL
Height	HT	Visibility	VSBY
Hertz	HZ	Warning	WRNG
Horizontal clearance	HOR CL	Weather	WEA
Hour	HR	Wreck	WK
International Regulations for Preventing Collisions at Sea, 1972	COLREGS	Yard(s)	YD
Kilohertz	KHZ	**Countries and States**	
Kilometer	KM	Alabama	AL
Knot(s)	KT(S)	Alaska	AK
Latitude	LAT	American Samoa	AS
Local Notice to Mariners	LNM	Arizona	AZ
Longitude	LONG	Arkansas	AR
Maintained	MAINTD	California	CA
Maximum	MAX	Canada	CN
Megahertz	MHZ	Colorado	CO
Millibar	MB	Connecticut	CT
Millimeter	MM	Delaware	DE
Minute (time; geo pos)	MIN	District of Columbia	DC
Moderate	MDT	Federated States of Micronesia	FSM
Mountain, Mount	MT	Florida	FL
Nautical Mile(s)	NM	Georgia	GA
Notice to Mariners	NTM	Guam	GU
Obstruction	OBSTR	Hawaii	HI
Occasion/Occasionally	OCCASION	Idaho	ID
Operating Area	OPAREA	Illinois	IL
Pacific	PAC	Indiana	IN
Point(s)	PT(S)	Iowa	IA
Position	PSN	Kansas	KS
Position Approximate	PA	Kentucky	KY
Pressure	PRES	Louisiana	LA
Private, Privately	PRIV	Maine	ME
		Maryland	MD
		Massachusetts	MA

ABBREVIATIONS USED IN COAST GUARD BROADCAST NOTICES TO MARINERS

Word/phrase	Abbrev	Word/phrase	Abbrev
Mexico	MX	Oregon	OR
Michigan	MI	Pennsylvania	PA
Minnesota	MN	Puerto Rico	PR
Mississippi	MS	Rhode Island	RI
Missouri	MO	South Carolina	SC
Montana	MT	South Dakota	SD
Nebraska	NE	Tennessee	TN
New Hampshire	NH	Texas	TX
Nevada	NV	United States	US
New Jersey	NJ	Utah	UT
New Mexico	NM	Vermont	VT
New York	NY	Virgin Islands	VI
North Carolina	NC	Virginia	VA
North Dakota	ND	Washington	WA
Northern Marianas	CM	West Virginia	WV
Ohio	OH	Wisconsin	WI
Oklahoma	OK	Wyoming	WY

RADIOBEACON SYSTEM – ATLANTIC COAST

SEQUENCED – By Frequency

Freq kHz	Sequence	Station	Characteristic	Range (n.m.)	Lat. (N) ° ' "	Long. (W) ° ' "
286	I	HIGHLAND	HI (.... ..)	100	42 02 24	70 03 40
	IV	AMBROSE	T (—)	125	40 27 32	73 49 52
	V	GREAT DUCK ISLAND	GD (——. —..)	50	44 08 32	68 14 47
	VI	MANANA ISLAND	MI (—— ..)	100	43 45 48	69 19 38
306	I, IV	CLINTON HARBOR	CL (—.—. .—..)	20	41 16 00	72 31 10
	II	LITTLE GULL	J (———)	20	41 12 22	72 06 29
	III, VI	HORTON POINT	HP (.... .——.)	20	41 05 06	72 26 48
	V	WATCH HILL	WH (.—— ....)	10	41 18 36	71 55 30
316	I, IV	EXECUTION ROCKS	XR (—..— .—.)	20	40 52 41	73 44 18
	II, V	OLDFIELD POINT	OP (——— .——.)	20	40 58 36	73 07 08
	III, VI	STRATFORD POINT	SP (... .——.)	20	41 09 06	73 06 13

CONTINUOUS – By Frequency

Freq kHz	Station	Characteristic	Range (n.m.)	Lat. (N) ° ' "	Long. (W) ° ' "
291	HALFWAY ROCK	HR (.... .—.)	10	43 39 21	70 02 15
291	NOBSKA POINT	NP (—. .——.)	20	41 30 58	70 39 20
291	FIRE ISLAND	RT (.—. —)	15	40 38 18	73 18 53
293	MONTAUK POINT	MP (—— .——.)	125	41 04 02	71 51 44
295	SCITUATE HARBOR	SH (... ....)	10	42 11 56	70 43 12
298	NANTUCKET LNB	NS (—. ...)	50	40 30 00	69 28 00
301	PORTLAND LIGHTED HORN BUOY P (LNB)	PH (.——. ....)	30	43 31 37	70 05 31
301	BLOCK ISLAND	BI (—... ..)	20	41 09 11	71 33 04
302	EAST ROCKAWAY INLET	ER (. .—.)	10	40 35 11	73 45 11
304	BOSTON LIGHTED HORN BUOY B (LNB)	BH (—... ....)	30	42 22 42	70 47 00
308	CLEVELAND LEDGE	CL (—.—. .—..)	10	41 37 51	70 41 42
308	MANASQUAN INLET	MI (—— ..)	20	40 06 03	74 02 03
310	BEAVERTAIL	N (—.)	20	41 26 58	71 23 58
311	CHATHAM	CH (—.—. ....)	20	41 40 17	69 57 02
311	SHINNECOCK INLET	SN (... —.)	20	40 50 32	72 28 44
314	MATINICUS ROCK	MR (.. .—.)	20	43 47 00	68 51 19

CONTINUOUS – By Frequency

Freq kHz	Station	Characteristic	Range (n.m.)	Lat. (N) ° ' "	Long. (W) ° ' "
314	BUZZARDS BAY	BB (—... —...)	20	41 23 47	71 02 02
318	CAPE COD CANAL BREAKWATER	CC (—.—. —.—.)	20	41 46 19	70 30 04
319	JONES INLET	JI (.——— ..)	10	40 34 50	73 34 24
320	THE CUCKOLDS	CU (—.—. ..—)	10	43 46 46	69 39 02
320	SAYBROOK BREAKWATER	SB (... —...)	10	41 15 47	72 20 36
322	PORTSMOUTH HARBOR (NEW CASTLE) LIGHT	NCE (—. —.—. .)	10	43 04 15	70 42 36
322	NEW BEDFORD	NB (—. —...)	10	41 37 28	70 54 22
325	EASTERN POINT	EP (. .——.)	10	42 34 50	70 39 54
325	POINT JUDITH	PJ (.——. .———)	10	41 21 39	71 28 55
325	BRANT POINT	BP (—... .——.)	10	41 17 23	70 05 27

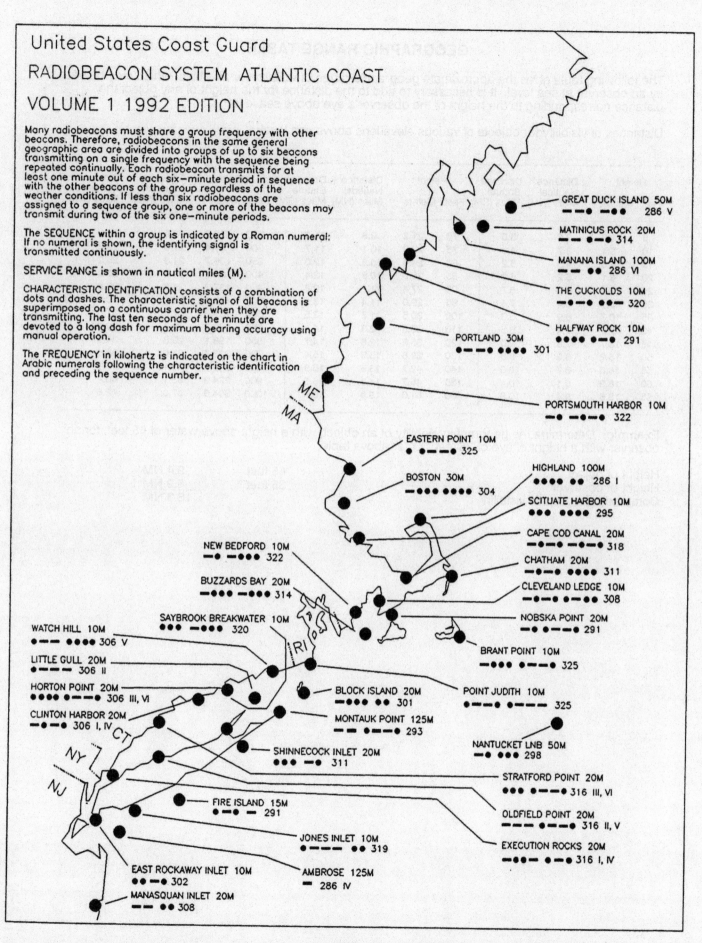

United States Coast Guard

RADIOBEACON SYSTEM ATLANTIC COAST

VOLUME 1 1992 EDITION

Many radiobeacons must share a group frequency with other beacons. Therefore, radiobeacons in the same general geographic area are divided into groups of up to six beacons transmitting on a single frequency with the sequence being repeated continually. Each radiobeacon transmits for at least one minute out of each six—minute period in sequence with the other beacons of the group regardless of the weather conditions. If less than six radiobeacons are assigned to a sequence group, one or more of the beacons may transmit during two of the six one—minute periods.

The SEQUENCE within a group is indicated by a Roman numeral: If no numeral is shown, the identifying signal is transmitted continuously.

SERVICE RANGE is shown in nautical miles (M).

CHARACTERISTIC IDENTIFICATION consists of a combination of dots and dashes. The characteristic signal of all beacons is superimposed on a continuous carrier when they are transmitting. The last ten seconds of the minute are devoted to a long dash for maximum bearing accuracy using manual operation.

The FREQUENCY in kilohertz is indicated on the chart in Arabic numerals following the characteristic identification and preceding the sequence number.

GREAT DUCK ISLAND 50M — — •• 286 V

MATINICUS ROCK 20M — — • • 314

MANANA ISLAND 100M — — •• 286 VI

THE CUCKOLDS 10M — • — • •• — 320

HALFWAY ROCK 10M •••• 291

PORTLAND 30M • — •• •••• 301

PORTSMOUTH HARBOR 10M — • — • — • 322

ME / MA

EASTERN POINT 10M • • — • — 325

BOSTON 30M — •••• •••• 304

HIGHLAND 100M •••• •• 286 I

SCITUATE HARBOR 10M ••• •••• 295

CAPE COD CANAL 20M — • — • — • 318

CHATHAM 20M — • — • 311

CLEVELAND LEDGE 10M — • — • — 308

NOBSKA POINT 20M — • — • — 291

NEW BEDFORD 10M — • — •••• 322

BUZZARDS BAY 20M — ••• — ••• 314

SAYBROOK BREAKWATER 10M ••• — ••• 320

BRANT POINT 10M — ••• • — • 325

WATCH HILL 10M • — — •••• 306 V

LITTLE GULL 20M • — — • 306 II

HORTON POINT 20M •••• • — • 306 III, VI

CLINTON HARBOR 20M — • — • 306 I, IV

RI

CT

NY

NJ

BLOCK ISLAND 20M — ••• • — • 301

POINT JUDITH 10M — • — • — 325

MONTAUK POINT 125M — — • — • 293

NANTUCKET LNB 50M — • — 298

SHINNECOCK INLET 20M ••• — • 311

STRATFORD POINT 20M ••• • — • 316 III, VI

OLDFIELD POINT 20M — • — • 316 II, V

FIRE ISLAND 15M — • — 291

JONES INLET 10M • — — • •• 319

EXECUTION ROCKS 20M — •• • — • 316 I, IV

EAST ROCKAWAY INLET 10M •• — • 302

AMBROSE 125M — 286 IV

MANASQUAN INLET 20M — •• 308

GEOGRAPHIC RANGE TABLE

The following table gives the approximate geographic range of visibility for an object which may be seen by an observer at sea level. It is necessary to add to the distance for the height of any object the distance corresponding to the height of the observer's eye above sea level.

Distances of visibility for objects of various elevations above sea level.

Height Feet	Height Meters	Distance Nautical Miles (NM)	Distance Statute Miles (SM)	Height Feet	Height Meters	Distance Nautical Miles (NM)	Distance Statute Miles (SM)	Height Feet	Height Meters	Distance Nautical Miles (NM)	Distance Statute Miles (SM)
5	1.5	2.6	3.0	70	21.3	9.8	11.3	250	76.2	18.5	21.3
10	3.1	3.7	4.3	75	22.9	10.1	11.7	300	91.4	20.3	23.3
15	4.6	4.5	5.2	80	24.4	10.5	12.0	350	106.7	21.9	25.2
20	6.1	5.2	6.0	85	25.9	10.8	12.4	400	121.9	23.4	26.9
25	7.6	5.9	6.7	90	27.4	11.1	12.8	450	137.2	24.8	28.6
30	9.1	6.4	7.4	95	29.0	11.4	13.1	500	152.4	26.2	30.1
35	10.7	6.9	8.0	100	30.5	11.7	13.5	550	167.6	27.4	31.6
40	12.2	7.4	8.5	110	33.5	12.3	14.1	600	182.9	28.7	33.0
45	13.7	7.8	9.0	120	36.6	12.8	14.7	650	198.1	29.8	34.3
50	15.2	8.3	9.5	130	39.6	13.3	15.4	700	213.4	31.0	35.6
55	16.8	8.7	10.0	140	42.7	13.8	15.9	800	243.8	33.1	38.1
60	18.3	9.1	10.4	150	45.7	14.3	16.5	900	274.3	35.1	40.4
65	19.8	9.4	10.9	200	61.0	19.0	16.5	1000	304.8	37.0	42.6

Example: Determine the geographic visibility of an object, with a height above water of 65 feet, for an observer with a height of eye of 35 feet. Enter above table;

Height of object	65 feet	9.4 NM
Height of observer	35 feet	6.9 NM
Computed geographic visibility		16.3 NM

LUMINOUS RANGE DIAGRAM

The nominal range given in this Light List is the maximum distance a given light can be seen when the meteorological visibility is 10 nautical miles (or 11.5 statute miles on Lake Champlain). If the existing visibility is less than 10 NM (11.5 SM), the range at which the light can be seen will be reduced below its nominal range. And, if the visibility is greater than 10 NM (11.5 SM), the light can be seen at greater distances. The distance at which a light may be expected to be seen in the prevailing visibility is called its luminous range.

Nautical Miles

Statute Miles
(For Lake Champlain)

METEOROLOGICAL VISIBILITY
(From International Visibility code)

Code	Metric	Nautical (approximate)	Statute (approximate)
0	Less than 50 meters	Less than 50 yards	Less than 50 yards
1	50–200 meters	50–200 yards	50–200 yards
2	200–500 meters	200–500 yards	200–500 yards
3	500–1,000 meters	500–1,000 yards	500–1,000 yards
4	1–2 kilometers	1,000–2,000 yards	1,000–2,000 yards
5	2–4 kilometers	1–2 nautical miles	1–2.5 statute miles
6	4–10 kilometers	2–5.5 nautical miles	2.5–6.5 statute miles
7	10–20 kilometers	5.5–11 nautical miles	6.5–13 statute miles
8	20–50 kilometers	11–27 nautical miles	13–31 statute miles
9	Greater than 50 km	Greater than 27 nm	Greater than 31 miles

This diagram enables the mariner to determine the approximate luminous range of a light when the nominal range and the prevailing meteorological visibility are known. The diagram is entered from the bottom border using the nominal range listed in column 6 of this book. The intersection of the nominal range with the appropriate visibility curve (or, more often, a point between two curves) yields, by moving horizontally to the left border, the luminous range.

CAUTION: When using this diagram is must be remembered that:
1. The ranges obtained are approximate.
2. The transparency of the atmosphere may vary between the observer and the light.
3. Glare from background lighting will considerably reduce the range at which lights are sighted.
4. The rolling motion of the mariner and/or of a lighted aid to navigation may reduce the distance at which lights can be detected and identified.

(1) No.	(2) Name and location	(3) Position	(4) Characteristic	(5) Height	(6) Range	(7) Structure	(8) Remarks

APPROACHES TO NEW YORK - NANTUCKET SHOALS TO FIVE FATHOM BANK (Chart 12300)

N/W

No.	Name and location	Position	Characteristic	Height	Range	Structure	Remarks
655	**Block Island Southeast Light**	41 09.2 71 33.1	Fl G 5s	258	24	On steel tower. 67	Emergency light of reduced intensity when main light is extinguished. Lighted throughout 24 hours.
656	**Block Island Southeast Radiobeacon**	41 09.2 71 33.1	BI (—••• ••)		20		FREQ: 301 kHz. Antenna 70 feet east south east of tower.
660	Southwest Ledge Lighted Bell Buoy 2 Marks southwest edge of shoals.	41 06.7 71 40.3	Fl R 2.5s		4	Red.	

APPROACHES TO NEW YORK - NANTUCKET SHOALS TO FIVE FATHOM BANK (Chart 12300)

No.	Name and location	Position	Characteristic	Height	Range	Structure	Remarks
665	Montauk Point Lighted Whistle Buoy MP	41 01.8 71 45.7	Mo (A) W		6	Red and white stripes with red spherical topmark.	
670	**Montauk Point Light**	41 04.2 71 51.5	Fl W 5s	168	24	White octagonal, pyramidal tower with brown band midway of height, covered way to gray dwelling.	HORN: 1 blast ev 15s (2s bl). Emergency light (F W 5s) when main light is extinguished. Lighted throughout 24 hours.
671	**Montauk Point Radiobeacon**	41 04.2 71 51.5	MP (—— •—••)		125		FREQ: 286 kHz, III. Antenna 690 yards, 227° from light.
675 27180	Shinnecock Inlet Approach Lighted Whistle Buoy SH	40 49.0 72 28.6	Mo (A) W		6	Red and white stripes with red spherical topmark.	
680 27175	**Shinnecock Light**	40 50.5 72 28.7	Fl (2) R 15s 0.1s fl 3.6s ec. 0.1s fl 11.2s ec.	75	21	Red skeleton tower.	HORN: 1 blast ev 15s (2s bl).
681 27176	**Shinnecock Radiobeacon**	40 50.5 72 28.8	SN (••• —•)		20		FREQ: 311 kHz. Antenna at light tower.
685	Moriches Inlet Approach Lighted Bell Buoy 2B	40 44.1 72 45.2	Fl R 6s		4	Red.	
690	Cedar Island Beach Outfall Buoy A					Yellow can.	Private aid.
695	**Fire Island Light**	40 37.9 73 13.1	Fl W 7.5s	167	24	Black and white banded tower; black on top.	Lighted throughout 24 hours.
700	**Fire Island Radiobeacon**	40 38.3 73 18.9	RT (•—• —)		15		FREQ: 291 kHz.
705	Fire Island Inlet Approach Lighted Whistle Buoy 4Fl	40 35.6 73 17.8	Fl R 2.5s		4	Red.	
720	Nantucket Traffic Lane Lighted Horn Buoy NA	40 25.7 73 11.5	Fl Y 6s		7	Yellow.	RACON: N (—•) HORN: 1 blast ev 15s (2s bl).
725	Nantucket Traffic Lane Lighted Whistle Buoy NB	40 26.5 73 40.8	Fl Y 4s		6	Yellow.	

(1) No.	(2) Name and location	(3) Position	(4) Characteristic	(5) Height	(6) Range	(7) Structure	(8) Remarks

		N/W					
	APPROACHES TO NEW YORK - NANTUCKET SHOALS TO FIVE FATHOM BANK (Chart 12300)						
730	**Ambrose Light**	40 27.6 73 49.9	Fl W 5s	136	24	Red tower on white square superstructure on four piles. AMBROSE on sides	HORN: 1 blast ev 15s (2s bl). Emergency light of reduced intensity when main light is extinguished. Obstruction lights showing Fl W from all four corners. Piles floodlighted from sunset to sunrise. Lighted throughout 24 hours. RACON: N (—•).
731	**Ambrose Radiobeacon**	40 27.6 73 49.9	T (—)		125		286 kHz, IV.

No.	Name and location	Position	Characteristic	Height	Range	Structure	Remarks
	APPROACHES TO NEW YORK - NANTUCKET SHOALS TO FIVE FATHOM BANK (Chart 12300)						
735	Hudson Canyon Traffic Lane Lighted Horn Buoy HA	40 07.6 73 21.4	Fl Y 4s		6	Yellow.	RACON: C (—•—•). HORN: 1 blast ev 30s (3s bl).
740	Barnegat Traffic Lane Lighted Whistle Buoy BA	40 20.7 73 47.7	Fl Y 6s		7	Yellow.	
745	Fishing Grounds Obstruction Lighted Bell Buoy FG	40 25.2 73 51.7	Fl (2+1) G 6s		4	Green and red bands.	
750	New York Bight Dumping Ground Lighted Buoy NY	40 22.8 73 50.7	Fl Y 6s		5	Yellow.	
755	New York Bight Dumping Ground Buoy KVK	40 22.2 73 51.2				Yellow nun.	
760	New York Bight Dumping Ground Buoy OM	40 22.7 73 50.4				Yellow can.	
765 32325	Shrewsbury Rocks Lighted Bell Buoy 1 Off east end of rocks.	40 20.5 73 55.6	Fl G 2.5s		4	Green.	
770 37325	Shark River Inlet Lighted Whistle Buoy SI	40 11.2 74 00.1	Mo (A) W		6	Red and white stripes with red spherical topmark.	
775 37345	MANASQUAN INLET NORTH BREAKWATER LIGHT 4	40 06.1 74 01.9	Fl R 4s	30	6	TR on skeleton tower.	
780 37350	**Manasquan Inlet South Breakwater Light 3**	40 06.0 74 01.9	Fl G 6s	35	10	SG on spindle.	HORN: 1 blast ev 30s (3s bl).
	Sea Girt						
785	– Buoy A Marks firing range.					Yellow spar.	Private aid.
790	– Buoy B Marks firing range.					Yellow spar.	Private aid
795	– Buoy C Marks firing range.					Yellow spar.	Private aid.
800	– Buoy D Marks firing range.					Yellow spar.	Private aid.

(1) No.	(2) Name and location	(3) Position	(4) Characteristic	(5) Height	(6) Range	(7) Structure	(8) Remarks

RHODE ISLAND – First District

NARRAGANSETT BAY (Chart 13221) N/W

Greenwich Bay

Warwick Cove

17970	– Buoy 5	41 41.0 71 23.5				Green can.	
17975	– Buoy 7	41 41.0 71 23.5				Green can.	
17980	– Buoy 9					Green can.	
17985	– Buoy 10					Red nun.	
17990	– Buoy 12					Red nun.	

Greenwich Bay

17995	– Buoy 3					Green can.	
18000	– Buoy 5					Green can.	
18005	– Buoy 6					Red nun.	
18010	– Buoy 7 On edge of shoal.					Green can.	
18015	Cedar Tree Point Buoy 2					Red nun.	
18020	Apponaug Cove Approach Buoy 1					Green can.	

Apponaug Cove Channel

18025	– Buoy 3					Green can.	
18030	– Buoy 5					Green can.	
18035	– Buoy 6					Red nun.	
18040	– Buoy 7					Green can.	
18045	– Buoy 8					Red nun.	

BLOCK ISLAND SOUND AND APPROACHES (Chart 13205)

West Passage

18050	**Point Judith Light**	41 21.7 71 28.9	Oc (3) W 15s 5s fl 2s ec. 2s fl 2s ec. 2s fl 2s ec.	65	16	Octagonal tower, lower half white, upper half brown. 51	HORN: I blast ev 15s (2s bl).
18051	**Point Judith Radiobeacon**	41 21.7 71 28.9	PJ (•——• •———)		20		FREQ: 325 kHz. Antenna 36 feet, 195° from light tower.
18055	*Point Judith Lighted Whistle Buoy 2*	41 19.3 71 28.6	Fl R 4s		4	Red.	
18060	Point Judith Bell Buoy 4					Red.	
18065	Nebraska Shoal Buoy 2NS	41 21.0 71 34.6				Red nun.	
18070	*Block Island North Reef Lighted Bell Buoy 1Bl*	41 15.5 71 34.6	Fl G 4s		4	Green.	

177

(1) No.	(2) Name and location	(3) Position	(4) Characteristic	(5) Height	(6) Range	(7) Structure	(8) Remarks

BLOCK ISLAND SOUND AND APPROACHES (Chart 13205) N/W

West Passage

18075	**Block Island North Light**	41 13.7 71 34.6	**Fl W** 5s	58	13	Black tower on grey granite dwelling. 52	

Point Judith Harbor of Refuge

18080	– EAST ENTRANCE LIGHT 2	41 21.5 71 29.6	**Fl R** 4s	31	5	TR on white pile structure.	
18085	– EAST ENTRANCE LIGHT 3	41 21.6 71 29.9	**Fl G** 4s	39	5	SG on post on concrete base.	
18090	– MAIN BREAKWATER CENTER LIGHT	41 21.3 71 30.5	**Fl W** 2.5s	37	7	NR on post on concrete base.	
18095	– WEST ENTRANCE LIGHT 2	41 21.7 71 30.8	**Fl R** 4s	35	5	TR on post on concrete base.	
18100	– WEST ENTRANCE LIGHT 3	41 21.9 71 30.9	**Fl G** 6s	35	6	SG on post on concrete base.	HORN: 1 blast ev 30s (3s bl).
18105	South Lump Buoy					Red and green bands; nun.	
18110	Point Judith Harbor Buoy 2					Red nun.	
18115	Point Judith Harbor Buoy 4					Red nun.	
18120	Point Judith Harbor Buoy 6					Red nun.	
18125	Point Judith Inner Harbor Daybeacon 8	41 22.5 71 30.8				TR on spindle.	

Great Island Channel

18126	– Buoy 1					Green can.	
18127	– Buoy 3					Green can.	
18128	– Buoy 5					Green can.	

Point Judith Pond

18130	– Junction Buoy					Red and green bands; nun.	
18135	– Channel Buoy 2					Red nun.	
18140	– Channel Buoy 2A					Red nun.	
18145	– Channel Buoy 2B					Red nun.	
18150	– Channel Buoy 3					Green can.	
18155	– Channel Buoy 4					Red nun.	
18160	– Channel Buoy 5					Green can.	
18165	– Channel Buoy 6					Red nun.	
18170	– Channel Buoy 6A					Red nun.	
18175	– Channel Buoy 7					Green can.	
18180	– Channel Buoy 8					Red nun.	
18185	– Channel Buoy 8A					Red nun.	
18190	– Channel Buoy 9					Green can.	

(1) No.	(2) Name and location	(3) Position	(4) Characteristic	(5) Height	(6) Range	(7) Structure	(8) Remarks

		N/W					
	BLOCK ISLAND SOUND AND APPROACHES (Chart 13205)						
	Point Judith Pond						
18195	– Channel Buoy 9A					Green can.	
18200	– Channel Buoy 10					Red nun.	
18205	– Channel Buoy 11					Green can.	
18210	– Channel Buoy 12					Red nun.	
18215	– Channel Buoy 14					Red nun.	
18220	– Channel Buoy 15					Green can.	
18225	– Channel Buoy 16					Red nun.	
18230	– Channel Buoy 18					Red nun.	
18235	– Channel Buoy 19					Green can.	
18240	– Channel Buoy 20					Red nun.	
18245	– Channel Buoy 21					Green can.	
18250	– Channel Buoy 24	41 23.4 71 29.8				Red nun.	
18255	– Channel Buoy 25					Green can.	
	BLOCK ISLAND (Chart 13217)						
	Block Island						
18260	Clay Head Buoy 3 Marks rock.					Green can.	
18265	– Northeast Whistle Buoy 5					Green.	
18270	– Old Harbor Channel Bell Buoy 1					Green.	
18275	– Old Harbor Channel Buoy 5 North end of shoal.					Green can.	
18280	– Old Harbor Channel Buoy 6					Red nun.	
18285	– Old Harbor Channel Buoy 7					Green can.	
18290	– Old Harbor Point Buoy 7	41 09.3 71 32.5				Green can.	
18295	Southeast Point Buoy 9	41 08.9 71 32.8				Green can.	
18300	– BREAKWATER LIGHT 3	41 10.6 71 33.3	Fl G 2.5s	27	8	SG on white skeleton tower, white house, concrete base.	HORN: 2 blasts ev 30s (2s bl 2s si 2s bl 24s si).
18305	**– Breakwater Outer Basin Light 8**	41 10.5 71 33.4	F R	23	11	TR on skeleton tower.	Lighted throughout 24 hours.
18310	Black Rock Point Buoy 2 On south side of rock.	41 08.4 71 35.8				Red nun.	
18315	*Southwest Point Lighted Whistle Buoy 4*	41 08.7 71 37.4	Fl R 6s		4	Red.	

(1) No.	(2) Name and location	(3) Position	(4) Characteristic	(5) Height	(6) Range	(7) Structure	(8) Remarks

BLOCK ISLAND (Chart 13217)

N/W

Block Island

(1) No.	(2) Name and location	(3) Position	(4) Characteristic	(5) Height	(6) Range	(7) Structure	(8) Remarks
18320	Dickens Point Shoal Bell Buoy 6					Red.	
	Great Salt Pond						
18325	– Entrance Bell Buoy 2	41 12.1 71 35.7				Red.	
18330	– BREAKWATER LIGHT 4	41 12.0 71 35.6	F R	49	8	TR on white cylindrical tower; red top.	HORN: 1 blast ev 10s (1s bl).
18335	– Entrance Buoy 5	41 12.0 71 35.5				Green can.	
18340	– Entrance Buoy 7					Green can.	
18345	– Entrance Buoy 8					Red nun.	
18355	– Buoy 10					Red nun.	
18360	– Buoy 11					Green can.	
18365	– Buoy 12					Red nun.	
18370	– Buoy 13	41 11.2 71 34.7				Green can.	
18375	– Buoy 14					Red nun.	

RHODE ISLAND – First District

BLOCK ISLAND SOUND AND APPROACHES (Chart 13205)

(1) No.	(2) Name and location	(3) Position	(4) Characteristic	(5) Height	(6) Range	(7) Structure	(8) Remarks
18380	**Watch Hill Light**	41 18.2 71 51.5	Al Oc W (2) R 15s 10.0s Wlt 1.1s ec 0.3s Rfl 2.2s ec 0.3s Rfl 1.1s ec	61	W 15 R 13	Square, gray granite tower attached to white building.	HORN: 1 blast ev 30s (3s bl). Emergency light of reduced intensity when main light is extinguished. Lighted throughout 24 hours.
18381	**Watch Hill Radiobeacon**	41 18.2 71 51.5	WH (•— ••••)		10		FREQ: 306 kHz, V. Antenna 136 yards, 021° from light.
18385	*Watch Hill Lighted Whistle Buoy WH*	41 15.8 71 51.0	Mo (A) W		6	Red and white stripes.	

NEW YORK – First District

BLOCK ISLAND SOUND AND GARDINERS BAY (Chart 13209)

(1) No.	(2) Name and location	(3) Position	(4) Characteristic	(5) Height	(6) Range	(7) Structure	(8) Remarks
18390	*Cerberus Shoal Lighted Gong Buoy 9* Northeast of shoal.	41 10.4 71 57.2	Fl G 4s		4	Green.	
18395	**Race Rock Light**	41 14.6 72 02.8	Fl R 10s	67	19	Granite tower attached to dwelling, on granite pier. 45	Lighted throughout 24 hours. HORN: 2 blasts ev 30s (2s bl-2s si-2s bl-24s si). Horn points southeast. Emergency light of reduced intensity when main light is extinguished.
18400	Race Point Buoy 2 On west edge of shoal.					Red nun.	

(1) No.	(2) Name and location	(3) Position	(4) Characteristic	(5) Height	(6) Range	(7) Structure	(8) Remarks
	BLOCK ISLAND SOUND AND GARDINERS BAY (Chart 13209)	N/W					
18405	*Valiant Rock Lighted Bell* *Buoy 1A* Northerly of rock.	41 13.8 72 04.0	Q G		4	Green.	
18410	**Little Gull Island Light**	41 12.4 72 06.5	F W	91	18	Gray granite tower, attached to red dwelling on pier.	HORN: 1 blast ev 15ˢ (2ˢ bl). Operates continuously. Emergency light of reduced intensity when main light is extinguished. Lighted throughout 24 hours.
18411	**Little Gull Island** **Radiobeacon**	41 12.4 72 06.5	J (•———)		20		FREQ: 306 kHz, II. Antenna 60 yards, 200° from light tower.
18415	Little Gull Island Reef Buoy 1 On east side of shoal spot.					Green can.	
18420	*Block Island Sound* *South Entrance* *Obstruction Lighted* *Buoy BIS*	41 06.9 71 43.1	Fl (2+1) G 6ˢ		4	Green and red bands.	
18425	*Endeavor Shoals Lighted* *Gong Buoy 1*	41 06.1 71 46.3	Fl G 4ˢ		4	Green.	
18435	Blackfish Rock Buoy 3 On north side of rock.					Green can.	
18440	*Shagwong Rock Lighted* *Buoy SR* On northeast side of rock.		Fl (2+1) G 6ˢ		4	Green and red bands.	
18445	*Shagwong Reef Lighted* *Bell Buoy 7SR* On north side of reef.	41 07.0 71 54.8	Fl G 2.5ˢ		4	Green.	
18450	*Montauk Harbor Entrance* *Lighted Bell Buoy M*	41 05.1 71 56.4	Mo (A) W		6	Red and white stripes with red spherical topmark.	
18455	MONTAUK EAST JETTY LIGHT 1	41 04.8 71 56.3	Fl G 4ˢ	30	4	SG on skeleton tower.	
18460	**Montauk West Jetty** **Light 2**	41 04.7 71 56.4	Fl R 5ˢ	32	14	TR on skeleton tower.	HORN: 1 blast ev 30ˢ (3ˢ bl).
18465	Montauk Channel Shoal Buoy 1S					Green can.	Removed when endangered by ice.
18470	Montauk Harbor West Side Daybeacon Marks rocks near edge of channel.					NW on pile worded DANGER ROCK.	Sides of daymark form 45° angle to the centerline of channel with apex toward channel.
	Montauk Harbor						
18475	– Buoy 1					Green can.	Maintained from May 1 to Nov. 1. Private aid.
18480	– Buoy 3					Green can.	Maintained from May 1 to Nov. 1. Private aid.

(1) No.	(2) Name and location	(3) Position	(4) Characteristic	(5) Height	(6) Range	(7) Structure	(8) Remarks
	NEW YORK – First District						
	N/W **BLOCK ISLAND SOUND AND GARDINERS BAY** (Chart 13209)						
	Montauk Harbor						
18485	– Buoy 5					Green can.	Maintained from May 1 to Nov. 1. Private aid.
18490	– Buoy 7					Green can.	Maintained from May 1 to Nov. 1. Private aid.
18495	– Buoy 8					Red nun.	Maintained from May 1 to Nov. 1 Private aid.
18500	– Buoy 9					Green can.	Maintained from May 1 to Nov. 1. Private aid.
18505	– Buoy 10					Red nun.	Maintained from May 1 to Nov. 1. Private aid.
18510	– Buoy 11					Green can.	Maintained from May 1 to Nov. 1. Private aid.
18515	– Buoy 12					Red nun.	Maintained from May 1 to Nov. 1. Private aid.
18520	– Buoy 13					Green can.	Maintained from May 1 to Nov. 1. Private aid.
18525	– Buoy 15					Green can.	Maintained from May 1 to Nov. 1. Private aid.
	Lake Montauk						
18530	– Buoy 1					Green Spar.	Maintained from May 1 to Nov. 1. Private aid.
18535	– Buoy 3					Green can.	Maintained from May 1 to Nov. 1. Private aid.
18540	– Buoy 4					Red nun.	Maintained from May 1 to Nov. 1. Private aid.
18545	– Buoy 5					Green can.	Maintained from May 1 to Nov. 1. Private aid.
18550	– Buoy 6					Red nun.	Maintained from May 1 to Nov. 1. Private aid.
18555	– Buoy 7					Green can.	Maintained from May 1 to Nov. 1. Private aid.
18560	– Buoy 8					Red nun.	Maintained from May 1 to Nov. 1. Private aid.

(1) No.	(2) Name and location	(3) Position	(4) Characteristic	(5) Height	(6) Range	(7) Structure	(8) Remarks

	BLOCK ISLAND SOUND AND GARDINERS BAY (Chart 13209)	N/W					
	Montauk Harbor						
18565	MONTAUK YACHT CLUB LIGHT	41 04.2 71 56.0	F W		65	On lighthouse tower.	Private aid.

CONNECTICUT – First District

	FISHERS ISLAND SOUND (Chart 13214)						
	Southeast Entrance						
18570	Catumb Passage Buoy 1C Off rock.	41 17.4 71 52.9				Green can.	
18575	Catumb Passage Buoy 3C Northeast side of Catumb Rocks.					Green can.	
18580	Catumb Rocks Buoy 2 Southwest of reef.					Red nun.	
18585	*Lords Passage Lighted Whistle Buoy L*	41 17.4 71 54.3	Mo (A) W		6	Red and white stripes with red spherical topmark.	
18590	Lords Passage Buoy 2L	41 17.5 71 54.0				Red nun.	
18595	Wicopesset Passage Bell Buoy W					Red and white stripes with red spherical topmark.	
18600	Wicopesset Passage Rock Buoy WP On north side of rock.					Green and red bands; can.	
	Main Channel						
18605	*Gangway Rock Lighted Bell Buoy 2*	41 18.0 71 51.5	Fl R 6s		4	Red.	Removed when endangered by ice.
18610	Watch Hill Reef Gong Buoy 1 On east side of reef.					Green.	
18615	Watch Hill Passage Buoy 3	41 17.9 71 51.7				Green can.	
18620	Sugar Reef Buoy 5					Green can.	
18625	*Napatree Point Ledge Lighted Bell Buoy 6*		Fl R 4s		4	Red.	
18630	Wicopesset Rock Buoy 7 Northeast of rock.					Green can.	
18635	Wicopesset Ledge Buoy 9					Green can.	
18640	Wicopesset Island Buoy 11					Green can.	
18645	Latimer Reef North Buoy N					Green and red bands; can.	
18650	Latimer Reef East Buoy E					Red and green bands; nun.	
18655	Seal Rocks Northeast Buoy S					Green and red bands; can.	
18660	Seal Rocks Buoy 13 On north side of rocks.					Green can.	

(1) No.	(2) Name and location	(3) Position	(4) Characteristic	(5) Height	(6) Range	(7) Structure	(8) Remarks

FISHERS ISLAND SOUND (Chart 13214) N/W

Main Channel

No.	Name and location	Position	Characteristic	Height	Range	Structure	Remarks
18665	LATIMER REEF LIGHT	41 18.3 71 56.0	Fl W 6s	55	9	White conical tower, brown midway of height; brown cylinder. 49	BELL: 2 strokes ev 15s.
18670	Youngs Rock Buoy 15 At north end of rock.					Green can.	
18675	Eel Grass Ground Southeast Buoy 16					Red nun.	
18680	East Clump Buoy 17	41 17.8 71 57.6				Green can.	
18685	Eel Grass Ground Northwest Buoy 18					Red nun.	
18690	*Ram Island Reef Lighted Bell Buoy 20*	41 18.2 71 58.4	Fl R 4s		4	Red.	
18695	Ram Island Reef Daybeacon RI On rocks.					NW on tower worded DANGER ROCKS.	
18700	Middle Clump Buoy 19					Green can.	
18705	Sweepers Ground Obstruction Buoy S					Red and green bands; nun.	
18710	Intrepid Rock Buoy IR On southeast side of rock					Red and green bands; nun.	
18715	Groton Long Point Buoy 22 On southwest end of reef.					Red nun.	
18720	Groton Long Point Buoy 24 On southwest side of 1/2 foot spot.					Red nun.	
18725	NORTH DUMPLING LIGHT	41 17.3 72 01.2	F W (R sector)	94	W 9 R 7	Square house with light tower. 60	HORN: 1 blast ev 30s (3s bl). Operates automatically. Red from 257° to 023°.
18730	Horseshoe Reef Buoy 26 On southwest side of reef.					Red nun.	
18735	SEAFLOWER REEF LIGHT On southwest part of reef.	41 17.7 72 02.0	Fl W 4s	28	7	NG on skeleton tower.	

Stonington Harbor

No.	Name and location	Position	Characteristic	Height	Range	Structure	Remarks
18740	– Approach Buoy 2	41 18.7 71 54.6				Red nun.	
18745	– Approach Gong Buoy 3 On southeast end of Noyes Shoal.					Green.	
18750	STONINGTON OUTER BREAKWATER LIGHT 4	41 19.0 71 54.5	Fl R 4s	46	5	TR on skeleton tower, small house, concrete base.	HORN: 1 blast ev 10s (1s bl).
18755	STONINGTON BREAKWATER LIGHT 5	41 19.5 71 54.8	Fl G 4s	31	5	SG on skeleton tower, concrete base.	
18760	Stonington Point Junction Buoy SP					Red and green bands; nun.	

(1) No.	(2) Name and location	(3) Position	(4) Characteristic	(5) Height	(6) Range	(7) Structure	(8) Remarks

FISHERS ISLAND SOUND (Chart 13214) N/W

Stonington Harbor

(1) No.	(2) Name and location	(3) Position	(4) Characteristic	(5) Height	(6) Range	(7) Structure	(8) Remarks
18765	STONINGTON INNER BREAKWATER LIGHT 8	41 19.8 71 54.6	Fl R 4s	27	5	TR on skeleton tower, concrete base.	
18770	– Buoy 7					Green can.	
18775	– Buoy 10 Marks end of outfall.					Red nun.	

Little Narragansett Bay

Channel buoys located 20-60 feet outside limit.

(1) No.	(2) Name and location	(3) Position	(4) Characteristic	(5) Height	(6) Range	(7) Structure	(8) Remarks
18780	*Academy Rock Lighted Buoy 2* Marks west side of rock.	41 19.6 71 54.3	Fl R 4s		3	Red.	Removed when endangered by ice.
18785	– Entrance Buoy 4 Marks northwesterly edge of shoal.					Red nun.	
18790	– *Entrance Lighted Buoy 3*		Fl G 4s		3	Green.	Removed when endangered by ice.
18795	– Buoy 5A On south side of rock.					Green can.	
18800	– Buoy 5					Green can.	
18805	– Buoy 6					Red nun.	
18810	– Channel Buoy 7	41 19.8 71 53.3				Green can.	
18815	– *Channel Lighted Buoy 9* 180 feet outside channel limit.		Fl G 4s		3	Green.	Removed when endangered by ice.
18820	– Channel Buoy 10					Red nun.	
18825	– Channel Buoy 11					Green can.	
18830	– Channel Buoy 12					Red nun.	
18835	– *Channel Lighted Buoy 13*		Fl G 2.5s		3	Green.	Removed when endangered by ice.
18840	– Channel Buoy 14					Red nun.	
18845	– Channel Buoy 16					Red nun.	
18850	– Channel Buoy 18					Red nun.	
18855	– *Channel Lighted Buoy 19* Marks south side of rock.		Fl G 4s		3	Green.	Removed when endangered by ice.
18860	Dennison Rock Buoy 2 Marks south side of rock.					Red nun.	

Pawcatuck River

Channel buoys located 20-30 feet outside channel limit.

(1) No.	(2) Name and location	(3) Position	(4) Characteristic	(5) Height	(6) Range	(7) Structure	(8) Remarks
18865	– Buoy 1 On south edge of shoal.	41 19.4 71 51.4				Green can.	

CONNECTICUT – First District

N/W
FISHERS ISLAND SOUND (Chart 13214)

Pawcatuck River

Channel buoys located 20-30 feet outside channel limit.

(1) No.	(2) Name and location	(3) Position	(4) Characteristic	(5) Height	(6) Range	(7) Structure	(8) Remarks
18870	– Buoy 3 On south point of shoal.					Green can.	
18875	– Channel Buoy 4 On south point of shoal.					Red nun.	
18880	– Channel Buoy 6					Red nun.	
18885	– Channel Buoy 7					Green can.	
18890	– Channel Buoy 8					Red nun.	
18895	– Channel Buoy 10					Red nun.	
18900	– Channel Buoy 12 On west edge of rocky area.					Red nun.	
18905	– Channel Buoy 14					Red nun.	
18910	– Channel Buoy 16					Red nun.	
18915	– Channel Buoy 17					Green can.	
18920	– Channel Buoy 19					Black can.	Private aid.
18925	Thompson Cove Buoy 1					Black can.	Maintained from May 1 to Nov. 30. Private aid.
18930	Thompson Cove Buoy 3					Black can.	Maintained from May 1 to Nov. 30. Private aid.
18935	– Channel Buoy 20					Red nun.	Private aid.
18940	– Channel Buoy 22					Red nun.	Private aid.
18945	– Channel Buoy 24					Red nun.	Private aid.
18950	– Channel Buoy 24A					Red nun.	Private aid.
18955	– Channel Buoy 25					Green can.	Private aid.
18960	– Channel Buoy 26					Red nun.	Private aid.
18965	– Channel Buoy 26A					Red nun.	Private aid.
18970	– Channel Buoy 27					Green can.	Private aid.
18975	– Channel Buoy 27A					Green can.	Private aid.
18980	– Channel Buoy 28					Red nun.	Private aid.
18985	Gavitt Point Outfall Buoy	41 21.2 71 50.2				White with orange bands and diamond worded DANGER SUB PIPE.	Private aid.
	Watch Hill Cove						
18990	– *Channel Lighted Buoy 2*	41 18.9 71 51.7	Fl R 4s		3	Red.	Removed when endangered by ice.
18995	– Channel Buoy 1					Green can.	

(1) No.	(2) Name and location	(3) Position	(4) Characteristic	(5) Height	(6) Range	(7) Structure	(8) Remarks
			CONNECTICUT – First District				
	FISHERS ISLAND SOUND (Chart 13214)	N/W					
	Silver Eel Pond						
19825	– LIGHT 2	41 15.5 72 02.0	Fl R 4s	14		Dolphin.	Private aid.
			LONG ISLAND SOUND (Connecticut and New York) – First District				
	LONG ISLAND SOUND (Eastern Part) (Chart 12354)						
19830	*Barlett Reef Lighted Bell Buoy 4*	41 15.6 72 08.4	Fl R 4s		4	Red.	Removed when endangered by ice.
19835	**Bartlett Reef Light** On south end of reef.	41 16.5 72 08.2	Fl W 5s	35	12	NR on skeleton tower.	HORN: 2 blasts ev 60s (3s bl-3s si-3s bl-51s si).
19840	Bartlett Reef Buoy 1A					Green can.	
19845	*Plum Island Lighted Whistle Buoy PI*	41 13.3 72 10.8	Mo (A) W		6	Red and white stripes with red spherical topmark.	
19850 26110	*Plum Gut Lighted Bell Buoy 2PG*		Fl R 4s		4	Red.	
19855 26105	PLUM GUT LIGHT	41 10.4 72 12.7	Fl W 2.5s	55	5	On brick shed.	
19860 26090	**Orient Point Light**	41 09.8 72 13.4	Fl W 5s	64	17	Black conical tower with white band in center.	HORN: 2 blasts ev 30s (2s bl-2s si-2s bl-24s si). Emergency light of reduced intensity when main light is extinguished. Lighted throughout 24 hours.
19865	Hatchett Reef Buoy 6 On south end of reef.					Red nun.	
19870	*Saybrook Bar Lighted Bell Buoy 8* On south point of shoal.	41 14.9 72 18.8	Fl R 4s		4	Red.	
19875	Long Sand Shoal East End Buoy E	41 14.6 72 19.4				Red and green bands; nun.	
19880 21160	**Saybrook Breakwater Light**	41 15.8 72 20.6	Fl G 6s	58	11	White conical tower on brown cylindrical pier. 49	HORN: 1 blast ev 30s (3s bl). Emergency light of reduced intensity when main light is extinguished. Lighted throughout 24 hours.
19881 21161	**Saybrook Breakwater Radiobeacon**	41 15.8 72 20.6	SB (••• –•••)		10		FREQ: 320 kHz. Antenna at light tower.
19885	Orient Shoal Buoy 3 On northeast side of shoal.	41 09.0 72 19.8				Green can.	
19895	*Long Sand Shoal Lighted Bell Buoy 8A*	41 13.5 72 23.1	Q R		4	Red.	
19900	*Cornfield Lighted Whistle Buoy CF*	41 11.3 72 22.3	Mo (A) W		6	Red and white stripes with red spherical topmark.	
19905	*Long Sand Shoal West End Lighted Horn Buoy W* At west point of shoal.	41 13.6 72 27.6	Fl (2+1) R 6s		4	Red and green bands.	HORN: 1 blast ev 30 (3 bl).

(1) No.	(2) Name and location	(3) Position	(4) Characteristic	(5) Height	(6) Range	(7) Structure	(8) Remarks
			LONG ISLAND SOUND (Connecticut and New York) – First District				
	LONG ISLAND SOUND (Eastern Part) (Chart 12354)	N/W					
19910	**Horton Point Light**	41 05.1 72 26.8	Fl G 10ˢ	103	14	White square tower, dwelling attached.	
19911	**Horton Point Radiobeacon**	41 05.1 72 26.8	HP (•••• •—–•)		20		FREQ: 306 kHz, III, VI. Antenna 72 yards 162° from Light tower.
19915	Sixmile Reef Lighted Bell Buoy 8C At southerly edge of reef.		Fl R 4ˢ		4	Red.	
19920	Twenty-Eight Foot Shoal Lighted Buoy TE	41 09.3 72 30.4	Fl (2+1) R 6ˢ		4	Red and green bands.	
19925	Kimberly Reef Lighted Horn Buoy KR	41 12.8 72 37.4	Fl (2+1) R 6ˢ		4	Red and green bands.	HORN: 1 blast ev 30ˢ (3ˢ bl).
19930	**Falkner Island Light**	41 12.7 72 39.2	Fl W 10ˢ	94	13	White octagonal tower. 46	
19935	Goose Island Lighted Bell Buoy 10GI Off south end of shoal.	41 12.1 72 40.5	Fl R 4ˢ		4	Red.	
19940	SACHEM HEAD BREAKWATER LIGHT On rock.	41 14.8 72 42.7	Fl R 3ˢ			Pile.	Maintained from June 1 to Oct. 1. Private aid.
19945	BRANFORD REEF LIGHT	41 13.3 72 48.4	Fl W 6ˢ	30	7	NR on skeleton tower.	
19950	Townsend Ledge Lighted Bell Buoy 10A Off south edge of ledge.		Fl R 4ˢ		4	Red.	
19955	New Haven Dumping Ground Lighted Buoy SP	41 09.0 72 53.2	Fl Y 4ˢ		5	Yellow.	
19960	CLIS Dumping Ground Lighted Buoy CDA	41 09.3 72 53.4	Fl Y 4ˢ		5	Yellow.	Maintained from June 1 to Oct. 1. Private aid.
19965 22425	New Haven Harbor Lighted Whistle Buoy NH	41 12.1 72 53.8	Mo (A) W		6	Red and white stripes with red spherical topmark.	
19970 22470	**Southwest Ledge Light**	41 14.1 72 54.7	Fl R 5ˢ	57	13	White octagonal house on brown cylindrical pier.	HORN: 1 blast ev 15ˢ (2ˢ bl). Emergency light of reduced intensity when main light is extinguished.
19975 22485	NEW HAVEN LIGHT	41 13.3 72 56.6	Fl W 4ˢ	35	7	NG on pipe tower.	
19980	Pond Point Shoal Buoy 12 On south point of shoal.					Red nun.	
19985	Charles Island Lighted Bell Buoy 16 South point of shoal.	41 11.0 73 03.1	Fl R 4ˢ		5	Red.	
19990	**Stratford Point Light**	41 09.1 73 06.2	Fl (2) W 20ˢ	52	16	White conical tower, brown band midway of height.	HORN: 2 blasts ev 30ˢ (2ˢ bl-2ˢ si-2ˢ bl-24ˢ si). Emergency light (Fl W 6ˢ) of reduced intensity when main light is extinguished.

(1) No.	(2) Name and location	(3) Position	(4) Characteristic	(5) Height	(6) Range	(7) Structure	(8) Remarks

(1) No.	(2) Name and location	(3) Position	(4) Characteristic	(5) Height	(6) Range	(7) Structure	(8) Remarks
	LONG ISLAND SOUND (Eastern Part) (Chart 12354)	N/W					
19991	**Stratford Point Radiobeacon**	41 09.1 73 06.2	**SP** (••• •—••)		20		FREQ: 316 kHz, III, VI. Antenna 150 feet, 010° from light tower.
19995	Stratford Point Buoy 20 On south side of Point No Point Shoal.	41 07.8 73 07.5				Red nun.	
20000	*Stratford Point Lighted Bell Buoy 18*		Fl R 6ˢ		4	Red.	Removed when endangered by ice.
	Stratford Shoal						
20005	– Buoy 1	41 04.2 73 05.2				Green can.	
20010	– Buoy 3 Off north point of shoal.					Green can.	
20015	– **(Middle Ground) Light**	41 03.6 73 06.1	Fl W 5ˢ	60	13	Gray, granite octagonal tower projection from house on pier.	HORN: 1 blast ev 15ˢ (2ˢ bl).
20020	*– Middle Ground Lighted Bell Buoy 2 South of shoal.*		Fl R 4ˢ		4	Red.	
20025	Mount Misery Shoal Buoy 11 On northeast point of shoal.					Green can.	
	LONG ISLAND SOUND (Western Part) (Chart 12363)						
20030	**Old Field Point Light**	40 58.6 73 07.1	Al R G 24ˢ R fl 12ˢ ec G fl 12ˢ ec	74	14	Black skeleton tower adjacent to old tower.	
20031	**Old Field Point Radiobeacon**	40 58.6 73 07.1	**OP** (——— •—•)		20		FREQ: 316 kHz, II, V.
20035	Old Field Point Gong Buoy 11A Off north point of shoal.					Green.	
20040	**Penfield Reef Light**		Fl R 6ˢ	51	18	White tower on granite dwelling on pier.	HORN: 1 blast ev 15ˢ (2ˢ bl). Emergency light of reduced intensity when main light is extinguished. Lighted throughout 24 hours.
20045	*Pine Creek Point Lighted Bell Buoy 22 On south point of shoal.*		Fl R 4ˢ		4	Red.	
20050	*Cockenoe Island Shoal Lighted Bell Buoy 24 Southeast of shoal.*	41 04.5 73 19.8	Fl R 2.5ˢ		4	Red.	Removed when endangered by ice.
20055	*Norwalk Islands Lighted Bell Buoy 26 Off southeast end of shoal.*	41 03.7 73 22.0	Fl R 4ˢ		4	Red.	Removed when endangered by ice.
20060	*Eatons Neck Point Lighted Gong Buoy 11B On north end of shoal.*		Fl G 4ˢ		5	Green.	Replaced by smaller LIB when endangered by ice.
20065	Eatons Neck Lump Buoy E On east side of shoal.					Green and red bands; can.	

(1) No.	(2) Name and location	(3) Position	(4) Characteristic	(5) Height	(6) Range	(7) Structure	(8) Remarks

LONG ISLAND SOUND (Western Part) (Chart 12363)

N/W

(1) No.	(2) Name and location	(3) Position	(4) Characteristic	(5) Height	(6) Range	(7) Structure	(8) Remarks
20250	**Stepping Stones Light** On outer end of reef.	40 49.5 73 46.5	F G	46	11	Red brick on granite pier; white band on southwest face of pier.	HORN: 1 blast ev 15s (2s bl). Emergency light of reduced intensity when main light is extinguished. Lighted throughout 24 hours.
20255	Locust Point Buoy 46A					Red nun.	
20260	*Throgs Neck Lighted Bell Buoy 48* Marks southern end of shoal.		Fl R 4s		4	Red.	
20265	**Throgs Neck Light**	40 48.3 73 47.5	F R	60	11	NB on tower.	
	WATCH HILL TO NEW HAVEN HARBOR (Chart 12372)						
	North Channel (Saybrook to New Haven)						
20275	Hatchett Reef Buoy 1 On northeast point of reef.	41 16.2 72 15.7				Green can.	
20280	*Cornfield Point Shoal Lighted Bell Buoy 2* South of shoal.	41 15.0 72 23.1	Fl R 4s		4	Red.	
20285	Hen and Chickens Buoy On southeast edge of shoal.					White can with orange bands and diamond worded ROCKS.	
	Old Saybrook Rock						
20290	– Regulatory Buoy A	41 15.7 72 24.1				White can with orange bands and diamond worded ROCKS.	Private aid.
20295	– Regulatory Buoy B					White can with orange bands and diamond worded ROCKS.	Private aid.
20300	– Regulatory Buoy C					White can with orange bands and diamond worded ROCKS.	Private aid.
20305	– Regulatory Buoy D					White can with orange bands and diamond worded ROCKS.	Private aid.
	North Channel (Saybrook to New Haven)						
20310	INDIAN TOWN EAST BREAKWATER LIGHT		Fl W 2s	28		On pile.	Maintained from Apr. 15 to Nov. 15. Private aid.
20315	Crane Reef Buoy 4 On south side of reef.					Red nun.	
20320	Duck Island Reef Buoy 6 On south end of reef.					Red nun.	
20325	Stone Island Reef Buoy 8 On south side of reef.					Red nun.	
20330	Hammonasset Point Reef Buoy 10 On southwest side of shoal.					Red nun.	

(1) No.	(2) Name and location	(3) Position	(4) Characteristic	(5) Height	(6) Range	(7) Structure	(8) Remarks
			LONG ISLAND SOUND (Connecticut and New York) – First District				
		N/W					
	WATCH HILL TO NEW HAVEN HARBOR (Chart 12372)						
	North Channel (Saybrook to New Haven)						
20335	Charles Reef Buoy 14 Off south end of reef.					Red nun.	
20340	*Falkner Island Reef Lighted Gong Buoy 15* North of shoal.		Fl G 4ˢ		4	Green.	
20345	Indian Reef Southwest Buoy 16 On south side of shoal.					Red nun.	
20350	Chimney Corner Reef Buoy 20 South side of reef.					Red nun.	
20355	JOSHUA POINT LIGHT		Iso W 6ˢ	10		Gray cement base.	Visible from 345.5° to 054° with higher intensity beam toward sound. Maintained from June 1 to to Oct. 15. Private aid.
20360	*Goose Rocks Shoal Lighted Bell Buoy 22* Marks southwest end of shoal.		Fl R 4ˢ		4	Red.	
20365	*Browns Reef Lighted Bell Buoy 26* South of reefs.		Fl R 4ˢ		5	Red.	
20370	*Negro Heads Lighted Buoy 28* On south end of reef.		Fl R 4ˢ		4	Red.	Replaced by nun when endangered by ice.
20375	Five Foot Rock Buoy 32 On southwest side of rock.					Red nun.	
20380	*Cow and Calf Lighted Bell Buoy 34*	41 14.3 72 50.5	Fl R 2.5ˢ		4	Red.	
20385	Round Rock Buoy 36 On south side of shoal.					Red nun.	
	SHELTER ISLAND SOUND AND PECONIC BAYS (Chart 12358)						
	South Side						
	Mattituck Inlet						
20390	– Buoy 1					Green can.	
20395	– Gong Buoy 3A					Green.	
	LONG ISLAND SOUND (Eastern Part) (Chart 12354)						
	South Side						
	Mattituck Inlet						
20400	– BREAKWATER LIGHT MI	41 00.9 72 33.7	Fl W 4ˢ	25	6	NR on skeleton tower.	
20405	– Buoy 2					Red nun.	

(1) No.	(2) Name and location	(3) Position	(4) Characteristic	(5) Height	(6) Range	(7) Structure	(8) Remarks

LONG ISLAND SOUND (Eastern Part) (Chart 12354)
N/W

South Side

Mattituck Inlet

20410	- Buoy 3					Green can.	

Mattituck Creek

20415	- Buoy 1					Green can.	Maintained from May 1 to Oct. 31. Private aid.
20420	- Buoy 3					Green can.	Maintained from May 1 to Oct. 31. Private aid.
20425	- Buoy 5					Green can.	Maintained from May 1 to Oct. 31. Private aid.

Jacobs Point

20430	- PLATFORM LIGHTS (4)	41 00.0 72 38.8	Q W	25		On platform.	HORN: 1 blast ev 20s (2s bl). Lights flash in unison. Private aids.
20435	- Rock Buoy 3					Black can.	Private aid.
20440	- Shoal Buoy 5					Black can.	Private aid.
20442	- *Aquaculture Lighted Buoys (4)*		Fl W 2s			White with orange bands worded LONG LINE.	Private aid.
20445	Roanoke Point Shoal Buoy 5 On northwest side of shoal.	41 00.2 72 42.3				Green can.	

South Side (Mattituck to Mt. Sinai)

20450	Herod Point Shoal Buoy 7 On north point of shoal.					Green can.	
20455	Rocky Point Buoy 9 On north end of shoal.					Green can.	

APPROACHES TO NEW LONDON HARBOR (Chart 13212)

Pine Island Channel

20460	Vixen Ledge Buoy VL Marks south side of ledge.	41 18.4 72 02.9				Red and green bands; nun.	
20465	*Pine Island Channel Lighted Bell Buoy 2* On southwest point of shoal.		Fl R 4s		4	Red.	
20470	Pine Island Channel Buoy 3 On north side of reef.					Green can.	
20475	*Pine Island Lighted Buoy 1* On southern tip of shoal.	41 18.9 72 03.7	Fl G 4s		3	Green.	Removed when endangered by ice.

LONG ISLAND SOUND (Connecticut) – First District

(1) No.	(2) Name and location	(3) Position	(4) Characteristic	(5) Height	(6) Range	(7) Structure	(8) Remarks
	APPROACHES TO NEW LONDON HARBOR (Chart 13212) N/W						
	Pine Island Channel						
20477	Pine Island Channel Avery Point Breakwater Light 1A Marks end of breakwater.	41 18.9 72 03.6	Q G			SG on spindle.	Private aid.
20480	Pine Island Buoy 2 On northern tip of shoal.					Red nun.	
	West Approach						
20485	Little Goshen Reef Buoy 3 On south point of shoal.	41 17.3 72 06.7				Green can.	
20490	Goshen Ledge Buoy 5 On south end of ledge.					Green can.	
20495	Rapid Rock Buoy R On southeast side of rock					Green and red bands; can.	
20500	Cormorant Rock Ledge Buoy 7 On point of ledge east of rock.					Green can.	
20505	Sarah Ledge Buoy SL					Green and red bands; can.	
20510	*Dumping Ground Lighted Buoy NL*	41 15.8 72 05.0	Fl Y 2.5s		5	Yellow.	
	NEW LONDON HARBOR AND VICINITY (Chart 13213)						
	New London Harbor						
20515	*– Channel Lighted Buoy 2*	41 17.6 72 04.7	Fl R 2.5s		4	Red.	
20520	*– Channel Lighted Buoy 1*	41 17.6 72 04.8	Fl G 2.5s		4	Green.	
20525	*– Channel Lighted Buoy 3*		Fl G 4s		4	Green.	
20530	– Channel Buoy 4	41 18.5 72 04.8				Red nun.	
20535	Black Ledge Buoy 2					Red nun.	
20540	Black Ledge Buoy 4					Red nun.	
20545	Black Ledge Buoy 6					Red nun.	
20550	**New London Ledge Light** On west side of Southwest Ledge.	41 18.3 72 04.7	Fl (3) W R 30s 0.3s W fl 4.7s ec 0.3s W fl 4.7s ec 0.3s W fl 9.7s ec 0.3s R fl 9.7s ec	58	W 17 R 14	Red brick dwelling on square pier.	HORN: 2 blast ev 20s (2s bl-2s si-2s bl-14s si). Emergency light of reduced intensity when main light is extinguished. Lighted throughout 24 hours.
20555	*New London Dumping Ground Lighted Buoy NDA*	41 16.4 72 04.3	Fl Y 4s			Yellow.	Maintained from Oct. 1 to June 1. Private aid.
20556	*New London Research Lighted Buoy (ODAS)*	41 15.8 72 04.0	Fl Y 4s			Yellow.	Private aid.
20560	Frank Ledge Buoy F On north side of ledge.					Green and red bands; can.	

(1) No.	(2) Name and location	(3) Position	(4) Characteristic	(5) Height	(6) Range	(7) Structure	(8) Remarks

NEW LONDON HARBOR AND VICINITY (Chart 13213)

N/W

New London Harbor

(1)	(2)	(3)	(4)	(5)	(6)	(7)	(8)
20565	– Light	41 19.0 72 05.4	Iso W 6s (R sector)	89	W 17 R 14	White octagonal pyramidal tower.	Red from 000° to 041°. Covers Sarah Ledge and shoals westward.
20570	– *Channel Lighted Buoy 5*		Fl G 2.5s		4	Green.	
20575	– *Channel Lighted Buoy 6*		Fl R 2.5s		4	Red.	
20580	– LOWER WHARF LIGHT	41 20.1 72 04.9	Fl R 15s	15		Pile.	Private aid.
20585	– UPPER WHARF LIGHT		Fl R 15s	15		Pile.	Private aid.
20587	*Groton Outfall Lighted Buoy*	41 20.2 72 04.9	Iso (2) W			White with orange bands.	Private aid.
20590	– *Channel Lighted Buoy 7*	41 20.3 72 05.1	Fl G 6s		5	Green.	
20595	– Channel Buoy 8					Red nun.	
20600	Powder Island Buoy 1 On north side of Melton Ledge.					Green can.	
20605	Fort Trumbull Outfall Buoy	41 20.5 72 05.2				White can with orange bands and diamond worded OUTFALL.	Private aid.
20610	GRAVING DOCK SOUTH LIGHT		Q R	22			Private aid.
20615	GRAVING DOCK CENTER LIGHT		Q R	22			Private aid.
20620	GRAVING DOCK NORTH LIGHT		Q R	22			Private aid.
20625	GRAVING DOCK 3 SOUTH LIGHT		Q R	18			Private aid.
20630	GRAVING DOCK 3 NORTH LIGHT		Q R	18			Private aid.
20635	– Buoy 9					Green can.	
20640	– Buoy 11					Green can.	
20645	– *Channel Lighted Buoy 13*	41 21.1 72 05.2	Fl G 4s		4	Green.	
20650	– Buoy 14					Red nun.	
20655	STATE PIER LIGHT		Iso G 6s	10		Mooring island.	Private aid.
20660	– Buoy 15					Green can.	
20665	– RANGE FRONT LIGHT	41 21.8 72 05.3	Iso R 6s	36		On southeast bridge abutment of railroad bridge.	Light obscured from 040° to 310° with higher intensity beam on channel line.
20670	– RANGE REAR LIGHT 3,814 yards, 354° from front light.		F G	80		Guyed tower.	Visible on rangeline only. Note: Does not mark center of channel at far end of range.

(1) No.	(2) Name and location	(3) Position	(4) Characteristic	(5) Height	(6) Range	(7) Structure	(8) Remarks
			LONG ISLAND SOUND (Connecticut) – First District				
	N/W **NEW LONDON HARBOR AND VICINITY (Chart 13213)**						
	Upper Thames River						
	Channel buoys located 30 feet outside channel limit.						
20860	INDIAN HILL LIGHT 29		Fl G 4s	9	4	SG on skeleton tower on concrete base.	
20865	PRIDE PIER LIGHT 30		Fl R 4s	20	4	TR on pile.	
20870	– Channel Buoy 31					Green can.	
20875	BURNT HOUSE PIER LIGHT 32	41 29.7 72 04.8	Fl R 2.5s	16	4	TR on pile.	
20880	PERCHE ROCK LIGHT 33 On rock.	41 29.8 72 05.0	Fl G 4s	16	4	SG on pile.	
20885	– Channel Buoy 34					Red nun.	
20890	– Channel Buoy 35					Green can.	
20895	SAND PIER LIGHT 37		Fl G 2.5s	16	4	SG on pile.	
20900	– Channel Buoy 38					Red nun.	
20905	LOWER COAL DOCK LIGHT 40		Fl R 4s	15	3	TR on skeleton tower on concrete base.	
20910	– Channel Buoy 41	41 30.7 72 04.8				Green can.	
20915	– Channel Buoy 43					Green can.	
	NIANTIC BAY AND VICINITY (Chart 13211)						
20920	Bartlett Reef North End Buoy 1	41 17.8 72 08.5				Green can.	
20925	Two Tree Island Shoal Buoy 3					Green can.	
20930	Flat Rock Buoy 2 On southwest side of rock					Red nun.	
20935	High Rock Buoy H					Green and red bands; can.	
20940	*White Rock Lighted Bell Buoy 4*		Fl R 4s		4	Red.	
20945	Threefoot Rock Buoy 5 On east side of rock.					Green can.	
20950	Black Rock Buoy 6 On west side of rock.					Red nun.	
20955	CRESCENT PARK BREAKWATER LIGHT		Fl W 6s	8		On pile.	Maintained from Apr. 15 to Nov. 15. Private aid.
20960	Crescent Beach Daybeacon					NW on pile.	Private aid.
20965	Wigwam Rock Danger Buoy					White with orange bands worded ROCKS.	Removed when endangered by ice.
	Niantic River						
	The position of buoys frequently shifted with changing conditions.						
20970	– Channel Daybeacon 1					SG on pile.	

(1) No.	(2) Name and location	(3) Position	(4) Characteristic	(5) Height	(6) Range	(7) Structure	(8) Remarks

NIANTIC BAY AND VICINITY (Chart 13211) N/W

Niantic River

The position of buoys frequently shifted with changing conditions.

No.	Name and location					Structure	Remarks
20975	– Channel Buoy 3					Green can.	
20980	– Channel Buoy 4					Red nun.	
20985	– Channel Buoy 6					Red nun.	Removed when endangered by ice.
20990	– Channel Daybeacon 7					SG on pile.	
20995	– Channel Daybeacon 8					TR on pile.	
21005	– Channel Buoy 10					Red nun.	Removed when endangered by ice.
21010	– Channel Buoy 11					Green can.	Removed when endangered by ice.
21015	– Channel Buoy 12					Red nun.	
21020	– Channel Daybeacon 13					SG on pile.	
21025	– Channel Daybeacon 14					TR on pile.	
21030	– Channel Buoy 15					Green can.	Removed when endangered by ice.
21035	– Channel Buoy 16					Red nun.	Removed when endangered by ice.
21040	– Channel Daybeacon 17					SG on pile.	
21045	– Channel Buoy 18					Red nun.	Removed when endangered by ice.
21050	– Channel Buoy 19					Green can.	Removed when endangered by ice.
21055	– Channel Buoy 21					Green can.	Removed when endangered by ice.
21060	– Channel Buoy 21A					Green can.	Removed when endangered by ice.
21065	– Channel Buoy 22					Red nun.	Removed when endangered by ice.
21070	– Channel Buoy 22A					Red nun.	Removed when endangered by ice.
21075	– Channel Buoy 23					Green can.	Removed when endangered by ice.
21080	– Channel Daybeacon 24					TR on pile.	
21085	– Channel Buoy 25					Green can.	Removed when endangered by ice.
21090	– Channel Buoy 26					Red nun.	Removed when endangered by ice.
21095	– Channel Daybeacon 27					SG on pile.	
21100	– Channel Daybeacon 28					TR on pile.	
21105	– Channel Buoy 29					Green can.	Removed when endangered by ice.

(1) No.	(2) Name and location	(3) Position	(4) Characteristic	(5) Height	(6) Range	(7) Structure	(8) Remarks

NIANTIC BAY AND VICINITY (Chart 13211) N/W

Niantic River

The position of buoys frequently shifted with changing conditions.

21110	– Channel Buoy 30					Red nun.	Removed when endangered by ice.
	Smith Cove						
21115	– Daybeacon 1	41 20.3 72 11.1				SB on pile.	Private aid.
21120	– Daybeacon 2					TR on pile.	Private aid.
21125	– Daybeacon 4					TR on pile.	Private aid.
21130	– Daybeacon 6					TR on pile.	Private aid.
21135	– Daybeacon 8					TR on pile.	Private aid.
21140	– Daybeacon 9					SB on pile.	Private aid.
	Pattaganset River						
21145	Blackboys Rocks Buoy 2 Marks southside of rock.					Red nun.	
21150	Long Rock Buoy 4 Marks southwest side of rocky shoal.					Red nun.	
21155	Seal Rock Buoy 5 Marks south end of rock.					Green can.	

CONNECTICUT RIVER - LONG ISLAND SOUND TO DEEP RIVER (Chart 12375)

Connecticut River

21160 19880	**Saybrook Breakwater Light**	41 15.8 72 20.6	Fl G 6s	58	11	White conical tower on brown cylindrical pier. 49	HORN: 1 blast ev 30s (3s bl). Emergency light of reduced intensity when main light is extinguished. Lighted throughout 24 hours.
21161 19881	**Saybrook Breakwater Radiobeacon**	41 15.8 72 20.6	SB (••• —•••)		10		FREQ: 320 kHz. Antenna at light tower.
21165	– Buoy 2	41 15.8 72 20.5				Red nun.	
21170	Saybrook Daybeacon	41 16.1 72 20.3				White globe on granite structure.	
21175	– Buoy 4					Red nun.	
21180	**Lynde Point Light**	41 16.3 72 20.6	F W	71	14	White stone tower.	
21185	– *Lighted Buoy 5*		Fl G 4s		3	Green.	Replaced by can when endangered by ice.
21190	– Buoy 6 Marks west edge of shoal					Red nun.	
21195	– Buoy 7 Marks east edge of shoal					Green can.	

LONG ISLAND SOUND (Connecticut) – First District

BODKIN ROCK TO HARTFORD (Chart 12377) N/W

Connecticut River

No.	Name and location	Position	Characteristic	Height	Range	Structure	Remarks
22015	NORTH OIL DOCK LIGHT	41 44.3 72 38.5	F R	26		On pile.	Private aid.
22020	– LIGHT 142		Fl R 4s	34	4	TR on skeleton tower.	
22025	HARTFORD JETTY LIGHT 143		Fl G 4s	34	4	SG on skeleton tower.	
22029	Sait Island Rock Buoy	41 16.5 72 26.4				White with orange band; can.	Maintained from Apr. 1 to Nov. 30. Private aid.
22030	Westbrook Harbor Buoy Marks south side of Lobster Rock.	41 16.1 72 26.5				Red and green bands; nun.	
22031	West Beach Shoal Buoy	41 16.3 72 27.2				White with orange band; can.	Maintained from Apr. 1 to Nov. 30. Private aid.
22032	Menunketesuck Island Shoal Buoy	41 15.6 72 27.6				White with orange band; can.	Maintained from Apr. 1 to Nov. 30. Private aid.
22034	Menunketesuck Island Rock Buoy	41 15.7 72 28.0				White with orange band; can.	Maintained from Apr. 1 to Nov. 30. Private aid.

DUCK ISLAND TO MADISON REEF (Chart 12374)

Duck Island Roads

No.	Name and location	Position	Characteristic	Height	Range	Structure	Remarks
22035	DUCK ISLAND NORTH BREAKWATER LIGHT	41 15.6 72 28.5	Fl W 4s	22	7	NR on skeleton tower.	
22040	DUCK ISLAND WEST BREAKWATER LIGHT 2DI	41 15.4 72 29.1	Fl R 4s	25	5	TR on skeleton tower.	

Patchogue River

No.	Name and location	Position	Characteristic	Height	Range	Structure	Remarks
22045	– BREAKWATER LIGHT 3A	41 16.1 72 28.5	Fl G 4s	21	4	SG on skeleton tower.	
22050	– Channel Lighted Buoy 2	41 15.9 72 28.4	Fl R 4s		4	Red.	Removed when endangered by ice.
22055	– Channel Buoy 3	41 16.0 72 28.4				Green can.	
22060	– Channel Buoy 4	41 16.1 72 28.4				Red nun.	
22065	– Channel Buoy 5					Black can.	Private aid.
22066	Menunketesuck River Junction Buoy M					Green and red bands; can.	Maintained from Apr. 1 to Nov. 30. Private aid.
22070	– Channel Buoy 6					Red nun.	Private aid.
22075	– Channel Daybeacon 7					SG on pile.	Private aid.
22080	– Channel Daybeacon 8					TR on pile.	Private aid.
22085	– Channel Daybeacon 10					TR on pile.	Private aid.
22090	KELSEY POINT BREAKWATER LIGHT	41 14.6 72 30.5	Fl W 2.5s	33	7	NG on skeleton tower.	

(1) No.	(2) Name and location	(3) Position	(4) Characteristic	(5) Height	(6) Range	(7) Structure	(8) Remarks

DUCK ISLAND TO MADISON REEF (Chart 12374) N/W

Clinton Harbor

22095	– Rock Buoy C West of rock.						White nun with orange bands worded ROCKS.
22100	– *Lighted Buoy 3*		Fl G 4s	4		Green.	Removed when endangered by ice.
22105	– **Radiobeacon**	41 16.0 72 31.2	CL (—•—• •—••)	20			FREQ: 306 kHz, I, IV.

Channel buoys located 20 feet outside channel limit.

22110	– Channel Buoy 6					Red nun.	
22115	– Channel Buoy 7					Green can.	
22120	– Channel Buoy 8	41 15.8 72 31.5				Red nun.	
22125	– Channel Buoy 9					Green can.	
22130	– Channel Buoy 11					Green can.	
22135	– Channel Buoy 11A					Green can.	
22140	– Channel Buoy 12					Red nun.	Maintained from May 1 to Dec. 1. Private aid.
22145	– Channel Buoy 13					Green can.	Maintained from May 1 to Dec. 1. Private aid.
22150	– Channel Buoy 14					Red nun.	Maintained from May 1 to Dec. 1. Private aid.
22155	– Channel Buoy 16					Red nun.	Maintained from May 1 to Dec. 1. Private aid.

Hammonasset River

22156	– Daybeacon 1H	41 16.0 72 32.1				SG on pile.	Private aid.
22156.1	– Daybeacon 2H					TR on pile.	Private aid.
22156.2	– Daybeacon 3H					SG on pile.	Private aid.
22156.3	– Daybeacon 4H					TR on pile	Private aid.
22156.4	– Daybeacon 5H					SG on pile.	Private aid.
22156.5	– Daybeacon 6H					TR on pile.	Private aid.
22156.6	– Daybeacon 8H					TR on pile.	Private aid.
22156.7	– Daybeacon 9H					SG on pile.	Private aid.
22156.8	– Daybeacon 10H					TR on pile.	Private aid.
22156.9	– Daybeacon 11H					SG on pile.	Private aid.
22157	– Daybeacon 12H					TR on pile.	Private aid.
22157.1	– Daybeacon 13H					SG on pile.	Private aid.

(1) No.	(2) Name and location	(3) Position	(4) Characteristic	(5) Height	(6) Range	(7) Structure	(8) Remarks

DUCK ISLAND TO MADISON REEF (Chart 12374) N/W

Hammonasset River

(1) No.	(2) Name and location	(3) Position	(4) Characteristic	(5) Height	(6) Range	(7) Structure	(8) Remarks
22157.2	– Daybeacon 14H					TR on pile.	Private aid.
22157.3	– Daybeacon 15H					SG on pile.	Private aid.
22157.4	– Daybeacon 16H					TR on pile.	Private aid.
22157.5	– Daybeacon 17H					SG on pile.	Private aid.
22157.6	– Daybeacon 18H					TR on pile.	Private aid.
22157.7	– Daybeacon 19H					SG on pile.	Private aid.
22157.8	– Daybeacon 21H					SG on pile.	Private aid.
22157.9	– Daybeacon 22H					TR on pile.	Private aid.
22158	– Daybeacon 23H					SG on pile.	Private aid.
22158.1	– Daybeacon 24H					TR on pile.	Private aid.
22158.2	– Daybeacon 25H					SG on pile.	Private aid.
22158.3	– Daybeacon 26H					TR on pile.	Private aid.
22158.4	– Daybeacon 27H					SG on pile.	Private aid.
22158.5	– Daybeacon 28H					TR on pile.	Private aid.
22158.6	– Daybeacon 29H					SG on pile.	Private aid.
22158.7	– Daybeacon 30H					TR on pile.	Private aid.
22158.8	– Daybeacon 31H					SG on pile.	Private aid.
22158.9	– Daybeacon 32H					TR on pile.	Private aid.
22159	– Daybeacon 33H					SG on pile.	Private aid.
22159.1	– Daybeacon 34H					TR on pile.	Private aid.
22159.2	– Daybeacon 35H					SG on pile.	Private aid.
22159.3	– Daybeacon 36H					TR on pile.	Private aid.
22159.4	– Daybeacon 37H					SG on pile.	Private aid.
22159.5	– Daybeacon 38H					TR on pile.	Private aid.
22159.6	– Daybeacon 39H					SG on pile.	Private aid.
22159.7	– Daybeacon 40H					TR on pile.	Private aid.
22159.8	– Daybeacon HR	41 15.9 72 32.8				Square daymark, green and red bands.	Private aid.

GUILFORD HARBOR TO FARM RIVER (Chart 12373)

Guilford Harbor

(1) No.	(2) Name and location	(3) Position	(4) Characteristic	(5) Height	(6) Range	(7) Structure	(8) Remarks
22160	– Lighted Bell Buoy 4	41 15.0 72 39.2	Fl R 4ˢ		4	Red.	Replaced by nun when endangered by ice.
22165	Indian Reef Buoy 1 South of reef.	41 14.6 72 40.5				Green can.	
22170	– Buoy 3 On southeast side of Netties Reef.					Green can.	

LONG ISLAND SOUND (Connecticut) – First District

N/W
GUILFORD HARBOR TO FARM RIVER (Chart 12373)

Guilford Harbor

(1) No.	(2) Name and location	(3) Position	(4) Characteristic	(5) Height	(6) Range	(7) Structure	(8) Remarks
22175	– Buoy 5 On east end of reef.					Green can.	
22180	– *Channel Lighted Buoy 7*		Fl G 4s		3	Green.	Removed when endangered by ice.
22185	– Channel Buoy 9					Green can.	
22190	– Channel Buoy 10					Red nun.	
22195	– Channel Buoy 11					Green can.	
22200	– Channel Buoy 12					Red nun.	
22205	– Channel Buoy 13					Green can.	
22210	– Channel Buoy 14					Red nun.	
	West River Entrance						
22211	– Buoy 1W	41 15.4 72 39.9				Green can.	Private aid.
22211.5	– Buoy 2W	41 15.4 72 39.9				Red nun.	Private aid.
22212	– Buoy 3					Green can.	Private aid.
22212.5	– Buoy 4					Red nun.	Private aid.
22213	– Buoy 5					Green can.	Private aid.
22213.5	– Buoy 6					Red nun.	Private aid.
22214	– Buoy 7					Green can.	Private aid.
22214.5	– Buoy 8					Red nun.	Private aid.
22214.6	WEST RIVER RANGE FRONT LIGHT	41 16.1 72 40.7	Q W	16		KRW on pole.	Visible on rangeline only. Private aid.
22214.7	WEST RIVER RANGE REAR LIGHT 215 yards, 321.3° from front light.		Fl W 6s	30		KRW on pile.	Visible on rangeline only. Private aid.
	The Thimbles						
	Thimble Shoals						
22215	– Buoy 4 At southwest edge of rocky shoal.					Red nun.	
22220	– Buoy 6					Red nun.	
22225	– Buoy 8					Red nun.	
22230	– Buoy 10					Red nun.	
22235	– Buoy 11 On east side of shoal.					Green can.	
	Stony Creek						
22240	– Buoy 1	41 15.6 72 45.7				Green can.	

(1) No.	(2) Name and location	(3) Position	(4) Characteristic	(5) Height	(6) Range	(7) Structure	(8) Remarks

	GUILFORD HARBOR TO FARM RIVER (Chart 12373) N/W						
	The Thimbles						
	Stony Creek						
22245	– Buoy 3					Green can.	
22250	– Buoy 4					Red nun.	
22260	– Buoy 5	41 15.9 72 45.2				Green can.	
	The Thimbles						
22270	Commander Rocks Buoy 2CR Marks southwest end of rocks.					Red nun.	
22275	High Island East Shoal Buoy 1 South of shoal.					Green can.	
22280	East Reef Buoy 1 Marks east side of reef.	41 13.9 72 45.8				Green can.	
22285	Wheaton Reef Buoy 3 On north side of reef.					Green can.	
22290	Inner Reef North Buoy 5 Marks northeast side of rock.	41 14.5 72 46.1				Green can.	
22295	Gangway Rock Buoy 1 Marks southeast side of rock.					Green can.	
22300	Northwest Reef Buoy 2NW Marks southwest side of reef.					Red nun.	
22305	Hookers Rock Buoy 3 Southeast side of rock.					Green can.	
22310	Inner Reef South Buoy 4 Marks southwest end of reef.					Red nun.	
22315	*Pine Orchard Approach Lighted Buoy 4A* Southeast of Hookers Rock.		Fl R 4s		4	Red.	Replaced by nun when endangered by ice.
22320	Pork Rocks Buoy 5 East of rocks.					Green can.	
22325	Dick Rocks Buoy 6 West of rocks.					Red nun.	
22330	*Pine Orchard Approach Lighted Buoy 8* Marks southwest edge of rocks.	41 15.3 72 46.2	Fl R 4s		4	Red.	Removed when endangered by ice.
	Duck Island Roads						
22342	JUNIPER POINT OBSTRUCTION LIGHTS (3)	41 15.8 72 46.0	Q Y	11		On dolphins.	Private aids.

(1) No.	(2) Name and location	(3) Position	(4) Characteristic	(5) Height	(6) Range	(7) Structure	(8) Remarks

GUILFORD HARBOR TO FARM RIVER (Chart 12373) N/W

Duck Island Roads

(1) No.	(2) Name and location	(3) Position	(4) Characteristic	(5) Height	(6) Range	(7) Structure	(8) Remarks
22345	QUARRY RANGE FRONT LIGHT	41 15.9 72 46.0	F R	20		Daymark consists of white arrows, vertically arranged.	Private aid.
22350	QUARRY RANGE MIDDLE LIGHT 40 yards, 028° from front light.		F R	27		Daymark consists of white arrows, vertically arranged.	Private aid.
22355	Quarry Range Rear Daybeacon					White diamond daymark with red center ball on skeleton structure.	Private aid.

Branford Harbor

(1) No.	(2) Name and location	(3) Position	(4) Characteristic	(5) Height	(6) Range	(7) Structure	(8) Remarks
22360	*Blyn Rock Lighted Buoy 2* On south side of rock.	41 14.8 72 49.9	Fl R 4s		3	Red.	Removed when endangered by ice.
22365	Bird Rock Buoy 4 On west side of reef.					Red nun.	
22370	Lovers Island Rock Buoy 5 East of rock.					Green can.	
22375	Little Mermaid Rock Buoy 6 West of rock.					Red nun.	
22380	BIG MERMAID LIGHT 7	41 15.4 72 49.7	Fl G 4s	28	5	SG on skeleton tower.	Higher intensity beam up and down channel.

Farm River

(1) No.	(2) Name and location	(3) Position	(4) Characteristic	(5) Height	(6) Range	(7) Structure	(8) Remarks
22385	- Approach Buoy 1					Green can.	
22390	- Approach Buoy 2					Red nun.	

NEW HAVEN HARBOR (Chart 12371)

New Haven Harbor

(1) No.	(2) Name and location	(3) Position	(4) Characteristic	(5) Height	(6) Range	(7) Structure	(8) Remarks
22395	- East Entrance Buoy 1 On northeast side of shoal.	41 14.2 72 53.7				Green can.	
22400	- East Entrance Buoy 2 On southwest side of shoal.					Red nun.	
22405	- East Entrance Buoy 4 On southwest side of shoal.					Red nun.	
22410	- East Entrance Buoy 5 On northeast end of Old Head Reef.					Green can.	
22415	Adams Fall Buoy A On southwest side of shoal.					Red and green bands; nun.	
22420	- East Entrance Channel Buoy 6 On southwest end of Lighthouse Point Shoal.					Red nun.	
22425 19965	- *Lighted Whistle Buoy NH*	41 12.1 72 53.8	Mo (A) W		6	Red and white stripes with red spherical topmark.	

(1) No.	(2) Name and location	(3) Position	(4) Characteristic	(5) Height	(6) Range	(7) Structure	(8) Remarks

LONG ISLAND SOUND (Connecticut) - First District

(1) No.	(2) Name and location	(3) Position	(4) Characteristic	(5) Height	(6) Range	(7) Structure	(8) Remarks
	NEW HAVEN HARBOR (Chart 12371) N/W						
	New Haven Harbor						
22430	– OUTER CHANNEL RANGE FRONT LIGHT	41 15.7 72 56.1	F G	35		White skeleton tower with concrete base.	Higher intensity on rangeline.
22435	– OUTER CHANNEL RANGE REAR LIGHT 800 yards, 333.6° from front light.		F G	65		White skeleton tower with concrete base.	Higher intensity on rangeline.
22440	– *Channel Lighted Gong Buoy 1*		Fl G 2.5s		4	Green.	
22445	– Buoy 2					Red nun.	
22450	– Buoy 3					Green can.	
22455	– *Channel Lighted Buoy 4*	41 13.7 70 54.7	Fl R 4s		4	Red.	
22460	– *Channel Lighted Bell Buoy 6*		Fl R 2.5s		4	Red.	Replaced by LIB of reduced intensity when endangered by ice.
22465	– *Channel Lighted Buoy 7*		Fl G 2.5s		4	Green.	Replaced by smaller LIB of reduced intensity when endangered by ice.
22470 19970	**Southwest Ledge Light**	41 14.1 72 54.7	Fl R 5s	57	13	White octagonal house on cylindrical pier.	HORN: 1 blast ev 15s (2s bl). Emergency light of reduced intensity when main light is extinguished.
22475	NEW HAVEN MIDDLE BREAKWATER EAST END LIGHT		Fl G 4s	43	4	NG on skeleton tower.	
22480	NEW HAVEN MIDDLE BREAKWATER WEST END LIGHT		Fl R 4s	38	4	NR on skeleton tower.	
22485 19975	NEW HAVEN LIGHT	41 13.3 72 56.6	Fl W 4s	35	7	NG on skeleton tower.	
22490	NEW HAVEN WEST BREAKWATER WEST END LIGHT 2	41 13.5 72 57.4	Fl R 6s	29	4	TR on skeleton tower.	
22495	– *Channel Lighted Buoy 8*		Q R		4	Red.	Replaced by smaller LIB of reduced intensity when endangered by ice.
22500	– *Channel Lighted Buoy 9*		Fl G 4s		4	Green.	Replaced by can when endangered by ice.
22505	– Channel Buoy 9A					Green can.	
22510	– Channel Buoy 10					Red nun.	
22515	– *Channel Lighted Buoy 10A*		Fl R 2.5s		4	Red.	Replaced by smaller LIB of reduced intensity when endangered by ice.
22520	– Channel Buoy 12					Red nun.	
22525	– *Channel Lighted Buoy 11*		Fl G 4s		4	Green.	Replaced by can when endangered by ice.
22530	– Channel Buoy 13					Green can.	

LONG ISLAND SOUND (New York) – First District

(1) No.	(2) Name and location	(3) Position	(4) Characteristic	(5) Height	(6) Range	(7) Structure	(8) Remarks
	N/W **HEMPSTEAD HARBOR TO TALLMAN ISLAND** (Chart 12366)						
	City Island						
	Hutchinson River						
24440	– Buoy 6					Red nun.	
24445	– Buoy 7					Green can.	
	PORT JEFFERSON AND MOUNT SINAI HARBORS (Chart 12362)						
	Mount Sinai Harbor						
24460	Mount Sinai Approach Buoy M					Red and white stripes; sphere.	
24465	MOUNT SINAI BREAKWATER LIGHT	40 57.9 73 02.6	Fl G 5^s	20		Concrete pedestal.	Private aid.
24470	– West Breakwater Daybeacon 2	40 57.9 73 02.7				TR on pile.	Private aid.
24475	– Buoy 1					Black can.	Private aid.
24480	– Buoy 2A					Red nun.	Private aid.
24485	– Buoy 3					Black can.	Private aid.
24490	– Buoy 4					Red nun.	Private aid.
24495	– Buoy 5					Black can.	Private aid.
24500	– Buoy 6					Red nun.	Private aid.
24505	– Buoy 8					Red nun.	Private aid.
24510	– Buoy 10					Red nun.	Private aid.
24515	– Buoy 12					Red nun.	Private aid.
	Port Jefferson Harbor						
24520	*Port Jefferson Approach* *Lighted Whistle* *Buoy PJ*	40 59.3 73 06.4	Mo (A) W		5	Red and white stripes with red spherical topmark.	
24525	*– Entrance Lighted* *Buoy 1*	40 58.4 73 05.6	Fl G 2.5^s		4	Green.	
24530	PORT JEFFERSON EAST BREAKWATER LIGHT	40 58.3 73 05.5	Fl W 4^s	35	7	NG on skeleton tower.	
24535	*– Entrance Lighted Bell* *Buoy 2*		Fl R 2.5^s		4	Red.	
24540	PORT JEFFERSON WEST BREAKWATER LIGHT 2A		Fl R 4^s	26	5	TR on skeleton tower.	
24545	LIGHTING COMPANY BOOM LIGHT		F R	71			Private aid.
24550	– RANGE FRONT LIGHT	40 56.9 73 04.3	Q R	20		KRW on pile.	
24555	– RANGE REAR LIGHT 225 yards, 146° from front light.		F R	32		KRW on pile.	
24560	– Buoy 4					Red nun.	

(1) No.	(2) Name and location	(3) Position	(4) Characteristic	(5) Height	(6) Range	(7) Structure	(8) Remarks

PORT JEFFERSON AND MOUNT SINAI HARBORS
(Chart 12362) N/W

Port Jefferson Harbor

(1) No.	(2) Name and location	(3) Position	(4) Characteristic	(5) Height	(6) Range	(7) Structure	(8) Remarks
24565	– Lighted Bell Buoy 5		Fl G 4s		3	Green.	
24566	– Buoy 7					Green can.	
24567	– Buoy 8					Red nun.	
24568	– Buoy 9					Green can.	

Setauket Harbor

(1) No.	(2) Name and location	(3) Position	(4) Characteristic	(5) Height	(6) Range	(7) Structure	(8) Remarks
24570	– Anchorage Buoy A					Yellow nun.	Maintained from May 1 to Nov. 1. Private aid.
24575	– Anchorage Buoy B					Yellow nun.	Maintained from May 1 to Nov. 1. Private aid.
24580	– Anchorage Buoy C					Yellow nun.	Maintained from May 1 to Nov. 1. Private aid.
24585	– Buoy 1					Green can.	Maintained from May 1 to Nov. 1. Private aid.
24590	– Buoy 2					Red nun.	Maintained from May 1 to Nov. 1. Private aid.
24595	– Buoy 3					Green can.	Maintained from May 1 to Nov. 1. Private aid.
24600	– Buoy 4					Red nun.	Maintained from May 1 to Nov. 1. Private aid.
24605	– Buoy 5					Green can.	Maintained from May 1 to Nov. 1. Private aid.
24610	– Buoy 6					Red nun.	Maintained from May 1 to Nov. 1. Private aid.

LONG ISLAND SOUND (Western Part) (Chart 12363)

Smithtown Bay

(1) No.	(2) Name and location	(3) Position	(4) Characteristic	(5) Height	(6) Range	(7) Structure	(8) Remarks
24615	Stony Brook Harbor Entrance Lighted Buoy 1	40 56.3 73 09.8	Fl G 4s		4	Green.	Replaced by can from Dec. 15 to Mar. 15.
24620	Stony Brook Harbor Daybeacon	40 55.6 73 08.9				On pile.	Maintained from June 1 to Oct. 1. Private aid.

Porpoise Channel

(1) No.	(2) Name and location	(3) Position	(4) Characteristic	(5) Height	(6) Range	(7) Structure	(8) Remarks
24625	– Lighted Buoy 1		Fl G 4s			Green.	Maintained from Apr. 1 to Nov. 1. Private aid.
24630	– Lighted Buoy 2		Fl R 4s			Red.	Maintained from Apr. 1 to Nov. 1. Private aid.

(1) No.	(2) Name and location	(3) Position	(4) Characteristic	(5) Height	(6) Range	(7) Structure	(8) Remarks

TALLMAN ISLAND TO QUEENSBORO BRIDGE
(Chart 12339)

N/W

South Brother Island Channel

26015	– Lighted Buoy 3	40 47.8 73 53.6	Fl G 4s		4	Green.	
26020	– Buoy 4	40 47.6 73 53.7				Red nun.	
26025	– Lighted Buoy 5	40 47.6 73 53.6	Fl G 6s		4	Green.	
26030	– Lighted Buoy 7		Fl G 2.5s		4	Green.	
26035	Rikers Island Basin Junction Lighted Buoy RI	40 47.3 73 53.7	Fl (2+1) R 6s		4	Red and green bands.	
26040	– Buoy 9					Green can.	
26045	STEINWAY CREEK WHARF LIGHT	40 47.1 73 53.8	F R	20			Private aid.

Rikers Island Channel

26050	LAWRENCE POINT LEDGE LIGHT LP On ledge.		Fl W 4s	25	5	NR on skeleton tower.	
26055	Lawrence Point Ledge Buoy 2					Red nun.	
26060	SOUTH BROTHER ISLAND LEDGE LIGHT 3 On ledge.		Fl G 4s	17	5	SG on skeleton tower.	

BLOCK ISLAND SOUND AND GARDINERS BAY
(Chart 13209)

North Entrance

26065	Gardiners Island Shoal Buoy 1	41 07.3 72 06.7				Green can.	
26070	Constellation Rock Buoy 2 Marks 17-foot rock.	41 10.5 72 06.6				Red nun.	
26075	Gardiners Island Lighted Gong Buoy 1GI	41 09.0 72 08.9	Fl G 4s		4	Green.	
26080	Plum Island Rock Buoy 4 On south side of rock.					Red nun.	

Plum Gut

26085	Midway Shoal Buoy MS On east side of shoal.	41 09.8 72 12.6				Green and red bands; can.	
26090 19860	**Orient Point Light**	41 09.8 72 13.4	Fl W 5s	64	17	Black conical tower with white band in center.	HORN: 2 blasts ev 30s (2s bl-2s si-2s bl-24s si). Emergency light of reduced intensity when main light is extinguished. Lighted throughout 24 hours.
26095	PLUM ISLAND HARBOR EAST DOLPHIN LIGHT		F R	10	6	On dolphin.	Maintained from sundown to 0130 daily. Maintained by the U.S. Dept. of Agriculture.

NEW YORK – First District

BLOCK ISLAND SOUND AND GARDINERS BAY N/W
(Chart 13209)

North Entrance

Plum Gut

No.	Name and location	Position	Characteristic	Height	Range	Structure	Remarks
26100	PLUM ISLAND HARBOR WEST DOLPHIN LIGHT	41 10.3 72 12.4	F G	12	6	On dolphin.	HORN: 1 blast ev 10s (5s bl). Sounded occasionally when USDA vessels are navigating in the area. Maintained from sundown to 0130 daily. Maintained by the U.S. Dept. Agriculture.
26105 19855	– LIGHT	41 10.4 72 12.7	Fl W 2.5s	55	5	On brick shed.	
26110 19850	– Lighted Bell Buoy 2PG		Fl R 4s		4	Red.	

North Entrance

| 26115 | CAR FERRY LIGHT | 41 09.3
72 14.4 | F W | 18 | | On dolphin. | Private aid. |

Research Basin

Aids are maintained by the U.S. Dept. of Agiculture.

26120	– APPROACH LIGHT	41 08.9 72 14.5	Fl G 4s	14		On pile.	Maintained from sundown to 0130 daily.
26125	– Bay Daybeacon 1					On piles.	
26130	– Bay Daybeacon 3					On piles.	
26135	– LIGHT	41 09.2 72 14.5	F R	10		On pile.	HORN: 1 blast ev 30s (1s bl). Maintained from sundown to 0130 daily.

Gardiners Bay South Entrance

26140	– Lighted Bell Buoy S	41 02.2 72 03.1	Mo (A) W		6	Red and white stripes with red spherical topmark. .	Replaced by red and white striped sphere from Nov. 15 to Apr. 15.
26145	– Buoy 2					Red nun.	
26147	NAPEAGUE HARBOR CLAM RAFT LIGHT		Fl W 2.5s			NW on raft.	Maintained from May 1 to Nov. 30. Private aid.
26150	– Buoy 4					Red nun.	
26155	– Buoy 6					Red nun.	
26160	– Buoy 8					Red nun.	
26165	– Buoy 11					Green can.	
26170	Lionhead Rock Buoy 13					Green can.	
26175	Crow Shoal Buoy 14 Southwest of shoal.					Red nun.	

Threemile Harbor

| 26180 | – Entrance Lighted Bell Buoy TM | 41 02.7
72 11.3 | Mo (A) W | | 6 | Red and white stripes with red spherical topmark. | Replaced by red and white striped sphere from Nov. 15 to Apr. 15. |

PART 1 - SECTION B

COAST PILOT 2

Atlantic Coast

covering

BLOCK ISLAND SOUND+EASTERN LONG ISLAND SOUND

including

general information and appendix

contents found on page vii

United States Coast Pilot

2

Atlantic Coast:
Cape Cod to Sandy Hook

U.S. DEPARTMENT OF COMMERCE
Barbara Hackman Franklin, Secretary

National Oceanic and Atmospheric Administration (NOAA)
Dr. John A. Knauss, Under Secretary of Commerce for Oceans
  and Atmosphere, and Administrator, NOAA

National Ocean Service
W. Stanley Wilson, Assistant Administrator for Ocean Services
  and Coastal Zone Management

Washington, DC
For sale by the National Ocean Service and its sales agents.

LIMITS OF UNITED STATES COAST PILOTS

Atlantic Coast
1 Eastport to Cape Cod
2 Cape Cod to Sandy Hook
3 Sandy Hook to Cape Henry
4 Cape Henry to Key West
5 Gulf of Mexico, Puerto Rico, and Virgin Islands

Pacific Coast
7 California, Oregon, Washington, and Hawaii
8 Alaska -- Dixon Entrance to Cape Spencer
9 Alaska -- Cape Spencer to Beaufort Sea

Great Lakes
6 The Lakes and their Connecting Waterways

Preface

The United States Coast Pilot is published by the National Ocean Service (NOS), Charting and Geodetic Services (C&GS), National Oceanic and Atmospheric Administration (NOAA), pursuant to the Act of 6 August 1947 (33 U.S.C. 883a and b) and the Act of 22 October 1968 (44 U.S.C. 1310).

The Coast Pilot supplements the navigational information shown on the nautical charts. The sources for updating the Coast Pilot include, but are not limited to, field inspections conducted by NOAA, information published in Notices to Mariners, reports from NOAA Hydrographic vessels and field parties, information from other Government agencies, State and local governments, maritime and pilotage associations, port authorities, and mariners.

This volume of Coast Pilot 2, Atlantic Coast, Cape Cod to Sandy Hook, cancels the 1991 (25th) Edition.

Notice.-Amendments are issued to this publication through U.S. Coast Guard Local Notices to Mariners. A subscription to the Local Notice to Mariners is available upon application to the appropriate Coast Guard District Commander (Aids to Navigation Branch). Consult appendix for address. All amendments are also issued in Defense Mapping Agency Notices to Mariners.

Mariners and others are urged to report promptly to the National Ocean Service errors, omissions, or any conditions found to differ from or to be additional to those published in the Coast Pilot or shown on the charts in order that they may be fully investigated and proper corrections made. A Coast Pilot Report form is included in the back of this book and a Marine Information Report form is published in the Defense Mapping Agency Hydrographic/Topographic Center Notice to Mariners for your convenience. These reports and/or suggestions for increasing the usefulness of the Coast Pilot should be sent to

Director,
Coast and Geodetic Survey (N/CG 2211),
National Ocean Service, NOAA,
Rockville, MD 20852-3806.

COAST PILOT 2 – GRAPHIC CHAPTER INDEX

IV

Contents

1. GENERAL INFORMATION

(1) The **UNITED STATES COAST PILOT.**–The National Ocean Service Coast Pilot is a series of nine nautical books that cover a wide variety of information important to navigators of U.S. coastal and intracoastal waters, and the waters of the Great Lakes. Most of this book information cannot be shown graphically on the standard nautical charts and is not readily available elsewhere. The subjects in the Coast Pilot include, but are not limited to, channel descriptions, anchorages, bridge and cable clearances, currents, tide and water levels, prominent features, pilotage, towage, weather, ice conditions, wharf descriptions, dangers, routes, traffic separation schemes, small-craft facilities, and Federal regulations applicable to navigation.

(2) **Notice-Amendments are issued to this publication through U.S. Coast Guard Local Notices to Mariners. A subscription to the Local Notice to Mariners is available upon application to the appropriate Coast Guard District Commander (Aids to Navigation Branch). Consult appendix for address.** All amendments are also issued in Defense Mapping Agency Notices to Mariners.

(3) **Bearings.**–These are true, and when given in degrees are clockwise from 000°(north) to 359°. Light-sector bearings are toward the light.

(4) **Bridges and cables.**–Vertical clearances of bridges and overhead cables are in feet above mean high water unless otherwise stated; clearances of drawbridges are for the closed position, although the open clearances are also given for vertical-lift bridges. Clearances given in the Coast Pilot are those approved for nautical charting, and are supplied by the U.S. Coast Guard (bridges) and U.S. Army Corps of Engineers (cables); they may be as-built (verified by actual inspection after completion of structures) or authorized (design values specified in permit issued prior to construction). No differentiation is made in the Coast Pilot between as-built and authorized clearances. (See charts for horizontal clearances of bridges, as these are given in the Coast Pilot only when they are less than 50 feet.) Submarine cables are rarely mentioned.

(5) **Cable ferries.**–Cable ferries are guided by cables fastened to shore and sometimes propelled by a cable rig attached to the shore. Generally, the cables are suspended during crossings and dropped to the bottom when the ferries dock. Where specific operating procedures are known they are mentioned in the text. Since operating procedures vary, mariners are advised to exercise extreme caution and seek local knowledge. **DO NOT ATTEMPT TO PASS A MOVING CABLE FERRY.**

(6) **Courses.**–These are true and are given in degrees clockwise from 000°(north) to 359°. The courses given are the courses to be made good.

(7) **Currents.**–Stated current velocities are the averages at strength. Velocities are in knots, which are nautical miles per hour. Directions are the true directions to which the currents set.

(8) **Depths.**–Depth is the vertical distance from the chart datum to the bottom and is expressed in the same units (feet, meters or fathoms) as soundings on the applicable chart. (See Chart Datum this chapter for further detail.) The **controlling depth** of a channel is the least depth within the limits of the channel; it restricts the safe use of the channel to drafts of less than that depth. The **centerline controlling depth** of a channel applies only to the channel centerline;

lesser depths may exist in the remainder of the channel. The **midchannel controlling depth** of a channel is the controlling depth of only the middle half of the channel. **Federal project depth** is the design dredging depth of a channel constructed by the Corps of Engineers, U.S. Army; the project depth may or may not be the goal of maintenance dredging after completion of the channel, and, for this reason, project depth must not be confused with controlling depth. **Depths alongside wharves** usually have been reported by owners and/or operators of the waterfront facilities, and have not been verified by Government surveys; since these depths may be subject to change, local authorities should be consulted for the latest controlling depths.

(9) In general, the Coast Pilot gives the project depths for deep-draft ship channels maintained by the Corps of Engineers. The latest controlling depths are usually shown on the charts and published in the Notices to Mariners. For other channels, the latest controlling depths available at the time of publication are given. **In all cases, however, mariners are advised to consult with pilots, port and local authorities, and Federal and State authorities for the latest channel controlling depths.**

(10) **Under-keel clearances.**–It is becoming increasingly evident that economic pressures are causing mariners to navigate through waters of barely adequate depth, with under-keel clearances being finely assessed from the charted depths, predicted tide levels, and depths recorded by echo sounders.

(11) It cannot be too strongly emphasized that even charts based on modern surveys may not show all sea-bed obstructions or the shoalest depths, and actual tide levels may be appreciably lower than those predicted.

(12) In many ships an appreciable correction must be applied to shoal soundings recorded by echo sounders due to the horizontal distance between the transducers. This separation corection, which is the amount by which recorded depths therefore exceed true depths, increases with decreasing depths to a maximum equal to half the distance apart of the transducers; at this maximum the transducers are aground. Ships whose transducers are more than 6 feet apart should construct a table of true and recorded depths using the Traverse Tables. (Refer to discussion of echo soundings elsewhere in chapter 1.)

(13) Other appreciable corrections, which must be applied to many ships, are for settlement and squat. These corrections depend on the depth of water below the keel, the hull form and speed of the ship.

(14) Settlement causes the water level around the ship to be lower than would otherwise be the case. It will always cause echo soundings to be less than they would otherwise be. Settlement is appreciable when the depth is less than seven times the draft of the ship, and increases as the depth decreases and the speed increases.

(15) Squat denotes a change in trim of a ship underway, relative to her trim when stopped. It usually causes the stern of a vessel to sit deeper in the water. However, it is reported that in the case of mammoth ships squat causes the bow to sit deeper. Depending on the location of the echo sounding transducers, this may cause the recorded depth to be greater or less than it ought to be. **Caution and common sense are continuing requirements for safe navigation.**

(16) **Distances.**—These are in nautical miles unless otherwise stated. A nautical mile is one minute of latitude, or approximately 2,000 yards, and is about 1.15 statute miles.

(17) **Heights.**—These are in feet above the tidal datum used for that purpose on the charts, usually mean high water. However, the heights of the decks of piers and wharves are given in feet above the chart datum for depths.

(18) **Light and fog signal characteristics.**These are not described, and light sectors and visible ranges are normally not defined. (See Coast Guard Light Lists.)

(19) **Obstructions.**—Wrecks and other obstructions are mentioned only if of a relatively permanent nature and in or near normal traffic routes.

(20) **Radio aids to navigation.**—These are seldom described. (See Coast Guard Light Lists and Defense Mapping Agency Radio Navigational Aids.)

(21) **Ranges.**—These are not fully described. "A 339° Range" means that the rear structure bears 339° from the front structure. (See Coast Guard Light Lists.)

(22) **Reported information.**—Information received by NOS from various sources concerning depths, dangers, currents, facilities, and other subjects, which has not been verified by Government surveys or inspections, is often included in the Coast Pilot; such **unverified information** is qualified as "reported," and should be regarded with caution.

(23) **Time.**—Unless otherwise stated, all times are given in local standard time in the 24-hour system. (Noon is 1200, 2:00 p.m. is 1400, and midnight is 0000.)

(24) **Winds.**—Directions are the true directions from which the winds blow. Unless otherwise indicated, speeds are given in knots, which are nautical miles per hour.

NOTICES TO MARINERS

(25) Notices to Mariners are published by Federal agencies to advise operators of vessels of marine information affecting the safety of navigation. The notices include changes in aids to navigation, depths in channels, bridge and overhead cable clearances, reported dangers, and other useful marine information. They should be used routinely for updating the latest editions of nautical charts and related publications.

(26) **Local Notice to Mariners** is issued by each Coast Guard District Commander for the waters under his jurisdiction. (See appendix for Coast Guard district(s) covered by this volume.) These notices are usually published weekly and may be obtained without cost by making application to the appropriate District Commander.

(27) **Notice to Mariners,** published weekly by the Defense Mapping Agency Hydrographic/Topographic Center, is prepared jointly with NOS and the Coast Guard. These notices contain selected items from the Local Notices to Mariners and other reported marine information required by oceangoing vessels operating in both **foreign** and **domestic** waters. Special items covering a variety of subjects and generally not discussed in the Coast Pilot or shown on nautical charts are published annually in Notice to Mariners No. 1. These items are important to the mariner and should be read for future reference. These notices may be obtained by operators or oceangoing vessels, without cost by making application to **Defense Mapping Agency** (see Defense Mapping Agency Procurement Information in appendix).

(28) Notices and reports of **improved channel depths** are also published by district offices of the Corps of Engineers,

U.S. Army (see appendix for districts covered by this volume). Although information from these notices/reports affecting NOS charts and related publications is usually published in the Notices to Mariners, the local district engineer office should be consulted where depth information is critical.

(29) **Marine Broadcast Notices to Mariners** are made by the Coast Guard through Coast Guard, Navy, and some commercial radio stations to report deficiencies and important changes in aids to navigation. (See Radio Navigation Warnings and Weather, this chapter.)

(30) Vessels operating within the limits of the Coast Guard districts can obtain information affecting NOS charts and related publications from the Local Notices to Mariners. Small craft using the Intracoastal Waterway and other waterways and small harbors within the United States that are not normally used by oceangoing vessels will require the Local Notices to Mariners to keep charts and related publications up-to-date. Information for oceangoing vessels can be obtained from the Notice to Mariners published by the Defense Mapping Agency Hydrographic/Topographic Center.

(31) Notices to Mariners may be consulted at Coast Guard district offices, NOS field offices, Defense Mapping Agency Hydrographic/Topographic Center offices and depots, most local marine facilities, and sales agents handling charts and related publications.

U.S. GOVERNMENT AGENCIES PROVIDING MARITIME SERVICES

(32) **Animal and Plant Health Inspection Service,** Department of Agriculture.—The Agricultural Quarantine Inspection Program and Animal Health Programs of this organization are responsible for protecting the Nation's animal population, food and fiber crops, and forests from invasion by foreign pests. They administer agricultural quarantine and restrictive orders issued under authority provided in various acts of Congress. The regulations prohibit or restrict the importation or interstate movement of live animals, meats, animal products, plants, plant products, soil, injurious insects, and associated items that may introduce or spread plant pests and animal diseases which may be new to or not widely distributed within the United States or its territories. Inspectors examine imports at ports of entry as well as the vessel, its stores, and crew or passenger baggage.

(33) The Service also provides an inspection and certification service for exporters to assist them in meeting the quarantine requirements of foreign countries. (See appendix for a list of ports where agricultural inspectors are located and inspections conducted.)

(34) **Customs Service,** Department of the Treasury.—The U.S. Customs Service administers certain laws relating to: entry and clearance of vessels and permits for certain vessel movements between points in the United States; prohibitions against coastwise transportation of passengers and merchandise; salvage, dredging and towing by foreign vessels; certain activities of vessels in the fishing trade; regular and special tonnage taxes on vessels; the landing and delivery of foreign merchandise (including unlading, appraisement, lighterage, drayage, warehousing, and shipment in bond); collection of customs duties, including duty on imported pleasure boats and yachts and 50% duty on foreign repairs to American vessels engaged in trade; customs treatment of sea and ship's stores while in port and the baggage of crewmen and passengers; illegally imported merchandise;

(35) and remission of penalties or forfeiture if customs or navigation laws have been violated. The Customs Service also cooperates with many other Federal agencies in the enforcement of statutes they are responsible for. Customs districts and ports of entry, including customs stations, are listed in the appendix.

(35) The Customs Service may issue, without charge, a **cruising license**, valid for a period of up to 6 months and for designated U.S. waters, to a yacht of a foreign country which has a reciprocal agreement with the United States. A foreign yacht holding a cruising license may cruise in the designated U.S. waters and arrive at and depart from U.S. ports without entering or clearing at the customhouse, filing manifests, or obtaining or delivering permits to proceed, provided it does not engage in trade or violate the laws of the United States or visit a vessel not yet inspected by a Customs Agent and does, within 24 hours of arrival at each port or place in the United States, report the fact of arrival to the nearest customhouse. Countries which have reciprocal agreements granting these privileges to U.S. yachts are Argentina, Australia, Bahama Islands, Bermuda, Canada, Federal Republic of Germany, Great Britain, Greece, Honduras, Jamaica, Liberia, the Netherlands, and New Zealand. Further information concerning cruising licenses may be obtained from the headquarters port for the customs district in which the license is desired. U.S. yacht owners planning cruises to foreign ports may contact the nearest customs district headquarters as to customs requirements.

(36) **National Ocean Service** (NOS), National Oceanic and Atmospheric Administration (NOAA), Department of Commerce.–The National Ocean Service provides charts and related publications for the safe navigation of marine and air commerce, and provides basic data for engineering and scientific purposes and for other commercial and industrial needs. The principal facilities of NOS are located in Rockville, Md.; in Norfolk, Va. (Atlantic Marine Center); and in Seattle, Wash. (Pacific Marine Center). NOAA ships are based at the marine centers. These offices maintain files of charts and other publications which are available for the use of the mariners, who are invited to avail themselves of the facilities afforded. (See appendix for addresses.)

(37) **Sales agents** for Charts, the Coast Pilot, Tide Tables, Tidal and Current Tables, Tidal Current Diagrams, and Tidal Current Charts of the National Ocean Service are located in many U.S. ports and in some foreign ports. A list of authorized sales agents and chart catalogs may be had free upon request from National Ocean Service, Distribution Branch (N/CG33). (See appendix for address.)

(38) **Nautical charts** are published primarily for the use of the mariner, but serve the public interest in many other ways. They are compiled principally from NOS basic field surveys, supplemented by data from other Government organizations.

(39) **Tide Tables** are issued annually by NOS in advance of the year for which they are prepared. These tables include predicted times and heights of high and low waters for every day in the year for a number of reference stations and differences for obtaining similar predictions for numerous other places. They also include other useful information such as a method of obtaining heights of tide at any time, local mean time of sunrise and sunset for various latitudes, reduction of local mean time to standard time, and time of moonrise and moonset for various ports.

(40) **Caution.**–In using the Tide Tables, slack water should not be confused with high or low water. For ocean stations there is usually little difference between the time of high or low water and the beginning of ebb or flood currents; but for places in narrow channels, landlocked harbors, or on tidal rivers, the time of slack current may differ by several hours from the time of high or low water. The relation of the times of high or low water to the turning of the current depends upon a number of factors, so that no simple general rule can be given. (To obtain the times of slack water, refer to the Tidal Current Tables.)

(41) **Tidal Current Tables** for the coasts of the United States are issued annually by NOS in advance of the year for which they are prepared. These tables include daily predictions of the times of slack water and the times and velocities of strength of flood and ebb currents for a number of waterways, together with differences for obtaining predictions for numerous other places. Also included is other useful information such as a method for obtaining the velocity of current at any time, duration of slack, coastal tidal currents, wind currents, combination of currents, and current diagrams. Some information on the Gulf Stream is included in the tables for the Atlantic coast.

(42) **Tidal Current Charts** are published by NOS for various localities. These charts depict the direction and velocity of the current for each hour of the tidal cycle. They present a comprehensive view of the tidal current movement in the respective waterways as a whole and when used with the proper current tables or tide tables supply a means for readily determining for any time the direction and velocity of the current at various localities throughout the areas covered.

(43) **Tidal Current Diagrams,** published annually by NOS, are a series of 12 monthly computer constructed diagrams used in conjunction with the Tidal Current Charts for a particular area. The diagrams present an alternate but more simplified method for calculating the speed and direction of the tidal currents in bays, estuaries, and harbors.

(44) **Coast Guard,** Department of Transportation.–The Coast Guard has among its duties the enforcement of the laws of the United States on the high seas and in coastal and inland waters of the U.S. and its possessions; enforcement of navigation and neutrality laws and regulations; establishment and enforcement of navigational regulations upon the Inland Waters of the United States, including the establishment of a demarcation line separating the high seas from waters upon which U.S. navigational rules apply; administration of the Oil Pollution Act of 1961, as amended; establishment and administration of vessel anchorages; approval of bridge locations and clearances over navigable waters; administration of the alteration of obstructive bridges; regulation of drawbridge operations; inspection of vessels of the Merchant Marine; admeasurement of vessels; documentation of vessels; preparation and publication of merchant vessel registers; registration of stack insignia; port security; issuance of Merchant Marine licenses and documents; search and rescue operations; investigation of marine casualties and accidents, and suspension and revocation proceedings; destruction of derelicts; operation of aids to navigation; publication of Light Lists and Local Notices to Mariners; and operation of ice-breaking facilities.

(45) The Coast Guard, with the cooperation of coast radio stations of many nations, operates the **Automated Mutual-assistance Vessel Rescue System (AMVER).** It is an international maritime mutual assistance program which provides important aid to the development and coordination of search and rescue (SAR) efforts in many offshore areas of the world. Merchant ships of all nations making offshore passages are encouraged to voluntarily send movement (sailing) reports and periodic position reports to the AMVER

Center at Coast Guard New York via selected radio stations. Information from these reports is entered into an electronic computer which generates and maintains dead reckoning positions for the vessels. Characteristics of vessels which are valuable for determining SAR capability are also entered into the computer from available sources of information.

(46)   A worldwide communications network of radio stations supports the AMVER System. Propagation conditions, location of vessel, and traffic density will normally determine which station may best be contacted to establish communications. To ensure that no charge is applied, all AMVER reports should be passed through specified radio stations. Those stations which currently accept AMVER reports and apply no coastal station, ship station, or landline charge are listed in each issue of the "AMVER Bulletin" publication. Also listed are the respective International radio call signs, locations, frequency bands, and hours of operation. The "AMVER Bulletin" is available from Commander, Atlantic Area (As), U.S. Coast Guard, AMVER Center, Governors Island, New York, N.Y. 10004. Although AMVER reports may be sent through nonparticipating stations, the Coast Guard cannot reimburse the sender for any charges applied.

(47)   Information concerning the predicted location and SAR characteristics of each vessel known to be within the area of interest is made available upon request to recognized SAR agencies of any nation or vessels needing assistance. Predicted locations are only disclosed for reasons related to marine safety.

(48)   Benefits of AMVER participation to shipping include: (1) improved chances of aid in emergencies, (2) reduced number of calls for assistance to vessels not favorably located, and (3) reduced time lost for vessels responding to calls for assistance. An AMVER participant is under no greater obligation to render assistance during an emergency than a vessel who is not participating.

(49)   All AMVER messages should be addressed to **Coast Guard New York** regardless of the station to which the message is delivered, except those sent to Canadian stations which should be addressed to **AMVER Halifax** or **AMVER Vancouver** to avoid incurring charges to the vessel for these messages.

(50)   Instructions guiding participation in the AMVER System are available in the following languages: Chinese, Danish, Dutch, English, French, German, Greek, Italian, Japanese, Korean, Norwegian, Polish, Portuguese, Russian, Spanish, and Swedish. The AMVER Users Manual is available from: Commander, Atlantic Area, U.S. Coast Guard, Governors Island, N.Y. 10004-5000; Commander, Pacific Area, U.S. Coast Guard, Coast Guard Island, Alameda, CA. 94501-5100; and at U.S. Coast Guard District Offices, Marine Safety Offices, Marine Inspection Offices, and Captain of the Port Offices in major U.S. ports. Requests for instructions should state the language desired if other than English.

(51)   For AMVER participants bound for U.S. ports there is an additional benefit. AMVER participation via messages which include the necessary information is considered to meet the requirements of 33 CFR 160. (See **160.201**, chapter 2, for rules and regulations.)

(52)   **AMVER Reporting Required.**–U.S. Maritime Administration regulations effective August 1, 1983, state that certain U.S. flag vessels and foreign flag "War Risk" vessels must report and regularly update their voyages to the **AMVER** Center. This reporting is required of the following: (a) U.S. flag vessels of 1,000 gross tons or greater, operating in foreign commerce; (b) foreign flag vessels of 1,000 gross tons or greater, for which an Interim War Risk Insurance Binder has been issued under the provisions of Title XII, Merchant Marine Act, 1936.

(53)   Details of the above procedures are contained in the AMVER Users Manual. The system is also published in DMAHTC Pub. 117.

(54)   Search and Rescue Operation procedures are contained in the International Maritime Organization (IMO) SAR Manual (MERSAR). U.S. flag vessels may obtain a copy of MERSAR from local Coast Guard Marine Safety Offices and Marine Inspection Offices or by writing to U.S. Coast Guard (G-OSR), Washington, D.C. 20593-0001. Other flag vessels may purchase MERSAR directly from IMO.

(55)   The Coast Guard conducts and/or coordinates **search and rescue** operations for surface vessels and aircraft that are in distress or overdue. (See Distress Signals and Communication Procedures this chapter.)

(56)   **Light Lists,** published by the Coast Guard, describe aids to navigation, consisting of lights, fog signals, buoys, lightships, daybeacons, and electronic aids, in United States (including Puerto Rico and U.S. Virgin Islands) and contiguous Canadian waters. Light Lists are for sale by the Government Printing Office (see appendix for address) and by sales agents in the principal seaports. Mariners should refer to these publications for detailed information regarding the characteristics and visibility of lights, and the descriptions of light structures, lightships, buoys, fog signals, and electronic aids.

(57)   **Documentation** (issuance of certificates of registry, enrollments, and licenses), admeasurements of vessels, and administration of the various navigation laws pertaining thereto are functions of the Coast Guard. Yacht commissions are also issued, and certain undocumented vessels required to be numbered by the Federal Boat Safety Act of 1971 are numbered either by the Coast Guard or by a State having an approved numbering system (the latter is most common). Owners of vessels may obtain the necessary information from any Coast Guard District Commander, Marine Safety Office, or Marine Inspection Office. Coast Guard District Offices, Coast Guard Stations, Marine Safety Offices, Captain of the Port Offices, Marine Inspection Offices, and Documentation Offices are listed in the appendix. (Note: A Marine Safety Office performs the same functions as those of a Captain of the Port and a Marine Inspection Office. When a function is at a different address than the Marine Safety Office, it will be listed separately in the appendix.)

(58)   **Corps of Engineers,** Department of the Army.–The Corps of Engineers has charge of the improvement of the rivers and harbors of the United States and of miscellaneous other civil works which include the administration of certain Federal laws enacted for the protection and preservation of navigable waters of the United States; the establishment of regulations for the use, administration, and navigation of navigable waters; the establishment of harbor lines; the removal of sunken vessels obstructing or endangering navigation; and the granting of permits for structures or operations in navigable waters, and for discharges and deposits of dredged and fill materials in these waters.

(59)   Information concerning the various ports, improvements, channel depths, navigable waters, and the condition of the Intracoastal Waterways in the areas under their jurisdiction may be obtained direct from the District Engineer Offices. (See appendix for addresses.)

(60) **Fishtraps.**–The Corps of Engineers has general supervision of location, construction, and manner of maintenance of all traps, weirs, pounds, or other fishing structures in the navigable waters of the United States. Where State and/or local controls are sufficient to regulate these structures, including that they do not interfere with navigation, the Corps of Engineers leaves such regulation to the State or local authority. (See **33 CFR 330** (not carried in this Pilot) for applicable Federal regulations.) Construction permits issued by the Engineers specify the lights and signals required for the safety of navigation.

(61) **Fish havens,** artificial reefs constructed to attract fish, can be established in U.S. coastal waters only as authorized by a Corps of Engineers permit; the permit specifies the location, extent, and depth over these "underwater junk piles."

(62) **Environmental Protection Agency (EPA).**–The U.S. Environmental Protection Agency provides coordinated governmental action to assure the protection of the environment by abating and controlling pollution on a systematic basis. The ocean dumping permit program of the Environmental Protection Agency provides that except when authorized by permit, the dumping of any material into the ocean is prohibited by the "Marine Protection, Research, and Sanctuaries Act of 1972, Public Law 92–532," as amended (33 USC 1401 et seq.).

(63) Permits for the **dumping of dredged material** into waters of the United States, including the territorial sea, and into ocean waters are issued by the Corps of Engineers. Permits for the dumping of fill material into waters of the United States, including the territorial sea, are also issued by the Corps of Engineers. Permits for the dumping of other material in the territorial sea and ocean waters are issued by the Environmental Protection Agency.

(64) Corps of Engineers regulations relating to the above are contained in **33 CFR 323-324**; Environmental Protection Agency regulations are in **40 CFR 220-229**. (See Disposal Sites, this chapter.)

(65) Persons or organizations who want to file for an application for an ocean dumping permit should write the Environmental Protection Agency Regional Office for the region in which the port of departure is located. (See appendix for addresses of regional offices and States in the EPA coastal regions.)

(66) The letter should contain the name and address of the applicant; name and address of person or firm; the name and usual location of the conveyance to be used in the transportation and dumping of the material involved; a physical description where appropriate; and the quantity to be dumped and proposed dumping site.

(67) Everyone who writes EPA will be sent information about a final application for a permit as soon as possible. This final application is expected to include questions about the description of the process or activity giving rise to the production of the dumping material; information on past activities of applicant or others with respect to the disposal of the type of material involved; and a description about available alternative means of disposal of the material with explanations about why an alternative is thought by the applicant to be inappropriate.

(68) **Federal Communications Commission.**–The Federal Communications Commission controls non-Government radio communications in the United States, Guam, Puerto Rico, and the Virgin Islands. Commission inspectors have authority to board ships to determine whether their radio stations comply with international treaties, Federal Laws, and Commission regulations. The commission has field offices in the principal U.S. ports. (See appendix for addresses.) Information concerning ship radio regulations and service documents may be obtained from the Federal Communications Commission, Washington, D.C. 20554, or from any of the field offices.

(69) **Immigration and Naturalization Service,** Department of Justice.–The Immigration and Naturalization Service administers the laws relating to admission, exclusion, and deportation of aliens, the registration and fingerprinting of aliens, and the naturalization of aliens lawfully resident in the United States.

(70) The designated ports of entry for aliens are divided into three classes. Class A is for all aliens. Class B is only for aliens who at the time of applying for admission are lawfully in possession of valid resident aliens' border-crossing identification cards or valid nonresident aliens' border-crossing identification cards or are admissible without documents under the documentary waivers contained in **8 CFR 212.1(a).** Class C is only for aliens who are arriving in the United States as crewmen as that term is defined in Section 101(a) (10) of the Immigration and Nationality Act. [The term "crewman" means a person serving in any capacity on board a vessel or aircraft. No person may enter the United States until he has been inspected by an immigration officer. A list of the offices covered by this Coast Pilot is given in the appendix.

(71) **Defense Mapping Agency Hydrographic/Topographic Center (DMAHTC),** Department of Defense.–The Defense Mapping Agency Hydrographic/Topographic Center provides hydrographic, navigational, topographic, and geodetic data, charts, maps, and related products and services to the Armed Forces, other Federal Agencies, the Merchant Marine and mariners in general. Publications include Sailing Directions, List of Lights, Distances Between Ports, Radio Navigational Aids, International Code of Signals, American Practical Navigator (Bowditch), and Notice to Mariners. (See Defense Mapping Agency Procurement Information in appendix.)

(72) **Public Health Service,** Department of Health and Human Services.–The Public Health Service administers foreign quarantine procedures at U.S. ports of entry.

(73) All vessels arriving in the United States are subject to public health inspection. Vessels subject routine boarding for quarantine inspection are only those which have had on board during the 15 days preceding the date of expected arrival or during the period since departure (whichever period of time is shorter) the occurrence of any death or ill person among passengers or crew (including those who have disembarked or have been removed). The master of a vessel must report such occurrences immediately by radio to the quarantine station at or nearest the port at which the vessel will arrive.

(74) In addition, the master of a vessel carrying 13 or more passengers must report by radio 24 hours before arrival the number of cases (including zero) of diarrhea in passengers and crew recorded in the ship's medical log during the current cruise. All cases that occur after the 24 hour report must also be reported not less than 4 hours before arrival.

(75) "Ill person" means person who:

(76)   1. Has a temperature of 100°F (or 38°C) or greater, accompanied by a rash, glandular swelling, or jaundice, or which has persisted for more than 48 hours; or

(77)   2. Has diarrhea, defined as the occurrence in a 24 hour period of three or more loose stools or of a greater than normal (for the person) amount of loose stools.

(78)   Vessels arriving at ports under control of the United States are subject to sanitary inspection to determine whether measures should be applied to prevent the introduction, transmission, or spread of communicable disease.

(79)   Specific public health laws, regulations, policies, and procedures may be obtained by contacting U.S. Quarantine Stations, U.S. Consulates or the Chief Program Operations, Division of Quarantine, Centers for Disease Control, Atlanta, Ga. 30333. (See appendix for addresses of U.S. Public Health Service Quarantine Stations.)

(80)   **Food and Drug Administration (FDA),** Public Health Service, Department of Health and Human Services.–Under the provisions of the Control of Communicable Diseases Regulations (**21 CFR 1240**) and Interstate Conveyance Sanitation Regulations (**21 CFR 1250**), vessel companies operating in interstate traffic shall obtain potable water for drinking and culinary purposes only at watering points found acceptable to the Food and Drug Administration. Water supplies used in watering point operations must also be inspected to determine compliance with applicable Interstate Quarantine Regulations (**42 CFR 72**). These regulations are based on authority contained in the Public Health Service Act (PL 78–410). Penalties for violation of any regulation prescribed under authority of the Act are provided for under Section 368 (42 USC 271) of the Act.

(81)   **Vessel Watering Points.**–FDA annually publishes a list of Acceptable Vessel Watering Points. This list is available from most FDA offices or from Interstate Travel Sanitation Subprogram Center for Food Safety and Applied Nutrition, FDA (HFF-312), 200 C Street SW., Washington, D.C. 20204. Current status of watering points can be ascertained by contacting any FDA office. (See appendix for addresses.)

(82)   **National Weather Service (NWS),** National Oceanic and Atmospheric Administration (NOAA), Department of Commerce.–The National Weather Service provides marine weather forecasts and warnings for the U.S. coastal waters, the Great Lakes, offshore waters, and high seas areas. Scheduled marine forecasts are issued four times daily from more than 20 **National Weather Service Forecast Offices (WSFOs)** around the country, operating 24 hours a day. Marine services are also provided by over 50 **National Weather Service Offices** with local areas of responsibility. (See appendix for Weather Service Forecast Offices and Weather Service Offices for the area covered by this Coast Pilot.)

(83)   Typically, the forecasts contain information on wind speed and direction, wave heights, visibility, weather, and a general synopsis of weather patterns affecting the region. The forecasts are supplemented with special marine warnings and statements, radar summaries, marine observations, small-craft advisories, gale warnings, storm warnings and various categories of tropical cyclone warnings e.g., tropical depression, tropical storm and hurricane warnings. Specialized products such as coastal flood, seiche, and tsunami warnings, heavy surf advisories, low water statements, ice forecasts and outlooks, and lake shore warnings and statements are issued as necessary.

(84)   The principal means of disseminating marine weather services and products in coastal areas is **NOAA Weather Radio.** This network or more than 350 stations nationwide is operated by the NWS and provides continuous broadcasts of weather information for the general public. These broadcasts repeat taped messages every 4-6 minutes. Tapes are updated periodically, usually every 2-3 hours and amended as required to include the latest information. When severe weather threatens, routine transmissions are interrupted and the broadcast is devoted to emergency warnings. (See appendix for NOAA Weather Radio Stations covered by this Coast Pilot.)

(85)   In coastal areas, the programming is tailored to the needs of the marine community. Each coastal marine forecast covers a specific area. For example, "Cape Henlopen to Virginia Beach, out 20 miles." The broadcast range is about 40 miles from the transmitting antenna site, depending on terrain and quality of the receiver used. When transmitting antennas are on high ground, the range is somewhat greater, reaching 60 miles or more. Some receivers are equipped with a warning alert device that can be turned on by means of a tone signal controlled by the NWS office concerned. This signal is transmitted for 13 seconds preceding an announcement of a severe weather warning.

(86)   NWS marine weather products are also disseminated to marine users through the broadcast facilities of the Coast Guard, Navy, National Bureau of Standards, certain Sea Grant Universities, and commercial marine radio stations. Details on these broadcasts including times, frequencies, and broadcast content are listed in the joint NWS/Navy publication Selected Worldwide Marine Weather Broadcasts. For marine weather services in the coastal areas, the NWS publishes a series of Marine Weather Services Charts showing locations of NOAA Weather Radio stations, sites, telephone numbers of recorded weather messages and NWS offices, and other useful marine weather information.

(87)   Ships of all nations share equally in the effort to report weather observations. These reports enable meteorologists to create a detailed picture of wind, wave, and weather patterns over the open waters that no other data source can provide and upon which marine forecasts are based. The effectiveness and reliability of these forecasts and warnings plus other services to the marine community are strongly linked to the observations received from mariners. There is an especially urgent need for ship observations in the coastal waters, and the NWS asks that these be made and transmitted whenever possible. Many storms originate and intensify in coastal areas. There may be a great difference in both wind direction and speed between the open sea, the offshore waters, and on the coast itself.

(88)   Information on how ships, commercial fishermen, offshore industries, and others in the coastal zone may participate in the marine observation program is available from **National Weather Service Port Meteorological Officers (PMOs).** Port Meteorological Officers are located in major U.S. port cities and the Republic of Panama, where they visit ships in port to assist masters and mates with the weather observation program, provide instruction on the interpretation of weather charts, calibrate barometers and other meteorological instruments, and discuss marine weather communications and marine weather requirements affecting the ships' operations. (See appendix for addresses of Port Meteorological Officers in or near the area covered by this Coast Pilot.)

(89)   **National Environmental Satellite, Data, and Information Service (NESDIS),** National Oceanic and Atmospheric Administration (NOAA), Department of Commerce.–Among its functions, NESDIS archives, processes,

and disseminates the non-realtime meteorological and oceanographic data collected by government agencies and private institutions. Marine weather observations are collected from ships at sea on a voluntary basis. About 1 million observations are received annually at NESDIS's National Climatic Center. They come from vessels representing every maritime nation. These observations, along with land data, are returned to the mariners in the form of climatological summaries and atlases for coastal and ocean areas. They are available in such NOAA publications as the **U.S. Coast Pilot, Mariners Weather Log,** and **Local Climatological Data, Annual Summary.** They also appear in the Defense Mapping Agency **Pilot Charts** and **Sailing Directions Planning Guides.**

DISTRESS SIGNALS AND COMMUNICATION PROCEDURES

(90) **Coast Guard search and rescue operations.**–The Coast Guard conducts and/or coordinates search and rescue operations for surface vessels or aircraft that are in distress or overdue. Search and Rescue vessels and aircraft have special markings, including a wide slash of red-orange and a small slash of blue on the forward portion of the hull or fuselage. Other parts of aircraft, normally painted white, may have other areas painted red to facilitate observation. The cooperation of vessel operators with Coast Guard helicopters, fixed-wing aircraft, and vessels may mean the difference between life and death for some seaman or aviator; such cooperation is greatly facilitated by the prior knowledge on the part of vessel operators of the operational requirements of Coast Guard equipment and personnel, of the international distress signals and procedures, and of good seamanship.

(91) **International distress signals.**–(1) A signal made by radiotelegraphy or by any other signalling method consisting of the group "SOS" in Morse Code.

(92) (2) A signal sent by radiotelephony consisting of the spoken word "MAYDAY."

(93) (3) The International Flag Code Signal of NC.

(94) (4) A signal consisting of a square flag having above or below it a ball or anything resembling a ball.

(95) (5) Flames on the craft (as from a burning oil barrel, etc.)

(96) (6) A rocket parachute flare or hand flare showing a red light.

(97) (7) Rockets or shells, throwing red stars fired one at a time at short intervals.

(98) (8) Orange smoke, as emitted from a distress flare.

(99) (9) Slowly and repeatedly raising and lowering arms outstretched to each side.

(100) (10) A gun or other explosive signal fired at intervals of about 1 minute.

(101) (11) A continuous sounding of any fog-signal apparatus.

(102) (12) The radiotelegraph alarm signal.

(103) (13) The radiotelephone alarm signal.

(104) (14) Signals transmitted by emergency position-indicating radiobeacons.

(105) (15) A piece of orange-colored canvas with either a black square and circle or other appropriate symbol (for identification from the air).

(106) (16) A dye marker.

(107) **Radio distress procedures.**–Distress calls are made on 500 kHz (SOS) for radiotelegraphy and on 2182 kHz or VHF-FM channel 16 (MAYDAY) for radiotelephony. For less serious situations than warrant the distress procedure, the urgency signal PAN-PAN (PAHN-PAHN, spoken three times), or the safety signal SECURITY (SAY-CURITAY, spoken three times), for radiotelephony, are used as appropriate. Since radiotelegraph transmissions are normally made by professional operators, and urgency and safety situations are less critical, only the distress procedures for voice radiotelephone are described. For complete information on emergency radio procedures, see **47 CFR 83** or DMAHTC Pub. 117. **(See appendix for a list of Coast Guard Stations which guard 2182 kHz and 156.80 MHz.)** Complete information on distress guards can be obtained from Coast Guard District Commanders.

(108) Distress calls indicate a vessel or aircraft is threatened by grave and imminent danger and requests immediate assistance. They have absolute priority over all other transmissions. All stations which hear a distress call must immediately cease any transmission capable of interfering with the distress traffic and shall continue to listen on the frequency used for the emission of the distress call. This call shall not be addressed to a particular station, and acknowledgement of receipt shall not be given before the distress message which follows it is sent.

(109) **Radiotelephone distress communications include the following actions:**

(110) (1) The **radiotelephone alarm signal** (if available): The signal consists of two audio tones, of different pitch, transmitted alternately; its purpose is to attract the attention of persons on radio watch or to actuate automatic alarm devices. It may only be used to announce that a distress call or message is about to follow.

(111) (2) The **distress call,** consisting of:–the distress signal MAYDAY (spoken three times);

(112) the words THIS IS (spoken once);

(113) the call sign or name of the vessel in distress (spoken three times).

(114) (3) The **distress message** follows immediately and consists of:

(115) the distress signal MAYDAY;

(116) the call sign and name of the vessel in distress;

(117) particulars of its position (latitude and longitude, or true bearing and distance from a known geographical position);

(118) the nature of the distress;

(119) the kind of assistance desired;

(120) the number of persons aboard and the condition of any injured;

(121) present seaworthiness of vessel;

(122) description of the vessel (length; type; cabin; masts; power; color of hull, superstructure, trim; etc.);

(123) any other information which might facilitate the rescue, such as display of a surface-to-air identification signal or a radar reflector;

(124) your listening frequency and schedule;

(125) THIS IS (call sign and name of vessel in distress). OVER.

(126) (4) **Acknowledgement of receipt of a distress message:** If a distress message is received from a vessel which is definitely in your vicinity, immediately acknowledge receipt. If it is not in your vicinity, allow a short interval of time to elapse before acknowledging, in order to permit vessels nearer to the vessel in distress to acknowledge receipt without interference. However, in areas where reliable communications with one or more shore stations are practicable, all vessels may defer this acknowledgement for a short interval so that a shore station may acknowledge receipt first. The acknowledgement of receipt of a distress is given as follows:

(127) the call sign or name of the vessel sending the distress (spoken three times);

(128)   the words THIS IS;

(129)   the call sign or name of acknowledging vessel (spoken three times);

(130)   The words RECEIVED MAYDAY.

(131)   After the above acknowledgement, allow a momentary interval of listening to insure that you will not interfere with another vessel better situated to render immediate assistance; if not, with the authority of the person in charge of the vessel, transmit:

(132)   the word MAYDAY;

(133)   the call sign and name of distressed vessel;

(134)   the words THIS IS;

(135)   the call sign and name of your vessel;

(136)   your position (latitude and longitude, or true bearing and distance from a known geographical position);

(137)   the speed you are proceeding towards, and the approximate time it will take to reach, the distressed vessel. OVER.

(138)   **(5) Further distress messages and other communications:** Distress communications consist of all messages relating to the immediate assistance required by the distressed vessel. Each distress communication shall be preceded by the signal MAYDAY. The vessel in distress or the station in control of distress communications may **impose silence** on any station which interferes. The procedure is:–the words SEELONCE MAYDAY (Seelonce is French for silence). Silence also may be imposed by nearby mobile stations other than the vessel in distress or the station in control of distress communications. The mobile station which believes that silence is essential may request silence by the following procedure:–the word SEELONCE, followed by the word DISTRESS, and its **own** call sign.

(139)   **(6) Transmission of the distress procedure by a vessel or shore station not itself in distress:** A vessel or a shore station which learns that a vessel is in distress shall transmit a distress message in any of the following cases:

(140)   **(a) When the vessel in distress is not itself able to transmit the distress message.**

(141)   (b) When a vessel or a shore station considers that further help is necessary.

(142)   (c) When, although not in a position to render assistance, it has heard a distress message that has not been acknowledged.

(143)   In these cases, the transmission shall consist of:

(144)   the radiotelephone alarm signal (if available);

(145)   the words MAYDAY RELAY (spoken three times);

(146)   the words THIS IS;

(147)   the call sign and name of vessel (or shore station), spoken three times.

(148)   When a vessel transmits a distress under these conditions, it shall take all necessary steps to contact the Coast Guard or a shore station which can notify the Coast Guard.

(149)   **(7) Termination of distress:** When distress traffic has ceased, or when silence is no longer necessary on the frequency used for the distress traffic, the station in control shall transmit on that frequency a message to all stations as follows:

(150)   the distress signal MAYDAY;

(151)   the call TO ALL STATIONS, spoken three times;

(152)   the words THIS IS;

(153)   the call sign and name of the station sending the message;

(154)   the time;

(155)   the name and call sign of the vessel in distress;

(156)   the words SEELONCE FEENEE (French for silence finished).

DISTRESS ASSISTANCE AND COORDINATION PROCEDURES

(157)   **Surface ship procedures for assisting distressed surface vessels.**

(158)   (1) The following immediate action should be taken by each ship on receipt of a distress message:

(159)   (a) Acknowledge receipt and, if appropriate, retransmit the distress message;

(160)   (b) Immediately try to take D/F bearings during the transmission of the distress message and maintain a D/F watch on 500 kHz and/or 2182 kHz;

(161)   (c) Communicate the following information to the ship in distress:

(162)   (i) identity;

(163)   (ii) position;

(164)   (iii) speed and estimated time of arrival (ETA);

(165)   (iv) when available, true bearing of the ship in distress.

(166)   (d) Maintain a continuous listening watch on the frequency used for the distress. This will normally be:

(167)   (i) 500 kHz (radiotelegraphy) and/or

(168)   (ii) 2182 kHz (radiotelephony).

(169)   (e) Additionally, maintain watch on VHF-FM channel 16 as necessary;

(170)   (f) Operate radar continuously;

(171)   (g) If in the vicinity of the distress, post extra lookouts.

(172)   (2) The following action should be taken when proceeding to the area of distress:

(173)   (a) Plot the position, course, speed, and ETA of other assisting ships.

(174)   (b) Know the communication equipment with which other ships are fitted. This information may be obtained from the International Telecommunication Union's List of Ship Stations.

(175)   (c) Attempt to construct an accurate "picture" of the circumstances attending the casualty. The important information needed is included under Distress Signals and Communication Procedures, this chapter. Should the ship in distress fail to transmit this information, a ship proceeding to assist should request what information is needed.

(176)   (3) The following on-board preparation while proceeding to the distress area should be considered:

(177)   (a) A rope (guest warp) running from bow to quarter at the waterline on each side and secured by lizards to the ship's side to assist boats and rafts to secure alongside;

(178)   (b) A derrick rigged ready for hoisting on each side of the ship with a platform cargo sling, or rope net, secured to the runner to assist the speedy recovery of exhausted or injured survivors in the water;

(179)   (c) Heaving lines, ladders, and scramble net placed ready for use along both sides of the ship on the lowest open deck and possibly crew members suitably equipped to enter the water and assist survivors;

(180)   (d) A ship's liferaft made ready for possible use as a boarding station;

(181)   (e) Preparations to receive survivors who require medical assistance including the provision of stretchers;

(182)   (f) When own lifeboat is to be launched, any means to provide communications between it and the parent ship will prove to be of very great help;

(183)   (g) A line throwing appliance with a light line and a heavy rope, ready to be used for making connection either with the ship in distress or with survival craft.

(184)   **Aircraft procedures for directing surface craft to scene of distress incident.**–The following procedures performed in sequence by an aircraft mean that the aircraft is

directing a surface craft toward the scene of a distress incident,

(185)   (a) Circling the surface craft at least once.

(186)   (b) Crossing the projected course of the surface craft close ahead at low altitude, rocking the wings, opening and closing the throttle, or changing the propeller pitch.

(187)   (c) Heading in the direction in which the surface craft is to be directed. The surface craft should acknowledge the signal by changing course and following the aircraft. If, for any reason, it is impossible to follow, the surface craft should hoist the international code flag NOVEMBER, or use any other signaling means available to indicate this.

(188)   The following procedures performed by an aircraft mean that the assistance of the surface craft is no longer required:

(189)   (a) Crossing the wake of the surface craft close astern at a low altitude, rocking the wings, opening and closing the throttle or changing the propeller pitch.

(190)   Since modern jet-engined aircraft cannot make the characteristic sound associated with opening and closing the throttle, or changing propeller pitch, ships should be alert to respond to the signals without the sounds, when jets or turboprop aircraft are involved.

(191)   **Surface ship procedures for assisting aircraft in distress.**

(192)   1. When an aircraft transmits a distress message by radio, the first transmission is generally made on the designated air/ground enroute frequency in use at the time between the aircraft and aeronautical station. The aircraft may change to another frequency, possibly another enroute frequency or the aeronautical emergency frequencies of 121.50 MHz or 243 MHz. In an emergency, it may use any other available frequency to establish contact with any land, mobile, or direction-finding station.

(193)   2. There is liaison between Coast Radio Stations aeronautical units, and land–based search and rescue organizations. Merchant ships will ordinarily be informed of aircraft casualties at sea by broadcast messages from Coast Radio Stations, made on the international distress frequencies of 500 kHz and 2182 kHz. Ships may, however, become aware of the casualty by receiving:

(194)   (a) An SOS message from an aircraft in distress which is able to transmit on 500 kHz or a distress signal from an aircraft using radiotelephone on 2182 kHz.

(195)   (b) A radiotelegraphy distress signal on 500 kHz from a hand-operated emergency transmitter carried by some aircraft.

(196)   (c) A message from a SAR aircraft.

(197)   3. For the purpose of emergency communications with aircraft, special attention is called to the possibility of conducting direct communications on 2182 kHz, if both ship and aircraft are so equipped.

(198)   4. An aircraft in distress will use any means at its disposal to attract attention, make known its position, and obtain help, including some of the signals prescribed by the applicable Navigation Rules.

(199)   5. Aircraft usually sink quickly (e.g. within a few minutes). Every endeavor will be made to give ships an accurate position of an aircraft which desires to ditch. When given such a position, a ship should at once consult any other ships in the vicinity on the best procedure to be adopted. The ship going to the rescue should answer the station sending the broadcast and give her identity, position, and intended action.

(200)   6. If a ship should receive a distress message direct from an aircraft, she should act as indicated in the immediately preceding paragraph and also relay the message to the nearest Coast Radio Station. Moreover, a ship which has received a distress message direct from an aircrft and is going to the rescue should take a bearing on the transmission and inform the Coast Radio Station and other ships in the vicinity of the call sign of the distressed aircraft and the time at which the distress message was received, followed by the bearing and time at which the signal ceased.

(201)   7. When an aircraft decides to ditch in the vicinity of a ship, the ship should:

(202)   (a) Transmit homing bearings to the aircraft, or (if so required) transmit signals enabling the aircraft to take its own bearings.

(203)   (b) By day, make black smoke.

(204)   (c) By night, direct a searchlight vertically and turn on all deck lights. Care must be taken not to direct a searchlight toward the aircraft, which might dazzle the pilot.

(205)   8. Ditching an aircraft is difficult and dangerous. A ship which knows that an aircraft intends to ditch should be prepared to give the pilot the following information:

(206)   (a) Wind direction and force.

(207)   (b) Direction, height, and length of primary and secondary swell systems.

(208)   (c) Other pertinent weather information.

(209)   The pilot of an aircraft will choose his own ditching heading. If this is known by the ship, she should set course parallel to the ditching heading. Otherwise the ship should set course parallel to the main swell system and into the wind component, if any.

(210)   9. A land plane may break up immediately on striking the water, and liferafts may be damaged. The ship should, therefore, have a lifeboat ready for launching, and if possible, boarding nets should be lowered from the ship and heaving lines made ready in the ship and the lifeboat. Survivors of the aircraft may have bright colored lifejackets and location aids.

(211)   10. The method of recovering survivors must be left to the judgment of the master of the ship carrying out the rescue operation.

(212)   11. It should be borne in mind that military aircraft are often fitted with ejection seat mechanisms. Normally, their aircrew will use their ejection seats, rather than ditch. Should such an aircraft ditch, rather than the aircrew bail out, and it becomes necessary to remove them from their ejection seats while still in the aircraft, care should be taken to avoid triggering off the seat mechanisms. The activating handles are invariably indicated by red and or black/yellow coloring.

(213)   12. A survivor from an aircraft casualty who is recovered may be able to give information which will assist in the rescue of other survivors. Masters are therefore asked to put the following questions to survivors and to communicate the answers to a Coast Radio Station. They should also give the position of the rescuing ship and the time when the survivors were recovered.

(214)   (a) What was the time and date of the casualty?

(215)   (b) Did you bail out or was the aircraft ditched?

(216)   (c) If you bailed out, at what altitude?

(217)   (d) How many others did you see leave the aircraft by parachute?

(218)   (e) How many ditched with the aircraft?

(219)   (f) How many did you see leave the aircraft after ditching?

(220)   (g) How many survivors did you see in the water?

(221)   (h) What flotation gear had they?

(222)   (i) What was the total number of persons aboard the aircraft prior to the accident?

(223)   (j) What caused the emergency?

(224) **Helicopter evacuation** of personnel.–Helicopter evacuation, usually performed by the Coast Guard, is a hazardous operation to the patient and to the flight crew, and should only be attempted in event of very serious illness or injury. Provide the doctor on shore with all the information you can concerning the patient, so that an intelligent evaluation can be made concerning the need for evacuation. Most rescue helicopters can proceed less than 150 miles offshore (a few new helicopters can travel 250 to 300 miles out to sea), dependent on weather conditions and other variables. If an evaluation is necessary, the vessel must be prepared to proceed within range of the helicopter, and should be familiar with the preparations which are necessary prior to and after its arrival.

(225) **When requesting helicopter assistance:**

(226) (1) Give the accurate position, time, speed, course, weather conditions, sea conditions, wind direction and velocity, type of vessel, and voice and CW frequency for your ship.

(227) (2) If not already provided, give complete medical information including whether or not the patient is ambulatory.

(228) (3) If you are beyond helicopter range, advise your diversion intentions so that a rendezvous point may be selected.

(229) (4) If there are changes to any items reported earlier, advise the rescue agency immediately. Should the patient die before the arrival of the helicopter, be sure to advise those assisting you.

(230) **Preparations prior to the arrival of the helicopter:**

(231) (1) Provide continuous radio guard on 2182 kHz or specified voice frequency, if possible. The helicopter normally cannot operate CW.

(232) (2) Select and clear the most suitable hoist area, preferably aft on the vessel with a minimum of 50 feet radius of clear deck. This must include the securing of loose gear, awnings, and antenna wires. Trice up running rigging and booms. If hoist is aft, lower the flag staff.

(233) (3) If the hoist is to take place at night, light the pickup areas as well as possible. Be sure you do not shine any lights on the helicopter, so that the pilot is not blinded. If there are any obstructions in the vicinity, put a light on them so the pilot will be aware of their positions.

(234) (4) Point searchlight vertically to aid the flight crew in locating the ship and turn them off when the helicopter is on the scene.

(235) (5) Be sure to advise the helicopter of the location of the pickup area on the ship before the helicopter arrives, so that the pilot may make his approach to aft, amidships, or forward, as required.

(236) (6) There will be a high noise level under the helicopter, so voice communications on deck are almost impossible. Arrange a set of hand signals among the crew who will assist.

(237) **Hoist operations:**

(238) (1) If possible, have the patient moved to a position as close to the hoist area as his condition will permit–**time is important.**

(239) (2) Normally, if a litter (stretcher) is required, it will be necessary to move the patient to the special litter which will be lowered by the helicopter. Be prepared to do this as quickly as possible. Be sure the patient is strapped in, face up, and with a life jacket on (if his condition will permit).

(240) (3) Be sure that the patient is tagged to indicate what medication, if any, was administered to him and when it was administered.

(241) (4) Have patient's medical record and necessary papers in an envelope or package ready for transfer with the patient.

(242) (5) Again, if the patient's condition permit, be sure he is wearing a life jacket.

(243) (6) Change the vessel's course to permit the ship to ride as easily as possible with the wind on the bow, preferably on the port bow. Try to choose a course to keep the stack gases clear of the hoist area. Once established, maintain course and speed.

(244) (7) Reduce speed to ease ship's motion, but maintain steerageway.

(245) (8) If you do not have radio contact with the helicopter, when you are in all respects ready for the hoist, signal the helicopter in with a "come on" with your hand, or at night by flashlight signals.

(246) (9) **Allow basket or stretcher to touch deck prior to handling to avoid static shock.**

(247) (10) If a trail line is dropped by the helicopter, guide the basket or stretcher to the deck with the line; keep the line free at all times. This line will not cause shock.

(248) (11) Place the patient in basket, sitting with his hands clear of the sides, or in the litter, as described above. Signal the helicopter hoist operator when ready for the hoist. Patient should signal by a nodding of the head if he is able. Deck personnel give thumbs up.

(249) (12) If it is necessary to take the litter away from the hoist point, unhook the hoist cable and keep it free for the helicopter to haul in. **Do not secure cable or trail line to the vessel or attempt to move stretcher without unhooking.**

(250) (13) When patient is strapped into the stretcher, signal the helicopter to lower the cable, attach cable to stretcher sling (bridle), then signal the hoist operator when the patient is ready to hoist. Steady the stretcher so it will not swing or turn.

(251) (14) If a trail line is attached to the basket or stretcher, use it to steady the patient as he is hoisted. Keep your feet clear of the line, and keep the line from becoming entangled.

(252) **Medical advice and/or evacuation.**–In the event a master of a vessel requires medical advice and/or there is a potential of evacuation the following should be volunteered by the master:

(253) Vessel's name and call sign.

(254) Vessel's position and time at position.

(255) Vessel's course, speed and next port and estimated time of arrival (ETA).

(256) Patient's name, nationality, age, race and sex.

(257) Patient's respiration, pulse and temperature.

(258) Patient's symptoms and nature of illness.

(259) Any known history of similar illness.

(260) Location and type of pain.

(261) Medical supplies carried on board vessel.

(262) Medication given to patient.

(263) Weather.

(264) Communication schedule and frequency.

(265) **Coast Guard droppable, floatable pumps.**–The Coast Guard often provides vessels in distress with emergency pumps by either making parachute drops, by lowering on helicopter hoist, or by delivering by vessel. The most commonly used type of pump comes complete in a sealed aluminum drum about half the size of a 50-gallon oil drum. One single lever on top opens it up. Don't be smoking as there may be gas fumes inside the can. The pump will draw about

90 gallons per minute. There should be a waterproof flashlight on top of the pump for night use. Operating instructions are provided inside the pump container.

(266) **Preparations for being towed by Coast Guard:**

(267) (1) Clear the forecastle area as well as you can.

(268) (2) If a line-throwing gun is used, keep everyone out of the way until line clears the boat. The Coast Guard vessel will blow a police whistle or otherwise warn you before firing.

(269) (3) Have material ready for chafing gear.

(270) **Radar reflectors on small craft.**–Operators of disabled wooden craft and persons adrift in rubber rafts or boats that are, or may consider themselves to be, the object of a search, should hoist on a halyard or otherwise place aloft as high as possible any metallic object that would assist their detection by radar. Coast Guard cutters and aircraft are radar equipped and thus are able to continue searching in darkness and during other periods of low visibility. It is advisable for coastal fishing boats, yachts, and other small craft to have efficient radar reflectors permanently installed aboard the vessel.

(271) **Filing Cruising schedules.**–Small-craft operators should prepare a cruising plan before starting on extended trips and leave it ashore with a yacht club, marina, friend, or relative. It is advisable to use a checking-in procedure by telephone for each point specified in the cruising plan. Such a trip schedule is vital for determining of a boat is overdue and will assist materially in locating a missing craft in the event search and rescue operations become necessary.

(272) **Medical advice.**–Free medical advice is furnished to seamen by radio through the cooperation of Governmental and commercial radio stations whose operators receive and relay messages prefixed **DH MEDICO** from ships at sea to the U.S. Coast Guard and/or directly to a hospital and then radio the medical advice back to the ships. (See appendix for list of radio stations that provide this service.)

RADIO NAVIGATION WARNINGS AND WEATHER

(273) Marine radio warnings and weather are disseminated by many sources and through several types of transmissions. Morse code radiotelegraph broadcasts of navigational warnings and other advisories are not described, since these transmissions are normally copied only by professional radio operators. U.S. Coast Guard NAVTEX, high-frequency (HF) narrow-band direct printing (radio telex), HF radiofacsimile, and radiotelephone broadcasts of maritime safety information are summarized here. (For complete information on radio warnings and weather see DMAHTC Pub. 117 and the joint National Weather Service/Navy publication Selected Worldwide Marine Weather Broadcasts.)

(274) **Frequency units.**–Hertz (Hz), a unit equal to one cycle per second, has been generally adopted for radio frequencies; accordingly, frequencies formerly given in the Coast Pilot in kilocycles (kc) and megacycles (mc) are now stated in **kilohertz (kHz)** and **Megahertz (MHz)**, respectively.

(275) **Coast Guard radio stations.**–Coast Guard radio stations provide urgent, safety, and scheduled marine information broadcasts with virtually complete coverage of the approaches and coastal waters of the United States, Puerto Rico, and the U.S. Virgin Islands.

(276) **Urgent and safety radiotelephone broadcasts** of important Notice to Mariners items, storm warnings, and other vital marine information are transmitted upon receipt, and urgent broadcasts are repeated 15 minutes later; additional broadcasts are made at the discretion of the originator. **Urgent** broadcasts are preceded by the urgent signal PAN-PAN (PAHN-PAHN, spoken three times). **Both the urgent signal and message are transmitted on 2182 kHz and/or VHF-FM channel 16. Safety** broacasts are preceded by the safety signal SECURITY (SAY-CURITAY, spoken three times). **The Safety signal is given on 2182 kHz and/or VHF-FM channel 16, and the message is given on 2670 kHz and/or VHF-FM channel 22A.**

(277) Scheduled radiotelephone broadcasts include routine weather, small-craft advisories, storm warnings, navigational information, and other advisories. Short-range broadcasts are made on **2670 kHz and/or VHF-FM channel 22A,** following a preliminary call on **2182 kHz and/or VHF-FM channel 16.** (See appendix for a list of stations and their broadcast frequencies and times for the area covered by this Coast Pilot.)

(278) Weather information is not normally broadcast by the Coast Guard on VHF-FM channel 22A in areas where NOAA Weather Radio service is available. See note below regarding VHF-FM channel 22A.

(279) HF single-sideband broadcasts of high seas weather information is available on the (carrier) frequencies 4428.7, 6506.4, 8765.4, 13113.2, and 17307.3 kHz from Portsmouth, VA and San Francisco, CA.

(280) Narrow-band direct printing (radio telex or sitor) broadcasts of NAVAREA and other navigational warnings are transmitted on the following assigned frequencies:

(281) Atlantic ice reports: 5320, 8502, and 12750 kHz.

(282) Other Atlantic warnings: 8490, 16968.8 kHz.

(283) Pacific: 8710.5, 8714.5, 8718, 13077, 13084.5, 17203, 22567, and 22574.5 kHz.

(284) HF radiofacsimile broadcasts of weather and ice charts are made on the following frequencies:

(285) Atlantic: 3242, 7530, 8502 (ice only), 12750 (ice only) kHz.

(286) Pacific: 4298 (Kodiak), 4336, 8459 (Kodiak), 8682, 12730, 17151.2 kHz.

(287) **Warning Regarding Coast Guard VHF-FM Channel 22A Broadcasts.**-The Coast Guard broadcasts urgent and routine maritime safety information to ships on channel 22A (157.10 MHz), the ship station transmit frequency portion of channel 22, of Appendix 18 of the International Telecommunications Union (ITU) Radio Regulations. This simplex use of channel 22A is not compatible with the international duplex arrangement of the channel (coast transmit 161.70 MHz, ship transmit 157.10 MHz). As a result, many foreign flag vessels having radios tuned to the international channel 22 can not receive these maritime safety broadcasts. A 1987 Coast Guard survey of foreign vessels in U.S. waters indicated that half of foreign vessels in U.S. waters did not have equipment on board capable of receiving channel 22A broadcasts.

(288) Operators of vessels which transit U.S. waters and who do not have VHF-FM radios tunable to USA channel 22A are urged to either obtain the necessary equipment, to monitor the radiotelephone frequency 2182 kHz and tune to 2670 kHz when a broadcast is announced, or to carry a NAVTEX receiver.

(289) **NAVTEX Marine Information Broadcasts.**- NAVTEX is an international system used in the United States to broadcast printed copies of Coast Guard district notices to mariners, distress notices, weather forecasts and warnings, ice warnings, and Gulf Stream location (where applicable), and radionavigation information to all types of

ships. NAVTEX consists of a small, low-cost and self-contained "smart" printing radio receiver installed in the pilot house of a ship or boat. The receiver checks each incoming message to see if it has been received during an earlier transmission, or if it is of a category of no interest to the ship's master. If it is a new and wanted message, it is printed onadding-machine size paper; if not, the message is ignored. The adding-machine size paper; if not, the message is ignored. The ship's master can, at his convenience, read the latest notices he needs to know. A new ship coming into the area will receive many previously-broadcast messages for the first time; ships already in the area which had already received the message will not receive it again. NAVTEX can be received either by a dedicated receiver, or by any narrow-band direct printing (radio telex) receiver operating in the forward error correcting (FEC) mode, tuned to 518 kHz.

(290)   The accompanying chart shows NAVTEX predicted coverage area for the U.S. east coast. The propagation predictions were based upon a 90% probability of reception during an average season and time of atmospheric radio noise, with a received character error rate of 1 in 1,000. The Coast Guard operates NAVTEX from stations in Boston (NMF), Portsmouth, VA (NMN), Miami (NMA), New Orleans (NMG), San Juan, PR (NMR), Long Beach, CA, San Francisco (NMC), Astoria, OR, Kodiak, AK (NOJ), Honolulu (NMO) and Guam (NRV). The Canadian Coast Guard also broadcasts NAVTEX information from Sydney, Nova Scotia.

(291)   As of January 1988, 43 NAVTEX stations in 19 countries were in operation worldwide, and 7 other countries indicated they might soon begin operating NAVTEX.

(292)   Broadcasts are planned internationally. Mandatory carriage of NAVTEX receivers is required for Safety of Life at Sea (SOLAS) Convention regulated vessels (merchant vessels greater than 300 gross tons and passenger vessels on international voyages) after 1993.

(293)   Questions and comments concerning the NAVTEX service in the United States are solicited. Correspondence should be addressed to:

(294)   Commandant (G-TTS-3/63)

(295)   United States Coast Guard

(296)   Washington, DC 20593-0001

(297)   Telex: 89-2427 COMDT COGARD Washington, D.C.

(298)   **NOAA Weather Radio.**–The National Weather Service operates **VHF-FM radio stations,** usually on frequencies **162.40, 162.475,** or **162.55 MHz,** to provide continuous recorded weather broadcasts. These broadcasts are available to those with suitable receivers within about 40 miles of the antenna site. (See the appendix for a list of these stations in the area covered by this Coast Pilot.)

(299)   **Commercial   radiotelephone   coast   stations.**–Broadcasts of coastal weather and warnings are made by some commercial radiotelephone coast stations (marine operators) on the normal transmitting frequencies of the stations. Vessels with suitable receivers and desiring this service may determine the frequencies and schedules of these broadcasts from their local stations, from Selected Worldwide Marine Weather Broadcasts, or from the series of Marine Weather Services Charts published by NWS.

(300)   **Local broadcast-band radio stations.**–Many local radio stations in the standard AM and FM broadcast band give local marine weather forecasts from NWS on a regular schedule. These stations are listed on the series of Marine Weather Services Charts published by NWS.

(301)   **Reports from ships.**–The master of every U.S. ship equipped with radio transmitting apparatus, on meeting with a tropical cyclone, dangerous ice, subfreezing air temperatures with gale force winds causing severe ice accretion on superstructures, derelict, or any other direct danger to navigation, is required to cause to be transmitted a report of these dangers to ships in the vicinity and to the appropriate Government agencies.

(302)   During the West Indies hurricane season, June 1 to November 30, ships in the Gulf of Mexico, Caribbean Sea area, southern North Atlantic Ocean, and the Pacific waters west of Central America and Mexico are urged to cooperate with NWS in furnishing these special reports in order that warnings to shipping and coastal areas may be issued.

(303)   **Time Signals.**–The **National Institute of Standards and Technology** broadcasts time signals continuously, day and night, from its radio stations WWV, near Fort Collins, Colorado, (40°49′49″N., 105°02′27″W.) on frequencies of 2.5, 5, 10, 15, and 20 MHz, and WWVH, Kekaha, Kauai, Hawaii (21°59′26″N., 159°46′00″W.) on frequencies 2.5, 5, 10, and 15 MHz. Services include time announcements, standard time intervals, standard audio frequencies, Omega Navigation System status reports, geophysical alerts, BCD (binary coded decimal) time code, UT1 time corrections, and high seas storm information.

(304)   Time announcements are made every minute, commencing at 15 seconds before the minute by a female voice and at 7½ seconds before the minute by a male voice, from WWVH and WWV, respectively. The time given is in Coordinated Universal Time (UTC) and referred to the time at Greenwich, England, i.e., Greenwich Mean Time.

(305)   **NIST Time and Frequency Dissemination Services, Special Publication 432,** gives a detailed description of the time and frequency dissemination services of the **National Institute of Standards and Technology.** Single copies may be obtained upon request from the National Institute of Standards and Technology, Time and Frequency Division, Boulder, CO 80303. Quantities may be obtained from the Government Printing Office (see appendix for address).

NAUTICAL CHARTS

(306)   **Reporting chart deficiencies.**–Users are requested to report all significant observed discrepancies in and desirable additions to NOS nautical charts, including depth information in privately maintained channels and basins; obstructions, wrecks, and other dangers; new landmarks or the nonexistence or relocation of charted ones; uncharted fixed private aids to navigation; and deletions or additions of small-craft facilities. All such reports should be sent to Director, Coast and Geodetic Survey (N/CG22), National Ocean Service, NOAA, Rockville, MD 20852-3806.

(307)   **Chart symbols and abbreviations.**–The standard symbols and abbreviations approved for use on all regular nautical charts published by the Defense Mapping Agency Hydrographic/Topographic Center and NOS are contained in **Chart No. 1,** United States of America **Nautical Chart Symbols and Abbreviations.** This publication is available from the Defense Mapping Agency Office of Distribution Services and NOS, and their sales agents.

(308)   On certain foreign charts reproduced by the United States, and on foreign charts generally, the symbols and abbreviations used may differ from U.S. approved standards. It is, therefore, recommended that navigators who acquire and use foreign charts and reproductions procure the symbol sheet or Chart No. 1 produced by the same foreign agency.

NAVTEX PREDICTED COVERAGE AREA
EAST COAST

LEGEND

------- 200 NMi
         (Approx.)

April 87

Longitude degrees — west

Latitude degrees — north

(309)   The mariner is warned that the buoyage systems, shapes, and colors used by other countries often have a different significance than the U.S. system.

(310)   **Chart Datum.**–Chart Datum is the particular tidal datum to which soundings and depth curves on a nautical chart or bathymetric map are referred. The tidal datum of **Mean Low Water** has been used as Chart Datum along the east coast of the United States and in parts of the West Indies. It is presently being changed to Mean Lower Low Water, with no adjustments to soundings, shorelines, low water lines, clearances, heights, elevations, or in the application of tide predictions for navigational purposes. The tidal datum of **Mean Lower Low Water** is used as Chart Datum along the Gulf and west coasts; the coasts of Alaska, Hawaii, and other United States and United Nations islands of the Pacific; and in parts of the West Indies.

(311)   Mean Low Water is defined as the arithmetic mean of all the low water heights observed over the National Tidal Datum Epoch. Mean Lower Low Water is defined as the arithmetic mean of the lower low water height of each tidal day (24.84 hours) observed over the National Tidal Datum Epoch. The National Tidal Datum Epoch is the specific 19-year period adopted by the National Ocean Service, NOAA, as the official time segment over which tide observations are taken and reduced to obtain mean values for tidal datums. The present Epoch is 1960 through 1978.

(312)   **Accuracy of a nautical chart.**–The value of a nautical chart depends upon the accuracy of the surveys on which it is based. The chart reflects what was found by field surveys and what has been reported to NOS Headquarters. The chart represents general conditions at the time of surveys or reports and does not necessarily portray present conditions. Significant changes may have taken place since the date of the last survey or report.

(313)   Each sounding represents an actual measure of depth and location at the time the survey was made, and each bottom characteristic represents a sampling of the surface layer of the sea bottom at the time of the sampling. Areas where sand and mud prevail, especially the entrances and approaches to bays and rivers exposed to strong tidal current and heavy seas, are subject to continual change.

(314)   In coral regions and where rocks and boulders abound, it is always possible that surveys may have failed to find every obstruction. Thus, when navigating such waters, customary routes and channels should be followed and areas avoided where irregular and sudden changes in depth indicate conditions associated with pinnacle rocks, coral heads, or boulders.

(315)   Information charted as "reported" should be treated with caution in navigating the area, because the actual conditions have not been verified by government surveys.

(316)   The **date of a chart** is of vital importance to the navigator. When charted information becomes obsolete, further use of the chart for navigation may be dangerous. Announcements of new editions of nautical charts are usually published in notices to mariners. A quarterly list of the latest editions is distributed to sales agents; free copies may be obtained from the sales agents or by writing to Distribution Branch (N/CG33), National Ocean Service. (See appendix for address.)

(317)   **U.S. Nautical Chart Numbering System.**– This chart numbering system, adopted by the National Ocean Service and the Defense Mapping Agency Hydrographic/Topographic Center, provides for a uniform method of identifying charts published by both agencies. Nautical charts published by the Defense Mapping Agency Hydrographic/

Topographic Center are identified in the Coast Pilot by an asterisk preceding the chart number.

(318)   **Corrections to charts.**–It is essential for navigators to keep charts corrected through information published in the notices to mariners, especially since the NOS no longer hand-corrects charts prior to distribution.

(319)   **Caution in using small-scale charts.**–Dangers to navigation cannot be shown with the same amount of detail on small-scale charts as on those of larger scale. Therefore, the largest scale chart of an area should always be used.

(320)   The **scales of nautical charts** range from 1:2,500 to about 1:5,000,000. Graphic scales are generally shown on charts with scales of 1:80,000 or larger, and numerical scales are given on smaller scale charts. NOS charts are classified according to scale as follows:

(321)   **Sailing charts,** scales 1:600,000 and smaller, are for use in fixing the mariner's position as he approaches the coast from the open ocean, or for sailing between distant coastwise ports. On such charts the shoreline and topography are generalized and only offshore soundings, and the principal lights, outer buoys, and landmarks visible at considerable distances are shown.

(322)   **General charts,** scales 1:150,000 to 1:600,000, are for coastwise navigation outside of outlying reefs and shoals.

(323)   **Coast charts,** scales 1:50,000 to 1:150,000 are for inshore navigation leading to bays and harbors of considerable width and for navigating large inland waterways.

(324)   **Harbor charts,** scales larger than 1:50,000, are for harbors, anchorage areas, and the smaller waterways.

(325)   **Special charts,** various scales, cover the Intracoastal waterways and miscellaneous small-craft areas.

(326)   **Blue tint in water areas.**–A blue tint is shown in water areas on many charts to accentuate shoals and other areas considered dangerous for navigation when using that particular chart.Since the danger curve varies with the intended purpose of a chart a careful inspection should be made to determine the contour depth of the blue tint areas.

(327)   **Caution on bridge and cable clearances.**–For bascule bridges whose spans do not open to a full vertical position, unlimited overhead clearance is not available for the entire charted horizontal clearance when the bridge is open, due to the inclination of the drawspans over the channel.

(328)   The charted clearances of overhead cables are for the lowest wires at mean high water unless otherwise stated. **Vessels with masts, stacks, booms, or antennas should allow sufficient clearance under power cables to avoid arcing.**

(329)   **Submarine cables and pipelines** cross many waterways used by both large and small vessels, but all of them may not be charted. For inshore areas, they usually are buried beneath the seabed, but, for offshore areas, they may lie on the ocean floor. Warning signs are often posted to warn mariners of their existence.

(330)   The installation of submarine cables or pipelines in U.S. waters or the Continental Shelf of the United States is under the jurisdiction of one or more Federal agencies, depending on the nature of the installation. They are shown on the charts when the necessary information is reported to NOS and they have been recommended for charting by the cognizant agency. The chart symbols for submarine cable and pipeline areas are usually shown for inshore areas, whereas, chart symbols for submarine cable and pipeline routes may be shown for offshore areas. Submarine cables and pipelines are not described in the Coast Pilots.

(331)   In view of the serious consequences resulting from damage to submarine cables and pipelines, vessel operators should take special care when anchoring, fishing, or engaging in underwater operations near areas where these cables

or pipelines may exist or have been reported to exist. Mariners are also warned that the areas where cables and pipelines were originally buried may have changed and they may be exposed; extreme caution should be used when operating vessels in depths of water comparable to the vessel's draft.

(332) Certain cables carry high voltage, while many pipelines carry natural gas under high pressure or petroleum products. Electrocution, fire, or explosion with injury, loss of life, or a serious pollution incident could occur if they are broached.

(333) Vessels fouling a submarine cable or pipeline should attempt to clear without undue strain. Anchors or gear that cannot be cleared should be slipped, but no attempt should be made to cut a cable or a pipeline.

(334) **Artificial obstructions to navigation.**–Disposal areas are designated by the Corps of Engineers for depositing dredged material where existing depths indicate that the intent is not to cause sufficient shoaling to create a danger to surface navigation. The areas are charted without blue tint, and soundings and depth curves are retained.

(335) **Disposal Sites** are areas established by Federal regulation **(40 CFR 220-229)** in which dumping of dredged and fill material and other nonbuoyant objects is allowed with the issuance of a permit. Dumping of dredged and fill material is supervised by the Corps of Engineers and all other dumping by the Environmental Protection Agency (EPA). (See Corps of Engineers and Environmental Protection Agency, this chapter, and appendix for office addresses.)

(336) **Dumping Grounds** are also areas that were established by Federal regulation **(33 CFR 205)**. However, these regulations have been revoked and the use of the areas discontinued. These areas will continue to be shown on nautical charts until such time as they are no longer considered to be a danger to navigation.

(337) Disposal Sites and Dumping Grounds are rarely mentioned in the Coast Pilot, but are shown on nautical charts. **Mariners are advised to exercise caution in and in the vicinity of all dumping areas.**

(338) **Spoil areas** are for the purpose of depositing dredged material, usually near and parallel to dredged channels; they are usually a hazard to navigation. Spoil areas are usually charted from survey drawings from Corps of Engineers after-dredging surveys, though they may originate from private or other Government agency surveys. Spoil areas are tinted blue on the charts and labeled, and all soundings and depth curves are omitted. Navigators of even the smallest craft should avoid crossing spoil areas.

(339) **Fish havens** are established by private interests, usually sport fishermen, to simulate natural reefs and wrecks that attract fish. The reefs are constructed by dumping assorted junk ranging from old trolley cars and barges to scrap building material in areas which may be of very small extent or may stretch a considerable distance along a depth curve; oil automobile bodies are a commonly used material. The Corps of Engineers must issue a permit, specifying the location and depth over the reef, before such a reef may be built. However, the reefbuilders' adherence to permit specifications can be checked only with a wire drag. Fish havens are outlined and labeled on the charts and show the minimum authorized depth when known. Fish havens are tinted blue if they have a minimum authorized depth of 11 fathoms or less or if the minimum authorized depth is unknown and they are in depths greater than 11 fathoms but still considered a danger to navigation. Navigators should be cautious about passing over fish havens or anchoring in their vicinity.

(340) **Fishtrap areas** are areas established by the Corps of Engineers, or State or local authority, in which traps may be built and maintained according to established regulations. The fish stakes which may exist in these areas are obstructions to navigation and may be dangerous. The limits of fishtrap areas and a cautionary note are usually charted. Navigators should avoid these areas.

(341) **Local magnetic disturbances.**–If measured values of magnetic variation differ from the expected (charted) values by several degrees, a magnetic disturbance note will be printed on the chart. The note will indicate the location and magnitude of the disturbance, but the indicated magnitude should not be considered as the largest possible value that may be encountered. Large disturbances are more frequently detected in the shallow waters near land masses than on the deep sea. Generally, the effect of a local magnetic disturbance diminishes rapidly with distance, but in some locations there are multiple sources of disturbances and the effects may be distributed for many miles.

(342) **Compass roses on charts.**–Each compass rose shows the date, magnetic variation, and the annual change in variation. Prior to the new edition of a nautical chart, the compass roses are reviewed. Corrections for annual change and other revisions may be made as a result of newer and more accurate information. On some general and sailing charts, the magnetic variation is shown by isogonic lines in addition to the compass roses.

(343) The **Mercator projection** used on most nautical charts has straight-line meridians and parallels that intersect at right angles. On any particular chart the distances between meridians are equal throughout, but distances between parallels increase progressively from the Equator toward the poles, so that a straight line between any two points is a rhumb line. This unique property of the Mercator projection is one of the main reasons why it is preferred by the mariner.

(344) **Echo soundings.**–Ship's echo sounders may indicate small variations from charted soundings; this may be due to the fact that various corrections (instrument corrections, settlement and squat, draft, and velocity corrections) are made to echo soundings in surveying which are not normally made in ordinary navigation, or to observational errors in reading the echo sounder. Instrument errors vary between different equipment and must be determined by calibration aboard ship. Most types of echo sounders are factory calibrated for a velocity of sound in water of 800 fathoms per second, but the actual velocity may differ from the calibrated velocity by as much as 5 percent, depending upon the temperature and salinity of the waters in which the vessel is operating; the highest velocities are found in warm, highly saline water, and the lowest in icy freshwater. Velocity corrections for these variations are determined and applied to echo soundings during hydrographic surveys. All echo soundings must be corrected for the vessel's draft, unless the draft observation has been set on the echo sounder.

(345) Observational errors include misinterpreting false echos from schools of fish, seaweed, etc., but the most serious error which commonly occurs is where the depth is greater than the scale range of the instrument; a 400–fathom scale indicates 15 fathoms when the depth is 415 fathoms. Caution in navigation should be exercised when wide variations from charted depths are observed.

AIDS TO NAVIGATION

(346) **Reporting of defects in aids to navigation.**–Promptly notify the nearest Coast Guard District Commander if an aid to navigation is observed to be missing, sunk, capsized,

out of position, damaged, extinguished, or showing improper characteristics.

(347) Radio messages should be prefixed "Coast Guard" and transmitted directly to any U.S. Government shore radio station for relay to the Coast Guard District Commander. If the radio call sign of the nearest U.S. Government radio shore station is not known, radiotelegraph communication may be established by the use of the general call "NCG" on the frequency of 500 kHz. Merchant ships may send messages relating to defects noted in aids to navigation through commercial facilities only when they are unable to contact a U.S. Government shore radio station. Charges for these messages will be accepted "collect" by the Coast Guard.

(348) **Lights.**–The range of visibility of lights as given in the Light Lists and as shown on the charts is the **Nominal range,** which is the maximum distance at which a light may be seen in clear weather (meteorological visibility of 10 nautical miles) expressed in nautical miles. The Light Lists give the Nominal ranges for all Coast Guard lighted aids except range and directional lights. **Luminous range** is the maximum distance at which a light may be seen under the existing visibility conditions. By use of the diagram in the Light Lists, Luminous range may be determined from the known Nominal range, and the existing visibility conditions. Both the Nominal and Luminous ranges do not take into account elevation, observer's height of eye, or the curvature of the earth. **Geographic range** is a function of only the curvature of the earth and is determined solely from the heights above sea level of the light and the observer's eye; therefore, to determine the actual Geographic range for a height of eye, the Geographic range must be corrected by a distance corresponding to the height difference, the distance correction being determined from a table of "distances of visibility for various heights above sea level." (See Light List or Coast Pilot table following appendix.) The maximum distances at which lights can be seen may at times be increased by abnormal atmospheric refraction and may be greatly decreased by unfavorable weather conditions such as fog, rain, haze, or smoke. All except the most powerful lights are easily obscured by such conditions. In some conditions of the atmosphere white lights may have a reddish hue. During weather conditions which tend to reduce visibility, colored lights are more quickly lost to sight than are white lights. Navigational lights should be used with caution because of the following conditions that may exist;

(349) A light may be extinguished and the fact not reported to the Coast Guard for correction, or a light may be located in an isolated area where it will take time to correct.

(350) In regions where ice conditions prevail the lantern panes of unattended lights may become covered with ice or snow, which will greatly reduce the visibility and may also cause colored lights to appear white.

(351) Brilliant shore lights used for advertising and other purposes, particularly those in densely populated areas, make it difficult to identify a navigational light.

(352) At short distances flashing lights may show a faint continuous light between flashes.

(353) The distance of an observer from a light cannot be estimated by its apparent intensity. The characteristics of lights in an area should always be checked in order that powerful lights visible in the distance will not be mistaken for nearby lights showing similar characteristics at low intensity such as those on lighted buoys.

(354) The apparent characteristic of a complex light may change with the distance of the observer, due to color and intensity variations among the different lights of the group.

The characteristic as charted and shown in the Light List may not be recognized until nearer the light.

(355) Motion of a vessel in a heavy sea may cause a light to alternately appear and disappear, and thus give a false characteristic.

(356) Where lights have different colored sectors, be guided by the correct bearing of the light; do not rely on being able to accurately observe the point at which the color changes. On either side of the line of demarcation of colored sectors there is always a small arc of uncertain color.

(357) On some bearings from the light, the range of visibility of the light may be reduced by obstructions. In such cases, the obstructed arc might differ with height of eye and distance. When a light is cut off by adjoining land and the arc of visibility is given, the bearing on which the light disappears may vary with the distance of the vessel from which observed and with the height of eye. When the light is cut off by a sloping hill or point of land, the light may be seen over a wider arc by a ship far off than by one close to.

(358) Arcs of circles drawn on charts around a light are not intended to give information as to the distance at which it can be seen, but solely to indicate, in the case of lights which do not show equally in all directions, the bearings between which the variation of visibility or obscuration of the light occurs.

(359) Lights of equal candlepower but of different colors may be seen at different distances. This fact should be considered not only in predicting the distance at which a light can be seen, but also in identifying it.

(360) Lights should not be passed close aboard, because in many cases riprap mounds are maintained to protect the structure against ice damage and scouring action.

(361) Many prominent towers, tanks, smokestacks, buildings, and other similar structures, charted as landmarks, display flashing and/or fixed red aircraft obstruction lights. Lights shown from landmarks are charted only when they have distinctive characteristics to enable the mariner to positively identify the location of the charted structure.

(362) **Articulated lights.**–An articulated light is a vertical pipe structure supported by a submerged buoyancy chamber and attached by a universal coupling to a weighted sinker on the seafloor. The light, allowed to move about by the universal coupling, is not as precise as a fixed aid. However, it has a much smaller watch circle than a conventional buoy, because the buoyancy chamber tends to force the pipe back to a vertical position when it heels over under the effects of wind, wave, or current.

(363) **Articulated daybeacons.**–Same description as for articulated lights (see above) except substitute daybeacon for light.

(364) **Bridge lights and clearance gages.**–The Coast Guard regulates marine obstruction lights and clearance gages on bridges across navigable waters. Where installed, clearance gages are generally vertical numerical scales, reading from top to bottom, and show the actual vertical clearance between the existing water level and the lowest point of the bridge over the channel; the gages are normally on the right-hand pier or abutment of the bridge, on both the upstream and downstream sides.

(365) Bridge lights are fixed red or green, and are privately maintained; they are generally not charted or described in the text of the Coast Pilot. All bridge piers (and their protective fenders) and abutments which are in or adjacent to a navigation channel are marked on all channel sides by red lights. On each channel span of a fixed bridge, there is a range of two green lights marking the center of the channel and a red light marking both edges of the channel, except

that when the margins of the channel are confined by bridge piers, the red lights on the span are omitted, since the pier lights then mark the channel edges; for multiplespan fixed bridges, the main-channel span may also be marked by three white lights in a vertical line above the green range lights.

(366) On all types of drawbridges, one or more red lights are shown from the drawspan (higher than the pier lights) when the span is closed; when the span is open, the higher red lights are obscured and one or two green lights are shown from the drawspan, higher than the pier lights. The number and location of the red and green lights depend upon the type of drawbridge.

(367) Bridges and their lighting, construction, maintenance, and operation are set forth in **33 CFR 114-118** (not carried in this Coast Pilot). Aircraft obstruction lights, prescribed by the Federal Aviation Administration, may operate at certain bridges. Drawbridge operation regulations are published in chapter 2 of the Coast Pilot.

(368) **Fog signals.**–Caution should be exercised in the use of sound fog signals for navigation purposes. They should be considered solely as warning devices.

(369) Sound travels through the air in a variable manner, even without the effects of wind; and, therefore, the hearing of fog signals cannot be implicitly relied upon.

(370) Experience indicates that distances must not be judged only by the intensity of the sound; that occasionally there may be areas close to a fog signal in which it is not heard; and that fog may exist not far from a station, yet not be seen from it, so the signal may not be operating. It is not always possible to start a fog signal immediately when fog is observed.

(371) **Avoidance of collision with offshore light stations and large navigational buoys (LNB).**–Courses should invariably be set to pass these aids with sufficient clearance to avoid the possibility of collision from any cause. Errors of observation, current and wind effects, other vessels in the vicinity, and defects in steering gear may be, and have been the cause of actual collisions, or imminent danger thereof, needlessly jeopardizing the safety of these facilities and their crews, and of all navigation dependent on these important aids to navigation.

(372) Experience shows that offshore light stations cannot be safely used as leading marks to be passed close aboard, but should always be left broad off the course, whenever sea room permits. When approaching fixed offshore light structures and large navigational buoys (LNB) on radio bearings, the risk of collision will be avoided by ensuring that radio bearing does not remain constant.

(373) It should be borne in mind that most large buoys are anchored to a very long scope of chain and, as a result, the radius of their swinging circle is considerable. The charted position is the location of the anchor. Furthermore under certain conditions of wind and current, they are subject to sudden and unexpected sheers which are certain to hazard a vessel attempting to pass close aboard.

(374) **Buoys.**–The aids to navigation depicted on charts comprise a system consisting of fixed and floating aids with varying degrees of reliability. Therefore, prudent mariners will not rely solely on any single aid to navigation, particularly a floating aid.

(375) The approximate position of a buoy is represented by the dot or circle associated with the buoy symbol. The approximate position is used because of practical limitations in positioning and maintaining buoys and their sinkers in precise geographical locations. These limitations include, but are not limited to, inherent imprecisions in position fixing methods, prevailing atmospheric and sea conditions, the slope of and the material making up the seabed, the fact that buoys are moored to sinkers by varying lengths of chain, and the fact that buoy body and/or sinker positions are not under continuous surveillance, but are normally checked only during periodic maintenance visits which often occur more than a year apart. The position of the buoy body can be expected to shift inside and outside of the charting symbol due to the forces of nature. The mariner is also cautioned that buoys are liable to be carried away, shifted, capsized, sunk, etc. Lighted buoys may be extinguished or sound signals may not function as a result of ice, running ice or other natural causes, collisions, or other accidents.

(376) For the foregoing reasons, a prudent mariner must not rely completely upon the charted position or operation of floating aids to navigation, but will also utilize bearings from fixed objects and aids to navigation on shore. Further, a vessel attempting to pass close aboard always risks collision with a yawing buoy or with the obstruction the buoy marks.

(377) Buoys may not always properly mark shoals or other obstructions due to shifting of the shoals or of the buoys. Buoys marking wrecks or other obstructions are usually placed on the seaward or channelward side and not directly over a wreck. Since buoys may be located some distance from a wreck they are intended to mark, and since sunken wrecks are not always static, extreme caution should be exercised when operating in the vicinity of such buoys.

(378) **Caution, channel markers.**–Lights, daybeacons, and buoys along dredged channels do not always mark the bottom edges. Due to local conditions, aids may be located inside or outside the channel limits shown by dashed lines on a chart. The Light List tabulates the offset distances for these aids in many instances.

(379) Aids may be moved, discontinued, or replaced by other types to facilitate dredging operations. Mariners should exercise caution when navigating areas where dredges with auxiliary equipment are working.

(380) Temporary changes in aids are not included on the charts.

(381) **Radiobeacons.**–A map showing the locations and operating details of marine radiobeacons is given in each Light List. This publication describes the procedure to follow in using radiobeacons to calibrate radio direction finders as well as listing special radio direction finder calibration stations.

(382) A vessel steering a course for a radiobeacon should observe the same precautions as when steering for a light or any other mark. If the radiobeacon is aboard a lightship, particular care should be exercised to avoid the possibility of collision, and sole reliance should never be placed on sighting the lightship or hearing its fog signal. If there are no dependable means by which the vessel's position may be fixed and the course changed well before reaching the lightship, a course should be selected that will ensure passing the lightship at a distance, rather than close aboard, and repeated bearings of the radiobeacon should show an increasing change in the same direction.

(383) **Radio bearings.**–No exact data can be given as to the accuracy to be expected in radio bearings taken by a ship, since the accuracy depends to a large extent upon the skill of the ship's operator, the condition of the ship's equipment, and the accuracy of the ship's calibration curve. Mariners are urged to obtain this information for themselves by taking frequent radio bearings, when their ship's position is accurately known, and recording the results.

(384) Radio bearings obtained at twilight or at night, and bearings which are almost parallel to the coast, should be

accepted with reservations, due to "night effect" and to the distortion of radio waves which travel overland. Bearings of aircraft ranges and standard broadcast stations should be used with particular caution due to coastal refraction and lack of calibration of their frequencies.

(385) **Conversion of radio bearings to Mercator bearings.**–Radio directional bearings are the bearings of the great circles passing through the radio stations and the ship, and, unless in the plane of the Equator or a meridian, would be represented on a Mercator chart as curved lines. Obviously it is impracticable for a navigator to plot such lines on a Mercator chart, so it is necessary to apply a correction to a radio bearing to convert it into a Mercator bearing, that is, the bearing of a straight line on a Mercator chart laid off from the sending station and passing through the receiving station.

(386) A table of corrections for the conversion of a radio bearing into a Mercator bearing follows the appendix. It is sufficiently accurate for practical purposes for distances up to 1,000 miles.

(387) The only data required are the latitudes and longitudes of the radiobeacons and of the ship by dead reckoning. The latter is scaled from the chart, and the former is either scaled from the chart or taken from the Light List.

(388) The table is entered with the differences of longitude in degrees between the ship and station (the nearest tabulated value being used), and opposite the middle latitude between the ship and station, the correction to be applied is read.

(389) The sign of the correction (bearings read clockwise from the north) will be as follows: In north latitude, the minus sign is used when the ship is east of the radiobeacon and the plus sign used when the ship is west of the radiobeacon. In south latitude, the plus sign is used when the ship is east of the radiobeacon, and the minus sign is used when the ship is west of the radiobeacon.

(390) To facilitate plotting, 180 degrees should be added to or subtracted from the corrected bearing, and the result plotted from the radiobeacon.

(391) Should the position by dead reckoning differ greatly from the true position of the ship as determined by plotting the corrected bearings, retrial should be made, using the new value as the position of the ship.

(392) **Radio bearings from other vessels.**–Any vessel with a radio direction-finder can take a bearing on a vessel equipped with a radio transmitter. These bearings, however, should be used only as a check, as comparatively large errors may be introduced by local conditions surrounding the radio direction-finder unless known and accounted for. Although any radio station, for which an accurate position is definitely known, may serve as a radiobeacon for vessels equipped with a radio direction-finder, extreme caution must be exercised in their use. Stations established especially for maritime services are more reliable.

(393) **SATELLITE POSITION INDICATING RADIO BEACON (EPIRB).**–Emergency position indicating radiobeacons (EPIRBs), devices which cost from $200 to over $2000, are designed to save your life if you get into trouble by alerting rescue authorities and indicating your location. EPIRB types are described in the accompanying table.

(394) **121.5/243 MHz EPIRBs.** These are the most common and least expensive type of EPIRB, designed to be detected by overflying commercial or military aircraft. Satellites were designed to detect these EPIRBs, but are limited for the following reasons:

(395) (i) Satellite detection range is limited for these EPIRBs (satellites must be within line of sight of both the

EPIRB Types		
Type	Frequency	Description
Class A	121.5/243 MHz	Float-free, automatically-activating, detectable by aircraft and satellite. Coverage limited (see Chart).
Class B	121.5/243 MHz	Manually activated version of Class A.
Class C	VHF ch 15/16	Manually activated, operates on maritime channels only. Not detectable by satellite.
Class S	121.5/243 MHz	Similar to Class B, except it floats, or is an integral part of a survival craft.
Cat I	406/121.5 MHz	Float-free, automatically activated EPIRB. Detectable by satellite anywhere in the world.
Cat II	406/121.5 MHz	Similar to Category I, except is manually activated.

EPIRB and a ground terminal for detection to occur) (see Chart),

(396) (ii) EPIRB design and frequency congestion cause these devices to be subject to a high false alert/false alarm rate (over 99%); consequently, confirmation is required before search and rescue forces can be deployed.

(397) (iii) EPIRBs manufactured before October 1989 may have design or construction problems (e.g. some models will leak and cease operating when immersed in water), or may not be detectable by satellite.

(398) **Class C EPIRBs.** These are manually activated devices intended for pleasure craft who do not venture far offshore and for vessels on the Great Lakes. They transmit a short burst on VHF-FM channel 16 and a longer homing signal on channel 15. Their usefulness depends upon a coast station or another vessel guarding channel 16 and recognizing the brief, recurring tone as an EPIRB. Class C EPIRBs are not recognized outside of the United States.

(399) **406 MHz EPIRBs.**–The 406 MHz EPIRB was designed to operate with satellites. Its signal allows a satellite local user terminal to accurately locate the EPIRB (much more accurately than 121.5/243 MHz devices), and identify the vessel (the signal is encoded with the vessel's identity) anywhere in the world (there is no range limitation). These devices also include a 121.5 MHz homing signal, allowing aircraft and rescue craft to quickly find the vessel in distress. These are the only type of EPIRB which must be certified by Coast Guard approved independent laboratories before they can be sold in the United States.

(400) An automatically activated, float-free version of this EPIRB will be required on Safety of Life at Sea Convention vessels (passenger ships and ships over 300 tons, on international voyages) of any nationality by 1 August 1993. The Coast Guard requires U.S. commercial fishing vessels carry this device (by May 1990, unless they carry a Class A EPIRB), and will require the same for other U.S. commercial uninspected vessels which travel more than 3 miles offshore.

(401) **The COSPAS-SARSAT system.**–COSPAS: Space System for Search of Distress Vessels (a Russian acronym); SARSAT: Search and Rescue Satellite-Aided Tracking. COSPAS-SARSAT is an international satellite-based search

Notes

LUTs
1 Archangelsk
2 Churchill
3 Edmonton
4 Goose Bay
5 Kodiak
6 Lasham
7 Moscow
8 Novosibirsk
9 Ottawa
10 Pt. Reyes
11 Scott AFB
12 Toulouse
13 Tromsø
14 Vladivostok

SARSAT satellite
Altitude   850 km
Elevation Angle   5 deg

1988 Satellite Visibility Area of SARSAT LUTs
(represents approximate System coverage at 121.5 MHz;
at 406 MHz, the System covers the entire globe)

and rescue system established by the U.S., U.S.S.R., Canada and France to locate emergency radio beacons transmitting on the frequencies 121.5, 243 and 406 MHz. Since its inception only a few years ago, COSPAS-SARSAT has contributed to the saving of 1240 lives (as of June 6, 1989), 554 of these mariners. The Coast Guard operates two local user terminals, satellite earth stations designed to received EPIRB distress calls forwarded from COSPAS-SARSAT satellites, located in Kodiak, Alaska and Point Reyes, California. The Air Force operates a third terminal at Scott Air Force Base, Illinois.

(402) **Testing EPIRBs.**–The Coast Guard urges those owning EPIRBs to periodically examine them for water tightness, battery expiration date and signal presence. FCC rules allow Class A, B, and S EPIRBs to be turned on briefly (for three audio sweeps, or one second only) during the first five minutes of each hour. Signal presence can be detected by an FM radio tuned to 99.5 MHz, or an AM radio tuned to any vacant frequency and located close to an EPIRB. FCC rules allow Class C EPIRBs to be tested within the first five minutes of every hour, for not more than five seconds. Class C EPIRBs can be detected by a marine radio tuned to channel 15 or 16. 406 MHz EPIRBs can be tested through its self-test function, which is an integral part of the device.

(403) **Radar beacons (Racons)** are low-powered radio transceivers that operate in the marine radar X-band frequencies. When activated by a vessel's radar signal, **Racons** provide a distinctive visible display on the vessel's radarscope from which the range and bearing to the beacon may be determined. (See Light List and DMAHTC Pub. 117 for details.)

(404) **LORAN-C.**–LORAN, an acronym for LOng RAnge Navigation, is an electronic aid to navigation consisting of shore-based radio transmitters. The LORAN system enables users equipped with a LORAN receiver to determine their position quickly and accurately, day or night, in practically any weather.

(405) A LORAN-C chain consists of three to five transmitting stations separated by several hundred miles. Within a chain, one station is designated as master while the other stations are designated as secondaries. Each secondary station is identified as either whiskey, x-ray, yankee, or zulu.

(406) The master station is always the first station to transmit. It transmits a series of nine pulses. The secondary stations then follow in turn, transmitting eight pulses each, at precisely timed intervals. This cycle repeats itself endlessly. The length of the cycle is measured in microseconds and is called a Group Repetition Interval (GRI).

(407) LORAN-C chains are designated by the four most significant digits of their GRI. For example, a chain with a GRI of 89,700 microseconds is referred to as 8970. A different GRI is used for each chain because all LORAN-C stations broadcast in the same 90 to 110 kilohertz frequency band and would otherwise interfere with one another.

(408) The LORAN-C system can be used in either a hyperbolic or range mode. In the widely used hyperbolic mode, a LORAN-C line of position is determined by measuring the time difference between sychronized pulses received from two separate transmitting stations. In the range mode, a line of position is determined by measuring the time required by LORAN-C pulses to travel from a transmitting station to the user's receiver.

(409) A user's position is determined by locating the crossing point of two lines of position on a LORAN-C chart. Many receivers have built-in coordinate converters which will automatically display the receiver's latitude and longitude. With a coordinate converter, a position can be determined using a chart that is not overprinted with LORAN-C lines of position.

(410) CAUTION: The latitude/longitude computation on some models is based upon an all seawater propagation path. This may lead to error if the LORAN-C signals from the various stations involve appreciable overland propagation paths. These errors may put the mariner at risk in areas requiring precise positioning if the proper correctors (ASF) are not applied. Therefore, it is recommended that mariners using Coordinate Converters check the manufacturer's operating manual to determine if and how corrections are to be applied to compensate for the discontinuity caused by the overland paths.

(411) There are two types of LORAN-C accuracy: absolute and repeatable. Absolute accuracy is a measure of the navigator's ability to determine latitude and longitude position from the LORAN-C time differences measured. Repeatable accuracy is a measure of the LORAN-C navigator's ability to return to a position where readings have been taken before.

(412) The absolute accuracy of LORAN-C is 0.25 nautical miles, 95% confidence within the published coverage area using standard LORAN-C charts and tables. Repeatable accuracy depends on many factors, so measurements must be taken to determine the repeatable accuracy in any given area. Coast Guard surveys have found repeatable accuracies between 30 and 170 meters in most ground wave coverage areas. LORAN-C position determination on or near the baseline extensions are subject to significant errors and, therefore, should be avoided whenever possible. The use of skywaves is not recommended within 250 miles of a station being used, and corrections for these areas are not usually tabulated.

(413) If the timing or pulse shape of a master-secondary pair deviates from specified tolerances, the first two pulses of the secondary station's pulse train will blink on and off. The LORAN-C receiver sees this blinking signal and indicates a warning to the user. This warning will continue until the signals are once again in tolerance. A blinking signal is not exhibited during off-air periods, so a separate receiver alarm indicates any loss of signal. Never use a blinking secondary signal for navigation.

(414) In coastal waters, LORAN-C should not be relied upon as the only aid to navigation. A prudent navigator will use radar, radio direction finder, fathometer and any other aid to navigation, in addition to the LORAN-C receiver.

(415) **LORAN-C Interference**

(416) Interference to LORAN-C may result from radio transmissions by public or private sources operating near the LORAN-C band of 90-110 kHz. Anyone using the LORAN-C system, who observes interference to LORAN-C, should promptly report it to one of the Coast Guard commands listed below. Include in such reports information regarding the date, time, identifying characteristics, strength of the interfering signals and your own vessel's position. These interference reports are very important and cooperation from users of LORAN-C will assist the Coast Guard in improving LORAN-C service.

(417) **Atlantic Ocean and Gulf of Mexico**
(418) Commander (Atl)
(419) Atlantic Area, U.S. Coast Guard
(420) Governors Island
(421) New York, NY 10004-5000
(422) **Pacific Ocean**
(423) Commander (Ptl)

(424)   Pacific Area, U.S. Coast Guard

(425)   Coast Guard Island

(426)   Alameda, CA 94501-5100

(427)   **All areas**

(428)   Commandant (G-NRN)

(429)   U.S. Coast Guard

(430)   Washington, DC 20593-0001

(431)   **LORAN-C Charts and Publications**

(432)   Navigational charts overprinted with LORAN-C lines of position are published by the National Ocean Service (NOS), Distribution Branch (N/CG33), 6501 Lafayette Avenue, Riverdale, MD 20737-1199 and the Defense Mapping Agency (DMA), Combat Support Center, Code: PMSR, Washington, DC 20315-0010, and may be purchased directly from NOS or DMA, or through local chart sales agents.

(433)   A general source of LORAN-C information is the LORAN-C User Handbook written by the U.S. Coast Guard. This publication can be purchased from the Government Printing Office, Washington, DC (see appendix for address).

(434)   **Omega.**–Omega is a continuous radionavigation system which provides hyperbolic lines of position through phase comparisons of very low frequency (10-14 kHz range) continuous wave signals transmitted on a common frequency on a time shared basis. With eight transmitting stations located throughout the world, Omega provides worldwide, all-weather navigation coverage. Six stations make Omega available in nearly all parts of the globe, with the two other stations providing redundancy and coverage during off-air time for maintenance.

(435)   Users are cautioned that the Omega system is in an implementation stage. System changes and station off-air periods are promulgated by Notice to Mariners and radio navigational warning messages. Current information on the status of individual Omega transmitting stations is broadcast on station WWV, 16 minutes after the hour, and on station WWVH, 47 minutes after the hour. Current status reports are available by telephone (202-245-0298).

(436)   At the present time the worldwide accuracy and reliability of this system cannot be precisely determined. Therefore positioning information derived from Omega should not be totally relied upon without reference to other positioning methods.

(437)   **Uniform State Waterway Marking System.**–Many bodies of water used by boatmen are located entirely within the boundaries of a State. The Uniform State Waterway Marking System (USWMS) has been developed to indicate to the small-boat operator hazards, obstructions, restricted or controlled areas, and to provide directions. Although intended primarily for waters within the state boundaries, USWMS is suited for use in all water areas, since it supplements and is generally compatible with the Coast Guard lateral system of aids to navigation. The Coast Guard is gradually using more aids bearing the USWMS geometric shapes described below.

(438)   Two categories of waterway markers are used. Regulatory markers, buoys, and signs use distinctive standard shape marks to show regulatory information. The signs are white with black letters and have a wide orange border. They signify speed zones, restricted areas, danger areas, and directions to various places. Aids to navigation on State waters use red and black buoys to mark channel limits. Red and black buoys are generally used in pairs. The boat should pass between the red buoy and its companion black buoy. If the buoys are not placed in pairs, the distinctive color of the buoy indicates the direction of dangerous water from the buoy. White buoys with red tops should be passed to the south or west, indicating that danger lies to the north or east of the buoy. White buoys with black tops should be passed to the north or east. Danger lies to the south or west. Vertical red and white striped buoys indicate a boat should not pass between the buoy and the nearest shore. Danger lies inshore of the buoy.

(439)   **DESTRUCTIVE WAVES.**–Unusual sudden changes in water level can be caused by tsunamis or violent storms. These two types of destructive waves have become commonly known as **tidal waves,** a name which is technically incorrect as they are not the result of tide-producing forces.

(440)   **Tsunamis (seismic sea waves)** are set up by submarine earthquakes. Many such seismic disturbances do not produce sea waves and often those produced are small, but the occasional large waves can be very damaging to shore installations and dangerous to ships in harbors.

(441)   These waves travel great distances and can cause tremendous damage on coasts far from their source. The wave of April 1, 1946, which originated in the Aleutian Trench, demolished nearby Scotch Cap Lighthouse and caused damages of $25 million in the Hawaiian Islands 2,000 miles away. The wave of May 22-23, 1960, which originated off Southern Chile, caused widespread death and destruction in islands and countries throughout the Pacific.

(442)   The speed of tsunamis varies with the depth of the water, reaching 300 to 500 knots in the deep water of the open ocean. In the open sea they cannot be detected from a ship or from the air because their length is so great, sometimes a hundred miles, as compared to their height, which is usually only a few feet. Only on certain types of shelving coasts do they build up into waves of disastrous proportions.

(443)   There is usually a series of waves with crests 10 to 40 minutes apart, and the highest may occur several hours after the first wave. Sometimes the first noticeable part of the wave is the trough which causes a recession of the water from shore, and people who have gone out to investigate this unusual exposure of the beach have been engulfed by the oncoming crest. Such an unexplained withdrawal of the sea should be considered as nature's warning of an approaching wave.

(444)   Improvements have been made in the quick determination and reporting of earthquake epicenters, but no method has yet been perfected for determining whether a sea wave will result from a given earthquake. The Pacific Tsunami Warning Center, Oahu, Hawaii, of the National Oceanic and Atmospheric Administration is headquarters of a warning system which has field reporting stations (seismic and tidal) in most countries around the Pacific. When a warning is broadcast, waterfront areas should be vacated for higher ground, and ships in the vicinity of land should head for the deep water of the open sea.

(445)   **Storm surge.**–A considerable rise or fall in the level of the sea along a particular coast may result from strong winds and sharp change in barometric pressure. In cases where the water level is raised, higher waves can form with greater depth and the combination can be destructive to low regions, particularly at high stages of tide. Extreme low levels can result in depths which are considerably less than those shown on nautical charts. This type of wave occurs especially in coastal regions bordering on shallow waters which are subject to tropical storms.

(446)   **Seiche** is a stationary vertical wave oscillation with a period varying from a few minutes to an hour or more, but somewhat less than the tidal periods. It is usually attributed

to external forces such as strong winds, changes in barometric pressure, swells, or tsunamis disturbing the equilibrium of the watersurface. Seiche is found both in enclosed bodies of water and superimposed upon the tides of the open ocean. When the external forces cause a short-period horizontal oscillation on the water, it is called **surge.**

(447)   The combined effect of seiche and surge sometimes makes it difficult to maintain a ship in its position alongside a pier even though the water may appear to be completely undisturbed, and heavy mooring lines have been parted repeatedly under such conditions. Pilots advise taut lines to reduce the effect of the surge.

SPECIAL SIGNALS FOR CERTAIN VESSELS

(448)   **Special signals for surveying vessels.**–National Oceanic and Atmospheric Administration (NOAA) vessels engaged in survey operations and limited in their ability to maneuver because of the work being performed (handling equipment over-the-side such as water sampling or conductivity-temperature-density (CTD) casts, towed gear, bottom samplers, etc., and divers working on, below or in proximity of the vessel) are required by Navigation Rules, International-Inland, Rule 27, to exhibit:

(449)   (b)(i) three all-round lights in a vertical line where they can best be seen. The highest and lowest of these lights shall be red and the middle light shall be white;

(450)   (ii) three shapes in a vertical line where they can best be seen. The highest and lowest of these shapes shall be balls and the middle one a diamond;

(451)   (iii) when making way through the water, masthead lights, sidelights and a sternlight, in addition to the lights prescribed in subparagraph (b)(i); and

(452)   (iv) when at anchor, in addition to the lights or shapes prescribed in subparagraphs(b)(i) and (ii) the light, lights or shapes prescribed in Rule 30, Anchored Vessels and Vessels Aground.

(453)   The color of the above shapes is black.

(454)   A NOAA vessel engaged in hydrographic survey operations (making way on a specific trackline while sounding the bottom) is not restricted in its ability to maneuver and therefore exhibits at night only those lights required for a power-driven vessel of its length.

(455)   **Warning signals for Coast Guard vessels while handling or servicing aids to navigation** are the same as those prescribed for surveying vessels. (See Special signals for surveying vessels, this chapter.)

(456)   **Minesweeper signals.**–U.S. vessels engaged in minesweeping operations or exercises are hampered to a considerable extent in their maneuvering powers. With a view to indicating the nature of the work on which they are engaged, these vessels will show the signals hereinafter mentioned. For the public safety, all other vessels, whether steamers or sailing craft, must endeavor to keep out of the way of vessels displaying these signals and not approach them inside the distances mentioned herein, especially remembering that it is dangerous to pass between the vessels of a pair or group sweeping together.

(457)   All vessels towing sweeps are to show: **By day,** a black ball at or near the foremast head and a black ball at each end of the fore yard. **By night,** all around green lights instead of the black balls, and in a similar manner.

(458)   Vessels or formations showing these signals indicate that it is dangerous for another vessel to approach within 1,000 meters (3,280 feet) of the mineclearance vessel. Under no circumstances is a vessel to pass through a formation of minesweepers. Minesweepers should be prepared to warn merchant vessels which persist in approaching too close by means of any of the appropriate signals from the International Code of Signals. In fog, mist, falling snow, heavy rainstorms, or any other condition similarly restricting visibility, whether by day or night, minesweepers while towing sweeps when in the vicinity of other vessels will sound whistle signals for a vessel towing (one prolonged blast followed by two short blasts).

(459)   The United States is increasingly using helicopters to conduct minesweeping operations and exercises. When so engaged, helicopters, like vessels, are considerably hampered in their ability to maneuver. Helicopters may function at night as well as during the day and in varying types of weather. Accordingly, surface vessels approaching helicopters engaged in minesweeping operations should take precautions similar to those described above with regard to minesweeping vessels.

(460)   Helicopters towing minesweeping gear, and surface escorts, if any, will use all practical means to warn approaching ships of the operations being conducted. Where practical, measures will be taken to mark or light the gear being towed. While towing, the helicopter's altitude varies from 49.2 to 311.6 feet (15 to 95 meters) above the water, and speeds vary from 0 to 30 knots.

(461)   Minesweeping helicopters are equipped with a rotating beacon which has a selectable red and amber mode. The amber mode is used during towing operations to notify and warn other vessels that the helicopter is towing.

(462)   **Submarine emergency identification signals.**–U.S. submarines are equipped with signal ejectors which may be used to launch identification signals, including emergency signals. Two general types of signals may be used: smoke floats and flares or stars. The smoke floats, which burn on the surface, produce a dense colored smoke for a period of 15 to 45 seconds. The flares or stars are propelled to a height of 300 to 400 feet from which they descend by small parachute. The flares or stars burn for about 25 seconds. The color of the smoke or flare/star has the following meaning:

(463)   **Green or black** is used under training exercise conditions only to indicate that a torpedo has been fired or that the firing of a torpedo has been simulated.

(464)   **Yellow** indicates the submarine is about to rise to periscope depth. Surface craft terminate antisubmarine counterattack and clear vicinity of submarine. Do not stop propellers.

(465)   **Red** indicates an emergency inside the submarine; she will try to surface immediately, if possible. Surface ships clear the area and stand by to assist. In case of repeated red signals, or if the submarine fails to surface in a reasonable time, she may be presumed disabled. Buoy the location, look for submarine buoy, and attempt to establish sonar communications. Advise U.S. Navy authorities immediately.

(466)   Submarine marker buoys consist of two spheres 3 feet in diameter with connecting structure, painted international orange. The buoy has a wire cable to the submarine, to act as a downhaul line for a rescue chamber. The buoy may be accompanied by an oil slick release to attract attention. A submarine on the bottom in distress may release this buoy. If sighted, such a buoy should be investigated and reported immediately to U.S. Navy authorities.

(467)   The submarine may transmit the International Distress Signal (SOS) on its sonar gear independently or in conjunction with the red signal. Submarines also may use these other means of attracting attention: release of dye marker or air bubble; ejection of oil; pounding on hull.

(468)   **Vessels Constrained by their Draft.**–International Navigation Rules, Rule 28, states that a vessel constrained

by her draft may, in addition to the lights prescribed for power-driven vessels in Rule 23, exhibit where they can best be seen three all-around red lights in a vertical line, or a cylinder.

NAVIGATION RESTRICTIONS AND REQUIREMENTS

(469) **Traffic Separation Schemes (Traffic Lanes).**–To increase the safety of navigation, particularly in converging areas of high traffic density, routes incorporating traffic separation have, with the approval of the International Maritime Organization (IMO), formerly the Inter-Governmental Maritime Consultative Organization (IMCO), been established in certain areas of the world. In the interest of safe navigation, it is recommended that through traffic use these schemes, as far as circumstances permit, by day and by night and in all weather conditions.

(470) General principles for navigation in Traffic Separation Schemes are as follows:

(471) 1. A ship navigating in or near a traffic separation scheme adopted by IMO shall in particular comply with Rule 10 of the 72 COLREGS to minimize the development of risk of collision with another ship. The other rules of the 72 COLREGS apply in all respects, and particularly the steering and sailing rules if risk of collision with another ship is deemed to exist.

(472) 2. Traffic separation schemes are intended for use by day and by night in all weather, in ice-free waters or under light ice conditions where no extraordinary maneuvers or assistance by icebreaker(s) are required.

(473) 3. Traffic separation schemes are recommended for use by all ships unless stated otherwise. Bearing in mind the need for adequate underkeel clearance, a decision to use a traffic separation scheme must take into account the charted depth, the possibility of changes in the seabed since the the time of last survey, and the effects of meteorological and tidal conditions on water depths.

(474) 4. A deepwater route is an allied routing measure primarily intended for use by ships which require the use of such a route because of their draft in relation to the available depth of water in the area concerned. Through traffic to which the above consideration does not apply should, if practicable, avoid following deepwater routes. When using a deepwater route mariners should be aware of possible changes in the indicated depth of water due to meteorological or other effects.

(475) 5. Users of traffic separation schemes adopted by IMO will be guided by Rule 10 of the 1972 International Regulations for Preventing Collisions at Sea (72 COLREGS) as follows:

(476) (a) This Rule applies to traffic separation schemes adopted by the Organization.

(477) (b) A vessel using a traffic separation scheme shall:

(478) (i) proceed in the appropriate traffic lane in the general direction of traffic flow for that lane;

(479) (ii) so far as practicable keep clear of a traffic separation line or separation zone;

(480) (iii) normally join or leave a traffic separation lane at the termination of the lane, but when joining or leaving from either side shall do so at as small an angle to the general direction of traffic flow as practicable.

(481) (c) A vessel shall so far as practicable avoid crossing traffic lanes, but if obliged to do so, shall cross as nearly as practicable at right angles to the general direction of traffic flow.

(482) (d) Inshore traffic zones shall not normally be used by through traffic which can safety use the appropriate traffic lane within the adjacent traffic separation scheme. However, vessels of less than 20 meters in length and sailing vessels may under all circumstances use inshore traffic zones.

(483) (e) A vessel, other than a crossing vessel, or a vessel joining or leaving a lane shall not normally enter a separation zone or cross a separation line except:

(484) (i) in cases of emergency to avoid immediate danger;

(485) (ii) to engage in fishing within a separate zone.

(486) (f) A vessel navigating in areas near the terminations of traffic separation schemes shall do so with particular caution.

(487) (g) A vessel shall so far as practicable avoid anchoring in a traffic separation scheme or in areas near its terminations.

(488) (h) A vessel not using a traffic separation scheme shall avoid it by as wide a margin as is practicable.

(489) (i) A vessel engaged in fishing shall not impede the passage of any vessel following a traffic lane.

(490) (j) A vessel of less than 20 meters in length or a sailing vessel shall not impede the safe passage of a power-driven vessel following a traffic lane.

(491) (k) A vessel restricted in her ability to maneuver when engaged in an operation for the maintenance of safety of navigation in a traffic separation scheme is exempted from complying with Rule 10 to the extent necessary to carry out the operation.

(492) (l) A vessel restricted in her ability to maneuver when engaged in an operation for laying, servicing or picking up of a submarine cable, within a traffic separation scheme, is exempted from complying with this Rule to the extent necessary to carry out the operation.

(493) 6. The arrows printed on charts merely indicate the general direction of traffic; ships need not set their courses strictly along the arrows.

(494) 7. The signal "YG" meaning "You appear not to be complying with the traffic separation scheme" is provided in the International Code of Signals for appropriate use.

(495) When approved or established, traffic separation scheme details are announced in Notice to Mariners, and later depicted on appropriate charts and included in the Coast Pilot and Sailing Directions.

(496) **Oil Pollution**–The Federal Water Pollution Control Act, as amended, prohibits the discharge of a harmful quantity of oil or a hazardous substance into or upon the United States navigable waters or adjoining shorelines, or into or upon the waters of the contiguous zone, or in connection with activities under the Outer Continental Shelf Lands Act or the Deepwater Port Act of 1974, or which may affect natural resources belonging to, appertaining to, or under the exclusive management authority of the United States including resources under the Fisher Conservation and Management Act of 1976. Discharges that do occur must be reported to the Coast Guard (National Response Center) by the most rapid available means. To assist in swift reporting of spills, a nationwide, 24-hour, toll-free telephone number has been established (1-800-424-8802).

(497) Hazardous quantities of oil have been defined by the Environmental Protection Agency as those which violate applicable water quality standards or cause a film or sheen upon or discoloration of the surface of the water or adjoining shorelines, or cause a sludge or emulsion to be deposited beneath the surface of the water or adjoining shorelines. (For regulations pertaining to this Act see **40 CFR 110.3**, not carried in this Pilot.)

(498)   The Refuse Act of 1899 (33 U.S.C. 407) prohibits anyone from throwing, discharging or depositing any refuse matter of any kind in U.S. navigable waters or tributaries of navigable waters. The only exceptions to this prohibition are liquid sewage flowing from streets or sewers and discharges made from shore facilities under a permit granted by the U.S. Army Corps of Engineers.

(499)   The Act to Prevent Pollution from Ships (33 U.S.C. 1901) is based on the International Convention for the Prevention of Pollution from Ships, as modified by the Protocol of 1978 (MARPOL 73/78). For tankers over 150 gross tons and all other ships over 400 gross tons, MARPOL 73/78 requires the installation of new equipment to control overboard discharges of oil and oily waste. This includes oily-water separating, monitoring and alarm systems for discharges from cargo areas, cargo pump rooms and machinery space bilges. New ships must have the equipment on board by October 2, 1983, while existing ships have until October 2, 1986 to comply.

(500)   Ships are also required to have an International Oil Pollution Prevention Certificate verifying that the vessel is in compliance with MARPOL 73/78 and that any required equipment is on board and operational, and they must maintain a new Oil Record Book reporting all oil transfers and discharges. The Oil Record Book is available from the Government Printing Office (see appendix for address).

(501)   **Other requirements for the protection of navigable waters.**–It is not lawful to tie up or anchor vessels or to float lografts in navigable channels in such manner as to obstruct normal navigation. When a vessel or raft is wrecked and sunk in a navigable channel it is the duty of the owner to immediately mark it with a buoy or beacon during the day and a light at night until the sunken craft is removed or abandoned.

(502)   **Obligation of deck officers.**–Licensed deck officers are required to acquaint themselves with the latest information published in Notice to Mariners regarding aids to navigation.

(503)   **Improper use of searchlights prohibited.**–No person shall flash or cause to be flashed the rays of a searchlight or other blinding light onto the bridge or into the pilothouse of any vessel underway. The International Code Signal "PG2" may be made by a vessel inconvenienced by the glare of a searchlight in order to apprise the offending vessel of the fact.

(504)   **Use of Radar.**–Navigation Rules, International-Inland, Rule 7, states, in part, that every vessel shall use all available means appropriate to the prevailing circumstances and conditions to determine if risk of collision exists. If there is any doubt such risk shall be deemed to exist. Proper use shall be made of radar equipment if fitted and operational, including long-range scanning to obtain early warning of risk of collision and radar plotting or equivalent systematic observation of detected objects.

(505)   This rule places an additional responsibility on vessels which are equipped and manned to use radar to do so while underway during periods of reduced visibility without in any way relieving commanding officers of the responsibility of carrying out normal precautionary measures.

(506)   Navigation Rules, International-Inland, Rules 6, 7, 8, and 19 apply to the use of radar.

(507)   **Danger signal.**–Navigation Rules, International-Inland, Rule 34(d), states that when vessels in sight of one another are approaching each other and from any cause either vessel fails to understand the intentions or actions of the other, or is in doubt whether sufficient action is being taken by the other to avoid collision, the vessel in doubt shall immediately indicate such doubt by giving at least five short and rapid blasts on the whistle. Such signal may be supplemented by a light signal of at least five short and rapid flashes.

(508)   **Narrow channels.**–Navigation Rules, International-Inland, Rule 9(b) states: A vessel of less than 65.6 feet (20 meters) in length or a sailing vessel shall not impede the passage of a vessel that can safety navigate only within a narrow channel or fairway.

(509)   **Control of shipping in time of emergency or war.**–In time of war or national emergency, merchant vessels of the United States and those foreign flag vessels, which are considered under effective U.S. control, will be subject to control by agencies of the U.S. Government. The allocation and employment of such vessels, and of domestic port facilities, equipment, and services will be performed by appropriate agencies of the War Transport Administration. The movement, routing, and diversion of merchant ships at sea will be controlled by appropriate naval commanders. The movement of merchant ships within domestic ports and dispersal anchorages will be coordinated by the U.S. Coast Guard. The commencement of naval control will be signaled by a general emergency message. (See DMAHTC Pub. 117 for emergency procedures and communication instructions.)

(510)   **Exclusive Economic Zone of the United States.**–Established by a Presidential Proclamation on March 10, 1983, the Exclusive Economic Zone (**EEZ**) of the United States is a zone contiguous to the territorial sea, including zones contiguous to the territorial sea of the United States, the Commonwealth of Puerto Rico, the Commonwealth of the Northern Mariana Islands (to the extent consistent with the Covenant and the United Nations Trusteeship Agreement), and United States overseas territories and possessions. The EEZ extends to a distance of 200 nautical miles from the baseline from which the breadth of the territorial sea is measured. In cases where the maritime boundary with a neighboring state remains to be determined, the boundary of the EEZ shall be determined by the United States and the other state concerned in accordance with equitable principles.

(511)   Within the EEZ, the United States has asserted, to the extent permitted by international law, (a) sovereign rights for the purpose of exploring, exploiting, conserving and managing natural resources, both living and nonliving, of the seabed and subsoil and the superjacent waters and with regard to other activities for the economic exploitation and exploration of the zone, such as the production of energy from the water, currents and winds; and (b) jurisdiction with regard to the establishment and use of artificial islands, and installations and structures having economic purposes, and the protection and preservation of the marine environment.

(512)   Without prejudice to the sovereign rights and jurisdiction of the United States, the EEZ remains an area beyond the territory and territorial sea of the United States in which all states enjoy the high seas freedoms of navigation, overflight, the laying of submarine cables and pipelines, and other internationally lawful uses of the sea.

(513)   This Proclamation does not change existing United States policies concerning the continental shelf, marine mammals and fisheries, including highly migratory species of tuna which are not subject to United States jurisdiction and require international agreements for effective management.

(514) The United States will exercise these sovereign rights and jurisdiction in accordance with the rules of international law.

(515) The seaward limit of the EEZ is shown on the nautical chart as a line interspersed periodically with EXCLUSIVE ECONOMIC ZONE. The EEZ boundary is coincidental with that of the Fishery Conservation Zone.

(516) **U.S. Fishery Conservation Zone.**– The United States exercises exclusive fishery management authority over all species of fish, except tuna, within the fishery conservation zone, whose seaward boundary is 200 miles from the baseline from which the U.S. territorial sea is measured; all anadromous species which spawn in the United States throughout their migratory range beyond the fishery conservation zone, except within a foreign country's equivalent fishery zone as recognized by the United States; all U.S. Continental Shelf fishery resources beyond the fishery conservation zone. Such resources include American lobster and species of coral, crab, abalone, conch, clam, and sponge, among others.

(517) No foreign vessel may fish, aid, or assist vessels at sea in the performance of any activity relating to fishing including, but not limited to preparation, supply, storage, refrigeration, transportation or processing, within the fishery conservation zone, or fish for anadromous species of the United States or Continental Shelf fishery resources without a permit issued in accordance with U.S. law. These permits may only be issued to vessels from countries recognizing the exclusive fishery management authority of the United States in an international agreement. The owners or operators of foreign vessels desiring to engage in fishing off U.S. coastal waters should ascertain their eligibility from their own flag state authorities. Failure to obtain a permit prior to fishing, or failure to comply with the conditions and restrictions established in the permit may subject both vessel and its owner or operators to administrative, civil, and criminal penalties. (Further details concerning foreign fishing are given in **50 CFR 611**.)

(518) Reports of foreign fishing activity within the fishery conservation zone should be made to the U.S. Coast Guard. Immediate reports are particularly desired, but later reports by any means also have value. Reports should include the activity observed, the position, and as much identifying information (name, number, homeport, type, flag, color, size, shape, etc.) about the foreign vessel as possible, and the reporting party's name and address or telephone number.

(519) **Bridge-to-bridge Radiotelephone Communication.**–Voice radio bridge-to-bridge communication between vessels is an effective aid in the prevention of collisions where there is restricted maneuvering room and/or visibility. VHF-FM radio is used for this purpose, due to its essentially line-of-sight characteristic and relative freedom from static. As VHF-FM has increasingly come into use for short-range communications in U.S. harbors and other high-traffic waters, so has the number of ships equipped with this gear increased.

(520) The Vessel Bridge-to-Bridge Radiotelephone Regulations, effective January 1, 1973, require vessels subject to the Act while navigating to be equipped with at least one single channel transceiver capable of transmitting and receiving on VHF-FM channel 13 (156.65 MHz), the Bridge-to-Bridge Radiotelephone frequency. Vessels with multichannel equipment are required to have an additional receiver so as to be able to guard VHF-FM channel 13 (156.65 MHz), the Bridge-to-Bridge Radiotelephone frequency, in addition to VHF-FM channel 16 (156.80 MHz), the National Distress, Safety and Calling frequency required by Federal Communications Commission regulations. (See **26.01 through 26.10**, chapter 2, for Vessel Bridge-to-Bridge Radiotelephone Regulations.)

(521) Mariners are reminded that the use of bridge-to-bridge voice communications in no way alters the obligation to comply with the provisions of the Navigation Rules, International-Inland.

(522) **VHF-FM Radiotelephone.**-The following table provides the frequency equivalents and general usage of selected VHF-FM channels which appear in the Coast Pilot. The letter "A" appended to a channel number indicates that U.S. operation of the particular channel is different than the international operation, i.e., U.S. stations transmit and receive on the same frequency and international stations use different frequencies.

(523) The information given here is extracted from the "Marine Radiotelephone Users Handbook" published by the Radio Technical Commission for Maritime Services. Ordering information for this valuable, comprehensive publication is included in the appendix.

(524) All channels given below are designated for both ship-to-ship and ship-to-coast communications except as noted.

Channel	Ship Frequency (MHz) Transmit	Receive	Channel Usage
1A	156.050	156.050	Port operations and commercial
5A	156.250	156.250	Port operations
6	156.300	156.300	Intership safety
7A	156.350	156.350	Commercial
8	156.400	156.400	Commercial (ship-to-ship only)
9	156.450	156.450	Commercial and non-commercial
10	156.500	156.500	Commercial
11	156.550	156.550	Commercial
12	156.600	156.600	Port operations (traffic advisories, including VTS in some ports)
13	156.650	156.650	Navigational (ship-to-ship), also used at locks and bridges
14	156.700	156.700	Port operations (traffic advisories, including VTS in some ports)
16	156.800	156.800	Distress, safety and calling
17	156.850	156.850	State or local government control
18A	156.900	156.900	Commercial

| Channel | Ship Frequency (MHz) | | Channel Usage |
	Transmit	Receive	
19A	156.950	156.950	Commercial
20	157.000	161.600	Port operations (traffic advisories)
22A	157.100	157.100	Coast Guard Liaison
24	157.200	161.800	Public correspondence (ship-to-coast)
25	157.250	161.850	Public correspondence (ship-to-coast)
26	157.300	161.900	Public correspondence (ship-to-coast)
27	157.350	161.950	Public correspondence (ship-to-coast)
28	157.400	162.000	Public correspondence (ship-to-coast)
63A	156.175	156.175	VTS New Orleans
65A	156.275	156.275	Port operations (traffic advisories)
66A	156.325	156.325	Port operations (traffic advisories)
67	156.375	156.375	Commercial (ship-to-ship only) (used in New Orleans VTS for ship-to-ship navigational purposes)
68	156.425	156.425	Non-commercial
69	156.475	156.475	Non-commercial
71	156.575	156.575	Non-commercial
72	156.625	156.625	Non-commercial (ship-to-ship only)
73	156.675	156.675	Port operations (traffic advisories)
74	156.725	156.725	Port operations (traffic advisories)
77	156.875	156.875	Port operations (ship-to-ship, to and from pilots docking ships)
78A	156.925	156.925	Non-commercial
79A	156.975	156.975	Commercial
80A	157.025	157.025	Commercial
84	157.225	161.825	Public correspondence (ship-to-coast)
85	157.275	161.875	Public correspondence (ship-to-coast)
86	157.325	161.925	Public correspondence (ship-to-coast)
87	157.375	161.975	Public correspondence (ship-to-coast)
88	157.425	162.025	Public correspondence in Puget Sound and parts of Great Lakes
88A	157.425	157.425	Commercial, fishing (ship-to-ship) (except in parts of Great Lakes)

2. NAVIGATION REGULATIONS

(1) This chapter contains the sections of **Code of Federal Regulations, Title 33, Navigation and Navigable Waters (33 CFR),** that are of most importance in the areas covered by Coast Pilot 2. The sections are from:

(2) Part 26, Vessel Bridge-to-Bridge Radiotelephone Regulations,

(3) Part 80, COLREGS Demarcation Lines;

(4) Part 110, Anchorage Regulations;

(5) Part 117, Drawbridge Operation Regulations;

(6) Part 160, Ports and Waterways Safety-General;

(7) Part 162, Inland Waterways Navigation Regulations;

(8) Part 164, Navigation Safety Regulations (in part);

(9) Part 165, Regulated Navigation Areas and Limited Access Areas;

(10) Part 166, Shipping Safety Fairways;

(11) Part 167, Offshore Traffic Separation Schemes;

(12) Part 207, Navigation Regulations; and

(13) Part 334, Danger Zones and Restricted Area Regulations.

(14) **Note.**-These regulations can only be amended by the enforcing agency or other authority cited in the regulations. Accordingly, requests for changes to these regulations should be directed to the appropriate agency for action. In those regulations where the enforcing agency is not cited or is unclear, recommendations for changes should be directed to the following Federal agencies for action: U.S. Coast Guard (33 CFR 26, 80, 110, 117, 160, 164, and 165); U.S. Army Corps of Engineers (33 CFR 207 and 334).

Part 26–Vessel Bridge-to-Bridge Radiotelephone Regulations

(15) **§26.01 Purpose.**

(16) (a) The purpose of this part is to implement the provisions of the Vessel Bridge-to-Bridge Radiotelephone Act. This part—

(17) (1) Requires the use of the vessel bridge-to-bridge radiotelephone;

(18) (2) Provides the Coast Guard's interpretation of the meaning of important terms in the Act;

(19) (3) Prescribes the procedures for applying for an exemption from the Act and the regulations issued under the Act and a listing of exemptions.

(20) (b) Nothing in this part relieves any person from the obligation of complying with the rules of the road and the applicable pilot rules.

(21) **§26.02 Definitions.**

(22) For the purpose of this part and interpreting the Act–

(23) "Secretary" means the Secretary of the Department in which the Coast Guard is operating;

(24) "Act" means the "Vessel Bridge-to-Bridge Radiotelephone Act", 33 U.S.C. sections 1201–1208;

(25) "Length" is measured from end to end over the deck excluding sheer;

(26) "Power-driven vessel" means any vessel propelled by machinery; and

(27) "Towing vessel" means any commercial vessel engaged in towing another vessel astern, alongside, or by pushing ahead.

(28) **§26.03 Radiotelephone required.**

(29) (a) Unless an exemption is granted under §26.09 and except as provided in paragraph (a)(4) of this section, section 4 of the Act provides that–

(30) (1) Every power-driven vessel of 300 gross tons and upward while navigating;

(31) (2) Every vessel of 100 gross tons and upward carrying one or more passengers for hire while navigating;

(32) (3) Every towing vessel of 26 feet or over in length while navigating; and

(33) (4) Every dredge and floating plant engaged in or near a channel or fairway in operations likely to restrict or affect navigation of other vessels: Provided, That an unmanned or intermittently manned floating plant under the control of a dredge need not be required to have separate radiotelephone capability;

(34) Shall have a radiotelephone capable of operation from its navigational bridge, or in the case of a dredge, from its main control station, and capable of transmitting and receiving on the frequency or frequencies within the 156–162 Mega-Hertz band using the classes of emissions designated by the Federal Communications Commission, after consultation with other cognizant agencies, for the exchange of navigational information.

(35) (b) The radiotelephone required by paragraph (a) of this section shall be carried on board the described vessels, dredges, and floating plants upon the navigable waters of the United States inside the lines established pursuant to section 2 of the Act of February 19, 1895 (28 Stat. 672), as amended.

(36) **§26.04 Use of the designated frequency.**

(37) (a) No person may use the frequency designated by the Federal Communications Commission under section 8 of the Act, 33 U.S.C. 1207(a), to transmit any information other than information necessary for the safe navigation of vessels or necessary tests.

(38) (b) Each person who is required to maintain a listening watch under section 5 of the Act shall, when necessary, transmit and confirm, on the designated frequency, the intentions of his vessel and any other information necessary for the safe navigation of vessels.

(39) (c) Nothing in these regulations may be construed as prohibiting the use of the designated frequency to communicate with shore stations to obtain or furnish information necessary for the safe navigation of vessels.

(40) **Note.**–The Federal Communications Commission (FCC) has designated the frequency 156.65 MHz (Channel 13) for the use of bridge-to-bridge stations in most of the United States. However, FCC rules designate the frequency 156.375 MHz (Channel 67) to be used instead of Channel 13 in the following areas, except to facilitate transition from these areas: The Mississippi River from South Pass Lighted Bell Buoy "2" and Southwest Pass Entrance (midchannel) Lighted Whistle Buoy SW to mile 242.4 AHP (Above Head of Passes) near Baton Rouge; and, in addition, over the full length of the Mississippi River-Gulf Outlet Canal from entrance to its junction with the Inner Harbor Navigation Canal, and over the full length of the Inner Harbor Navigation Canal from its junction with the Mississippi River to its entry to Lake Pontchartrain at the New Seabrook vehicular bridge.

(41) **§26.05 Use of radiotelephone.**

(42) Section 5 of the Act states–

(43) (a) The radiotelephone required by this Act is for the exclusive use of the master or person in charge of the vessel, or the person designated by the master or person in charge

of the vessel, or the person designated by the master or person in charge to pilot or direct the movement of the vessel, who shall maintain a listening watch on the designated frequency. Nothing contained herein shall be interpreted as precluding the use of portable radiotelephone equipment to satisfy the requirements of this Act.

(44) **§26.06 Maintenance of radiotelephone; failure of radiotelephone.**

(45) Section 6 of the Act states—

(46) (a) Wherever radiotelephone capability is required by this Act, a vessel's radiotelephone equipment shall be maintained in effective operating condition. If the radiotelephone equipment carried aboard a vessel ceases to operate, the master shall exercise due diligence to restore it or cause it to be restored to effective operating condition at the earliest practicable time. The failure of a vessel's radiotelephone equipment shall not, in itself, constitute a violation of this Act, nor shall it obligate the master of any vessel to moor or anchor his vessel; however, the loss of radiotelephone capability shall be given consideration in the navigation of the vessel.

(47) **§26.07 English language.**

(48) No person may use the services of, and no person may serve as a person required to maintain a listening watch under section 5 of the Act, 33 U.S.C. 1204 unless he can speak the English language.

(49) **§26.08 Exemption procedures.**

(50) (a) Any person may petition for an exemption from any provision of the Act or this part;

(51) (b) Each petition must be submitted in writing to U.S. Coast Guard Office of Navigation Safety and Waterway Services, 2100 Second Street SW., Washington, DC 20593-0001, and must state—

(52) (1) The provisions of the Act or this part from which an exemption is requested; and

(53) (2) The reasons why marine navigation will not be adversely affected if the exemption is granted and if the exemption relates to a local communication system how that system would fully comply with the intent of the concept of the Act but would not conform in detail if the exemption is granted.

(54) **§26.09 List of exemptions.**

(55) (a) All vessels navigating on those waters governed by the navigation rules for Great Lakes and their connecting and tributary waters (33 U.S.C. 241 et seq.) are exempt from the requirements of the Vessel Bridge-to-Bridge Radiotelephone Act and this part until May 6, 1975.

(56) (b) Each vessel navigating on the Great Lakes as defined in the Inland Navigational Rules Act of 1980 (33 U.S.C. 2001 et seq.) and to which the Vessel Bridge-to-Bridge Radiotelephone Act (33 U.S.C. 1201–1208) applies is exempt from the requirements in 33 U.S.C. 1203, 1204, and 1205 and the regulations under §§26.03, 26.04, 26.05, 26.06, and 26.07. Each of these vessels and each person to whom 33 U.S.C. 1208(a) applies must comply with Articles VII, X, XI, XII, XIII, XV, and XVI and Technical Regulations 1–7 of "The Agreement Between the United States of America and Canada for Promotion of Safety on the Great Lakes by Means of Radio, 1973."

(57) **§26.10 Penalties**

(58) Section 9 of the Act states—

(59) (a) Whoever, being the master or person in charge of a vessel subject to the Act, fails to enforce or comply with the Act or the regulations hereunder; or whoever, being designated by the master or person in charge or a vessel subject to the Act to pilot or direct the movement of a vessel fails to enforce or comply with the Act or the regulations hereunder—is liable to a civil penalty of not more than $500 to be assessed by the Secretary.

(60) (b) Every vessel navigated in violation of the Act or the regulations hereunder is liable to a civil penalty of not more than $500 to be assessed by the Secretary, for which the vessel may be proceeded against in any District Court of the United States having jurisdiction.

(61) (c) Any penalty assessed under this section may be remitted or mitigated by the Secretary, upon such terms as he may deem proper.

Part 80—COLREGS Demarcation Lines

(62) **§80.01 General basis and purpose of demarcation lines.**

(63) (a) The regulations in this part establish the lines of demarcation delineating those waters upon which mariners shall comply with the International Regulations for Preventing Collisions at Sea, 1972 (72 COLREGS) and those waters upon which mariners shall comply with the Inland Navigation Rules.

(64) (b) The waters inside of the lines are Inland Rules waters. The waters outside the lines are COLREGS waters.

(65) (c) Geographic coordinates expressed in terms of latitude or longitude, or both, are not intended for plotting on maps or charts whose referenced horizontal datum is the North American Datum of 1983 (NAD 83), unless such geographic coordinates are expressly labeled NAD 83. Geographic coordinates without the NAD 83 reference may be plotted on maps or charts referenced to NAD 83 only after application of the appropriate corrections that are published on the particular map or chart being used.

(66) **§80.135 Hull, Mass. to Race Point, Mass.** (a) Except inside lines described in this section, the 72 COLREGS apply on the harbors, bays, and inlets on the east coast of Massachusetts from the easternmost radio tower at Hull, charted in approximate position latitude 42°16.7′N., longitude 70°52.6′W., to Race Point on Cape Cod.

(67) (b) A line drawn from Canal Breakwater Light 4 south to the shoreline.

(68) **§80.145 Race Point, Mass., to Watch Hill, R.I.** (a) Except inside lines specifically described in this section, the 72 COLREGS shall apply on the sounds, bays, harbors, and inlets along the coast of Cape Cod and the southern coasts of Massachusetts and Rhode Island from Race Point to Watch Hill.

(69) (b) A line drawn from Nobska Point Light to Tarpaulin Cove Light on the southeastern side of Naushon Island; thence from the southernmost tangent of Naushon Island to the easternmost extremity of Nashawena Island; thence from the southwesternmost extremity of Nashawena Island to the easternmost extremity of Cuttyhunk Island; thence from the southwestern tangent of Cuttyhunk Island to the tower on Gooseberry Neck charted in approximate position latitude 41°29.1′N., longitude 71°02.3′W.

(70) (c) A line drawn from Sakonnet Breakwater Light 2 tangent to the southernmost part of Sachuest Point charted in approximate position latitude 41°28.5′N., longitude 71°14.8′W.

(71) (d) An east-west line drawn through Beavertail Light between Brenton Point and the Boston Neck shoreline.

(72) **§80.150 Block Island, R.I.**

(73) The 72 COLREGS shall apply on the harbors of Block Island.

(74) **§80.155 Watch Hill, R.I. to Montauk Point, N.Y.** (a) A line drawn from Watch Hill Light to East Point on Fishers Island.

(75) (b) A line drawn from Race Point to Race Rock Light; thence to Little Gull Island Light thence to East Point on Plum Island.

(76) (c) A line drawn from Plum Island Harbor East Dolphin Light to Plum Island Harbor West Dolphin Light.

(77) (d) A line drawn from Plum Island Light to Orient Point Light; thence to Orient Point.

(78) (e) A line drawn from the lighthouse ruins at the southwestern end of Long Beach Point to Cornelius Point.

(79) (f) A line drawn from Coecles Harbor Entrance Light to Sungic Point.

(80) (g) A line drawn from Nichols Point to Cedar Island Light.

(81) (h) A line drawn from Threemile Harbor West Breakwater Light to Threemile Harbor East Breakwater Light.

(82) (i) A line drawn from Montauk West Jetty Light 1 to Montauk East Jetty Light 2.

(83) **§80.160 Montauk Point, N.Y. to Atlantic Beach, N.Y.** (a) A line drawn from Shinnecock Inlet East Breakwater Light to Shinnecock Inlet West Breakwater Light 1.

(84) (b) A line drawn from Moriches Inlet East Breakwater Light to Moriches Inlet West Breakwater Light.

(85) (c) A line drawn from Fire Island Inlet Breakwater Light 348° true to the southernmost extremity of the spit of land at the western end of Oak Beach.

(86) (d) A line drawn from Jones Inlet Light 322° true across the southwest tangent of the island on the north side of Jones Inlet to the shoreline.

(87) **§80.165 New York Harbor.**

(88) A line drawn from East Rockaway Inlet Breakwater Light to Sandy Hook Light.

Part 110–Anchorage Regulations

(89) **§110.1 General.** (a) The areas described in Subpart A of this part are designated as special anchorage areas pursuant to the authority contained in an act amending laws for preventing collisions of vessels approved April 22, 1940 (54 Stat. 150); Article 11 of section 1 of the Act of June7, 1897, as amended (30 Stat. 98; 33 U.S.C. 180), Rule 9 of section 1 of the act of February 8, 1895, as amended (28 Stat. 647; 33 U.S.C. 258), and Rule Numbered 13 of section 4233 of the Revised Statutes as amended (33 U.S.C. 322). Vessels not more than 65 feet in length, when at anchor in any special anchorage area shall not be required to carry or exhibit the white anchor lights required by the Navigation Rules.

(90) (b) The anchorage grounds for vessels described in Subpart B of this part are established, and the rules and regulations in relation thereto adopted, pursuant to the authority contained in section 7 of the act of March 4, 1915, as amended (38 Stat. 1053; 33 U.S.C. 471).

(91) (c) All bearings in the part are referred to true meridian.

(92) (d) Geographic coordinates expressed in terms of latitude or longitude, or both, are not intended for plotting on maps or charts whose referenced horizontal datum is the North American Datum of 1983 (NAD 83), unless such geographic coordinates are expressly labeled NAD 83. Geographic coordinates without the NAD 83 reference may be plotted on maps or charts referenced to NAD 83 only after application of the appropriate corrections that are published on the particular map or chart being used.

(93) **§110.1a Anchorages under Ports and Waterways Safety Act.** (a) The anchorages listed in this section are regulated under the Ports and Waterways Safety Act (33 U.S.C. 1221 et seq.):

(94) (1) Section 110.155 Port of New York.

(95) (b) Any person who violates any regulation issued under the Ports and Waterways Safety Act–

(96) (1) Is liable to a civil penalty, not to exceed $25,000 for each violation;

(97) (2) If the violation is willful, is fined not more than $50,000 for each violation or imprisoned for not more than five years, or both.

Subpart A–Special Anchorage Areas

(98) **§110.38 Edgartown Harbor, Mass.** An area in the inner harbor easterly of the project channel and south of Chappaquiddick Point bounded as follows: Beginning at

(99) 41°23′19″N., 70°30′32″W.; thence along the shore to

(100) 41°22′52″N., 70°30′12″W.; thence

(101) 287°30′, 1,600 feet; thence

(102) 327°30′, 700 feet; thence

(103) 359°, 800 feet; thence

(104) 024°15′, approximately 900 feet to the point of beginning.

(105) NOTE: The area is reserved for yachts and other small recreational craft. Fore and aft moorings and temporary floats or buoys for marking anchors in place will be allowed. All moorings shall be so placed that no vessel when anchored shall extend into waters beyond the limits of the area. Fixed mooring piles or stakes are prohibited.

(106) **§110.40 Silver Beach Harbor, North Falmouth, Mass.** All the waters of the harbor northward of the inner end of the entrance channel.

(107) **§110.45 Onset Bay, Mass.** Northerly of a line extending from the northernmost point of Onset Island to the easternmost point of Wickets Island; easterly of a line extending from the easternmost point of Wickets Island to the southwest extremity of Point Independence; southerly of the shore line; and westerly of the shore line and of a line bearing due north from the northernmost point of Onset Island.

(108) **§110.45a Mattapoisett Harbor, Mattapoisett, Mass.**

(109) (a) Area No. 1 beginning at a point on the shore at

(110) 41°39′23″N., 70°48′50″W.; thence 138.5°T. to

(111) 41°38′45″N., 70°48′02″W.; thence 031°T. to

(112) 41°39′02″N., 70°47′48″W.; thence along the shore to the point of beginning.

(113) (b) Area No. 2 beginning at a point on the shore at

(114) 41°39′24″N., 70°49′02″W.; thence 142.5°T to

(115) 41°38′10″N., 70°47′45″W.; thence 219°T. to

(116) 41°37′54″N., 70°48′02″W.; thence along the shore to the point of beginning.

(117) **Note.–**Administration of the Special Anchorage Area is exercised by the Harbormaster, Town of Mattapoisett pursuant to a local ordinance. The town of Mattapoisett will install and maintain suitable navigational aids to mark the perimeter of the anchorage area.

(118) **§110.46 Newport Harbor, Newport, R.I.** (a) Area No. 1. The waters of Brenton Cove south of a line extending from

(119) 41°28′50″N., 71°18′58″W.; to

(120) 41°28′45″N., longitude 71°20′08″W.; thence along the shoreline to the point of beginning.

(121) (b) Area No. 2. The waters east of Goat Island beginning at a point bearing 090°, 245 yards from Goat Island Shoal Light; thence

(122) 007°, 505 yards; thence

(123) 054°, 90 yards; thence

(124) 086°, 330 yards; thence

(125) 122°, 90 yards; thence

(126) 179°, 290 yards; thence

(127) 228°, 380 yards; thence

(128) 270°, 250 yards to the point of beginning.

(129) (c) Area No. 3. The waters north of Goat Island Causeway Bridge beginning at Newport Harbor Light; thence 023° to the southwest corner of Anchorage E; thence 081° following the southerly boundary of Anchorage E to the shoreline; thence south along the shoreline to the east foot of the Goat Island Causeway Bridge; thence west following Goat Island Causeway Bridge to the shoreline of Goat Island; thence north following the east shore of Goat Island to the point of beginning.

(130) **§110.47 Little Narragansett Bay, Watch Hill, R.I.** All of the navigable waters of Watch Hill Cove southeasterly of a line beginning at the shore end of the United States project groin on the southerly shore of the cove and running 41°30′ true, to the northerly shore of the cove at a point about 200 feet west of the west side of the shore end of Meadow Lane, with the exception of a 100-foot wide channel running from the westerly end of the cove in a southeasterly direction to the Watch Hill Yacht Club pier, thence along in front of the piers on the easterly side of the cove northerly to the shore at the north end of the cove.

(131) **§110.48 Thompson Cove on east side of Pawcatuck River below Westerly, R.I.** Eastward of a line extending from the channelward end of Thompson Dock at the northern end of Thompson Cove 184° to the shore at the southern end of Thompson Cove.

(132) **§110.50 Stonington Harbor, Conn.** (a) Area No. 1. Beginning at the southeastern tip of Wamphassuc Point; thence to the northwesterly end of Stonington Inner Breakwater; thence along the breakwater to

(133) longitude 71°54′50.5″; thence to

(134) 41°20″25.3″, 71°54′50.5″; thence to a point on the shoreline at

(135) 41°20′32″, 71°54′54.8″; thence along the shoreline to the point of beginning.

(136) (b) Area No. 2. Beginning at a point on the shoreline at

(137) 41°19′55.8″N., 71°54′28.9″W.; thence to

(138) 41°19′55.8″N., 71°54′37.1″W.; thence to

(139) 41°20′01.6″N., 71°54′38.8″W.; thence to

(140) 41°20′02.0″N., 71°54′34.3″W.; thence along the shoreline to the point of beginning.

(141) (c) Area No. 3. Beginning at a point on the shoreline at

(142) 41°20′29.5″N., 71°54′43.0″W.; thence to

(143) 41°20′25.6″N., 71°54′48.5″W.; thence to

(144) 41°20′10.7″N., 71°54′48.5″W.; thence to the shoreline at

(145) 41°20′10.7″N.; thence along the shoreline to the point of beginning.

(146) NOTE: A fixed mooring stake or pile is prohibited. The General Statutes of the State of Connecticut authorizes the Harbor Master of Stonington to station and control a vessel in the harbor.

(147) **§110.50a Fishers Island Sound, Stonington, Conn.** An area on the east side of Mason Island bounded as follows:

(148) Beginning at the shore line on the easterly side of Mason Island at latitude 41°20′06″; thence due east about 600 feet to latitude 41°20′06″, longitude 71°57′37″; thence due south about 2,400 feet to latitude 41°19′42″, longitude 71°57′37″; thence due west about 1,000 feet to the shore line on the easterly side of Mason Island at latitude 41°19′42″; thence along the shore line to the point of beginning.

(149) NOTE: The area will be principally for use by yachts and other recreational craft. Temporary floats or buoys for marking anchors will be allowed. Fixed mooring piles or stakes will be prohibited. The anchoring of vessels and the placing of temporary moorings will be under the jurisdiction and the discretion of the local Harbor Master.

(150) **§110.50b Mystic Harbor, Groton and Stonington, Conn.** (a) Area No. 1. Beginning at Ram Point on the westerly side of Mason Island at

(151) 41°19′44″N., 71°58′42″W.; thence to

(152) 41°19′30″N., 71°58′43″W.; thence to

(153) 41°19′36″N., 71°58′58″W.; thence to

(154) 41°19′45″N., 71°58′56″W.; thence to the point of beginning.

(155) (b) Area No. 2. Beginning at a point about 250 feet southerly of Area 1 and on line with the easterly limit of Area 1 at

(156) 41°19′27″N., 71°58′44″W.; thence to

(157) 41°19′19″N., 71°58′45″W.; thence to

(158) 41°19′25″N., 71°58′59″W.; thence to

(159) 41°19′33″N., 71°58′48″W.; thence to the point of beginning.

(160) NOTE: The areas will be principally for use by yachts and other recreational craft. Temporary floats or buoys for marking anchors will be allowed. Fixed mooring piles or stakes are prohibited. All moorings shall be so placed that no vessel, when anchored, shall at any time extend beyond the limits of the areas. The anchoring of vessels and the placing of temporary moorings will be under the jurisdiction and at the discretion of the local Harbor Master.

(161) **§110.50c Mumford Cove, Groton, Conn.** (a) Area No. 1. Beginning at a point on the easterly shore of Mumford Cove at

(162) 41°19′36″N., 72°01′06″W.; to

(163) 41°19′30″N., 72°01′04″W.; thence to the shore at

(164) 41°19′31″N., 72°01′00″W.; and thence along the shoreline to the point of beginning.

(165) (b) Area No. 2. Beginning at a point on the easterly shore of Mumford Cove at

(166) 41°19′15.0″N., 72°00′54.0″W.; thence to

(167) 41°19′14.5″N., 72°00′59.0″W.; thence to

(168) 41°19′11.0″N., 72°00′58.0″W.; thence to

(169) 41°19′10.0″N., 72°00′54.0″W.; thence to

(170) 41°19′12.5″N., 72°00′52.0″W.; thence to

(171) 41°19′14.0″N., 72°00′55.0″W.; and thence to the point of beginning.

(172) NOTE. The areas are principally for use by yachts and other recreational craft. Temporary floats or buoys for marking anchors will be allowed. Fixed mooring piles or stakes will be prohibited. The anchoring of vessels and placing of temporary moorings will be under the jurisdiction, and at the discretion, of the local Harbor Master.

(173) **§110.50d Mystic Harbor, Noank, Conn.** (a) The area comprises that portion of the harbor off the easterly side of Morgan Point beginning at a point at

(174) 41°19′15.0″N., 71°59′13.5″W.; thence to

(175) 41°19′15.0″N., 71°59′00.0″W.; thence to

(176) 41°19′02.5″N., 71°59′00.0″W.; thence to

(177) 41°19′06.0″N., 71°59′13.5″W.; and thence to the point of beginning.

(178) (b) The following requirements shall govern this special anchorage area:

(179) (1) The area will be principally for use by yachts and other recreational craft.

(180) (2) Temporary floats or buoys for marking anchors will be allowed but fixed piles or stakes are prohibited. All moorings shall be so placed that no vessel, when anchored, shall extend beyond the limits of the area.

to such adjustments as may be necessary to accommodate all classes of vessels which may require anchorage room.

(476)   (ii) Temporary floats or buoys for marking anchors or moorings in place will be allowed in this area. Fixed mooring piles or stakes will not be allowed.

(477)   (5) **Anchorage E.** South of Coasters Harbor Island, east of a line bearing 341° from the outer end of Briggs Wharf to the southwestern shore of Coasters Harbor Island near the War College Building; and north of a line ranging 265° from the flagstaff at Fort Greene toward Rose Island Light.

(478)   (i) In this area the requirements of the naval service will predominate from May 1 to October 1, but will at all times be subject to such adjustment as may be necessary to accommodate all classes of vessels that may require anchorage room.

(479)   (ii) Temporary floats or buoys for marking anchors or moorings in place will be allowed in this area. Fixed mooring piles or stakes will not be allowed.

(480)   (b) **West Passage (1) Anchorage H.** North of a line 1,000 yards long bearing 88° from Bonnet Point; west of a line bearing 3° from the eastern end of the last-described line; and south of a line ranging 302° through a point 200 yards south of the Kearny wharf toward the church spire at South Ferry, Boston Neck.

(481)   (i) Temporary floats or buoys for marking anchors or moorings in place will be allowed in this area. Fixed mooring piles or stakes will not be allowed.

(482)   (2) **Anchorage I.** North of a line 1,000 yards long bearing 88° from Bonnet Point to the shore at Austin Hollow; east of a line bearing 183° from Dutch Island Light; and south of a line ranging 302° through a point 200 yards south of the Kearny wharf toward the church spire at South Ferry, Boston Neck.

(483)   (i) Temporary floats or buoys for marking anchors or moorings in place will be allowed in this area. Fixed mooring piles or stakes will not be allowed.

(484)   (3) **Anchorage J.** At Saunderstown, south of a line ranging 110° from the south side of the ferry wharf toward the cable crossing sign on Dutch Island; west of a line ranging 192° from Plum Beach Shoal Buoy 1 PB toward the east shore of The Bonnet; and north of a line from the shore ranging 108° toward Dutch Island Light and the north end of the wharf at Beaver Head.

(485)   (i) Temporary floats or buoys for marking anchors or moorings in place will be allowed in this area. Fixed mooring piles or stakes will not be allowed.

(486)   (4) **Anchorage K.** In the central and southern portion of Dutch Island Harbor, north of a line ranging 106° from Beaver Head Point Shoal Buoy 2 toward the Jamestown standpipe; east of a line ranging 14° from Beaver Head Point Shoal Buoy 2 toward the inshore end of the engineer wharf, Dutch Island; southeast of a line ranging 50° from Dutch Island Light toward the windmill north of Jamestown; and south of a line parallel to and 100 yards southwesterly from a line ranging 132° from the engineer wharf, Dutch Island, and the west ferry wharf, Jamestown.

(487)   (i) Temporary floats or buoys for marking anchors or moorings in place will be allowed in this area. Fixed mooring piles or stakes will not be allowed.

(488)   (5) **Anchorage L.** North of a line ranging 101° from a point on shore 300 yards northerly of the Saunderstown ferry wharf toward the entrance to Round Swamp, Conanicut Island; west of a line bearing 15° parallel to and 1,000 feet westerly from a line joining the western point of Dutch Island and Twenty-three Foot Rock Buoy 4, and a line ranging 6° from Dutch Island Light toward Warwick Light; and south of a line ranging 290° from Sand Point,

Conanicut Island, to Wickford Harbor Light, and a line bearing 226° from Wickford Harbor Light to Poplar Point tower.

(489)   (i) Temporary floats or buoys for marking anchors or moorings in place will be allowed in this area. Fixed mooring piles or stakes will not be allowed.

(490)   (6) **Anchorage M.** East and north of Dutch Island, northeast of a line ranging 316° from the inshore end of the west ferry wharf, Jamestown, toward the north end of Dutch Island to a point bearing 88°, 200 yards, from the engineer wharf, Dutch Island, thence ranging 3° toward the shore of Conanicut Island at Slocum Ledge; north of a line 200 yards off the Dutch Island shore ranging 281° from the entrance to Round Swamp toward a point on shore 300 yards northerly from the Saunderstown ferry wharf; east of a line ranging 15° from the western point of Dutch Island to Twenty-three Foot Rock Buoy 4; and south of a line bearing 77° from Twenty-three Foot Rock Buoy 4 to the shore.

(491)   (i) Temporary floats or buoys for marking anchors or moorings in place will be allowed in this area. Fixed mooring piles or stakes will not be allowed.

(492)   (7) **Anchorage N.** West of the north end of Conanicut Island, south of a line bearing 262° from Conanicut Island Light; east of a line bearing 8° from Twenty-three Foot Rock Buoy 4; and north of a line ranging 290° from Sand Point toward Wickford Harbor Light.

(493)   (i) Temporary floats or buoys for marking anchors or moorings in place will be allowed in this area. Fixed mooring piles or stakes will not be allowed.

(494)   (c) **Bristol Harbor–(1) Anchorage O.** South of the south line of Franklin Street extended westerly; west of a line bearing 164°30′ parallel to and 400 feet westerly from the State harbor line between Franklin and Constitution Streets, and of a line ranging 244° from a point on the north line of Constitution Street extended 400 feet beyond the State harbor line toward Usher Rock Buoy 3; and north of the north line of Union Street extended to the Popasquash Neck Shore.

(495)   (i) Temporary floats or buoys for marking anchors or moorings in place will be allowed in this area. Fixed mooring piles or stakes will not be allowed.

(496)   (d) **The regulations.** (1) Except in cases of great emergency, no vessels shall be anchored in the entrances to Narragansett Bay, in Newport Harbor, or in Bristol Harbor, outside of the anchorage areas defined in paragraphs (a), (b) and (c) of this section.

(497)   (2) Anchors must not be placed outside the anchorage areas, nor shall any vessel be so anchored that any portion of the hull or rigging shall at any time extend outside the boundaries of the anchorage area.

(498)   (3) Any vessel anchoring under the circumstances of great emergency outside the anchorage areas must be placed near the edge of the channel and in such position as not to interfere with the free navigation of the channel, nor obstruct the approach to any pier, nor impede the movement of any boat, and shall move away immediately after the emergency ceases, or upon notification by an officer of the Coast Guard.

(499)   (4) A vessel upon being notified to move into the anchorage limits or to shift its position on anchorage grounds must get under way at once or signal for a tug, and must change position as directed with reasonable promptness.

(500)   (5) Whenever the maritime or commercial interests of the United States so require, any officer of the Coast Guard is hereby empowered to shift the position of any vessel anchored within the anchorage areas, of any vessel anchored outside the anchorage areas, and of any vessel

which is so moored or anchored as to impede or obstruct vessel movements in any channel.

(501)   (6) Nothing in this section shall be construed as relieving the owner or person in charge of any vessel from the penalties of the law for obstructing navigation or for obstructing or interfering with range lights, or for not complying with the navigation laws in regard to lights, fog signals, or for otherwise violating the law.

(502)   §110.147 New London Harbor, Conn. (a) The anchorage grounds–(1) Anchorage A. In the Thames River east of Shaw Cove, bounded by lines connecting points which are the following bearings and distances from Monument, Groton (latitude 41°21′18″N., longitude 72°04′48″W.): 243°, 1,400 yards; 246°, 925 yards; 217°, 1,380 yards; and 235°, 1,450 yards.

(503)   (2) Anchorage B. In the Thames River southward of New London, bounded by lines connecting points which are the following bearings and distances from New London Harbor Light (latitude 41°18′59″N., longitude 72°05′25″W.): 002°, 2,460 yards; 009°, 2,480 yards; 026°, 1,175 yards; and 008°, 1,075 yards.

(504)   (3) Anchorage C. In the Thames River southward of New London Harbor, bounded by lines connecting a point bearing 100°, 450 yards from New London Harbor Light, a point bearing 270°, 575 yards from New London Ledge Light (latitude 41°18′21″N., longitude 72°04′41″W.), and a point bearing 270°, 1,450 yards from New London Ledge Light.

(505)   (4) Anchorage D. In Long Island Sound approximately two miles west-southwest of New London Ledge Light, bounded by lines connecting points which are the following bearings and distances from New London Ledge Light; 246°, 2.6 miles; 247°, 2.1 miles; 233°, 2.1 miles; and 235°, 2.6 miles.

(506)   (5) Anchorage E. The waters at the mouth of New London Harbor one mile southeast of New London Ledge Light beginning at latitude 41°17′26″N., longitude 72°04′21″W.;

(507)   thence northeasterly to 41°17′38″N., 72°03′54″W.;

(508)   thence southeasterly to 41°16′50″N., 72°03′16″W.;

(509)   and thence southwesterly to 41°16′38″N., 72°03′43″W.;

(510)   and thence northwesterly to the point of beginning.

(511)   (6) Anchorage F. The waters off the mouth of New London Harbor two miles southeast of New London Ledge Light beginning at latitude 41°16′00″N., longitude 72°03′13″W.;

(512)   thence westerly to 41°16′00″N., 72°03′38″W.;

(513)   thence northerly to 41°16′35″N., 72°03′38″W.;

(514)   thence easterly to 41°16′35″N., 72°03′13″W.;

(515)   and thence southerly to the point of beginning.

(516)   (b) The regulations–(1) Anchorage A is for barges and small vessels drawing less than 12 feet.

(517)   (2) Anchorage F is reserved for the use of naval vessels, except in cases of emergency, no other vessel may anchor in Anchorage F without permission from the Captain of the Port, New London, CT.

(518)   (3) Except in emergencies, vessels shall not anchor in New London Harbor or the approaches thereto outside the anchorages defined in paragraph (a) of this section unless authorized to do so by the Captain of the Port.

(519)   §110.148 Johnsons River at Bridgeport, Conn. (a) The anchorage grounds. In Johnsons River, beginning at

(520)   point "A" 41°10′12.3″N., 73°09′50.2″W.; to

(521)   point "B" 41°10′12.3″N., 73°09′52.1″W.; to

(522)   point "C" 41°10′10.0″N., 73°09′54.9″W.; to

(523)   point "D" 41°10′05.0″N., 73°09′56.1″W.; to

(524)   point "E" 41°10′04.0″N., 73°09′55.9″W.; to

(525)   point "F" 41°10′05.0″N., 73°00′54.5″W,; to

(526)   point "G" 41°10′05.8″N., 73°09′54.5″W.; thence to the point of beginning.

(527)   (b) The regulations. The anchorage is for use by commercial and pleasure craft. Temporary floats or buoys for marking anchors or moorings will be allowed. The anchoring of vessels and placing of temporary anchors or mooring piles are under the jurisdiction of the local harbor master. Fixed mooring piles or stakes will not be allowed.

(528)   §110.150 Block Island Sound N.Y. (a) The anchorage ground. A ¾- by 2-mile rectangular area approximately 3 miles east-northeast of Gardiners Island with the following coordinates:

(529)   41°06′12″N., 72°00′05″W.

(530)   41°07′40″N., 72°01′54″W.

(531)   41°08′12″N., 72°01′10″W.

(532)   41°06′46″N., 71°59′18″W.

(533)   (b) The regulations. This anchorage ground is for use of U.S. Navy submarines. No vessel or person may approach or remain within 500 yards of a U.S. Navy submarine anchored in this anchorage ground.

(534)   §110.155 Port of New York. (a) Long Island Sound–(1) Anchorage No. 1. Southwest of a line between Neptune Island and Glen Island ranging from Aunt Phebe Rock Light and tangent to the north edge of Glen Island; southwest of a line tangent to the northeast edge of Glen Island and Goose Island breakwater; southwest of a line bearing southeasterly from the southwest end of Goose Island breakwater and on range with the south gable of the Casino on the northeast end of Glen Island; west of a line ranging from the east edge of Goose Island breakwater to the west edge of the north end of Hart Island; west of Hart Island; and northwest of a line extending from Hart Island Light to Locust Point; excluding from this area, however, (i) the waters northeast of a line ranging 303° from the southwest end of Hart Island; northwest of a line ranging from the water tank at the north end of Davids Island 207°40′ to the northwest end of City Island; and south of latitude 40°52′12″; and (ii) the waters west of Hunter Island; and south of a line ranging from the most southerly end of Glen Island tangent to the most northerly end of Hunter Island.

(535)   (i) Boats shall not anchor in this area in buoyed channels.

(536)   (ii) Boats shall be so anchored as to leave at all times an open, usable channel, at least 50 feet wide, west and south of Glen Island.

(537)   NOTE: Special anchorage areas in this anchorage are described in §110.60.

(538)   (2) Anchorage No. 1–A. Southwest of a line ranging from Duck Point, Echo Bay, through Bailey Rock Lighted Buoy 3 BR; northwest of a line ranging from Hicks Ledge Buoy 2H to Old Tom Head Rocks Buoy 4; and north of a line ranging from Old Tom Head Rocks Buoy 4 to the southernmost point of Davenport Neck.

(539)   NOTE: The special anchorage area in this anchorage is described in §110.60(b–1).

(540)   (3) Anchorage No. 1–B. West of a line ranging from the point on the southwest side of the entrance of Horseshoe Harbor, Larchmont, to Hicks Ledge Buoy 2H; north of a line ranging from Hicks Ledge Buoy 2H to Duck Point; and in Echo Bay north and west of the channel.

(541)   NOTE: The special anchorage area in this anchorage is described in §110.60(b–1).

(542)   (4) Anchorage No. 2. West of a line from Locust Point tangent to the northeasterly sea wall at Throgs Neck.

(543)   NOTE: Special anchorage areas in this anchorage are described in §110.60.

(829) Except as otherwise required by this subpart, draw-bridges shall open promptly and fully for the passage of vessels when a request to open is given in accordance with this subpart.

(830) **§117.7 General duties of drawbridge owners and tenders.**

(831) (a) Drawbridge owners and tenders shall operate the draw in accordance with the requirement in this part.

(832) (b) Except for drawbridges not required to open for the passage of vessels, owners of drawbridges shall ensure that:

(833) (1) The necessary drawtenders are provided for the safe and prompt opening of the draw;

(834) (2) The operating machinery of the draw is maintained in a serviceable condition; and

(835) (3) The draws are operated at sufficient intervals to assure their satisfactory operation.

(836) **§117.9 Delaying opening of a draw.**

(837) No person shall unreasonably delay the opening of a draw after the signals required by §117.15 have been given.

(838) **Note.**—Trains are usually controlled by the block method. That is, the track is divided into blocks or segments of a mile or more in length. When a train is in a block with a drawbridge, the draw may not be able to open until the train has passed out of the block and the yardmaster or other manager has "unlocked" the drawbridge controls. The maximum time permitted for delay is defined in Subpart B for each affected bridge. Land and water traffic should pass over or through the draw as soon as possible in order to prevent unnecessary delays in the opening and closure of the draw.

(839) **§117.11 Appurtenances unessential to navigation.**

(840) No vessel owner or operator shall signal a draw-bridge to open for any nonstructural vessel appurtenance which is not essential to navigation or which is easily lowered.

(841) **§117.15 Signals.**

(842) (a) General. (1) The operator of each vessel requesting a drawbridge to open shall signal the drawtender and the drawtender shall acknowledge that signal. The signal shall be repeated until acknowledged in some manner by the drawtender before proceeding.

(843) (2) The signals used to request the opening of the draw and to acknowledge that request shall be sound signals, visual signals, or radiotelephone communications described in this subpart.

(844) (3) Any of the means of signaling described in this subpart sufficient to alert the bridge being signaled may be used.

(845) (b) Sound signals. (1) Sound signals shall be made by whistle, horn, megaphone, hailer, or other device capable of producing the described signals loud enough to be heard by the drawtender.

(846) (2) As used in this section, "prolonged blast" means a blast of four to six seconds duration and "short blast" means a blast of approximately one second duration.

(847) (3) The sound signal to request the opening of a draw is one prolonged blast followed by one short blast sounded not more than three seconds after the prolonged blast. For vessels required to be passed through a draw during a scheduled closure period, the sound signal to request the opening of the draw during that period is five short blasts sounded in rapid succession.

(848) (4) When the draw can be opened immediately, the sound signal to acknowledge a request to open the draw is one prolonged blast followed by one short blast sounded not more than 30 seconds after the requesting signal.

(849) (5) When the draw cannot be opened immediately, or is open and shall be closed promptly, the sound signal to acknowledge a request to open the draw is five short blasts sounded in rapid succession not more than 30 seconds after the vessel's opening signal. The signal shall be repeated until acknowledged in some manner by the requesting vessel.

(850) (c) Visual signals. (1) The visual signal to request the opening of a draw is—

(851) (i) A white flag raised and lowered vertically; or

(852) (ii) A white, amber, or green light raised and lowered vertically.

(853) (2) When the draw can be opened immediately, the visual signal to acknowledge a request to open the draw, given not more than 30 seconds after the vessel's opening signal, is—

(854) (i) A white flag raised and lowered vertically;

(855) (ii) A white, amber, or green light raised and lowered vertically, or

(856) (iii) A fixed or flashing white, amber, or green light or lights.

(857) (3) When the draw cannot be opened immediately, or is open and must be closed promptly, the visual signal to acknowledge a request to open the draw is—

(858) (i) A red flag or red light swung back and forth horizontally in full sight of the vessel given not more than 30 seconds after the vessel's opening signal; or

(859) (ii) A fixed or flashing red light or lights given not more than 30 seconds after the vessel's opening signal.

(860) (4) The acknowledging signal when the draw cannot open immediately or is open and must be closed promptly shall be repeated until acknowledged in some manner by the requesting vessel.

(861) (d) Radiotelephone communications. (1) Radiotelephones may be used to communicate the same information provided by sound and visual signals.

(862) **NOTE:** Call signs and radio channels for draw-bridges equipped with radiotelephones are included with the bridge descriptions in chapters 4 through 12.

(863) (2) The vessel and the drawtender shall monitor the frequency used until the vessel has cleared the draw.

(864) (3) When radiotelephone contact cannot be initiated or maintained, sound or visual signals under this section shall be used.

(865) **§117.17 Signalling for contiguous drawbridges.**

(866) When a vessel must pass two or more drawbridges close together, the opening signal is given for the first bridge. After acknowledgment from the first bridge that it will promptly open, the opening signal is given for the second bridge, and so on until all bridges that the vessel must pass have been given the opening signal and have acknowledged that they will open promptly.

(867) **§117.19 Signalling when two or more vessels are approaching a drawbridge.**

(868) When two or more vessels are approaching the same drawbridge at the same time, or nearly the same time, whether from the same or opposite directions, each vessel shall signal independently for the opening of the draw and the drawtender shall reply in turn to the signal of each vessel. The drawtender need not reply to signals by vessels accumulated at the bridge for passage during a scheduled open period.

(869) **§117.21 Signalling for an opened drawbridge.**

(870) When a vessel approaches a drawbridge with the draw in the open position, the vessel shall give the opening signal. If no acknowledgment is received within 30 seconds, the vessel may proceed, with caution, through the open draw.

(871) **§117.23 Installation of radiotelephones.**

(872)   (a) When the District Commander deems it necessary for reasons of safety of navigation, the District Commander may require the installation and operation of a radiotelephone on or near a drawbridge.

(873)   (b) The District Commander gives written notice of the proposed requirement to the bridge owner.

(874)   (c) All comments the owner wishes to submit shall be submitted to the District Commander within 30 days of receipt of the notice under paragraph (b) of this section.

(875)   (d) If, upon consideration of the comments received, the District Commander determines that a radiotelephone is necessary, the District Commander notifies the bridge owner that a radiotelephone shall be installed and gives a reasonable time, not to exceed six months, to install the radiotelephone and commence operation.

(876)   **§117.24 Radiotelephone installation identification.**

(877)   (a) The Coast Guard authorizes, and the District Commander may require the installation of a sign on drawbridges, on the upstream and downstream sides, indicating that the bridge is equipped with and operates a VHF radiotelephone in accordance with §117.23.

(878)   (b) The sign shall give notice of the radiotelephone and its calling and working channels—

(879)   (1) In plain language; or

(880)   (2) By a sign consisting of the outline of a telephone handset with the long axis placed horizontally and a vertical three-legged lightning slash superimposed over the handset. The slash shall be as long vertically as the handset is wide horizontally and normally not less than 27 inches and no more than 36 inches long. The preferred calling channel should be shown in the lower left quadrant and the preferred working channel should be shown in the lower right quadrant.

(881)   **§117.31 Closure of draw for emergency vehicles.**

(882)   When a drawtender is informed by a reliable source that an emergency vehicle is due to cross the draw, the drawtender shall take all reasonable measures to have the draw closed at the time the emergency vehicle arrives at the bridge.

(883)   **§117.33 Closure of draw for natural disasters or civil disorders.**

(884)   Drawbridges need not open for the passage of vessels during periods of natural disasters or civil disorders declared by the appropriate authorities unless otherwise provided for in Subpart B or directed to do so by the District Commander.

(885)   **§117.35 Operations during repair or maintenance.**

(886)   (a) When operation of the draw must deviate from the regulations in this part for scheduled repair or maintenance work, the drawbridge owner shall request approval from the District Commander at least 30 days before the date of the intended change. The request shall include a brief description of the nature of the work to be performed and the times and dates of requested changes. The District Commander's decision is forwarded to the applicant within five working days of the receipt of the request. If the request is denied, the reasons for the denial are forwarded with the decision.

(887)   (b) When the draw is rendered inoperative because of damage to the structure or when vital, unscheduled repair or maintenance work shall be performed without delay, the drawbridge owner shall immediately notify the District Commander and give the reasons why the draw is or should be rendered inoperative and the expected date of completion of the repair or maintenance work.

(888)   (c) All repair or maintenance work under this section shall be performed with all due speed in order to return the draw to operation as soon as possible.

(889)   (d) If the operation of the draw will be affected for periods of less than 60 days, the regulations in this part will not be amended. Where practicable, the District Commander publishes notice of temporary deviations from the regulations in this part in the Federal Register and Local Notices to Mariners. If operation of the draw is expected to be affected for more than 60 days, the District Commander publishes temporary regulations covering the repair period.

(890)   **§117.37 Opening or closure of draw for public interest concerns.**

(891)   (a) For reasons of public health or safety or for public functions, such as street parades and marine regattas, the District Commander may authorize the opening or closure of a drawbridge for a specified period of time.

(892)   (b) Requests for opening or closure of a draw shall be submitted to the District Commander at least 30 days before the proposed opening or closure and include a brief description of the proposed event or other reason for the request, the reason why the opening or closure is required, and the times and dates of the period the draw is to remain open or closed.

(893)   (c) Approval by the District Commander depends on the necessity for the opening or closure, the reasonableness of the times and dates, and the overall effect on navigation and users of the bridge.

(894)   **§117.39 Closure of draw due to infrequent use.**

(895)   Upon written request by the owner or operator of a drawbridge, the District Commander may, after notice in the Federal Register and opportunity for public comment, permit the draw to be closed and untended due to infrequency of use of the draw by vessels. The District Commander may condition approval on the continued maintenance of the operating machinery.

(896)   **§117.41 Maintenance of draw in fully open position.**

(897)   The draw may be maintained in the fully open position to permit the passage of vessels and drawtender service discontinued if the District Commander is notified in advance. The draw shall remain in the fully open position until drawtender service is restored or authorization under §117.39 is given for the draw to remain closed and untended.

(898)   **§117.43 Changes in draw operation requirements for regulatory purposes.**

(899)   In order to evaluate suggested changes to the drawbridge operation requirements, the District Commander may authorize temporary deviations from the regulations in this part for periods not to exceed 60 days. Notice of these deviations is disseminated in the Local Notices to Mariners and published in the Federal Register.

(900)   **§117.45 Operation during winter in the Great Lakes area.**

(901)   (a) The Commander, Ninth Coast Guard District, may determine that drawbridges located in the Ninth Coast Guard District need not open during the winter season when general navigation is curtailed, unless a request to open the draw is given at least 12 hours before the time of the intended passage.

(902)   (b) Notice of these determinations is disseminated in Local Notices to Mariners and other appropriate media. Notices indicate—

(903)   (1) The name and location of the bridge affected;

(904)   (2) The period of time covered; and

(905)   (3) The telephone number and address of the party to whom requests for openings are given.

(906)   **§117.47 Clearance gages.**

(907)   (a) Clearance gages are required for drawbridges across navigable waters of the United States discharging into the Atlantic Ocean south of Delaware Bay (including

and maintained according to the provisions of §118.160 of these regulations.

(1230)   (3) Trains and locomotives shall be controlled so that any delay in opening the draw shall not exceed five minutes. However, if a train moving toward the bridge has crossed the home signal for the bridge before the signal requesting opening of the bridge is given, that train may continue across the bridge and must clear the bridge and must clear the bridge interlocks before stopping.

(1231)   (4) Except as provided in paragraphs (b) through (e) of this section, each draw shall open on signal.

(1232)   (b) The draws of the Long Island Railroad bridges, mile 1.1 across Dutch Kills, both at New York City shall open on signal if at least six hours notice is given to the Long Island Railroad Movement Bureau except as provided in paragraphs (a)(1) and (a)(3) of this section.

(1233)   (c) The draw of the Borden Avenue bridge, mile 1.2 across Dutch Kills at New York City (NYC), shall open on signal if at least one hour advance notice is given to the drawtender at the Grand Street/Avenue bridge, mile 3.1 across Newton Creek (East Branch), the New York City Department of Transportation (NYCDOT) Radio Hotline, or NYCDOT Bridge Operations Office. In the event the drawtender is at the Roosevelt Island bridge, mile 6.4 across East River of the Hunters Point Avenue bridge, mile 1.4 across Dutch Kills, New York, up to an additional half hour delay may be required.

(1234)   (d) The draw of the Hunters Point Avenue bridge, mile 1.4 across Dutch Kill, New York City, shall open on signal if at least one hour advance notice is given to the drawtender at the Grand Street/Avenue bridge, mile 3.1 across Newtown Creek (East Branch), the New York City Department of Transportation (NYCDOT) Radio Hotline or NYCDOT Bridge Operations Office. In the event the drawtender is at the Roosevelt Island bridge, mile 6.4 across East River, or the Borden Avenue bridge, mile 1.2 across Dutch Kills, up to an additional half hour may be required.

(1235)   (e) The draw of Grand Street/Avenue bridge, mile 3.1 across Newtown Creek (East Branch), at New York City, shall open on signal unless the drawtender is at the Borden Avenue or Hunters Point Avenue Bridges, mile 1.2 and 1.4, respectively, across Dutch Kills, New York or the Roosevelt Island bridge, mile 6.4 across East River. In this event, a notice to New York City Department of Transportation Radio Hotline, or NYCDOT Bridge Operations Office shall be given, to which a delay of up to one hour may be required.

(1236)   **§117.805 Peekskill (Annsville) Creek.**

(1237)   The draw of the Conrail bridge, mile 0.0 at Peekskill, need not be opened for the passage of vessels.

(1238)   **§117.807 Richmond Creek.**

(1239)   The draw of the Richmond Avenue bridge, mile 2.0 at New York City, need not open for the passage of vessels.

(1240)   **§117.813 Wappinger Creek.**

(1241)   The draw of the Metro-North Commuter railroad bridge, mile 0.0 at New Hamburg, need not be opened for the passage of vessels. However, the draw shall be returned to operable condition within six months after notification by the District Commander to do so.

(1242)   **§117.815 Westchester Creek.**

(1243)   The draw of the Bruckner Boulevard bridge, mile 1.7, shall open on signal; except that, from 7 a.m. to 9 a.m. and 4 p.m. to 6 p.m. Monday through Friday, the draw need not be opened for the passage of vessels. Public vessels of the United States, state or local vessels used for public safety, or vessels in distress shall be passed without delay. The owners of the bridge shall provide and keep in good legible condition two board gages painted white with black figures not

less than nine inches high to indicate the vertical clearance under the closed draw at all stages of the tide. The gages shall be so placed on the bridge that they are plainly visible to operators of vessels approaching the bridge either up or downstream.

(1244)   **RHODE ISLAND**

(1245)   **§117.907 Providence River.**

(1246)   The draw of the US1 (Point Street) bridge, mile 7.5 at Providence, need not be opened for the passage of vessels from 7 a.m. to 9 a.m. and 4 p.m. to 6 p.m. At all other times, the draw shall open on signal if at least 24 hours notice is given to the Director of Public Works, City Hall, Providence. Public vessels of the United States, state and local vessels used for public safety, loaded, self-propelled cargo vessels, and assisting tugs shall be passed as soon as possible.

(1247)   **Note.**–Call signs and radio channels for drawbridges equipped with radiotelephones are included with the bridge descriptions in chapters 4 through 12.

Part 160–Ports and Waterways Safety-General

Subpart A–General:

(1248)   **§ 160.1 Purpose.**

(1249)   Part 160 contains regulations implementing the Ports and Waterways Safety Act (33 U.S.C. 1221) and related statutes.

(1250)   **§160.3 Definitions.**

(1251)   (a) For the purposes of this part:

(1252)   (1) "Commandant" means the Commandant of the United States Coast Guard.

(1253)   (2) "District Commander" means the officer of the Coast Guard designated by the Commandant to command a Coast Guard District described in 33 CFR 3.

(1254)   (3) "Captain of the Port" means the Coast Guard officer commanding a Captain of the Port zone described in 33 CFR 3.

(1255)   (4) "Person" means an individual, firm, corporation, association, partnership, or governmental entity.

(1256)   (5) "State" means each of the several States of the United States, the District of Columbia, the Commonwealth of Puerto Rico, Guam, American Samoa, the United States Virgin Islands, the Trust Territories of the Pacific Islands, the Commonwealth of the Northern Marianas Islands, and any other commonwealth, territory, or possession of the United States.

(1257)   (6) "Vessel" means every description of watercraft or other artificial contrivance used, or capable of being used, as a means of transportation on water.

(1258)   (7) "Vehicle" means every type of conveyance capable of being used as a means of transportation on land.

(1259)   **§160.5 Delegations.**

(1260)   (a) District Commanders and Captains of the Ports are delegated the authority to establish safety zones.

(1261)   (b) Under the provisions of 33 CFR 6.04-1 and 6.04-6, District Commanders and Captains of the Ports have been delegated authority to establish security zones.

(1262)   (c) Under the provisions of 33 CFR §1.05-1, District Commanders have been delegated authority to establish regulated navigation areas.

(1263)   (d) Under the direction of the Captain of the Port Honolulu, the Commander, Marianas Section, may exercise the authority of a Captain of the Port within the waters surrounding Guam, and the Commonwealth of Marianas, all of which are in the Honolulu Captain of the Port Zone.

(1264)   **§160.7 Appeals.**

(1265)   (a) Any person directly affected by a safety zone or an order or direction issued under this subchapter (33 CFR

Subchapter P) may request reconsideration by the official who issued it or in whose name it was issued. This request may be made orally or in writing, and the decision of the official receiving the request may be rendered orally or in writing.

(1266)   (b) Any person directly affected by the establishment of a safety zone or by an order or direction issued by, or on behalf of, a Captain of the Port may appeal to the District Commander through the Captain of the Port. The appeal must be in writing, except as allowed under paragraph (d) of this section, and shall contain complete supporting documentation and evidence which the appellant wishes to have considered. Upon receipt of the appeal, the District Commander may direct a representative to gather and submit documentation or other evidence which would be necessary or helpful to a resolution of the appeal. A copy of this documentation and evidence is made available to the appellant. The appellant is afforded five working days from the date of receipt to submit rebuttal materials. Following submission of all materials, the District Commander issues a ruling, in writing, on the appeal. Prior to issuing the ruling, the District Commander may, as a matter of discretion, allow oral presentation on the issues.

(1267)   (c) Any person directly affected by the establishment of a safety zone or by an order or direction issued by a District Commander, or who receives an unfavorable ruling on an appeal taken under paragraph (b) of this section, may appeal through the District Commander to the Chief, Office of Marine Safety, Security and Environmental Protection, U.S. Coast Guard, Washington, D.C. 20593. The appeal must be in writing, except as allowed under paragraph (d) of this section. The District Commander forwards the appeal, all the documents and evidence which formed the record upon which the order or direction was issued or the ruling under paragraph (b) of this section was made, and any comments which might be relevant, to the Chief, Office of Marine Safety, Security and Environmental Protection. A copy of this documentation and evidence is made available to the appellant. The appellant is afforded five working days from the date of receipt to submit rebuttal materials to the Chief, Office of Marine Safety, Security and Environmental Protection. The decision of the Chief, Office of Marine Safety, Security and Environmental Protection is based upon the materials submitted, without oral argument or presentation. The decision of the Chief, Office of Marine Safety, Security and Environmental Protection is issued in writing and constitutes final agency action.

(1268)   (d) If the delay in presenting a written appeal would have significant adverse impact on the appellant, the appeal under paragraphs (b) and (c) of this section may initially be presented orally. If an initial presentation of the appeal is made orally, the appellant must submit the appeal in writing within five days of the oral presentation to the Coast Guard official to whom the presentation was made. The written appeal must contain, at a minimum, the basis for the appeal and a summary of the material presented orally. If requested, the official to whom the appeal is directed may stay the effect of the action while the ruling is being appealed.

Subpart B—Control of Vessel and Facility Operations
(1269)   **§160.101 Purpose.**
(1270)   This subpart describes the authority exercised by District Commanders and Captains of the Ports to insure the safety of vessels and waterfront facilities, and the protection of the navigable waters and the resources therein. The controls described in this subpart are directed to specific situations and hazards.
(1271)   **§160.103 Applicability.**

(1272)   (a) This subpart applies to any—
(1273)   (1) Vessel on the navigable waters of the United States, except as provided in paragraphs (b) and (c) of this section;
(1274)   (2) Bridge or other structure on or in the navigable waters of the United States; and
(1275)   (3) Land structure or shore area immediately adjacent to the navigable waters of the United States.
(1276)   (b) This subpart does not apply to any vessel on the Saint Lawrence Seaway.
(1277)   (c) Except pursuant to international treaty, convention, or agreement, to which the United States is a party, this subpart does not apply to any foreign vessel that is not destined for, or departing from, a port or place subject to the jurisdiction of the United States and that is in—
(1278)   (1) Innocent passage through the territorial sea of the United States;
(1279)   (2) Transit through the navigable waters of the United States which form a part of an international strait.
(1280)   **§160.105 Compliance with orders.**
(1281)   Each person who has notice of the terms of an order issued under this subpart must comply with that order.
(1282)   **§160.107 Denial of entry.**
(1283)   Each District Commander or Captain of the Port, subject to recognized principles of international law, may deny entry into the navigable waters of the United States or to any port or place under the jurisdiction of the United States, and within the district or zone of that District Commander or Captain of the Port, to any vessel not in compliance with the provisions of the Port and Tanker Safety Act (33 U.S.C. 1221-1232) or the regulations issued thereunder.
(1284)   **§160.109 Waterfront facility safety.**
(1285)   (a) To prevent damage to, or destruction of, any bridge or other structure on or in the navigable waters of the United States, or any land structure or shore area immediately adjacent to those waters, and to protect the navigable waters and the resources therein from harm resulting from vessel or structure damage, destruction, or loss, each District Commander or Captain of the Port may—
(1286)   (1) Direct the handling, loading, unloading, storage, stowage, and movement (including the emergency removal, control, and disposition) of explosives or other dangerous articles and substances, including oil or hazardous material as those terms are defined in Section 4417a of the Revised Statutes, as amended, (46 U.S.C. 391a) on any structure on or in the navigable waters of the United States, or any land structure or shore area immediately adjacent to those waters; and
(1287)   (2) Conduct examinations to assure compliance with the safety equipment requirements for structures.
(1288)   **§160.111 Special orders applying to vessel operations.**
(1289)   Each District Commander or Captain of the Port may order a vessel to operate or anchor in the manner directed when—
(1290)   (a) The District Commander or Captain of the Port has reasonable cause to believe that the vessel is not in compliance with any regulation, law or treaty;
(1291)   (b) The District Commander or Captain of the Port determines that the vessel does not satisfy the conditions for vessel operation and cargo transfers specified in §160.113; or
(1292)   (c) The District Commander or Captain of the Port has determined that such order is justified in the interest of safety by reason of weather, visibility, sea conditions, temporary port congestion, other temporary hazardous circumstances, or the condition of the vessel.
(1293)   **§160.113 Prohibition of vessel operation and cargo transfers.**

(1294)   (a) Each District Commander or Captain of the Port may prohibit any vessel subject to the provisions of section 4417a of the Revised Statutes (46 U.S.C. 391a) from operating in the navigable waters of the United States, or from transferring cargo or residue in any port or place under the jurisdiction of the United States, and within the district or zone of that District Commander or Captain of the Port, if the District Commander or the Captain of the Port determines that the vessel's history of accidents, pollution incidents, or serious repair problems creates reason to believe that the vessel may be unsafe or pose a threat to the marine environment.

(1295)   (b) The authority to issue orders prohibiting operation of the vessels or transfer of cargo or residue under paragraph (a) of this section also applies if the vessel:

(1296)   (1) Fails to comply with any applicable regulation;

(1297)   (2) Discharges oil or hazardous material in violation of any law or treaty of the United States;

(1298)   (3) Does not comply with applicable vessel traffic service requirements;

(1299)   (4) While underway, does not have at least one licensed deck officer on the navigation bridge who is capable of communicating in the English language.

(1300)   (c) When a vessel has been prohibited from operating in the navigable waters of the United States under paragraphs (a) or (b) of this section, the District Commander or Captain of the Port may allow provisional entry into the navigable waters of the United States, or into any port or place under the jurisdiction of the United States and within the district or zone of that District Commander or Captain of the Port, if the owner or operator of such vessel proves to the satisfaction of the District Commander or Captain of the Port, that the vessel is not unsafe or does not pose a threat to the marine environment, and that such entry is necessary for the safety of the vessel or the persons on board.

(1301)   (d) A vessel which has been prohibited from operating in the navigable waters of the United States, or from transferring cargo or residue in a port or place under the jurisdiction of the United States under the provisions of paragraph (a) or (b)(1), (2) or (3) of this section, may be allowed provisional entry if the owner or operator proves, to the satisfaction of the District Commander or Captain of the Port that has jurisdiction, that the vessel is no longer unsafe or a threat to the environment, and that the condition which gave rise to the prohibition no longer exists.

(1302)   **§160.115 Withholding of clearance.**

(1303)   (a) Each District Commander or Captain of the Port may request the Secretary of the Treasury, or the authorized representative thereof, to withold or revoke the clearance required by 46 U.S.C. 91 of any vessel, the owner or operator of which is subject to any penalties under 33 U.S.C. 1232.

Subpart C–Notifications of Arrivals, Departures, Hazardous Conditions, and Certain Dangerous Cargoes

(1304)   **§160.201 Applicability and exceptions to applicability.**

(1305)   (a) This subpart prescribes notification requirements for U.S. and foreign vessels bound for or departing from ports or places in the United States.

(1306)   (b) This subpart does not apply to boats under the Federal Boat Safety Act of 1971 (46 U.S.C. 1451, et seq.) and, except §161.215, does not apply to passenger and supply vessels when they are employed in the exploration for or in the exploitation of oil, gas, or mineral resources on the continental shelf.

(1307)   (c) Sections 160.207 and 160.209 do not apply to the following:

(1308)   (1) Each vessel of less than 1,600 gross tons.

(1309)   (2) Each vessel operating exclusively within a Captain of the Port zone.

(1310)   (3) Each vessel operating upon a route that is described in a schedule that is submitted to the Captain of the Port for each port or place of destination listed in the schedule at least 24 hours in advance of the first date and time of arrival listed on the schedule and contains—

(1311)   (i) Name, country of registry, and call sign or official number of the vessel;

(1312)   (ii) Each port or place of destination; and

(1313)   (iii) Dates and times of arrivals and departures at those ports or places.

(1314)   (4) Each vessel arriving at a port or place under force majeure.

(1315)   (5) Each vessel entering a port of call in the United States in compliance with the Automated Mutual Assistance Vessel Rescue System (AMVER).

(1316)   (6) Each vessel entering a port of call in the United States in compliance with the U.S. Flag Merchant Vessel Locator Filing System (USMER).

(1317)   (7) Each barge.

(1318)   (8) Each public vessel.

(1319)   (9) United States or Canadian flag vessels, except tank vessels or vessels carrying certain dangerous cargo, which operate solely on the Great Lakes.

(1320)   (d) Sections 160.207, 160.211, and 160.213 apply to each vessel upon the waters of the Mississippi River between its mouth and mile 235, Lower Mississippi River, above Head of Passes. Sections 160.207, 160.211, and 160.213 do not apply to each vessel upon the waters of the Mississippi River between its sources and mile 235, above Head of Passes, and all the tributaries emptying thereinto and their tributaries, and that part of the Atchafalaya River above its junction with the Plaquemine-Morgan City alternate waterway, and the Red River of the North.

(1321)   **§160.203 Definitions.**

(1322)   As used in this subpart:

(1323)   "Agent" means any person, partnership, firm, company or corporation engaged by the owner or charterer of a vessel to act in their behalf in matters concerning the vessel.

(1324)   "Carried in bulk" means a commodity that is loaded or carried on board a vessel without containers or labels and received and handled without mark or count.

(1325)   "Certain dangerous cargo" includes any of the following:

(1326)   (a) Class A explosives, as defined in 46 CFR 146.20–7 and 49 CFR 173.53.

(1327)   (b) Oxidizing materials or blasting agents for which a permit is required under 49 CFR 176.415.

(1328)   (c) Highway route controlled quantity radioactive material, as defined in 49 CFR 173.403(1), or Fissile Class III shipments of fissile radioactive material, as defined in 49 CFR 173.455(a)(3).

(1329)   (d) Each cargo under Table 1 of 46 CFR Part 153 when carried in bulk.

(1330)   (e) Any of the following when carried in bulk:

(1331)   Acetaldehyde

(1332)   Ammonia, anhydrous

(1333)   Butadiene

(1334)   Butane

(1335)   Butene

(1336)   Butylene Oxide

(1337)   Chlorine

(1338)   Ethane

(1339)   Ethylene

(1340)   Ethylene Oxide

(1341)   Methane

(1342) Methyl Acetylene, Propadiene Mixture, Stabilized
(1343) Methyl Bromide
(1344) Methyl Chloride
(1345) Phosphorous, elemental
(1346) Propane
(1347) Propylene
(1348) Sulfur Dioxide
(1349) Vinyl Chloride
(1350) "Great Lakes" means Lakes Superior, Michigan, Huron, Erie, and Ontario, their connecting and tributary waters, the Saint Lawrence River as far east as Saint Regis, and adjacent port areas.
(1351) "Hazardous condition" means any condition that could adversely affect the safety of any vessel, bridge, structure, or shore area or the environmental quality of any port, harbor, or navigable water of the United States. This condition could include but is not limited to, fire, explosion, grounding, leakage, damage, illness of a person on board, or a manning shortage.
(1352) "Port or place of departure" means any port or place in which a vessel is anchored or moored.
(1353) "Port or place of destination" means any port or place to which a vessel is bound to anchor or moor.
(1354) "Public vessel" means a vessel owned by and being used in the public service of the United States. This definition does not include a vessel owned by the United States and engaged in a trade or commercial service or a vessel under contract or charter to the United States.

(1355) **§160.205 Waivers.**
(1356) The Captain of the Port may waive, within that Captain of the Port's designated zone, any of the requirements of this subpart for any vessel or class of vessels upon finding that the vessel, route, area of operations, conditions of the voyage, or other circumstances are such that application of this subpart is unnecessary or impractical for purposes of safety, environmental protection, or national security.

(1357) **§160.207 Notice of arrival: vessels bound for ports or places in the United States.**
(1358) (a) The owner, master, agent or person in charge of a vessel on a voyage of 24 hours or more shall report under paragraph (c) of this section at least 24 hours before entering the port or place of destination.
(1359) (b) The owner, master, agent, or person in charge of a vessel on a voyage of less than 24 hours shall report under paragraph (c) of this section before departing the port or place of departure.
(1360) (c) The Captain of the Port of the port or place of destination in the United States must be notified of—
(1361) (1) The name and country of registry of the vessel;
(1362) (2) The name of the port or place of departure.
(1363) (3) The name of the port or place of destination; and
(1364) (4) The estimated time of arrival at the port or place.
(1365) If the estimated time of arrival changes by more than six hours from the latest reported time, the Captain of the Port must be notified of the correction as soon as the change is known.

(1366) **§160.209 Notice of arrival: vessels bound from the high seas for ports or places on the Great Lakes.**
(1367) In addition to complying with the requirement of §160.207, the owner, master, agent, or person in charge of a vessel bound from the high seas for any port or place of destination on the Great Lakes shall notify the Commander, Ninth Coast Guard District, at least 24 hours before arriving at the Snell Locks, Massena, New York of—
(1368) (a) The name and country of registry of the vessel; and
(1369) (b) The estimated time of arrival at the Snell Locks, Massena, New York.

(1370) **§160.211 Notice of arrival: vessels carrying certain dangerous cargo.**
(1371) (a) The owner, master, agent, or person in charge of a vessel, except a barge, bound for a port or place in the United States carrying certain dangerous cargo shall notify the Captain of the Port of the port or place of destination at least 24 hours before entering that port or place of—
(1372) (1) The name and country of registry of the vessel;
(1373) (2) The location of the vessel at the time of the report;
(1374) (3) The name of each certain dangerous cargo carried;
(1375) (4) The amount of each certain dangerous cargo carried;
(1376) (5) The stowage location of each certain dangerous cargo;
(1377) (6) The operational condition of the equipment under 33 CFR 164.35;
(1378) (7) The name of the port or place of destination; and
(1379) (8) The estimated time of arrival at that port or place. If the estimated time of arrival changes by more than six hours from the latest reported time, the Captain of the Port must be notified of the correction as soon as the change is known.
(1380) (b) The owner, master, agent or person in charge of a barge bound for a port or place in the United States carrying certain dangerous cargo shall report the information required in paragraph (a)(1) through (a)(8) of this section to the Captain of the Port of the port or place of destination at least 4 hours before entering that port or place.

(1381) **§160.213 Notice of departure; vessels carrying certain dangerous cargo.**
(1382) (a) The owner, master, agent, or person in charge of a vessel, except a barge, departing from a port or place in the United States for any other port or place and carrying certain dangerous cargo shall notify the Captain of the Port or place of departure at least 24 hours before departing, unless this notification was made within 2 hours after the vessel's arrival, of—
(1383) (1) The name and country of registry of the vessel;
(1384) (2) The name of each certain dangerous cargo carried;
(1385) (3) The amount of each certain dangerous cargo carried;
(1386) (4) The stowage location of each certain dangerous cargo carried;
(1387) (5) The operational condition of the equipment under 33 CFR 164.35;
(1388) (6) The name of the port or place of departure; and
(1389) (7) The estimated time of departure from the port or place.
(1390) If the estimated time of departure changes by more than six hours from the latest reported time, the Captain of the Port must be notified of the correction as soon as the change is known.
(1391) (b) The owner, master, agent, or person in change of a barge departing from a port or place in the United States for any other port or place and carrying certain dangerous cargo shall report the information required in paragraph (a)(1) through (a)(7) of this section to the Captain of the Port of the port or place of departure at least 4 hours before departing, unless this report was made within 2 hours after the barge's arrival.

(1392) **§160.215 Notice of hazardous conditions.**
(1393) Whenever there is a hazardous condition on board a vessel, the owner, master, agent or person in charge shall immediately notify the Captain of the Port of the port or place of destination and the Captain of the Port of the port

or place in which the vessel is located of the hazardous condition.

(1394) **Part 161 - Vessel Traffic Management**

(1395) **New York Vessel Traffic Service**

(1396) **General rules**

(1397) **§161.501 Purpose and applicability.**

(1398) (a) Sections 161.501 through 161.580 of this part prescribe rules for vessel operation in the Vessel Traffic Service New York Area (VTSNY Area) to prevent collisions and groundings and to protect the navigable waters of the VTSNY Area from environmental harm resulting from collisions and groundings.

(1399) (b) The General Rules in §§ 161.501 through 161.505 and 161.507 through 161.510, and the Use of Designated Frequency Rule in §161.523 of this part apply to the operation of all vessels.

(1400) (c) The Requirement to Carry Regulations Rule in §161.506, the Communications Rules in §§ 161.520 through 161.522 and 161.524 through 161.532, the Vessel Movement Reporting Rules in §§ 161.536 through 161.542, and the Special Rules of §161.575 of this part apply only to the operation of -

(1401) (1) Power driven vessels of 300 gross tons and upward while navigating;

(1402) (2) Vessels of 100 gross tons and upward carrying one or more passengers for hire while navigating;

(1403) (3) Commercial vessels of 26 feet or more in length engaged in towing another vessel astern, alongside, or by pushing ahead; and

(1404) (4) Every dredge and floating plant.

(1405) (d) Geographic coordinates expressed in terms of latitude and longitude are not intended for plotting on maps or charts whose referenced horizontal datum is the North American Datum of 1983 (NAD 83), unless such geographic coordinates are expressly labeled NAD 83. Geographic coordinates without the NAD 83 reference may be plotted on maps or charts referenced to NAD 83 only after application of the appropriate corrections that are published on the particular map or charts used.

(1406) **§161.503 Definitions.**

(1407) As used in any section of this part:

(1408) Commercial Vessel means any vessel operating in return for payment or other type of compensation.

(1409) ETA means estimated time of arrival.

(1410) Floating Plant means any vessel, other than a vessel underway and making way, engaged in any construction, manufacturing, or exploration operation, and which may restrict the navigation of other vessels. Master means a licensed master or operator or, on vessels not requiring a licensed operator, the person directing the movement of the vessel.

(1411) Person includes an individual, firm, corporation, association, partnership, and governmental entity.

(1412) Vessel Movement Reporting System (VMRS) is a method for monitoring vessel progress based on position reports from the vessel rather than on electronic surveillance.

(1413) Vessel Traffic Center (VTC) means the shore based facility that operates the New York Vessel Traffic Service.

(1414) Vessel Traffic Service New York Area (VTSNY Area) means the area described in §161.580 of this part.

(1415) **§161.504 Vessel operation in the VTSNY Area.**

(1416) No person may cause or authorize the operation of a vessel in the VTSNY Area contrary to the rules in this part.

(1417) **§161.505 VTC directions.**

(1418) (a) During conditions of vessel congestion, adverse weather, reduced visibility, other hazardous circumstances, the VTC may issue directions to control and supervise traffic by specifying times when vessels may enter, move within or

through, or depart from ports, harbors or other waters in the VTSNY Area.

(1419) (b) The master or pilot of a vessel in the VTSNY Area shall comply with each direction issued to the vessel under this section.

(1420) **§161.506 Requirement to carry regulations.**

(1421) The master of a vessel shall ensure that a copy of the current edition of the Vessel Traffic Service New York regulations, Title 33, Code of Federal Regulations, §§161.501 through 161.580, is available on board the vessels at all times when it is navigating in the VTSNY Area.

(1422) Note.-The New York VTS Operating Manual includes the VTS regulations described above. Additional information for efficient operation in the VTS system is also included. The manual may be obtained free-of-charge from U.S. Coast Guard Marine Inspection Office, Battery Park Building, New York, NY 16004, and from Commanding Officer, U.S. Coast Guard Vessel Traffic Service, Governors Island, New York, NY 10004.

(1423) **§161.507 Laws and regulations not affected.**

(1424) Nothing in this part is intended to relieve any person from complying with any other applicable laws or regulations.

(1425) **§161.508 Authorization to deviate from these rules.**

(1426) (a) The Commander, First Coast Guard District may, upon written request, issue an authorization to deviate from any rule in this part if he or she finds that the proposed operation can be done safely. An application for an authorization to deviate from a rule must state the need for the deviation and describe the proposed operation.

(1427) (b) The VTC may, upon verbal request, issue an authorization to deviate from any rule in this part for the voyage on which a vessel is embarked or about to embark.

(1428) **§161.510 Emergencies.**

(1429) In an emergency, any master or pilot may deviate from any rule in this part to the extent necessary to avoid endangering persons, property, or the environment but shall report the deviation to the VTC as soon as possible.

(1430) **Communications Rules**

(1431) **§161.520 Radiotelephone listening watch.**

(1432) The master or pilot shall continuously monitor the VTS radiotelephone frequency when operating in the VTS Area, except when transmitting on that frequency.

(1433) **§161.522 Radiotelephone equipment.**

(1434) The master or pilot shall ensure all reports and communications required by this part are made from the navigational bridge of the vessel, or in the case of a dredge, at its main control station. Such reports and communications must be made to the VTC on designated frequencies using a radiotelephone that is in effective operating condition.

(1435) **§161.523 Use of designated frequencies.**

(1436) (a) In accordance with Federal Communications Commission regulations, no person may use the frequencies designated in this section to transmit any information other than information necessary for the safety of vessel traffic.

(1437) (b) All transmissions on the VTS frequencies shall be initiated on low power, if available; high power may only be used if low power communications are unsuccessful or in an emergency.

(1438) (c) The following frequencies must be used when communicating with the VTC:

(1439) (1) Primary frequencies: 156.550 MHz (channel 11), 156.600 MHz (channel 12), and 156.700 MHz (channel 14).

(1440) (2) Secondary frequency (to be used if communication is not possible on a primary frequency): 156.650 MHz (channel 13).

(1441) **§161.524 English language.**

(1442)   Each report required by this part must be made in the English language.

(1443)   **§161.526 Time.**

(1444)   Each report required by this part must specify time using:

(1445)   (a) The time zone in effect in the VTSNY Area and

(1446)   (b) The 24-hour clock system.

(1447)   **§161.528 Radiotelephone failure.**

(1448)   Whenever a vessel's radiotelephone equipment fails -

(1449)   (a) While underway in the VTSNY Area or is inoperative when entering the VTSNY Area- (1) Compliance with §§ 161.520 and 161.538 of this part is not required; and

(1450)   (2) Compliance with §§ 161.536, 161.537, and 161.542 of this part is not required unless those reports can be made by other means.

(1451)   (b) Before getting underway in the VTSNY Area, permission to get underway must be obtained from the VTC; and

(1452)   (c) The master shall restore the radiotelephone to operating condition as soon as possible.

(1453)   **§161.530 Report of radiotelephone failure.**

(1454)   Whenever the master or pilot of a vessel deviates from any rule in this part because of radiotelephone failure, the deviation and radiotelephone failure shall be reported to the VTC by the most expedient means available.

(1455)   **§161.532 Report of impairment to the operation of the vessel.**

(1456)   The master of a vessel in the VTSNY Area shall report to the VTC as soon as possible -

(1457)   (a) Any condition on the vessel that may impair its navigation, such as fire, malfunctioning propulsion machinery, malfunctioning steering equipment, or malfunctioning radar;

(1458)   (b) Whenever the vessel has difficulty controlling its tow; and

(1459)   (c) Any grounding, collision or allision with a fixed or floating object.

(1460)   **Note.**–In the VTSNY Area, the reports required in 33 CFR part 164 are to be made to the VTC instead.

(1461)   **Vessel Movement Reporting Rules**

(1462)   **§161.536 Initial report.**

(1463)   Fifteen minutes before a vessel enters or gets underway in the VTSNY Area, the master of the vessel shall report the following information to the VTC:

(1464)   (a) The type and name of the vessel.

(1465)   (b) The estimated time and point of entry in the VTSNY Area.

(1466)   (c) Destination and route in the VTSNY Area.

(1467)   (d) Deepest draft of the vessel.

(1468)   (e) Speed of advance of the vessel.

(1469)   (f) Whether or not any dangerous cargo listed in part 160, subpart C, of this chapter, is onboard the vessel or its tow.

(1470)   (g) Any impairment to the operation of the vessel as described in §161.532 (a) and (b) of this part.

(1471)   (h) Any planned maneuvers that may impede traffic.

(1472)   **§161.537 Follow-up reports.**

(1473)   When entering or beginning to navigate in the VTSNY Area, or if the vessel deviates from its route plan as reported in the initial report, the master of the vessel shall report the following information by radiotelephone to the VTC:

(1474)   (a) Vessel name.

(1475)   (b) Location of the vessel.

(1476)   (c) Any revision to the initial report required by §161.536 of this part.

(1477)   **§161.538 Movement reports.**

(1478)   When the VMRS is in operation, or at other times when directed by the VTC, the master of a vessel passing a reporting point listed in §161.540 of this part shall report the following to the VTC by radiotelephone:

(1479)   (a) Vessel name.

(1480)   (b) Reporting point or location of the vessel.

(1481)   **§161.539 Invoking of the VMRS rules.**

(1482)   In the event of impairment of surveillance capability or when otherwise required for the safety of navigation, the Vessel Movement Reporting System (VMRS) may be invoked by the VTC.

(1483)   **§161.540 VMRS reporting points.**

No.	Position description	Geographic location
1	Verrazano-Narrows Bridge.	Upper New York Bay.
2	Brooklyn Bridge	East River.
3	Holland Tunnel Ventilator.	Hudson River.
4	Caven Point	Upper New York Bay.
5	Red Hook	Buttermilk Channel.
6	Constable Hook	Kill Van Kull.
7	Bayonne Bridge	Kill Van Kull.
8	AK Rail Bridge	Arthur Kill.
9	Lehigh Valley Draw Bridge.	Newark Bay.
10	Texaco Bayonne Facility.	Newark Bay.

(1484)   **§161.542 Final report.**

(1485)   When a vessel anchors in, moors in, or departs from the VTSNY Area, the master shall report the place of anchoring, mooring, or departing to the VTC.

(1486)   **Special Rules**

(1487)   **§161.575 Action during reduced visibility.**

(1488)   When visibility is less than 2 nautical miles in the VTSNY Area, any vessel that is operating without radar shall notify the VTC immediately.

(1489)   **Descriptions and Geographic Coordinates**

(1490)   **§161.580 VTSNY Area.**

(1491)   The VTSNY Area consists of the navigable waters of the United States bounded by the Verrazano-Narrows Bridge to the south, the Brooklyn Bridge to the east, and to the north, at a line drawn east-west from the Holland Tunnel ventilator shaft at latitude 40°43.7′N, longitude 74°01.6′W. The Kill Van Kull to the AK Rail Bridge and Newark Bay to the Lehigh Valley Draw Bridge are also included in the VTSNY Area.

Part 162–Inland Waterways Navigation Regulations

(1492)   **§162.1 General.**

(1493)   Geographic coordinates expressed in terms of latitude or longitude, or both, are not intended for plotting on maps or charts whose referenced horizontal datum is the North American Datum of 1983 (NAD 83), unless such geographic coordinates are expressly labeled NAD 83. Geographic coordinates without the NAD 83 reference may be plotted on maps or charts referenced to NAD 83 only after application of the appropriate corrections that are published on the particular map or chart being used.

(1494)   **§162.15 Manhasset Bay, N.Y.; seaplane restricted area.** (a) The restricted area. An area in Manhasset Bay between the shore at Manorhaven on the north and the southerly limit line of the special anchorage area in Manhasset Bay, west area at Manorhaven (described in 33 CFR 110.60), on the south; its axis being a line bearing 166°50′ true from latitude 40°50′17.337″, longitude 73°43′03.877″, which point is on the south side of Orchard Beach Boulevard at Manorhaven; and being 100 feet wide for a distance of 380 feet in a southerly direction from the south side of Orchard Beach Boulevard, and thence flaring to a width of 300 feet at the southerly limit line.

(1495) (b) The regulations. (1) Vessels shall not anchor or moor within the restricted area.

(1496) (2) All vessels traversing the area shall pass directly through without unnecessary delay, and shall give seaplanes the right-of-way at all times.

(1497) **§162.20 Flushing Bay near La Guardia Airport, Flushing, N.Y.; restricted area.** (a) The area. An area in the main channel in Flushing Bay extending for a distance of 300 feet on either side of the extended center line of Runway No. 13–31 at La Guardia Airport.

(1498) (b) The regulations. (1) All vessels traversing in the area shall pass directly through without unnecessary delay.

(1499) (2) No vessels having a height of more than 35 feet with reference to the plane of mean high water shall enter or pass through the area whenever visibility is less than one mile.

(1500) **§162.25 Ambrose Channel, New York Harbor, N.Y.; navigation.** (a) The use of Ambrose Channel (formerly and before improvement called "East Channel") is hereby restricted to navigation by vessels under efficient control with their own motive power and not having barges or other vessels or floats in tow. Sailing vessels and vessels carrying tows are not permitted to use this channel except under permit as provided in paragraph (b) of this section.

(1501) (b) The Captain of the Port, New York may authorize vessels under tow to use Ambrose Channel in special cases when, in his judgement, the draft of such vessels or other conditions may render unsafe the use of other channels.

(1502) (c) Vessels permitted to use Ambrose Channel under paragraphs (a) and (b) of this section must proceed through the channel at a reasonable speed such as not to endanger other vessels and not to interfere with any work which may become necessary in maintaining, surveying, or buoying the channel; and they must not anchor in the channel except in cases of emergency, such as fog or accident, which would render progress unsafe or impossible.

(1503) (d) This section is not to be construed as prohibiting any necessary use of the channel by any Government boats while on Government duty, nor in emergencies by pilot boats whether steam or sail, nor by police boats.

(1504) (e) This section shall remain in force until modified or rescinded, and shall supplant all prior regulations governing the use of Ambrose Channel, which are hereby revoked.

Part 164—Navigation Safety Regulations (in part). For a complete description of this part see 33 CFR 164.

(1505) **§164.01 Applicability.**

(1506) (a) This part (except as specifically limited herein) applies to each self-propelled vessel of 1600 or more gross tons (except foreign vessels described in §164.02) when it is operating in the navigable waters of the United States except the St. Lawrence Seaway.

(1507) **§164.02 Applicability exception for foreign vessels.**

(1508) (a) This part (including §§164.38 and 164.39) does not apply to vessels that:

(1509) (1) Are not destined for, or departing from, a port or place subject to the jurisdiction of the United States; and

(1510) (2) Are in:

(1511) (i) Innocent passage through the territorial sea of the United States; or

(1512) (ii) Transit through navigable waters of the United States which form a part of an international strait.

(1513) **§164.03 Incorporation by reference.**

(1514) (a) Certain materials are incorporated by reference into this part with the approval of the Director of the Federal Register. The Office of the Federal Register publishes a table, "Material Approved for Incorporation by Reference," which appears in the Finding Aids section of this volume. In that table is found the date of the edition approved, citations to the particular sections of this part where the material is incorporated, addresses where the material is available, and the date of the approval by the Director of the Federal Register. To enforce any edition other than the one listed in the table, notice of the change must be published in the FEDERAL REGISTER and the material made available. All approved material is on file at the Office of the Federal Register, Washington, DC 20408 and at Room 4402, U.S. Coast Guard Headquarters, 2100 Second St. SW, Washington, DC.

(1515) (b) The materials approved for incorporation by reference in this part are: Radio Technical Commission For Marine Services (RTCM) Paper 12-78/DO-100 dated 12/20/77.

(1516) **§164.11 Navigation underway: General.**

(1517) The owner, master, or person in charge of each vessel underway shall ensure that:

(1518) (a) The wheelhouse is constantly manned by persons who—

(1519) (1) Direct and control the movement of the vessel; and

(1520) (2) Fix the vessel's position;

(1521) (b) Each person performing a duty described in paragraph (a) of this section is competent to perform that duty;

(1522) (c) The position of the vessel at each fix is plotted on a chart of the area and the person directing the movement of the vessel is informed of the vessel's position;

(1523) (d) Electronic and other navigational equipment, external fixed aids to navigation, geographic reference points, and hydrographic contours are used when fixing the vessel's position;

(1524) (e) Buoys alone are not used to fix the vessel's position;

(1525) **Note:** Buoys are aids to navigation placed in approximate positions to alert the mariner to hazards to navigation or to indicate the orientation of a channel. Buoys may not maintain an exact position because strong or varying currents, heavy seas, ice, and collisions with vessels can move or sink them or set them adrift. Although buoys may corroborate a position fixed by other means, buoys cannot be used to fix a position: however, if no other aids are available, buoys alone may be used to establish an estimated position.

(1526) (f) The danger of each closing visual or each closing radar contact is evaluated and the person directing the movement of the vessel knows the evaluation;

(1527) (g) Rudder orders are executed as given;

(1528) (h) Engine speed and direction orders are executed as given;

(1529) (i) Magnetic variation and deviation and gyrocompass errors are known and correctly applied by the person directing the movement of the vessel;

(1530) (j) A person whom he has determined is competent to steer the vessel is in the wheelhouse at all times (See also 46 U.S.C. 672, which requires an able seaman at the wheel on U.S. vessels of 100 gross tons or more in narrow or crowded waters or during low visibility.);

(1531) (k) If a pilot other than a member of the vessel's crew is employed, the pilot is informed of the draft, maneuvering characteristics, and peculiarities of the vessel and of any abnormal circumstances on the vessel that may affect its safe navigation.

(1532)   (1) Current velocity and direction for the area to be transited are known by the person directing the movement of the vessel;

(1533)   (m) Predicted set and drift are known by the person directing movement of the vessel;

(1534)   (n) Tidal state for the area to be transited is known by the person directing movement of the vessel;

(1535)   (o) The vessel's anchors are ready for letting go;

(1536)   (p) The person directing the movement of the vessel sets the vessel's speed with consideration for—

(1537)   (1) The prevailing visibility and weather conditions;

(1538)   (2) The proximity of the vessel to fixed shore and marine structures;

(1539)   (3) The tendency of the vessel underway to squat and suffer impairment of maneuverability when there is small underkeel clearance;

(1540)   (4) The comparative proportions of the vessel and the channel;

(1541)   (5) The density of marine traffic;

(1542)   (6) The damage that might be caused by the vessel's wake;

(1543)   (7) The strength and direction of the current; and

(1544)   (8) Any local vessel speed limit;

(1545)   (q) The tests required by §164.25 are made and recorded in the vessel's log; and

(1546)   (r) The equipment required by this part is maintained in operable condition.

(1547)   (s) Upon entering U.S. waters, the steering wheel or lever on the navigating bridge is operated to determine if the steering equipment is operating properly under manual control, unless the vessel has been steered under manual control from the navigating bridge within the preceding 2 hours, except when operating on the Great Lakes and their connecting and tributary waters.

(1548)   (t) At least two of the steering gear power units on the vessel are in operation when such units are capable of simultaneous operation, except when operating on the Great Lakes and their connecting and tributary waters.

(1549)   **§164.15 Navigation bridge visibility.**

(1550)   (a) The arrangement of cargo, cargo gear, and trim of all vessels entering or departing from U.S. ports must be such that the field of vision from the navigation bridge conforms as closely as possible to the following requirements:

(1551)   (1) From the conning position, the view of the sea surface must not be obscured by more than the lesser of two hip lengths or 500 meters (1640 feet) from dead ahead to 10 degrees on either side of the vessel. Within this arc of visibility any blind sector caused by cargo, cargo gear, or other permanent obstructure must not exceed 5 degrees.

(1552)   (2) From the conning position, the horizontal field of vision must extend over an arc from at least 22.5 degrees abaft the beam on one side of the vessel, through dead ahead, to at least 22.5 degrees abaft the beam on the other side of the vessel. Blind sectors forward of the beam caused by cargo, cargo gear, or other permanent obstruction must not exceed 10 degrees each, nor total more than 20 degrees, including any blind sector within the arc of visibility described in paragraph (a)(1) of this section.

(1553)   (3) From each bridge wing, the field of vision must extend over an arc from at least 45 degrees on the opposite bow, through dead ahead, to at least dead astern.

(1554)   (4) From the main steering position, the field of vision must extend over an arc from dead ahead to at least 60 degrees on either side of the vessel.

(1555)   (b) A clear view must be provided through at least two front windows at all times regardless of weather conditions.

(1556)   **§164.19 Requirements for vessels at anchor.**

(1557)   The master or person in charge of each vessel that is anchored shall ensure that—

(1558)   (a) A proper anchor watch is maintained;

(1559)   (b) Procedures are followed to detect a dragging anchor; and

(1560)   (c) Whenever weather, tide, or current conditions are likely to cause the vessel's anchor to drag, action is taken to ensure the safety of the vessel, structures, and other vessels, such a being ready to veer chain, let go a second anchor, or get underway using the vessel's own propulsion or tug assistance.

(1561)   **§164.25 Tests before entering or getting underway.**

(1562)   (a) Except as provided in paragraphs (b) and (c) of this section no person may cause a vessel to enter into or get underway on the navigable waters of the United States unless no more than 12 hours before entering or getting underway, the following equipment has been tested:

(1563)   (1) Primary and secondary steering gear. The test procedure includes a visual inspection of the steering gear and its connecting linkage, and where applicable, the operation of the following:

(1564)   (i) Each remote steering gear control system.

(1565)   (ii) Each steering position located on the navigating bridge.

(1566)   (iii) The main steering gear from the alternative power supply, if installed.

(1567)   (iv) Each rudder angle indicator in relation to the actual position of the rudder.

(1568)   (v) Each remote steering gear control system power failure alarm.

(1569)   (vi) Each remote steering gear power unit failure alarm.

(1570)   (vii) The full movement of the rudder to the required capabilities of the steering gear.

(1571)   (2) All internal vessel control communications and vessel control alarms.

(1572)   (3) Standby or emergency generator, for as long as necessary to show proper functioning, including steady state temperature and pressure readings.

(1573)   (4) Storage batteries for emergency lighting and power systems in vessel control and propulsion machinery spaces.

(1574)   (5) Main propulsion machinery, ahead and astern.

(1575)   (b) Vessels navigating on the Great Lakes and their connecting and tributary waters, having once completed the test requirements of this sub-part, are considered to remain in compliance until arriving at the next port of call on the Great Lakes.

(1576)   (c) Vessels entering the Great Lakes from the St. Lawrence Seaway are considered to be in compliance with this sub-part if the required tests are conducted preparatory to or during the passage of the St. Lawrence Seaway or within one hour of passing Wolfe Island.

(1577)   (d) No vessel may enter, or be operated on the navigable waters of the United States unless the emergency steering drill described below has been conducted within 48 hours prior to entry and logged in the vessel logbook, unless the drill is conducted and logged on a regular basis at least once every three months. This drill must include at a minimum the following:

(1578)   (1) Operation of the main steering gear from within the steering gear compartment.

(1579)   (2) Operation of the means of communications between the navigating bridge and the steering compartment.

(1580)   (3) Operation of the alternative power supply for the steering gear if the vessel is so equipped.

(1581)   **§164.30 Charts, publications, and equipment: General.**

(1582) No person may operate or cause the operation of a vessel unless the vessel has the marine charts, publications, and equipment as required by §§164.33 through 164.41 of this part.

(1583) **§164.33 Charts and publications.**

(1584) (a) Each vessel must have the following:

(1585) (1) Marine charts of the area to be transited, published by the National Ocean Service, U.S. Army Corps of Engineers, or a river authority that—

(1586) (i) Are of a large enough scale and have enough detail to make safe navigation of the area possible; and

(1587) (ii) Are currently corrected.

(1588) (2) For the area to be transited, a currently corrected copy of, or applicable currently corrected extract from, each of the following publications:

(1589) (i) U.S. Coast Pilot.

(1590) (ii) Coast Guard Light List.

(1591) (3) For the area to be transited, the current edition of, or applicable current extract from:

(1592) (i) Tide tables published by the National Ocean Service.

(1593) (ii) Tidal current tables published by the National Ocean Service, or river current publication issued by the U.S. Army Corps of Engineers, or a river authority.

(1594) (b) As an alternative to the requirements for paragraph (a) of this section, a marine chart or publication, or applicable extract, published by a foreign government may be substituted for a U.S. chart and publication required by this section. The chart must be of large enough scale and have enough detail to make safe navigation of the area possible, and must be currently corrected. The publication, or applicable extract, must singly or in combination contain similar information to the U.S. Government publication to make safe navigation of the area possible. The publication, or applicable extract must be currently corrected, with the exceptions of tide and tidal current tables, which must be the current editions.

(1595) (c) As used in this section, "currently corrected" means corrected with changes contained in all Notices to Mariners published by Defense Mapping Agency Hydrographic/Topographic Center, or an equivalent foreign government publication, reasonably available to the vessel, and that is applicable to the vessel's transit.

(1596) **§164.35 Equipment: All vessels.**

(1597) Each vessel must have the following:

(1598) (a) A marine radar system for surface navigation.

(1599) (b) An illuminated magnetic steering compass, mounted in a binnacle, that can be read at the vessel's main steering stand.

(1600) (c) A current magnetic compass deviation table or graph or compass comparison record for the steering compass, in the wheelhouse.

(1601) (d) A gyrocompass.

(1602) (e) An illuminated repeater for the gyrocompass required by paragraph (d) of this section that is at the main steering stand, unless that gyrocompass is illuminated and is at the main steering stand.

(1603) (f) An illuminated rudder angle indicator in the wheelhouse.

(1604) (g) The following maneuvering information prominently displayed on a fact sheet in the wheelhouse:

(1605) (1) A turning circle diagram to port and starboard that shows the time and distance and advance and transfer required to alter course 90 degrees with maximum rudder angle and constant power settings, for either full and half speeds, or for full and slow speeds. For vessels whose turning circles are essentially the same for both directions, a diagram showing a turning circle in one direction, with a note on the diagram stating that turns to port and starboard are essentially the same, may be substituted.

(1606) (2) The time and distance to stop the vessel from either full and half speeds, or from full and slow speeds, while maintaining approximately the initial heading with minimum application of rudder.

(1607) (3) For each vessel with a fixed propeller, a table of shaft revolutions per minute for a representative range of speeds.

(1608) (4) For each vessel with a controllable pitch propeller, a table of control settings for a representative range of speeds.

(1609) (5) For each vessel that is fitted with an auxiliary device to assist in maneuvering, such as a bow thruster, a table of vessel speeds at which the auxiliary device is effective in maneuvering the vessel.

(1610) (6) The maneuvering information for the normal load and normal ballast condition for—

(1611) (i) Calm weather-wind 10 knots or less, calm sea;

(1612) (ii) No current;

(1613) (iii) Deep water conditions-water depth twice the vessel's draft or greater; and

(1614) (iv) Clean hull.

(1615) (7) At the bottom of the fact sheet, the following statement;

(1616) **Warning.**

(1617) The response of the (name of the vessel) may be different from that listed above if any of the following conditions, upon which the maneuvering information is based, are varied:

(1618) (1) Calm weather-wind 10 knots or less, calm sea;

(1619) (2) No current;

(1620) (3) Water depth twice the vessel's draft or greater;

(1621) (4) Clean hull; and

(1622) (5) Intermediate drafts or unusual trim.

(1623) (h) An echo depth sounding device.

(1624) (i) A device that can continuously record the depth readings of the vessel's echo depth sounding device, except when operating on the Great Lakes and their connecting and tributary waters.

(1625) (j) Equipment on the bridge for plotting relative motion.

(1626) (k) Simple operating instructions with a block diagram, showing the changeover procedures for remote steering gear control systems and steering gear power units, permanently displayed on the navigating bridge and in the steering gear compartment.

(1627) (l) An indicator readable from the centerline conning position showing the rate of revolution of each propeller, except when operating on the Great Lakes and their connecting and tributary waters.

(1628) (m) If fitted with controllable pitch propellers, an indicator readable from the centerline conning position showing the pitch and operational mode of such propellers, except when operating on the Great Lakes and their connecting and tributary waters.

(1629) (n) If fitted with lateral thrust propellers, an indicator readable from the centerline conning position showing the direction and amount of thrust of such propellers, except when operating on the Great Lakes and their connecting and tributary waters.

(1630) **§164.37 Equipment: Vessels of 10,000 gross tons or more.**

(1631) (a) Each vessel of 10,000 gross tons or more must have, in addition to the radar system under §164.35(a), a second marine radar system that operates independently of the first.

(1632) **Note:** Independent operation means two completely separate systems, from separate branch power supply circuits or distribution panels to antennas, so that failure of any component of one system will not render the other system inoperative.

(1633) (b) On each tanker of 10,000 gross tons or more that is subject to Section 5 of the Port and Tanker Safety Act of 1978 (46 U.S.C. 391a), the dual radar system required by this part must have a short range capability and a long range capability and each radar must have true north features consisting of a display that is stabilized in azimuth.

(1634) **§164.38 Automatic radar plotting aids (ARPA). (See 33 CFR 164.)**

(1635) **§164.39 Steering gear: Tankers. (See 33 CFR 164.)**

(1636) **§164.40 Devices to indicate speed and distance.**

(1637) (a) Each vessel required to be fitted with an Automatic Radar Plotting Aid (ARPA) under §164.38 must be fitted with a device to indicate speed and distance of the vessel either through the water, or over the ground. Vessels constructed prior to September 1, 1984, must have this equipment according to the following schedule:

(1638) (1) Each tank vessel constructed before September 1, 1984, operating on the navigable waters of the United States-

(1639) (i) If of 40,000 gross tons or more, by January 1, 1985;

(1640) (ii) If of 10,000 gross tons or more but less than 40,000 gross tons, by January 1, 1986.

(1641) (2) Each self-propelled vessel constructed before September 1, 1984, that is not a tank vessel, operating on the navigable waters of the United States-

(1642) (i) If of 40,000 gross tons or more, by September 1, 1986;

(1643) (ii) If of 20,000 gross tons or more, but less than 40,000 gross tons, by September 1, 1987;

(1644) (iii) If of 15,000 gross tons or more, but less than 20,000 gross tons, by September 1, 1988.

(1645) (b) The device must meet the following specifications:

(1646) (1) The display must be easily readable on the bridge by day or night.

(1647) (2) Errors in the indicated speed, when the vessel is operating free from shallow water effect, and from the effects of wind, current, and tide, should not exceed 5 percent of the speed of the vessel, or 0.5 knot, whichever is greater.

(1648) (3) Errors in the indicated distance run, when the vessel is operating free from shallow water effect, and from the effects of wind, current, and tide, should not exceed 5 percent of the distance run of the vessel in one hour or 0.5 nautical mile in each hour, whichever is greater.

(1649) **§164.41 Electronic position fixing devices.**

(1650) (a) Each vessel calling at a port in the continental United States, including Alaska south of Cape Prince of Wales, except each vessel owned or bareboat chartered and operated by the United States, or by a state or its political subdivision, or by a foreign nation, and not engaged in commerce, must have one of the following:

(1651) (1) A Type I or II LORAN C receiver as defined in Section 1.2(e), meeting Part 2 (Minimum Performance Standards) of the Radio Technical Commission for Marine Services (RTCM) Paper 12-78/DO-100 dated December 20, 1977, entitled "Minimum Performance Standards (MPS) Marine Loran-C Receiving Equipment". Each receiver installed on or after June 1, 1982, must have a label with the information required under paragraph (b) of this section. If the receiver is installed before June 1, 1982, the receiver must have the label with the information required under paragraph (b) by June 1, 1985.

(1652) (2) A satellite navigation receiver with:

(1653) (i) Automatic acquisition of satellite signals after initial operator settings have been entered; and

(1654) (ii) Position updates derived from satellite information during each usable satellite pass.

(1655) (3) A system that is found by the Commandant to meet the intent of the statements of availability, coverage, and accuracy for the U.S. Coastal Confluence Zone (CCZ) contained in the U.S. "Federal Radionavigation Plan" (Report No. DOD-NO 4650.4-P, I or No. DOT-TSC-RSPA-80-16, I). A person desiring a finding by the Commandant under this subparagraph must submit a written application describing the device to the Office of Navigation Safety and Waterway Services, 2100 Second Street, SW., Washington, DC 20593-0001. After reviewing the application, the Commandant may request additional information to establish whether or not the device meets the intent of the Federal Radionavigation Plan.

(1656) **Note.**–The Federal Radionavigation Plan is available from the National Technical Information Service, Springfield, Va. 22161, with the following Government Accession Numbers:

(1657)   Vol 1, ADA 116468

(1658)   Vol 2, ADA 116469

(1659)   Vol 3, ADA 116470

(1660)   Vol 4, ADA 116471

(1661) (b) Each label required under paragraph (a)(1) of this section must show the following:

(1662) (1) The name and address of the manufacturer.

(1663) (2) The following statement by the manufacturer:

(1664) This receiver was designed and manufactured to meet Part 2 (Minimum Performance Standards) of the RTCM MPS for Marine Loran-C Receiving Equipment.

(1665) **§164.42 Rate of turn indicator.**

(1666) Each vessel of 100,000 gross tons or more constructed on or after September 1, 1984, shall be fitted with a rate of turn indicator.

(1667) **§164.51 Deviations from rules: Emergency.**

(1668) Except for the requirements of §164.53(b), in an emergency, any person may deviate from any rule in this part to the extent necessary to avoid endangering persons, property, or the environment.

(1669) **§164.53 Deviations from rules and reporting: Nonoperating equipment.**

(1670) (a) If during a voyage any equipment required by this part stops operating properly, the person directing the movement of the vessel may continue to the next port of call, subject to the directions of the District Commander or the Captain of the Port, as provided by 33 CFR 160.

(1671) (b) If the vessel's radar, radio navigation receivers, gyrocompass, echo depth sounding device, or primary steering gear stops operating properly, the person directing the movement of the vessel must report or cause to be reported that it is not operating properly to the nearest Captain of the Port, District Commander, or, if participating in a Vessel Traffic Service, to the Vessel Traffic Center, as soon as possible.

(1672) **§164.55 Deviations from rules: Continuing operation or period of time.**

(1673) The Captain of the Port, upon written application, may authorize a deviation from any rule in this part if he determines that the deviation does not impair the safe navigation of the vessel under anticipated conditions and will not result in a violation of the rules for preventing collisions at sea. The authorization may be issued for vessels operating in the waters under the jurisdiction of the Captain of the Port for any continuing operation or period of time the Captain of the Port specifies.

(1674) **§164.61 Marine casualty reporting and record retention.**

(1675) When a vessel is involved in a marine casualty as defined in 46 CFR 4.03-1, the master or person in charge of the vessel shall–

(1676) (a) Ensure compliance with 46 CFR 4.05, "Notice of Marine Casualty and Voyage Records," and

(1677) (b) Ensure that the voyage records required by 46 CFR 4.05-15 are retained for–

(1678) (1) 30 days after the casualty if the vessel remains in the navigable waters of the United States; or

(1679) (2) 30 days after the return of the vessel to a United States port if the vessel departs the navigable waters of the United States within 30 days after the marine casualty.

Part 165–Regulated Navigation Areas and Limited Access Areas

Subpart A–General

(1680) **§165.1 Purpose of part.**

(1681) The purpose of this part is to–

(1682) (a) Prescribe procedures for establishing different types of limited or controlled access areas and regulated navigation areas;

(1683) (b) Prescribe general regulations for different types of limited or controlled access areas and regulated navigation areas;

(1684) (c) Prescribe specific requirements for established areas; and

(1685) (d) List specific areas and their boundaries.

(1686) **§165.5 Establishment procedures.**

(1687) (a) A safety zone, security zone, or regulated navigation area may be established on the initiative of any authorized Coast Guard official.

(1688) (b) Any person may request that a safety zone, security zone, or regulated navigation area be established. Except as provided in paragraph (c) of this section, each request must be submitted in writing to either the Captain of the Port or District Commander having jurisdiction over the location as described in 33 CFR 3, and including the following:

(1689) (1) The name of the person submitting the request;

(1690) (2) The location and boundaries of the safety zone, security zone, or regulated navigation area;

(1691) (3) The date, time, and duration that the safety zone, security zone, or regulated navigation area should be established;

(1692) (4) A description of the activities planned for the safety zone, security zone, or regulated navigation area;

(1693) (5) The nature of the restrictions or conditions desired; and

(1694) (6) The reason why the safety zone, security zone, or regulated navigation area is necessary.

(1695) (Requests for safety zones, security zones, and regulated navigation areas are approved by the Office of Management and Budget under control numbers 2115-0076, 2115-0219, and 2115-0087.)

(1696) (c) Safety Zones and Security Zones. If, for good cause, the request for a safety zone or security zone is made less than 5 working days before the zone is to be established, the request may be made orally, but it must be followed by a written request within 24 hours.

(1697) **§165.7 Notification.**

(1698) (a) The establishment of these limited access areas and regulated navigation areas is considered rulemaking. The procedures used to notify persons of the establishment of these areas vary depending upon the circumstances and emergency conditions. Notification may be made by marine broadcasts, local notice to mariners, local news media, distribution in leaflet form, and on-scene oral notice, as well as publication in the Federal Register.

(1699) (b) Notification normally contains the physical boundaries of the area, the reasons for the rule, its estimated duration, and the method of obtaining authorization to enter the area, if applicable, and special navigational rules, if applicable.

(1700) (c) Notification of the termination of the rule is usually made in the same form as the notification of its establishment.

(1701) **§165.8 Geographic coordinates.**

(1702) Geographic coordinates expressed in terms of latitude or longitude, or both, are not intended for plotting on maps or charts whose referenced horizonal datum is the North American Datum of 1983 (NAD 83), unless such geographic coordinates are expressly labeled NAD 83. Geographic coordinates without the NAD 83 reference may be plotted on maps or charts referenced to NAD 83 only after application of the appropriate corrections that are published on the particular map or chart being used.

Subpart B–Regulated Navigation Areas

(1703) **§165.10 Regulated navigation area.**

(1704) A regulated navigation area is a water area within a defined boundary for which regulations for vessels navigating within the area have been established under this part.

(1705) **§165.11 Vessel operating requirements (regulations).**

(1706) Each District Commander may control vessel traffic in an area which is determined to have hazardous conditions, by issuing regulations–

(1707) (a) Specifying times of vessel entry, movement, or departure to, from, within, or through ports, harbors, or other waters;

(1708) (b) Establishing vessel size, speed, draft limitations, and operating conditions; and

(1709) (c) Restricting vessel operation, in a hazardous area or under hazardous conditions, to vessels which have particular operating characteristics or capabilities which are considered necessary for safe operation under the circumstances.

(1710) **§165.13 General regulations.**

(1711) (a) The master of a vessel in a regulated navigation area shall operate the vessel in accordance with the regulations contained in Subpart F.

(1712) (b) No person may cause or authorize the operation of a vessel in a regulated navigation area contrary to the regulations in this Part.

Subpart C–Safety Zones

(1713) **§165.20 Safety zones.**

(1714) A Safety Zone is a water area, shore area, or water and shore area to which, for safety or environmental purposes, access is limited to authorized persons, vehicles, or vessels. It may be stationary and described by fixed limits or it may be described as a zone around a vessel in motion.

(1715) **§165.23 General regulations.**

(1716) Unless otherwise provided in this part–

(1717) (a) No person may enter a safety zone unless authorized by the COTP or the District Commander;

(1718) (b) No person may bring or cause to be brought into a safety zone any vehicle, vessel, or object unless authorized by the COTP or the District Commander;

(1719) (c) No person may remain in a safety zone or allow any vehicle, vessel, or object to remain in a safety zone unless authorized by the COTP or the District Commander; and

(1720) (d) Each person in a safety zone who has notice of a lawful order or direction shall obey the order or direction of the COTP or District Commander issued to carry out the purposes of this subpart.

Subpart D–Security Zones
(1721) **§165.30 Security zones.**
(1722) (a) A security zone is an area of land, water, or land and water which is so designated by the Captain of the Port or District Commander for such time as is necessary to prevent damage or injury to any vessel or waterfront facility, to safeguard ports, harbors, territories, or waters of the United States or to secure the observance of the rights and obligations of the United States.
(1723) (b) The purpose of a security zone is to safeguard from destruction, loss, or injury from sabotage or other subversive acts, accidents, or other causes of a similar nature–
(1724) (1) Vessels,
(1725) (2) Harbors,
(1726) (3) Ports and
(1727) (4) Waterfront facilities– in the United States and all territory and water, continental or insular, that is subject to the jurisdiction of the United States.
(1728) **§165.33 General regulations.**
(1729) Unless otherwise provided in the special regulations in Subpart F of this part–
(1730) (a) No person or vessel may enter or remain in a security zone without the permission of the Captain of the Port;
(1731) (b) Each person and vessel in a security zone shall obey any direction or order of the Captain of the Port;
(1732) (c) The Captain of the Port may take possession and control of any vessel in the security zone;
(1733) (d) The Captain of the Port may remove any person, vessel, article, or thing from a security zone;
(1734) (e) No person may board, or take or place any article or thing on board, any vessel in a security zone without the permission of the Captain of the Port; and
(1735) (f) No person may take or place any article or thing upon any waterfront facility in a security zone without the permission of the Captain of the Port.

Subpart E–Restricted Waterfront Areas
(1736) **§165.40 Restricted Waterfront Areas.**
(1737) The Commandant, may direct the COTP to prevent access to waterfront facilities, and port and harbor areas, including vessels and harbor craft therein. This section may apply to persons who do not possess the credentials outlined in 33 CFR 125.09 when certain shipping activities are conducted that are outlined in 33 CFR 125.15.

Subpart F–Specific Regulated Navigation Areas and Limited Access Areas
(1738) **§165.121 Safety Zone Rhode Island Sound, Narragansett Bay, Providence River.**
(1739) (a) Location. The following areas are established as safety zones:
(1740) (1) For Liquefied Petroleum Gas (LPG) vessels while at anchor in the waters of Rhode Island Sound; in position 41°25N., 71°23W., a Safety Zone with a radius of one-half mile around the LPG vessel.
(1741) (2) For Liquefied Petroleum Gas (LPG) vessels while transitting Narragansett Bay and the Providence River; a moving Safety Zone from a distance of two (2) miles ahead to one (1) mile astern to the limits of the navigable channel around the LPG vessel.
(1742) (3) For Liquefied Petroleum Gas (LPG) vessels while moored at the LPG facility, Port of Providence; a

Safety Zone within 50 feet around the vessel. No vessel shall moor within 400 feet from the LPG vessel. All vessels transitting the area are to proceed with caution to minimize the effects of wake around the LPG vessel.
(1743) (4) For Liquefied Petroleum Gas (LPG) vessels while moored with manifolds connected at the LPG Facility, Port of Providence; a Safety Zone within a 100 foot radius around the shoreside manifold while connected. This is in addition to the requirements for LPG vessels while moored at the LPG Facility, Port of Providence.
(1744) (b) The Captain of the Port Providence will notify the maritime community of periods during which this safety zone will be in effect by providing advance notice of scheduled arrivals and departures of LPG vessels via Marine Safety Information Radio Broadcast on VHF Marine Band Radio, Channel 22 (157.1 MHz).
(1745) (c) Regulations. The general regulations governing safety zones contained in §165.23 apply.
(1746) **§165.130 Sandy Hook Bay, New Jersey-security zone.**
(1747) (a) Naval Ammunition Depot Piers.–The waters within the following boundaries are a security zone-A line beginning on the shore at
(1748) 40°25'57"N., 74°04'32"W.; then to
(1749) 40°27'52.5"N., 74°03'14.5"W.; then to
(1750) 40°27'28.3"N., 74°02'12.4"W.; then to
(1751) 40°26'29.2"N., 74°02'53"W.; then to
(1752) 40°26'31.1"N., 74°02'57.2"W.; then to
(1753) 40°25'27.3"N., 74°03'41"W.; then along the shoreline to the beginning point.
(1754) (b) Terminal Channel. The waters within the following boundaries are a security zone-A line beginning at
(1755) 40°27'41.2"N., 74°02'46"W.; then to
(1756) 40°28'27"N., 74°02'17.2"W.; then to
(1757) 40°28'21.1"N., 74°02'00"W.; then to
(1758) 40°28'07.8"N., 74°02'22"W.; then to
(1759) 40°27'39.8"N., 74°02'41.4"W.; then to the beginning.
(1760) (c) The following rules apply to the security zone established in paragraph (b) of this section (Terminal Channel) instead of the rule in §165.33(a)
(1761) (1) No vessel shall anchor, stop, remain or drift without power at any time in the security zone.
(1762) (2) No vessel shall enter, cross, or otherwise navigate in the security zone when a public vessel, or any other vessel, that cannot safely navigate outside the Terminal Channel, is approaching or leaving the Naval Ammunition Depot Piers at Leonardo, New Jersey.
(1763) (3) Vessels may enter or cross the security zone, except as provided in paragraph (c)(2) of this section.
(1764) (4) No person may swim in the security zone.
(1765) **§165.140 New London Harbor, Connecticut-security zone.**
(1766) (a) Security zones–
(1767) (1) Security Zone A. The waters of the Thames River off State Pier enclosed by a line beginning at the midpoint of the southeast face of State Pier; then to
(1768) 41°21'24"N., 72°05'21.2"W.; then to
(1769) 41°21'26.2"N., 72°05'19.3"W.; then to
(1770) 41°21'34"N., 72°05'18.1"W.; then extending northwest through buoy C15 to the shoreline at
(1771) 41°21'43.5"N., 72°05'23"W.; then along the shoreline and pier to the point of beginning.
(1772) (2) Security Zone B. The waters of the Thames River west of the Electric Boat Division Shipyard enclosed by a line beginning at a point on the shoreline at
(1773) 41°20'22.1"N., 72°04'52.8"W.; then west to
(1774) 41°20'28.7"N., 72°05'03.5"W.; then to
(1775) 41°20'53.3"N., 72°05'06.6"W.; then to

(1776) 41°21'03"N., 72°05'06.7"W.; then due east to a point on the shoreline at

(1777) 41°21'03"N., 72°05'00"W.; then along the shoreline to the point of beginning.

(1778) (3) Security Zone C. The waters of the Thames River, west of the Naval Submarine Base, New London, Conn., enclosed by a line beginning at a point on the shoreline at

(1779) 41°23'15.8"N., 72°05'17.9"W.; then to

(1780) 41°23'15.8"N., 72°05'22"W.; then to

(1781) 41°23'25.9"N., 72°05'29.9"W.; then to

(1782) 41°23'33.8"N., 72°05'34.7"W.; then to

(1783) 41°23'37.0"N., 72°05'38.0"W.; then to

(1784) 41°23'41.0"N., 72°05'40.3"W.; then to

(1785) 41°23'47.2"N., 72°05'42.3"W.; then to

(1786) 41°23'53.8"N., 72°05'43.7"W.; then to

(1787) 41°23'59.8"N., 72°05'43.0"W.; then to

(1788) 41°24'12.4"N., 72°05'43.2"W.; then to a point on the shoreline at

(1789) 41°24'14.4"N., 72°05'38"W.; then along the shoreline to the point of beginning.

(1790) (4) Security Zone D. The waters of the Thames River east of the Naval Underwater Systems Center, New London, enclosed by a line beginning at

(1791) 41°20'36.0"N., 72°05'34.1"W.; then to

(1792) 41°20'36.0"N., 72°05'20"W.; then to

(1793) 41°20'41"N., 72°05'20"W.; then to

(1794) 41°20'43.7"N., 72°05'25.9"W.; then to

(1795) 41°20'41.6"N., 72°05'35.0"W.; then along the shoreline to the points of beginning.

(1796) (b) Special regulation. Section 165.33 does not apply to public vessels when operating in Security Zones A or B, or to vessels owned by, under hire to, or performing work for the Electric Boat Division when operating in Security Zone B.

(1797) §165.150 New Haven Harbor, Quinnipiac River, Mill River.

(1798) (a) The following is a regulated navigation area: The waters surrounding the Tomlinson Bridge located within a line extending from a point A at the southeast corner of the Wyatt terminal dock at 41°17'50"N., 72°54'36"W.; thence along a line 126°T to point B at the southwest corner of the Gulf facility at 41°17'42"N., 72°54'21"W.; thence north along the shoreline to point C at the northwest corner of the Texaco terminal dock 41°17'57"N., 72°54'06"W.; thence along a line 303°T to point D at the west bank of the mouth of the Mill River 41°18'05"N., 72°54'23"W.; thence south along the shoreline to point A.

(1799) (b) Regulations. (1) No person may operate a vessel or tow a barge in this Regulated Navigation Area in violation of these regulations.

(1800) (2) Applicability. The regulations apply to barges with a freeboard greater than ten feet and to any vessel towing or pushing these barges on outbound transits of the Tomlinson Bridge.

(1801) (3) Regulated barges may not transit the bridge—

(1802) (i) During the period from one hour to five hours after high water slack,

(1803) (ii) When the wind speed at the bridge is greater than twenty knots, and

(1804) (iii) With the barge being towed on a hawser, stern first.

(1805) (4) Regulated barges with a beam greater than fifty feet must be pushed ahead through the bridge.

(1806) (5) If the tug operator does not have a clear view over the barge when pushing ahead, the operator shall post a lookout on the barge with a means of communication with the operator.

(1807) (6) Regulated barges departing the Mill River may transit the bridge only between sunrise and sunset. Barges must be pushed ahead of the tug, bow first, with a second tug standing by to assist at the bow.

(1808) (7) Nothing in this section is intended to relieve any person from complying with—

(1809) (i) Applicable Navigation and Pilot Rules for Inland Waters;

(1810) (ii) Any other laws or regulations;

(1811) (iii) Any order or direction of the Captain of the Port.

(1812) (8) The Captain of the Port, New Haven, may issue an authorization to deviate from any rule in this section if the COTP finds that an alternate operation can be done safely.

(1813) §165.155 Northville Industries Offshore Platform, Riverhead, Long Island, New York-safety zone.

(1814) (a) The following area is established as a safety zone during the specified condition:

(1815) (1) The waters within a 500 yard radius of the Northville Industries Offshore Platform, Long Island, New York, 1 mile North of the Riverhead shoreline at 41°00'N., 072°38'W., while a liquefied Petroleum Gas (LPG) vessel is moored at the Offshore Platform. The safety zone remains in effect until the LPG vessel departs the Offshore Platform.

(1816) (b) The general regulations governing safety zone contained in 33 CFR 165.23 apply.

(1817) (c) The Captain of the Port will notify the maritime community of periods during which this safety zone will be in effect by providing notice of scheduled moorings at the Northville Industries Offshore Platform of LPG vessels via Marine Safety Information Radio Broadcast.

(1818) §165.160 New York, New Jersey, Sandy Hook Channel, Raritan Bay, Arthur Kill-Safety Zone.

(1819) (a) The following areas are established as Safety Zones during the specified conditions:

(1820) (1) For incoming tank vessels loaded with Liquefied Petroleum Gas, the waters within a 100 yard radius of the LPG carrier while the vessel transits the Sandy Hook Channel, Raritan Bay East and West Reach, Ward Point Bend East and West Reach, and the Arthur Kill to the LPG receiving facility. The Safety Zone remains in effect until the LPG vessel is moored at the LPG receiving facility in the Arthur Kill.

(1821) (2) For outgoing tank vessels loaded with LPG, the waters within a 100 yard radius of the LPG carrier while the vessel departs the LPG facility and transits the Arthur Kill, Ward Point Bend West and East Reach, Raritan Bay West and East Reach, and Sandy Hook Channel. The safety zone remains in effect until the LPG vessel passes the Scotland Lighted Horn Buoy "S" (LLNR 1619) at the entrance to the Sandy Hook Channel.

(1822) (b) The general regulations governing safety zones contained in 33 CFR 165.23 apply.

(1823) (c) The Captain of the Port will notify the maritime community of periods during which this safety zone will be in effect by providing advance notice of scheduled arrivals and departures of loaded LPG vessels via a Marine Safety Information Radio Broadcast.

Part 166-Shipping Safety Fairways

(1824) **Subpart A-General**

(1825) §166.100 Purpose.-The purpose of these regulations is to establish and designate shipping safety fairways and fairway anchorages to provide unobstructed approaches for vessels using U.S. ports.

(1826) §166.103 Geographic Coordinates.

(1827) Geographic coordinates expressed in terms of latitude or longitude, or both, are not intended for plotting on maps or charts whose referenced horizontal datum is the North American Datum of 1983 (NAD 83), unless such geographic coordinates are expressly labeled NAD 83. Geographic coordinates without the NAD 83 reference may be plotted on maps or charts referenced to NAD 83 only after application of the appropriate corrections that are published on the particular map or chart being used.

(1828) **§166.105 Definitions.**

(1829) (a) "Shipping safety fairway" or "fairway" means a lane or corridor in which no artificial island or fixed structure, whether temporary or permanent, will be permitted. Temporary underwater obstacles may be permitted under certain conditions described for specific areas in Subpart B. Aids to navigation approved by the U.S. Coast Guard may be established in a fairway.

(1830) (b) "Fairway anchorage" means an anchorage area contiguous to and associated with a fairway, in which fixed structures may be permitted within certain spacing limitations, as described for specific areas in Subpart B.

(1831) **§166.110 Modification of areas.**

(1832) Fairways and fairway anchorages are subject to modification in accordance with 33 U.S.C. 1223(c); 92 Stat. 1473. Subpart B-Designation of Fairways and Fairway Anchorages (in part)

(1833) **§166.500 Areas along the Atlantic Coast.**

(1834) (a) Purpose. Fairways, as described in this section are established to control the erection of structures therein to provide safe vessel routes along the Atlantic Coast.

(1835) (b) Designated areas.-(1) Off New York Shipping Safety Fairway.

(1836) (i) Nantucket to Ambrose Safety Fairway. The area enclosed by rhumb lines, (North American Datum of 1927 (NAD-27)), joining points at:

(1837) 40°32'20"N., 73°04'57"W.
(1838) 40°30'58"N., 71°58'25"W.
(1839) 40°34'07"N., 70°19'23"W.
(1840) 40°35'37"N., 70°14'09"W.
(1841) 40°30'37"N., 70°14'00"W.
(1842) 40°32'07"N., 70°19'19"W.
(1843) 40°28'58"N., 72°58'25"W.
(1844) 40°27'20"N., 73°04'57"W.

(1845) (ii) Ambrose to Nantucket Safety Fairway. The area enclosed by rhumb lines, NAD-27, joining points at:

(1846) 40°24'20"N., 73°04'58"W.
(1847) 40°22'58"N., 72°58'26"W.
(1848) 40°26'07"N., 70°19'09"W.
(1849) 40°27'37"N., 70°13'46"W.
(1850) 40°22'37"N., 70°13'36"W.
(1851) 40°24'07"N., 70°19'05"W.
(1852) 40°20'58"N., 72°58'26"W.
(1853) 40°19'20"N., 73°04'58"W.

Part 167-Offshore Traffic Separation Schemes

(1854) **Subpart A-General**

(1855) **§167.1 Purpose.** The purpose of the regulations in this part is to establish and designate traffic separation schemes and precautionary areas to provide access routes for vessels proceeding to and from U.S. ports.

(1856) **§167.5 Definitions.**

(1857) (a) "Traffic separation scheme" (TSS) means a designated routing measure which is aimed at the separation of opposing streams of traffic by appropriate means and by the establishment of traffic lanes.

(1858) (b) "Traffic lane" means an area within defined limits in which one-way traffic is established. Natural obstacles, including those forming separation zones, may constitute a boundary.

(1859) (c) "Separation zone or line" means a zone or line separating the traffic lanes in which ships are proceeding in opposite or nearly opposite directions; or separating a traffic lane from the adjacent sea area; or separating traffic lanes designated for particular classes of ships proceeding in the same direction.

(1860) (d) "Precautionary area" means a routing measure comprising an area within defined limits where ships must navigate with particular caution and within which the direction of traffic flow may be recommended.

(1861) **§166.10 Operating rules.**

(1862) The operator of a vessel in a TSS shall comply with Rule 10 of the International Regulations for Preventing Collisions at Sea, 1972, as amended.

(1863) **§167.15 Modification of schemes.**

(1864) (a) A traffic separation scheme or precautionary area described in this Part may be permanently amended in accordance with 33 U.S.C. 1223 (92 Stat. 1473), and with international agreements.

(1865) (b) A traffic separation scheme or precautionary area in this Part may be temporarily adjusted by the Commandant of the Coast Guard in an emergency, or to accommodate operations which would create an undue hazard for vessels using the scheme or which would contravene Rule 10 of the International Regulations for Preventing Collisions at Sea, 1972. Adjustment may be in the form of a temporary traffic lane shift, a temporary suspension of a section of the scheme, a temporary precautionary area overlaying a lane, or other appropriate measure. Adjustments will only be made where, in the judgment of the Coast Guard, there is no reasonable alternative means of conducting an operation and navigation safety will not be jeopardized by the adjustment. Notice of adjustments will be made in the appropriate Notice to Mariners and in the Federal Register. Requests by members of the public for temporary adjustments to traffic separation schemes must be submitted 150 days prior to the time the adjustment is desired. Such Requests, describing the interference that would otherwise occur to a TSS, should be submitted to the District Commander of the Coast Guard District in which the TSS is located. Atlantic East Coast

(1866) **§167.150 Off New York Traffic Separation Scheme and Precautionary Areas.**

(1867) The specific areas in the Off New York Traffic Separation Scheme and Precautionary Areas are described in §§167.151, 167.152, 167.153, 167.154, and 167.155 of this chapter.

(1868) **§167.151 Precautionary areas.**

(1869) (a) A circular precautionary area with a radius of seven miles is established centered upon Ambrose Light in geographic position

(1870) 40°27.50'N., 73°49.90'W.

(1871) (b) A precautionary area is established between the traffic separation scheme "Eastern Approach, off Nantucket" and the traffic separation scheme "In the Approach to Boston, Massachusetts." (1) The precautionary area is bounded to the east by a circle of radius 15.5 miles, centered upon geographic position

(1872) 40°35.00'N., 69°00.00'W., and is intersected by the traffic separation scheme "In the Approach to Boston, Massachusetts" and "Off New York" at the following geographic positions:

(1873) 40°50.33'N., 68°57.00'W.
(1874) 40°23.75'N., 69°14.63'W.

(279) The cove has several boatyards. Berths, electricity, gasoline, water, diesel fuel, ice, marine supplies, wet and dry storage, launching ramps, lifts to 21 tons, and complete engine and hull repairs are available. The **harbormaster** in the cove controls anchoring and berthing; contact can be made through the Warwick City Hall.

(280) From **Sandy Point**, the eastern extremity of Potowomut Neck, shoals with depths of 2 to 9 feet extend northeasterly for about 0.6 mile. Extensive shoals extend off the eastern side of Warwick Neck to Ohio Ledge. **Rocky Point** is on the eastern side of the neck, 1.7 miles north-northeastward of Warwick Point.

(281) The natural channel between the shoals off Warwick Neck and the shoals northward of Patience and Prudence Islands has depths of 19 to 50 feet. A buoy marks the shoal off **Providence Point**, the northernmost point of Prudence Island.

(282) **Chart 13218.**–The shoreline of **Point Judith Neck** between West Passage and Point Judith should be given a berth of at least 0.6 mile. From Narragansett Pier to **Black Point**, a rocky promontory 1.9 miles southward, the shoreline is a rugged rocky ledge with deep water close inshore. The waters between Black Point and Point Judith are boulder-strewn and shoal up gradually.

(283) Three very prominent landmarks are Point Judith Light, the elevated water tank 1.7 miles north of Point Judith, and Hazard's Tower, a high, square stone tower 0.5 mile south of Narragansett Pier. Closer inshore the stone bathing pavilion at the State-operated **Scarborough Beach**, 0.5 mile south of Black Point, and an open stone tower on a house 0.4 mile north of Black Point are prominent.

7. BLOCK ISLAND SOUND

(1) This chapter describes Block Island Sound, Fishers Island Sound, Gardiners Bay, Little Peconic Bay, Great Peconic Bay, and the ports and harbors in the area, the more important of which are Point Judith Harbor, Great Salt Pond, Stonington, Mystic Harbor, and Greenport.

(2) **COLREGS Demarcation Lines.** –The lines established for this part of the coast are described in **80.150 and 80.155,** chapter 2.

(3) **Charts 13205, 13215.–Block Island North Reef** is a is a deep navigable waterway forming the eastern approach to Long Island Sound, Fishers Island Sound, and Gardiners Bay from the Atlantic Ocean. The sound is a link for waterborne commerce between Cape Cod and Long Island Sound. It has two entrances from the Atlantic; an eastern entrance from Rhode Island Sound between Block Island and Point Judith, and a southern entrance between Block Island and Montauk Point. The sound is connected with Long Island Sound by The Race and other passages to the southwestward, and with Fishers Island Sound by several passages between rocky reefs from Watch Hill Point to East Point, Fishers Island.

(4) The north shoreline of Block Island Sound and Fishers Island Sound from Point Judith to New London is generally rocky and broken with short stretches of sandy beach. Many inlets and harbors, especially in the vicinity of Fishers Island, afford harbors of refuge for vessels. Most of the rocks and shoals near the channels are marked with navigational aids.

(5) The southern part of Block Island Sound is bounded by Block Island on the east, the eastern extremity of Long Island, and Gardiners Island on the west. Plum Island and Fishers Island are at the western end of the sound.

(6) The deep water in the central part of Block Island Sound will accommodate vessels of the greatest draft.

(7) Westward of Gardiners Island, enclosed between the northeastern and eastern ends of Long Island, are Gardiners Bay, Shelter Island Sound, Little Peconic Bay, and Great Peconic Bay. This area is well protected but generally shallow, and is not suited for deep-draft vessels. The shoreline is marked by many indentations and shallow harbors. These waters are much used by commercial fishing vessels and small pleasure craft because of the protection afforded and the many anchorages.

(8) **Block Island North Reef** is a sand shoal with depths of 14 feet or less extending 1 mile northward from **Sandy Point** at the north end of Block Island. The shoal should be avoided by all vessels; its depths change frequently, and its position is also subject to a slow change. It is practically steep-to on all sides, so that soundings alone cannot be depended on to clear it. A lighted bell buoy is 1.5 miles northward of the point.

(9) **Southwest Ledge,** 5.5 miles west-southwestward of Block Island Southeast Light, has a least known depth of 23 feet and is marked on its southwest side by Southwest Ledge Lighted Bell Buoy 2. Rocky patches with least depths of 27 and 29 feet extend 1.5 miles northeastward from the ledge. The sea breaks on the shoaler places on the ledge in heavy weather.

(10) Several other dangers that must be guarded against are northward and westward of Southwest Ledge Lighted Bell Buoy 2. These dangers are: two obstructions, about 300 yards apart, covered 31 and 32 feet, marked by a lighted buoy, about 2.2 miles 280° from the lighted bell buoy; and two obstructions, cleared to a depth of 35 feet, about 0.75 mile north of the lighted bell buoy.

(11) The deepest passage in the southern entrance to Block Island Sound is just westward of Southwest Ledge and has a width of over 2 miles; this is the best passage for deep-draft vessels. In heavy weather vessels desiring to enter the sound westward of Block Island should pass westward of Southwest Ledge Lighted Bell Buoy 2, taking care to pass clear of the obstructions mentioned above.

(12) Between the inner patch of rocks and the shoals, which extend 0.9 mile from Block Island, is a channel 1.3 miles wide, with a depth of about 34 feet. Vessels using this channel round the southwest end of Block Island at a distance of 1.5 miles. It is not advisable to use this passage during heavy weather.

(13) The entrance between Point Judith and Block Island is used by vessels coming from the bays and sounds eastward to Long Island Sound. The route generally used is through The Race. Tows of light barges and vessels of 14 feet or less draft sometimes go through Fishers Island Sound, especially during daylight with a smooth sea. This entrance is clear with the exception of Block Island North Reef and the numerous large boulders extending about 4 miles south-southeastward of Point Judith. The coast from Point Judith nearly to Watch Hill should be given a berth of over 1 mile, avoiding the broken ground with depths less than 30 feet.

(14) (Full tidal information, including daily predictions is given in the Tide Tables.)

(15) The effect of strong winds, in combination with the regular tidal action, may at times cause the water to fall several feet below or rise the same amount above the plane of reference of the chart. The mean range of **tide** throughout Block Island Sound varies from about 3 feet at Point Judith to 2 feet at Montauk Point.

(16) **Tidal current** data for a number of locations in Block Island Sound are given in the Tidal Current Tables. Current directions and velocities throughout the sound for each hour of the tidal cycle are shown on Tidal Current Charts, Block Island Sound and Eastern Long Island Sound.

(17) The tidal currents throughout Block Island Sound have considerable velocity; the greatest velocities occur in the vicinity of The Race and in the entrances between Montauk Point, Block Island, and Point Judith. Soundings alone cannot be depended upon to locate the position; the shoaling is generally abrupt in approaching the shores or dangers.

(18) In the middle of the passage between Point Judith and Block Island, the velocity is 0.7 knot. The flood sets westward, and the ebb eastward.

(19) In the passage between Block Island and Montauk Point, the flood sets generally northwestward and the ebb southeastward. In the middle of the passage the velocity is 1.5 knots on the flood and 1.9 knots on the ebb. About 1.2 miles eastward of Montauk Point, the flood sets 346°, ebb 162°, with a velocity of 2.8 knots.

(20) In Block Island Sound and in the eastern part of Long Island Sound, **fogs** are generally heaviest with southeast winds. In these waters the usual duration of a fog is from 4 to 12 hours, but periods of from 4 to 6 days have been known with very short clear intervals. In the autumn, **land fogs,** as they are termed locally, sometimes occur with

northerly breezes, but are generally burned off before midday.

(21) The Race may be said to be the only locality where tidal currents have any decided influence on the movements of the ice. Large quantities of floe ice usually pass through The Race during the ebb, especially if the wind is westerly, and in severe winters this ice causes some obstruction in Block Island Sound and around Montauk Point. These obstructions are the most extensive around the middle of February.

(22) **Weather.**-Land influences the weather only at the northern edge of the Sound, with a northerly wind. Otherwise the waters are open, similar to the nearby ocean. Winds from all other directions have ample time to increase in strength and the Sound can be as turbulent as any water off the coast. Wind speeds can be double those found on the coast, especially in winter, when average speeds of 16 to 17 knots are common. Gales occur up to 5 percent of the time in winter and are most likely from the west and northwest. Seas built by winds from the southeast through southwest are usually highest since there is no land to interfere with the fetch. Seas of 10 feet or more are likely 5 to 7 percent of the time in winter.

(23) Because of relatively cold water, summer fog occurs two to three times more often in these waters than in either Narragansett or Buzzard Bays. For example, in June visibilities drop below 1/2 mile nearly 9 percent of the time.

(24) **Pilotage, Block Island Sound and Long Island Sound.**-Pilotage is compulsary for foreign vessels under register in Block Island Sound and Long Island Sound. A vessel traversing Block Island is enroute to or from Long Island Sound. See Pilotage, Long Island Sound (indexed as such), chapter 8. Vessels bound for Long Island Sound ports may board pilots in the vicinity of Point Judith Lighted Whistle Buoy 2, within a 1-mile radius circle centered in 41°17.2'N., 71°30.4'W.

(25) **Chart 13217.**-Block Island, 5 miles long, is hilly with elevations up to about 200 feet. The shore of the island is fringed in most places by boulders and should be given a berth of over 0.5 mile even by small craft; the shoaling is generally abrupt in approaching the island.

(26) **Weather.**-Block Island, formed by glaciers, consists of nearly 7,000 acres and lies in the Atlantic Ocean about 12 miles east-northeast of Long Island and about the same distance south of Charlestown, R.I. Hence, the climate is typically maritime, but under conditions of extreme cold or heat the effect is felt on the island as well as on the mainland. Temperatures of -10°F and 95°F have been recorded.

(27) Summers are usually dry. Recorded rainfall for any 1 month ranges from a trace to 12.93 inches. In July and August maximum temperatures average 74°F. The island is too small to build up cumulonimbus clouds, and local thunderstorms do not occur. Fog occurs on 1 out of 4 days in the early summer, when the ocean is relatively cold.

(28) Winters are distinguished for their comparative mildness, maximums average 4° to 10°F above freezing and minimums average 25°F in February. Since the surface winds are usually easterly when snow begins it soon changes to rain or melts rapidly after it piles up. The ocean temperatures are of course always somewhat above freezing and not far off shore are relatively high.

(29) The ocean has a dampening effect on hot winds in summer and an accelerating effect on cold winds from the mainland in the winter. Katabatic winds from Narragansett Bay and Long Island reach as high as 35 knots when anticyclonic conditions prevail on the mainland in winter.

The wind velocity averages 15 knots for the year, but the mean is 17 knots in the winter, when gales are frequent. In the early fall most of the tropical storms moving up the coast affect the island to some extent.

(30) (See page T-3 for **Block Island climatological table.**)

(31) **Communications.**-A ferry operates daily from Galilee to Great Salt Pond or Old Harbor, carrying mail, passengers, freight, and vehicles. There is summer ferry service from Old Harbor to Providence, via Newport, and to New London. The island has telephone service to the mainland. Air service is also available.

(32) **Block Island Southeast Light** (41°09.2' N., 71°33.1'W.), 258 feet above the water, is shown from a steel tower on **Mohegan Bluffs** on the southeast point of the island. A radiobeacon is close east-southeast of the light.

(33) About 0.2 mile southeast of the light is the wreck of the large tanker SS LIGHTBURNE. The wreck is marked by a buoy. At **Clay Head,** on the northeast side of Block Island, is a lone white house on top of the bluff. Two nearby silos are conspicuous.

(34) **Block Island North Light** (41°13.7'N., 71°34.6'W.), 58 feet above the water, is shown from a black tower on a gray granite dwelling on Sandy Point at the north end of the island.

(35) **Old Harbor,** frequently used as a harbor of refuge, is an artificial harbor formed by two breakwaters on the east side of Block Island, 1.4 miles northward of Block Island Southeast Light. In March-November 1989, the controlling depth was 13 feet in the entrance, thence depths of 10 to 15 feet were available in the inner harbor anchorage with lesser depths along the north, northwest, and southwest sides, and thence 5½ feet was available in the basin in the southeast corner of the inner harbor. The harbor is occupied by pleasure craft during the summer. The eastern part of the inner harbor is left clear for the passage of the ferry to the wharf. The basin in the southeast corner of the inner harbor is usually occupied by fishing boats and local craft which tie up along the sides. Gasoline, diesel fuel, and berths are available. The **harbormaster** has an office at the Old Harbor town dock.

(36) The east breakwater extends about 300 yards northward of the entrance of the inner harbor, and is marked at its end by a light and fog signal. A bell buoy is 0.55 mile northward of the breakwater. A light marks the end of the breakwater on the west side at the entrance to the inner harbor.

(37) **Great Salt Pond (New Harbor),** on the west side of Block Island, is the best harbor in Block Island Sound for vessels of 15-foot draft or less. In easterly gales when the sea is too heavy to enter Old Harbor, a landing can be made at Great Salt Pond. The entrance, about 2 miles south-southwestward of Block Island North Light, is a dredged cut through the narrow beach. The southwestern side of the entrance is protected by a jetty, marked by a light and fog signal at its outer end and by a light at the inner end.

(38) In June 1987, the midchannel controlling depth in the entrance channel was 8½ feet. The channel is well marked, but subject to shoaling. Strangers should seek local knowledge before entering.

(39) The usual anchorage in Great Salt Pond is near the southeast end, off the ferry landing, in 15 to 48 feet, taking care to leave a fairway to the landing. A channel with a reported depth of about 8 feet in July 1981 leads to **Trim Pond,** where local fishing craft are moored.

(40) Small-craft facilities in Great Salt Pond can provide berths, electricity, gasoline, diesel fuel, water, ice, and marine supplies. The marina about 0.3 mile westward of the ferry landing had a reported depth of 16 feet at the face of

the dock in July 1981. Sail and engine repairs are available nearby.

(41) The mean range of tide is about 2.6 feet.

(42) Tidal currents in the entrance to Great Salt Pond have a velocity of 0.3 knot. (See Tidal Current Tables for predictions.)

(43) **Chart 13219.–Point Judith Light** (41°21.7'N., 71°28.9'W.), 65 feet above the water, is shown from an octagonal tower, 51 feet high, with the lower half white, upper half brown. The station has a fog signal and a radiobeacon. About 100 yards north of the light is **Point Judith Coast Guard Station.** A lighted whistle buoy is about 2.4 miles southward of the light. (See chart 13218.) A prominent elevated water tank is about 1.8 miles northward of the light, and another globular water tank is about 3 miles northwestward of the light.

(44) The area around Point Judith, including the approaches to Point Judith Harbor of Refuge, is irregular with rocky bottom and indications of boulders. Caution is advised to avoid the shoal spots, even with a smooth sea, and to exercise extra care where the depths are not more than 6 feet greater than the draft.

(45) **Point Judith Harbor of Refuge,** on the west side of Point Judith, is formed by a main V-shaped breakwater and two shorearm breakwaters extending to the shore. The harbor is easy of access for most vessels except with a heavy southerly sea. It is little used by tows. The only soft bottom in the harbor is found in the southern part of the deeper water enclosed by the main breakwater. On the north side the shoaling is gradual; the 18-foot curve is about 0.3 to 0.5 mile offshore.

(46) Near the central part of the harbor are two shoals; the northernmost one has depths of 14 to 18 feet, and the southernmost one has depths of 14 to 16 feet and is marked by a buoy.

(47) The area within the V-shaped breakwater affords protected anchorage for small craft. The breakwater should be given a berth of 200 yards to avoid broken and hard bottom; a rocky shoal area about 100 yards wide, paralleling the west side of the main breakwater northward from the angle should be avoided. A good berth for a vessel is on a line between Point Judith Harbor of Refuge East Entrance Light 3 and Point Judith Harbor of Refuge West Entrance Light 2, midway between them in 22 to 30 feet. This position falls on the edge of the east-west thorofare used by pleasure craft and fishing boats.

(48) In August 1984, a submerged obstruction was reported about 270 yards southeast of Point Judith Harbor of Refuge West Entrance Light 2 in about 41°21'37"N., 71°30'40"W. In July 1991, an obstruction, covered 5 feet, was reported in about 41°21'28"N., 71°30'20"W.

(49) The southern entrance to the Harbor of Refuge, known locally as the East Gap, is 400 yards wide; in July 1981, it had a reported controlling depth of about 24 feet with deeper water in the western half of the channel.

(50) The western entrance to the Harbor of Refuge, known locally as the West Gap, is 500 yards wide; in July 1981, it had a reported controlling depth of about 18 feet, with lesser depths on the north side of the entrance.

(51) **Tides and Currents.**–The mean range of tide in the Harbor of Refuge is 3.1 feet. The tidal currents have a velocity of about 0.7 knot at the south entrance. The currents off the west entrance are rotary, with a velocity at strength of 0.5 knot. (See Tidal Current Tables for predictions.)

(52) Considerably stronger currents have been reported to develop especially when the tide is ebbing.

(53) **Point Judith Pond** is a saltwater tidal pond entered between two rock jetties at **The Breachway** in the northwestern part of Point Judith Harbor of Refuge. The east jetty is marked near its seaward end by a daybeacon. The pond extends 3.3 miles northerly to the town of **Wakefield.** It is used extensively by small fishing vessels and pleasure craft, and numerous fish wharves are inside the entrance. The north end of Point Judith Pond affords good anchorage for boats of 4 feet draft or less during a heavy blow.

(54) The village of **Galilee** on the east side of the entrance and **Jerusalem** on the west side at **Succotach Point** have State piers and numerous small piers chiefly used by fishermen. A State fisheries laboratory is just above the State pier at Jerusalem. A State pier superintendent controls the State piers at Galilee and Jerusalem; his office is at the head of the Galilee State Pier.

(55) A channel with three dredged sections marked by buoys and a daybeacon extends from Point Judith Harbor of Refuge along the west side of the pond to the State Pier at Jerusalem, and thence northerly to the turning basin at Wakefield. A branch channel, on the east side, extends northeasterly from the entrance to the pond to the State Pier at Galilee, and into anchorage areas westward of Galilee and southward of Little Comfort Island.

(56) In February 1983, the controlling depths were 11 feet (13 feet at midchannel) to the junction with the Galilee branch channel, thence 11 feet to the State Pier at Jerusalem, thence in December 1985, 4½ feet to the turning basin at Wakefield with 6 feet in the basin except for shoaling to 5 feet along the west limit. In February 1983, the east branch channel had a controlling depth of 15 feet to the State Pier at Galilee, thence 11 feet (14 feet at midchannel) to the anchorage basin southward of Little Comfort Island, thence in October 1985, depths of 4½ to 7 feet were available in the anchorage except for shoaling to 1½ feet along the northeast limit. In February 1983, the anchorage westward of Galilee had depths of 10 feet.

(57) **Tides and Currents.**–The mean range of tide in the pond is 2.8 feet and occurs later than in the Harbor of Refuge by about 10 minutes just inside the entrance and 30 minutes at the north end. The tidal currents in the entrance have a velocity of 1.8 knots on the flood and 1.5 knots on the ebb, and cause slight rips and overfalls at changes of tide. Higher current velocities are reported to occur. (See Tidal Current Tables for predictions.)

(58) Several boatyards and marinas are at Galilee, Jerusalem, Wakefield, and at Snug Harbor, on the west side of the pond about 0.8 mile above the entrance. Berths, electricity, gasoline, diesel fuel, water, ice, marine supplies, storage, launching ramps, and hull and engine repairs are available. The largest marine railway in the area, at the southern end of the waterfront at Snug Harbor, can handle craft up to 150 feet long or 400 tons. In July 1981, a reported depth of 12 feet could be carried to the railway.

(59) Daily ferry service is available to Block Island from Galilee. Daily bus service is operated to Providence.

(60) **Potter Pond,** shallow and landlocked, is joined with Point Judith by a narrow channel near **Snug Harbor.** Local knowledge should be obtained before using this channel, which has depths of 2 to 4 feet and is crossed by overhead power and telephone cables with a clearance of 30 feet at the channel entrance and by a fixed highway bridge with a clearance of 5 feet about 0.4 mile above the entrance. A current of more than 3 knots develops through the channel on the ebb. The mean range of tide in the pond is about 1 foot, and it occurs about 2.5 hours later than in the Harbor of Refuge.

(61) **Chart 13215.**–From Point Judith to Watch Hill the shore is low and for the most part consists of sandy beaches which are broken by several projecting rocky points. Back from the immediate shore are areas of cultivation interspersed with rolling grass-covered or wooded hills. Except for Point Judith Pond, most pond outlets are used only by small local craft. The coast is fringed by broken ground and boulders in places, which should be avoided by deep-draft vessels where the depths are less than 36 to 42 feet.

(62) **Matunuck** is a summer resort about 3 miles west of Point Judith. Southwest of **Matunuck Point** is **Nebraska Shoal**, a patch of boulders covered 18 feet and marked by a buoy. The shoal is at the south end of broken ground, with depths less than 30 feet offshore; the water deepens abruptly around the patch.

(63) **Charlestown Breachway**, 4.5 miles westward of Matunuck Point, is a narrow inlet which leads to **Ninigret Pond**, also known as **Charlestown Pond**, to the westward, and the village of **Charlestown** to the northward. In July 1981, a reported depth of about 2 feet could be taken in the inlet, with depths of about 3 to 6 feet inside. The southern part of Ninigret Pond is mostly mud flats. Local knowledge is required in entering and moving about inside. A small-craft facility is at Charlestown, and one is at the western end of Ninigret Pond; berths, gasoline, electricity, marine supplies, and launching ramps are at both facilities.

(64) **Quonochontaug**, 10.8 miles westward of Point Judith, is a summer settlement at the outlet of **Quonochontaug Pond**. In July 1981, a reported depth of about 3 feet could be carried in **Quonochontaug Breachway**, with depths of 15 to 20 feet reported in the pond. Vessels favor the west side of the entrance to avoid rocks in the easterly half of the entrance.

(65) **Weekapaug Point**, 12.5 miles west of Point Judith, is bold, rocky, and prominent from the southwest and southeast. Two stone jetties, 1,500 feet long, protect the entrance to **Winnapaug Pond** just westward of the point. In July 1981, a reported depth of about 5 feet could be carried in **Weekapaug Breachway** to the pond; vessels favor the west side of the breachway above the bridge. Reported depths in Winnapaug Pond vary from bare to 10 feet. There are numerous shoals and sandbars. Southerly winds cause breakers at the ends of the jetties; extreme caution is advised. The fixed bridge over the entrance has a clearance of 6 feet.

(66) **Old Reef**, with a depth of 5 feet over it, is about 1.5 miles west of Weekapaug Point and about 0.5 mile offshore.

(67) **Chart 13214.**–**Watch Hill**, about 17.5 miles west of Point Judith, is a high bare bluff on its easterly side with several large hotels and summer houses.

(68) **Watch Hill Light** (41°18.2′N., 71°51.5′W.), 61 feet above the water, is shown from a square gray granite tower, 45 feet high, attached to a white building with a red roof, on **Watch Hill Point**. It is reported that the fog signal at the station is not easily heard eastward of the light, but from the southwest can be heard nearly to Montauk Point. A radiobeacon is 136 yards north-northeast of the light. A lighted whistle buoy, 2.5 miles southward of the light, marks a passage through Block Island Sound.

(69) **Gangway Rock**, awash at low water, is part of a boulder reef extending about 0.2 mile southward from Watch Hill Light. A lighted bell buoy marks the south end of the reef. A submerged rock is about 50 yards northward of the buoy.

(70) **Watch Hill Passage** is the principal entrance to Fishers Island Sound from eastward, and the only one used by strangers. It has a least depth of about 17 feet. A spot with

12 feet over it in the passage is marked by a buoy; the best channel is northward of this buoy, giving it a berth of about 150 yards.

(71) **Watch Hill Reef**, on the southwest side of Watch Hill Passage, has rocks that bare and is marked by a gong buoy.

(72) **Sugar Reef Passage**, between Watch Hill Reef and Sugar Reef, has a width of 0.3 mile; the least depths are about 22 feet.

(73) **Sugar Reef**, some 500 to 600 yards in extent, is covered 2 to 12 feet and should be avoided; it is marked by a buoy off its north side.

(74) **Catumb Passage**, between Sugar Reef and Catumb Rocks, has a width of 150 yards; its least depth is 13 feet.

(75) **Catumb Rocks**, the highest of which are awash, are marked by buoys on the north, southeast, and southwest sides. Rocks covered 1 to 18 feet extend 0.8 mile westward of Catumb Rocks to the buoy that marks the east side of **Lords Passage**. This passage, about 0.3 mile wide, has a least depth of 16 feet.

(76) **Wicopesset Rock**, on the northwesterly side of Lords Passage, is the easterly part of foul ground extending about 0.3 mile to **Wicopesset Island**, which is low and rocky.

(77) **Wicopesset Passage**, between Wicopesset Island and East Point, is narrow and is obstructed by a rock in the middle marked by a buoy; it is suitable only for small craft and should not be used by strangers. A bell buoy marks the southern entrance. Extreme caution is recommended when using the passage as the ebb current is apt to set boats on the foul ground.

(78) Information about the tides and tidal currents in the passages is given with the discussion of Fishers Island Sound.

(79) **Charts 13214, 13212.**–**Fishers Island**, 6 miles long, is hilly and sparsely wooded. **Chocomount**, 136 feet high, is the highest point on the island. **East Point**, at the east end of the island, is marked by several large houses. The former Coast Guard station at East Harbor, about 1 mile from East Point of Fishers Island, is prominent; numerous buildings on the western part of Fishers Island and a large yellow hotel building are conspicuous. The radar antenna on **Mount Prospect**, near the west end of the island, south shore, is the most prominent landmark on Fishers Island from seaward. The south side of the island is fringed with foul ground which rises abruptly from depths of 42 to 48 feet; but by giving the shore a berth of 0.5 mile, all dangers will be avoided.

(80) **Race Point Ledge**, partly bare at low water, extends about 0.2 mile southwestward from **Race Point**, the southwest extremity of Fishers Island, and is marked at its end by a buoy. Inside the buoy are boulders with 2 to 9 feet over them. The passage between the buoy and Race Rock Light has very irregular bottom; the least depth is about 24 feet. It is suitable only for small vessels with a comparatively smooth sea.

(81) **Race Rock**, on the northeast side of The Race, is nearly 200 yards in diameter, with a depth of 8 feet. A ridge with a least depth of 25 feet is reported extending about 370 yards south of Race Rock. Another ridge, oriented north-south and with a least depth of 40 feet, is about 380 yards east of Race Rock.

(82) **Race Rock Light** (41°14.6′N., 72°02.8′W.), 67 feet above the water, is shown from a granite tower attached to a dwelling on a granite pier on the rock. A fog signal is sounded at the station. The fog signal is reported at times to be inaudible when a vessel is approaching from eastward and is close southward of Fishers Island.

(83) **Charts 13209, 13212.–The Race,** the main entrance to Long Island Sound from eastward, extends between Fishers Island and Little Gull Island, between which is a width of about 3.5 miles. The only dangers are Valiant Rock, nearly in the middle, and Little Gull Island with its reefs.

(84) **Current.**–In the middle of The Race, the flood sets 295° and the ebb 100°, with average velocities of 2.9 knots and 3.5 knots, respectively. There are always strong rips and swirls in the wake of all broken ground in The Race, except for about one-half hour at slack water. The rips are exceptionally heavy during heavy weather, and especially when a strong wind opposes the current, or the current sets through against a heavy sea. (Predicted times of slack water and times and velocities of strength of current are given in the Tidal Current Tables.)

(85) **Little Gull Reef,** with little depth over it and foul ground, extends 0.3 mile east-northeastward from **Little Gull Island.** Deep-draft vessels should avoid this locality. **Little Gull Island Light** (41°12.4'N., 72°06.5'W.), 91 feet above the water, is shown from a gray granite tower, 81 feet high, attached to a red dwelling on a pier. A fog signal is at the light, and a radiobeacon is about 60 yards south-southwest of the light. The light and Race Rock Light are the guides, as soundings cannot be depended upon.

(86) In passing north of Valiant Rock, vessels should keep from 0.5 to 0.8 mile southwestward of Race Rock Light, and craft passing southward of Valiant Rock should hold to a course about 1 mile northeastward of Little Gull Island Light.

(87) **Cerberus Shoal,** 6 miles southeast of Race Rock Light, is about 0.4 mile in diameter, with a least depth of 19 feet on a small rocky patch near its north end. The seas break on this shoal during heavy swells. It is marked by a lighted gong buoy. Near the shoal, tide rips are unusually strong.

(88) **Great Gull Island,** 0.6 mile southwest of Little Gull Island, was formerly a military reservation, but is now privately owned. The pier on the north side is in ruins. A lookout tower on the island is conspicuous.

(89) **Valiant Rock,** with a least depth of 19 feet, is surrounded by shoal area, and the 10-fathom curve surrounding the rock marks the area which should be avoided by deep-draft vessels and preferably all vessels, on account of the heavy swirls and rips. A lighted bell buoy is northward of the rock.

(90) **The Sluiceway,** the passage between Great Gull Island and Plum Island, has several known dangers and very irregular bottom with boulders, and should be avoided. The velocity of the **tidal current** in the passage is 2.6 knots on the flood, and 3.2 knots on the ebb; flood sets 299°, and ebb 133°. Considerably higher velocities occur at times, and tide rips are very bad in heavy weather. Boulders covered 3 to 10 feet are between **Old Silas Rock** and Plum Island. Old Silas Rock is awash at high water. **Middle Shoal Rock,** 0.3 mile northeastward of Old Silas Rock, has a depth of 8 feet.

(91) **Bedford Reef** is broken ground, on which the least found depths are 14 to 16 feet, extending about 1.5 miles southward from broken ground lying between Great Gull and Plum Islands. It should be avoided. **Constellation Rock,** on the southeasterly extension on this broken ground, has 17 feet over it, is marked by a buoy, and lies 1.9 miles southward of Little Gull Island Light.

(92) **Chart 13209.**–**Montauk Point,** the easterly extremity of Long Island, is a high sandy bluff, on the summit of which is the light. The land is grass covered, with a height of 165 feet at **Prospect Hill,** 2 miles westward of the point. The south side of the point is bold, the 10-fathom curve is about

0.5 mile from shore; depths of 24 feet and less extend 0.8 mile off the northeast side of the point.

(93) **Montauk Point Light** (41°04.2'N., 71°51.5'W.), 168 feet above the water, is shown from a white octagonal, pyramidal tower, 108 feet high, with a brown band midway of its height and a covered way to a gray dwelling. A fog signal is at the light. A radiobeacon is 0.3 mile south-southwestward of the light.

(94) Surrounding Montauk Point for about 4 miles is a shoal area that has been closely surveyed (see also chart 13215); the bottom is very broken, and extra caution should be observed where the depths are less than 10 feet greater than the draft. In general, the shoals are a series of long narrow ridges, in places only a few yards wide, and their positions are indicated by the rips over them at the strength of the tidal currents.

(95) **Montauk Shoal,** about 2.5 miles south-southeastward of the light, has least depths of 28 feet. **Great Eastern Rock,** 1.5 miles east-northeast of the light, has a least depth of 24 feet. **Phelps Ledge,** just northerly of Great Eastern Rock, is covered by 24 feet. **Endeavor Shoals,** about 2.3 miles northeast of the light, are covered by 19 to 24 feet on a narrow ridge about 0.4 mile long. A lighted gong buoy is off the eastern end of the ridge. In 1981, a sunken wreck was reported about 1 mile north-northeast of Montauk Point Light in about 41°05.2'N., 71°50.8'W.

(96) Vessels drawing up to 20 feet can avoid the dangers eastward and northeastward of Montauk Point in smooth weather by giving the point a berth of over 1 mile and avoiding Great Eastern Rock.

(97) Broken ground with rocky bottom and boulders extends about 2 miles off the north coast west of Montauk Point. **Shagwong Reef,** with a least depth of 8 feet and marked by a lighted bell buoy, is the northern limit of this area. **Shagwong Rock,** with a least depth of 7½ feet and marked by a lighted buoy, and **Washington Shoal,** with a least depth of 15 feet, are between the shore and Shagwong Reef. The principal danger outside Shagwong Reef is a shoal with a depth of 30 feet, 5.3 miles northwestward of Montauk Point.

(98) **Pilotage Pickup Locations Off Montauk Point.**–Pilots generally, or by prearrangement, meet a ship "off Montauk Point". The following pilot associations meet vessels "off Montauk Point" at the locations indicated. For telephone number, FAX number, cable address, description of the boat, frequencies, etc., consult the name of the association under Pilotage, Narraganset Bay and Other Rhode Island Waters (indexed as such), chapter 6; Pilotage, Long Island Sound (indexed as such), chapter 8; and Pilotage, New York Harbor and Approaches (indexed as such), chapter 11.

(99) Sound Pilots, Inc. (division of Northeast Marine Pilots, Inc.), 2 miles east of Montauk Point Lighted Whistle Buoy MP;

(100) Connecticut State Pilots, 3 miles east-southeast of Montauk Point Lighted Whistle Buoy MP;

(101) Constitution State Pilots Association, 3 miles east of Montauk Point Lighted Whistle Buoy MP;

(102) Long Island Sound State Pilots Association, Inc., at Montauk Point Lighted Whistle Buoy MP.

(103) **Montauk Harbor,** in the northern part of **Lake Montauk,** is entered through a dredged channel on the northern shore about 3 miles west of Montauk Point. The entrance is protected by jetties, each of which is marked by a light, and the west jetty has a fog signal. A lighted bell buoy, about 0.3 mile north of the entrance, marks the approach to the harbor. In June 1988, the reported controlling depth in the channel was 12 feet to the boat basin northwestward of Star Island and to the yacht basin east of the island; in 1982, the

boat basin had depths of 9½ feet except for shoaling along the edges. The channel is marked by private seasonal buoys.

(104) **Star Island**, just inside Montauk Harbor, is connected to the mainland by a causeway. A private light is shown from the eastern side of the island. Depths of 8 to 16 feet are reported in the yacht basin off the eastern side of the island; caution is advised in selecting anchorage because lesser depths may be found. A privately marked channel with a reported controlling depth of about 3 feet in June 1981 leads from the yacht basin to the southern part of Lake Montauk where there are depths of 6 to 8 feet in the center.

(105) **COLREGS Demarcation Lines.**–The lines established for Montauk Harbor are described in **80.155**, chapter 2.

(106) The mean range of **tide** is 1.9 feet.

(107) Tidal **currents** at the entrance to Montauk Harbor have a velocity of 1.2 knots on the flood and about 0.5 knot on the ebb. They are reported to decrease rapidly after entering the harbor and are practically negligible near the yacht club landing on the east side of Star Island. (See Tidal Current Tables for predictions.) **Montauk Coast Guard Station** is at the northern end of Star Island.

(108) There are several small-craft facilities on both sides of the entrance to Montauk Harbor, and a yacht club and several marinas are on the east side of Star Island. Gasoline, diesel fuel, water, ice, marine supplies, and space for transients are available. Lifts to 80 tons can handle craft for complete engine and hull repairs. Groceries and other supplies may be obtained at the village of Montauk.

(109) **Fort Pond Bay** is a semicircular bight about 1 mile wide on the north side of Long Island, 5 miles westward of Montauk Point. The bay is free of dangers, but flats with 8 to 12 feet over them make out 0.2 mile from its eastern shore. The bay affords anchorage in 40 to 50 feet, soft bottom, but is exposed to northerly and northwesterly winds; the shoaling is abrupt on its east and south sides.

(110) **Montauk**, a summer resort at the southeast end of the bay, is the terminus of the Long Island Railroad. A depth of 10 feet was reported alongside the commercial pier on the east side of the bay. There are no public piers available.

(111) **Napeague Bay**, 8 miles westward of Montauk Point, is shallow in the western and southwestern part. **Promised Land Channel**, the buoyed passage southward of Gardiners and Cartwright Islands, has a least centerline depth of about 14 feet; however, the depth is continually changing due to the shifting shoals.

(112) The tidal currents have a velocity of about 1.5 knots through all the channels between the shoals. It is not advisable for vessels drawing more than 10 feet to attempt the passage without local knowledge, and then only when the buoys can be seen.

(113) **Napeague Harbor**, a small-craft refuge in the southwest part of Napeague Bay, can be entered through privately dredged channels northward and southward of **Hicks Island**. In June 1981, the reported controlling depths were 4 feet in the northerly and southerly entrances. Depths in the central part of the harbor range from 1½ to 7 feet; the chart is the best guide. The harbor is especially useful in northeasterly weather when the adjoining bays are unsafe. There are no landings in the harbor.

(114) **Promised Land** is a former fishing village on the southwest side of Napeague Bay. A depth of about 4 feet can be carried to the landing at the yacht club, 1.3 miles westward of Promised Land.

(115) **Gardiners Island**, 11 miles westward of Montauk Point, is partly wooded and has an elevation of 130 feet near its middle. **Cartwright Island** is narrow, low, and sandy, and

extends 1 mile in a southerly direction off the south tip of Gardiners Island. Its size and shape are subject to considerable change by storms.

(116) **Crow Head** is the high bluff at the western end of Gardiners Island. Shoal water with depths of 9 to 16 feet extends 1.8 miles southwestward from **Cherry Hill Point**, the westerly end of Gardiners Island, and terminates at **Crow Shoal**. The shoal has depths of 3 to 11 feet and is marked by a buoy. An obstruction covered 12 feet is 200 yards eastward of the buoy.

(117) The bight between the southern part of Gardiners Island and Crow Shoal is **Cherry Harbor**. It has depths of 24 to 27 feet with mud bottom and affords shelter from northeasterly winds. **Bostwick Bay** is the bight on the northwest side of Gardiners Island. It affords excellent anchorage in easterly winds in depths of about 25 feet, but is exposed to all westerly winds.

(118) **Gardiners Point**, a low spit, is at the northerly end of a very shoal bar which extends 1.5 miles north-northwestward from Gardiners Island. This shoal is steep-to on its north and west sides and is marked by a lighted gong buoy. A rock with a depth of 2 feet over it is about 0.8 mile eastward of the north point of Gardiners Island and is marked by a buoy.

(119) The **Ruins**, a concrete structure on Gardiners Point, is Government property and formerly a naval aircraft bombing target; it is prohibited to the public. The Ruins and the area within 300 yards radius of it is dangerous due to the possible existence of undetonated explosives.

(120) A **restricted anchorage** for U.S. Navy submarines is about 3 miles eastward of Gardiners Island. (See **110.1** and **110.150**, chapter 2, for limits and regulations.)

(121) **Gardiners Bay** is at the western end of Block Island Sound from which it is separated by Gardiners Island. The bay is an excellent anchorage easily entered day or night, and is the approach to Shelter Island Sound and the Peconic Bays. The principal entrance is northward of Gardiners Point. The entrance from Long Island Sound is through Plum Gut. The entrance southward of Gardiners Island is used by fishing vessels.

(122) The principal guides for the entrance to Gardiners Bay from Block Island Sound are the lighted gong buoy north of Gardiners Point, Little Gull Light, and Orient Point Light. The white church spires at Orient and Sag Harbor are prominent. When past the lighted gong buoy north of Gardiners Point, vessels can select the anchorage in Gardiners Bay which affords the best lee in the prevailing winds.

(123) The principal dangers in approaching Gardiners Bay from the northward are the broken ground between Constellation Rock and Plum Island, and the shoal making out to Gardiners Point. In the bay, Crow Shoal should be avoided. In general, the shoaling is rather abrupt in approaching these dangers and gradual in approaching the shoals on the western side of the bay.

(124) **Plum Island**, about 2 miles westward of Great Gull Island, is 2.5 miles long, hilly, and bare of trees except near the southwest end, and has several large buildings, and a prominent tank and flagpole. The island is a Government reservation and closed to the public.

(125) The bight in the southeast side of Plum Island is foul to **Plum Island Rock**, which is 0.5 mile from shore abreast of the middle of the island, has 1 foot over it and is marked by a buoy.

(126) **Plum Gut Harbor**, on the southwest side of Plum Island, has an entrance between jetties with private seasonal lights on dolphins off the outer ends. The lights are shown daily from sundown to 0130. A private fog signal at the west

jetty light is sounded occasionally when Department of Agriculture vessels are navigating in the area. A depth of about 14 feet is in the entrance. Small yachts seeking shelter in an emergency lie alongside the wharves. The harbor is under the supervision of the Department of Agriculture and the Coast Guard, and may be used only with permission.

(127) **COLREGS Demarcation Lines.**–The lines established for Plum Gut Harbor are described in **80.155**, chapter 2.

(128) **Plum Gut**, the entrance to Gardiners Bay from Long Island Sound, is nearly 0.6 mile wide and has sufficient water for vessels of the deepest draft; in the passage are several rocks with depths of 17 to 19 feet over them. Tidal currents set through the passage with great velocity. Steamers, or sailing vessels with a strong favorable wind, should have no difficulty in passing through.

(129) Velocities of the current on flood and ebb are 3.5 and 4.3 knots, respectively. The flood sets northwestward and the ebb southeastward. Heavy tide rips occur. In November 1983, NOAA Ships RUDE and HECK reported that during the flood a countercurrent normally develops along the north shore of Plum Island. This countercurrent is most prevalent within 0.5 mile of the island. Caution is recommended when using this passage.

(130) **Oyster Pond Reef**, extending about 0.5 mile east-northeastward from **Orient Point**, is marked by a light and fog signal. Caution is recommended regarding the fog signal, as it may be difficult to hear at times, particularly with an easterly wind. Numerous boulders and little depth are between the light and Orient Point. **Midway Shoal**, about 0.5 mile east of the light, has 17 feet over it and is marked by a buoy.

(131) When using Plum Gut it is well to give Plum Island and Orient Point Light a berth of 0.2 mile. The best water in the passage will be found on a **295°** course, passing **Pine Point** and the buoy marking Midway Shoal at a distance of 350 yards and passing midway between Orient Point Light and the western end of Plum Island.

(132) A wharf with a depth of 8 feet at its end is on the south side of Orient Point, 1 mile westward of Orient Point Light. A ferry operates between here and New London. A small-craft facility is about 0.1 mile westward of the wharf. Berths, electricity, gasoline, diesel fuel, water, ice, and a launching ramp are available. In June 1981, a reported depth of about 6 feet could be carried to the facility.

(133) **Acabonack Harbor**, at the southeast end of Gardiners Bay, is entered through a privately maintained and marked channel with a reported controlling depth of 2½ feet in the entrance in June 1981. There is deeper water inside.

(134) **Hog Creek Point**, on the southerly side of Gardiners Bay, is generally flat, with bluffs approximately 25 feet in height. **Lionhead Rock**, off the point and marked by a buoy, is awash at high water. Fishtraps are westward of the point.

(135) **Threemile Harbor**, on the south side of Gardiners Bay 1.7 miles southwestward of Hog Creek Point, is entered through a channel with two privately dredged sections. In September 1980, a portion of the wooden bulkhead on the west side of the entrance collapsed into the channel. In June 1981, it was reported that by favoring the east side of the entrance channel a depth of 8 feet could be carried to a point opposite **Maidstone Park**, thence 7 feet to the basin at the head of the harbor. The approach to the harbor is marked by a seasonal lighted bell buoy, and the channel is marked by lighted and unlighted buoys. The jetties at the harbor entrance are marked on the outer ends by private lights. A public commercial landing with reported depths of 8 feet is on the east side of the channel about 0.6 mile above the entrance. A 5 mph **speed limit** is enforced in the harbor.

(136) Anchorage is available in Threemile Harbor in depths of 9 to 14 feet with soft bottom and good holding ground; this is a good anchorage during strong winds. The range of **tide** in the entrance to the harbor is 2.4 feet. The **tidal current** has a velocity of about 3 knots through the entrance.

(137) Small-craft facilities on the east and south sides of Threemile Harbor can provide berths, electricity, gasoline, diesel fuel, water, ice, launching ramps, storage, lifts to 40 tons, and hull and engine repair. Provisions can be obtained at the town of **East Hampton**, 3.5 miles south of Threemile Harbor.

(138) In June 1989, the public pier maintained by the town of East Hampton at the head of the harbor had reported depths of 7 feet at its face and 4 feet on its west side.

(139) **COLREGS Demarcation Lines.**–The lines established for Threemile Harbor are described in **80.155**, chapter 2.

(140) **Chart 12358.**–**Shelter Island Sound** and Peconic Bays extend westward from Gardiners Bay about 22 miles to Riverhead, the head of navigation on Peconic River. They are much frequented by yachts and other small craft in the summer. Fishtraps and oyster stakes are on many of the shoals.

(141) A depth of about 26 feet can be carried through the channel north of Shelter Island and through Little Peconic Bay as far as Robins Island, and about 13 feet through the channel south of Shelter Island. Across the bar between Little and Great Peconic Bays about 13 feet can be carried. With local knowledge greater depths can be carried in the channels and across the bar. A depth of about 6 feet can be taken to South Jamesport and Riverhead.

(142) The mean range of **tide** is about 2.5 feet. The **tidal currents** have considerable velocity wherever the channel is narrowed. The velocity in the narrower places is about 1.8 knots.

(143) **Ice** obstructs navigation in the coves and shallow harbors during January and February. In severe winters, drift ice is reported to interfere with navigation for short periods of time. In the south arm of Shelter Island Sound, the ice is heavy enough at times to destroy structures exposed to it.

(144) Diesel fuel, gasoline, ice, water, marine supplies, and other provisions can best be obtained at Greenport and Sag Harbor. Several boatyards, shipyards, marine railways, and enclosed basins with excellent repair facilities are at Greenport.

(145) **Ram Head** is a prominent sandy bluff on the western shore of Gardiners Bay. A lower bluff is nearly 1.5 miles westward of Ram Head with numerous houses along the top. A shoal with 7 to 17 feet over it extends about 2.4 miles southeastward from Ram Head.

(146) A boulder with 1 foot over it is 230 yards from shore about 0.3 mile northeastward of the northern point of the entrance to Coecles Harbor. Other boulders with little depth are between this boulder and Ram Head.

(147) The entrance to **Coecles Harbor** is at the south end of Ram Head; the channel is marked by private seasonal buoys and a private seasonal light. In June 1981, the reported controlling depth in the privately maintained entrance channel was 7 feet. The **speed limit** is 5 mph. A marina and boatyard are in the harbor. A mobile hoist at the boatyard can haul out craft up to 35 tons; gasoline, water, ice, diesel fuel, marine supplies, sewage pumpout, berths, guest moorings, storage facilities, and complete engine and hull repairs are available. In June 1981, a reported depth of 5½ feet could be carried to the marina and boatyard.

(148) A **special anchorage** is in Coecles Harbor. (See **110.1 and 110.60(y)**, chapter 2, for limits and regulations.)

(149) **COLREGS Demarcation Lines.**—The lines established for Coecles Harbor are described in **80.155**, chapter 2.

(150) Extensive flats make off from Ram Head and the shore between it and **Hay Beach Point**, the northernmost point of Shelter Island, which is a low flat with a clump of scrub at its end and backed by wooded highland. **Long Beach Point** is a low spit eastward of Hay Beach Point. A bar with little depth extends southwesterly from Long Beach Point to the ruins of a former lighthouse of which only the 10-foot concrete foundation remains. A private light marks the ruins.

(151) Shoals with depths of 10 to 12 feet extend 0.5 mile eastward from Long Beach Point. The south and west sides of this shoal have depths of 12 to 15 feet, and rise abruptly from the channel. The limits of the shoal south of the point are marked by buoys. The bar has extended southward enough to be a real danger to small craft.

(152) **COLREGS Demarcation Lines.**—The lines established for the Long Island bays are described in **80.155**, chapter 2.

(153) **Orient Harbor**, about 4 miles northwestward of Ram Head, is an excellent anchorage; the depths range from over 20 feet in its southern part to 16 feet at its northern end. **Orient** is a village at the northeast end of Orient Harbor. At the end of the main wharf the depth is 8½ feet. The eastern part of Orient Harbor has depths of 7 to 9 feet. Fish traps are on the shoals.

(154) About 0.4 mile northeastward of **Cleaves Point**, at the southwest end of Orient Harbor, the shore has been cut through to a small pond which is used as a private basin for small craft. The entrance, between two jetties, has a depth of about 3 feet over the bar, with about 6 feet in the basin. Permission is required before anchoring in the basin. Rocks are 0.2 mile south of the entrance.

(155) **Hallock Bay** makes eastward from Orient Harbor on the north side of Long Beach Point. A channel, marked by uncharted private daybeacons, leads into the bay. The bay is shallow and dangers and shoaling have been reported. Local knowledge is advised prior to entering.

(156) **Gull Pond** is 0.3 mile westward of Cleaves Point at the southwest end of Orient Harbor. In July 1981, a reported depth of 4 feet could be carried through the entrance, with depths of 10 to 15 feet reported in the pond. A State launching ramp is available in the pond.

(157) **Greenport** is an important town and the terminus of a branch of the Long Island Railroad. The white church spires, near the northern end of town, and a tank and TV radio tower in the center of town are prominent.

(158) **Greenport Harbor** is formed on the northeast by a 5-foot-high breakwater, which extends 0.2 mile southeastward from **Youngs Point**, nearly to the 18-foot curve, and is marked at its outer end by a light. The depths at the wharves range from 7 to 21 feet. The railroad wharf on the south side of the waterfront can accommodate a vessel up to 100 feet.

(159) **Stirling Basin**, on the northeast side of Greenport, is a part of Greenport Harbor. In July 1981, the reported controlling depth was 8 feet in the entrance channel with 10 to 12 feet in the mooring areas. The entrance channel is marked by private seasonal buoys. Two smaller privately dredged channels with depths of about 9 feet reported are in the northeastern part of the basin. The **harbormaster** for Greenport Harbor controls mooring and berthing in the basin. The **speed limit** is 5 mph.

(160) Small-craft facilities at Greenport can provide berths, electricity, gasoline, diesel fuel, water, ice, storage, marine supplies, and hull and engine repairs. The largest marine railway, at a shipbuilding company at the southeast end of the waterfront, can handle craft up to 400 tons and 15 feet in draft and has a 15-ton crane. Mobile hoists to 50 tons are available. A well-equipped machine shop is also in the town.

(161) A ferry operates between Greenport and Shelter Island. During the summer, bus service is available from Greenport to Orient Point where there is ferry service to New London.

(162) **Dering Harbor**, southward of Greenport and at the northwest end of Shelter Island, is a favorite anchorage for yachts and motorboats. The entrance to the harbor, marked by private buoys, is partially constricted by a disposal area in about midentrance and shoal area with a reported depth of 4 feet in June 1981 that extends from the southwestern entrance point to near the disposal area; caution is advised. In April 1989, it was reported that about 10 feet could be carried into the harbor with local knowledge. Depths of 10 to 14 feet are available in the central part of the harbor, with much lesser depths around the edges. Moorings and float landings for small craft are in the bight at the southwest end of the harbor. Vessels too large to enter can anchor outside the harbor in depths of 14 to 30 feet. The **speed limit** is 5 mph. Small-craft facilities, on the west side of the harbor, can provide berths, electricity, gasoline, diesel fuel, water, ice, marine supplies, sewage pumpout, and hull and outboard engine repairs. A launching ramp is also available. **Shelter Island Heights** is on the southwestern side of Dering Harbor.

(163) **Fanning Point** is on the north shore at the southwest end of Greenport. A shoal extends 300 yards off the point and is marked by a buoy. Four dolphins, part of a former oil facility, are northward of the point. Currents of 2 knots, running fair with the channel, have been reported in the vicinity of Fanning Point.

(164) **Conkling Point**, on the north shore 1 mile southwestward of Fanning Point, is low and sandy at the end and has deep water as close as 150 yards. A marina on the southwest side of the point had a reported depth of 5½ feet in the approach in July 1981. Berths, electricity, gasoline, marine supplies, storage, a launching ramp, and a 30-ton mobile hoist are available. Hull and engine repairs can be made.

(165) **Mill Creek** is the entrance to **Hashamomuck Pond**, about 1.1 miles westward of Conkling Point. In July 1981, the privately dredged entrance channel into the creek had a controlling depth of 4 feet, thence 3½ feet was reported in the channel along the northwest shore of Mill Creek. The entrance channel is marked by private seasonal buoys. About 400 yards eastward of the creek is a small bight entered through a channel with a depth of about 4 feet and marked by private seasonal lights and buoys.

(166) **Jennings Point**, the western end of Shelter Island, is high and wooded. Rocks are off the point close-to, and it should be given a berth of over 150 yards. A lighted buoy is off the point. A gazebo on the point is prominent.

(167) The town of **Southold** is at the head of **Southold Bay**, which is the bight at the western end of Shelter Island Sound westward of Jennings Point. For about a mile northeastward of the entrance jetty, shoals with 12 feet or less extend nearly 0.4 mile from shore and are generally steep-to. The southwest part of the bay is shoal for about 0.3 mile from shore. Anchorage can be selected east-southeast of the jetty at a distance of from 0.2 to 0.4 mile, in 12 to 18 feet.

(168) A small jettied basin is about 0.5 mile northeast of Southold entrance. The overhead power cable crossing the entrance has a clearance of 31 feet. There are no public landings in the basin.

(169)   In April 1989, the reported controlling depth was about 3 feet in the privately maintained channels in **Town Creek, Jockey Creek,** and **Goose Creek.** The common entrance to Town Creek and Jockey Creek is marked by private seasonal buoys. The highway bridge at the mouth of Goose Creek has a clearance of 9 feet and the bridge that crosses Jockey Creek has a 45-foot fixed span with a vertical clearance of 6½ feet.

(170)   On the shore south of Southold entrance jetty is a prominent white tower.

(171)   There are several small-craft facilities on the creeks and along the west shore of Southold Bay from Paradise Point to Conkling Point. Berths, electricity, gasoline, water, ice, marine supplies, launching ramps, storage, lifts, and cranes are available. Provisions can be obtained at Southold.

(172)   **Paradise Point,** on the west side of Shelter Island Sound, is low and wooded, and from the point a sloping sandspit extends about 0.3 mile eastward and is marked by a lighted buoy. Southward of Paradise Point, shoals with depths of 10 to 15 feet extend from the west shore to midsound; the southeast point of the shoals is marked by a buoy.

(173)   The channel south of Shelter Island has numerous shoals, but is easily followed by vessels of 13 feet or less draft when the buoys can be seen. The channel is used by vessels going to Sag Harbor. Vessels operating between Greenport and Sag Harbor prefer the inside route around the western end of Shelter Island. The **tidal current** in the channel between Shelter Island and North Haven Peninsula has a velocity of about 2.4 knots. The approach from Gardiners Bay is across a shoal or bar which extends in a southeasterly direction from Ram Head to the south shore, the depths on which vary from 7 to 11 feet about 1.6 miles from Ram Head, and thence 13 to 17 feet to the buoys which mark the entrance.

(174)   **Dangerous Rock,** awash at low water in surrounding depths of about 12 feet, is 0.2 mile south of the channel.

(175)   A shoal extends 0.3 to 0.4 mile north of the shore of **Cedar Point** which is marked by a light. The shoal has boulders, and its edge is marked by buoys.

(176)   Shoals with boulders and little water over them in places extend nearly 0.5 mile southeastward from **Nicoll Point.** Buoys mark the limit of the channel in this area.

(177)   **Northwest Harbor,** between Cedar Island Light and **Barcelona Point,** is strewn with boulders covered by 4 to 6 feet.

(178)   **Sand Spit,** an extensive shoal partly bare at half-tide, is between **Mashomack Point,** the southeastern extremity of Shelter Island, and Sag Harbor. The spit is marked by buoys and a light.

(179)   A group of rocks locally known as **Gull Island,** showing bare at half-tide, is nearly 0.4 mile northeastward of the breakwater at Sag Harbor.

(180)   **Sag Harbor,** about 2.5 miles southwestward of the light on Cedar Point, is protected on the northeast by a breakwater marked at the outer end by a light. A spherical tank, a radio tower, and several flagpoles are prominent landmarks.

(181)   In entering Sag Harbor, do not round the breakwater too closely, as a depth of about 6 feet is found near its end. The deepest water is near the buoy. Anchor eastward or northeastward of the end of the former ferry wharf, locally known as Long Wharf. A 5 mph **speed limit** is enforced.

(182)   In July 1974, the dredged channel into Sag Harbor had a controlling depth of 8 feet (10 feet at midchannel) through the entrance to the turning basin, 9 feet in the turning basin, 5 feet in the southerly anchorage area, and 7 feet in the main anchorage area. The channel to **Sag Harbor**

Cove is about 8 feet deep; this channel and the cove are marked by private seasonal lights and buoys. A 37-foot-wide fixed bridge at the entrance has a clearance of 20 feet. Berths, electricity, gasoline, diesel fuel, storage, marine supplies, water, ice, launching ramps, and complete engine, hull, rigging, and sail repairs are available at Sag Harbor; a 30-ton mobile hoist, near the inner end of the breakwater, can haul out craft up to about 60 feet.

(183)   **Smith Cove,** a small bight on the south side of Shelter Island, is a good anchorage for small craft in northerly weather. Depths range from 11 to 30 feet. A marina on the west side of the cove can provide moorings, limited berths, gasoline, electricity, water, and some marine supplies. In June 1981, a depth of 6 feet was reported alongside the pier at the marina. A ferry operates between **South Ferry** on the southwest side of the cove to **North Haven Peninsula.**

(184)   **West Neck Harbor** and **West Neck Bay** are shallow bodies of water on the southwest side of Shelter Island. In June 1989, it was reported that a depth of 2 feet could be carried over the bar and into the harbor from Shelter Island Sound. The entrance is close eastward of the seaward end of a peninsula, marked by a private lighted buoy, that separates the harbor from the sound, and the channel follows along the north side of this peninsula. The channel is marked by private buoys. The harbor has numerous private landings. A boatyard with a marine railway can handle craft up to 40 feet for hull and engine repairs. Berths, gasoline, water, ice, a launching ramp, and some marine supplies are available.

(185)   A special anchorage is in West Neck Harbor. (See 110.1 and 110.60 y-1, chapter 2, for limits and regulations.)

(186)   **Noyack (Noyac) Bay** is between North Haven Peninsula and Jessup Neck and southward of the western end of Shelter Island. No dangers will be encountered if the shores are given a berth of 0.4 mile.

(187)   **Mill Creek,** in the southern part of Noyack Bay, is entered through a privately dredged channel that leads to a basin. The channel is marked by private seasonal lights and buoys. In June 1981, the reported controlling depths were 8 feet in the channel and 6 feet in the basin. A clubhouse on the west side of the entrance is prominent. Small-craft facilities in the creek can provide berths, electricity, gasoline, water, ice, storage, a launching ramp, marine supplies, and hull and engine repairs; a 25-ton mobile hoist is available.

(188)   **Jessup Neck** is a long narrow strip, partly high and wooded, separating Noyack Bay from Little Peconic Bay. The north end of the neck is a sandspit from which a shoal with 4 to 12 feet over it extends nearly 0.4 mile north-north-westward. A lighted buoy marks the outer end of the shoal area.

(189)   A shoal with depths of 5 to 7 feet extends 1.5 miles southwestward from **Great Hog Neck,** on the northwest side at the entrance to Little Peconic Bay; this shoal is marked by a buoy.

(190)   Heavy tide rips occur southeast of Great Hog Neck during the flood with a southwesterly wind. At such times, small craft can avoid the worst of them by favoring the shore on the northwest side of the passage.

(191)   **Richmond Creek** and **Corey Creek** are at the head of **Hog Neck Bay.** A depth of about 7 feet can be taken in the privately dredged channel leading to a basin in Richmond Creek; the channel is marked by private seasonal buoys. In 1964, the dredged channel leading into and connecting with small boat channels in Corey Creek had a controlling depth of 7 feet. Controlling depths in the small-boat channels inside Corey Creek were 5½ to 6 feet. The entrance channel is marked by private buoys.

(192) **Little Peconic Bay** is about 5 miles long. The southerly shore of the bay is clear if given a berth of 0.4 mile, but shoals extend 0.6 mile from the south end of the bay.

(193) An aquaculture site, marked by private seasonal buoys, is at the south end of Little Peconic Bay about 1 mile north-northwest of the entrance to North Sea Harbor.

(194) A prominent sandy bluff, known locally as **Holmes Hill**, is just west of the entrance to **North Sea Harbor.** In June 1981, the reported controlling depth through the dredged channel into the harbor was 4 feet. The channel is marked by private seasonal buoys and by a private seasonal light at the entrance. This is an excellent harbor of refuge for small craft with drafts not exceeding 3½ feet. The bottom is soft with good holding ground.

(195) A marina in the harbor has gasoline, ice, water, some marine supplies, and a lift that can handle craft to 10 tons; hull and engine repairs can be made.

(196) **Wooley Pond**, 1 mile northeastward of North Sea Harbor, is entered through a dredged channel which, in June 1981, had a reported controlling depth of 6 feet. The channel is marked by private seasonal buoys and by a private seasonal light on the north side of the entrance.

(197) A marina in the pond can provide berths, eletricity, gasoline, water, ice, storage, marine supplies, and hull and engine repairs; a 45-foot marine railway and a 12-ton forklift are available. In June 1981, depths of 5 to 6 feet were reported available at the marina.

(198) **Nassau Point**, the long neck on the northwest side of Little Peconic Bay, has high bluffs on the eastern side. A shoal with little depth over it extends 0.5 mile southward from Nassau Point and is marked by a lighted buoy.

(199) **Cutchogue Harbor**, between Nassau Point and New Suffolk, is used by local boats drawing 6 to 10 feet. On the east shore of the harbor, northwestward of Nassau Point, three channels leading into the ponds have been dredged by private interests. At the middle of the three channels, 0.9 mile northwest of the extremity of Nassau Point, are several private wharves. The channel leads between two jetties, and a depth of about 3 feet can be carried into the pond and 1 foot to some of the wharves.

(200) **Haywater Cove, Broadwater Cove, Mud Creek,** and **East Creek,** used by local interests and sharing a common entrance, are at the head of Cutchogue Harbor. The entrance channel and the channels through these waterways have been privately dredged. The controlling depths are: 6 feet reported in the entrance channel in July 1981, thence 7 feet in Haywater Cove, Broadwater Cove, and Mud Creek, and 6 feet in East Creek in 1966. Shoaling is reported to occur in these areas; caution is advised.

(201) A depth of 8 feet can be taken within 100 feet of the wharves at **New Suffolk** by passing eastward and about 200 yards northward of the buoy westward of Nassau Point and steering westward for the wharves. A small basin, with a depth of about 8 feet reported in 1981, is northward of the wharf. In July 1981, shoaling to 2 feet was reported in the southern part of Cutchogue Harbor, about 0.4 mile east of New Suffolk.

(202) A larger basin at the north end of New Suffolk, locally known as **School House Creek**, extends to the highway. The entrance channel is protected by a short rock jetty, covered at high water, on the south. The depth to the boatyard at the head of the basin was reported to be about 4 feet in June 1981. Berths, gasoline, storage, marine supplies, hull and engine repairs, and a 30-ton moblie hoist are available at the boatyard.

(203) **Wickham Creek,** locally known as Boatmens Harbor, 0.7 mile north of New Suffolk, is entered through a privately dredged entrance channel with a reported controlling depth of 6 feet in July 1981. The channel is marked by private seasonal buoys and bush stakes. Gasoline, water, ice, storage, a launching ramp, and some marine supplies are available in the basin. A flatbed trailer can haul out craft to 32 feet.

(204) In southeast gales, local craft of less than 6-foot draft seek shelter in the small cove, locally known as **Horseshoe Cove**, in the northeast part of Cutchogue Harbor.

(205) The through channel in **North Race**, northward of **Robins Island**, is marked and used only by light-draft boats. **South Race**, the channel southward of Robins Island, has a controlling depth of about 13 feet and is marked by buoys.

(206) An aquaculture site, marked by private buoys, is 0.6 mile southwest of the south end of Robins Island.

(207) Tide rips occur between the mainland and the south end of Robins Island when the tidal current sets against the wind.

(208) **Great Peconic Bay**, about 5 miles in diameter, is used mostly by local motorboats from Shinnecock Canal and by yachts. The bay is generally clear, but extensive shoals make off from the shores, except on its south side. Shinnecock Canal, the entrance from the south, is described in chapter 10.

(209) **Rodgers Rock**, about 1.3 miles west-southwestward of **Cow Neck** and about 1.2 miles south-southwest of Robins Island, has a depth of 6 feet over it and is marked on the northeast side by a buoy. **Robins Island Rock**, 0.8 mile westward of the south end of Robins Island, is awash at low water. It is marked by a buoy. Caution is recommended in this vicinity.

(210) **Sebonac Creek**, on the southeast side of Great Peconic Bay, is used extensively by yachts, and serves as a yacht harbor for the town of Southampton. A privately dredged channel, marked by private seasonal lights and buoys, leads into the creek and had a reported controlling depth of 8 feet in June 1981. The landings are at **West Neck**, a small settlement northeastward of **Ram Island in Bullhead Bay.** An obstruction buoy is locally maintained during the summer to mark a rock, covered 1½ feet, about 100 feet westward of the town landing. In June 1981, a reported depth of 5 feet could be carried to the town landing. A 5 mph **speed limit** is enforced.

(211) **Cold Spring Pond**, about 1.6 miles southwestward of Sebonac Creek and 1.1 miles eastward of Shinnecock Canal entrance, is entered through a privately dredged channel which had a reported depth of 2 feet in June 1981. The entrance channel to the pond is marked by a private seasonal light and buoy. An overhead power cable at the entrance to the pond has a clearance of 34 feet.

(212) **James Creek**, on the north shore of Great Peconic Bay opposite the entrance to Shinnecock Canal, is entered through a privately dredged channel that had a reported controlling depth of 6 feet in 1981. The entrance is marked by private seasonal buoys. Small-craft facilities on the creek can provide berths, gasoline, storage, launching ramps, and hull and engine repairs. A flatbed trailer can haul out craft to 30 feet.

(213) **South Jamesport** is a village on **Miamogue Point**, 3.4 miles southwestward of James Creek. Local knowledge is necessary to avoid the shoals in this area, and strangers should take soundings frequently to keep in the best water. A small-craft facility at South Jamesport can provide berths, electricity, gasoline, water, ice, launching ramps, storage, marine supplies, and hull and engine repairs; a 25-ton mobile hoist is available. In June 1981, a reported depth of about 8 feet could be taken to the facility. The town has railroad passenger and bus service.

(214) **Peconic River** empties into the western end of Flanders Bay, about 1.5 miles westward of South Jamesport. The

river is entered through a dredged channel marked by private seasonal lights that leads from Flanders Bay to the head of navigation at **Riverhead,** about 2.4 miles above the channel entrance. The dredged channel is approached from deep water in Great Peconic Bay through a marked channel. In August-September 1981, the dredged channel had a centerline controlling depth of 4½ feet. A fixed highway bridge with a clearance of 25 feet crosses the river about 0.9 mile above the mouth.

(215)   **Flanders Bay** is the scene of considerable small boat activity. A yacht club is at Riverhead; limited berths, electricity, and water are available.

(216)   **Meetinghouse Creek, Terrys Creek, and Reeves Creek,** which empty into the northwestern part of Flanders Bay, are entered through privately dredged channels. In June 1981, the channels had reported controlling depths of 5 feet. The entrance channel leading to, and connecting with, Terrys Creek and Meetinghouse Creek is marked by private seasonal buoys and a private seasonal light. A marina is on Meetinghouse Creek. Berths, electricity, gasoline, water, ice, a 5-ton forklift, 30-ton mobile hoist, launching ramp, storage facilities, and hull and engine repairs are available. In June 1981, a reported depth of 7 feet was available at the marina.

(217)   **Reeves Bay,** on the southwest side of Flanders Bay, is entered through a privately dredged channel that leads to the town of **Flanders** on the south side of the bay. In June 1981, the channel had a reported controlling depth of 4 feet. Other dredged channels lead from the entrance channel into several arms of the bay. A boatyard at Flanders has gasoline, storage facilities, marine supplies, and a 10-ton marine railway; hull and engine repairs can be made.

(218)   **Chart 13214.**–Fishers Island Sound extends between the mainland of Connecticut and Fishers Island, and forms one of the entrances into Long Island Sound that is used to some extent by light tows and other vessels up to 14-foot draft. The sound has numerous shoals and lobster trap buoys, and the entire area is exceedingly treacherous, characterized by boulder patches that rise abruptly from deep water. Vessels should follow the deeper channels between the shoals and proceed with caution if obliged to cross shoal areas. In general, all shoal spots or abrupt changes of depth are indications of boulders and should be avoided as anchorages.

(219)   **Tides and currents.**–In Watch Hill Passage the tidal currents are strong and necessitate caution in navigating. Buoys may be towed under. The flood current sets nearly in the direction of the channel, but has a tendency to northward and the ebb a tendency to southward. The northerly and southerly set is more marked between Napatree Point and Latimer Reef Light.

(220)   In Sugar Reef and Catumb Passages the tidal currents set obliquely across the axis of the channel. The flood sets northwestward and the ebb southeastward. The tidal currents in Sugar Reef Passage are about the same velocity as in Watch Hill Passage, but are stronger in Catumb Passage.

(221)   In Lords Passage the tidal currents set diagonally across the channel and have a velocity of nearly 2 knots, the ebb being greater than the flood.

(222)   In the main channel of Fishers Island Sound, the flood sets westward and the ebb eastward. In the main channel between Napatree Point and Wicopesset Island, the velocity of flood is 1.7 knots and ebb 2.2 knots. The flood sets 284° and the ebb 113°.

(223)   In the channel south of Ram Island Reef, the velocities of flood and ebb are 1.3 and 1.6 knots, respectively. The flood sets 255° and the ebb 088°. The direction and velocity of the current are affected by strong winds that may change the duration of flood or ebb.

(224)   The strong tidal currents prevent the formation of heavy local ice, except in shoal tributaries. The only ice to give trouble is that set in from Long Island Sound by wind and current. The ice formations in Little Narragansett Bay are sufficiently heavy to be destructive to structures exposed to them.

(225)   On the south side of Fishers Island Sound, off the north side of **East Point** on Fishers Island, are **Seal Rocks,** partly bare at low water and marked by a buoy. A rocky patch covered 11 feet and marked by a buoy is about 500 yards northeastward of Seal Rocks. **Youngs Rock,** about 0.4 mile westward of Seal Rocks, has about 1 foot over it and is marked by a buoy. A rocky patch extends about 400 yards to the east-northeastward.

(226)   **East Harbor** and **Chocomount Cove,** in the north shore of Fishers Island, are sometimes used as anchorages by small craft. There is considerable foul ground in East Harbor and in the approach to Chocomount Cove. The harbor and cove are exposed to northerly winds. A former Coast Guard Station with a boathouse and dock is prominent near the south side of East Harbor. Several small private piers with about 6 feet at their ends are in East Harbor.

(227)   The north shore of Fishers Island from East Harbor around into West Harbor has several private landings.

(228)   **East Clump** is a cluster of rocks partly bare at high water and marked by a buoy about 0.8 mile north of Fishers Island. From East Clump for some 2.8 miles westward to North Dumpling, there are rocky islets and dangers which must be avoided. These are 0.5 to 0.8 mile off the Fishers Island shore, and most are buoyed. **North Dumpling,** an islet marked by a light and fog signal, is surrounded by rocks awash and foul ground. **Seaflower Reef,** marked by a light, is near the middle of the western entrance of Fishers Island Sound and 0.8 mile northwestward of North Dumpling Light.

(229)   **West Harbor,** on the north side of Fishers Island southeastward of North Dumpling Light, affords shelter from southerly winds. In April 1986, the dredged channel leading into the harbor along the west shore had a controlling depth of 12 feet. Foul ground extends across the entrance of West Harbor to near the eastern edge of the dredged channel; the northern limits of the foul ground are buoyed.

(230)   A yacht club wharf and another small-craft facility are on the southwest side of the harbor. Gasoline, diesel fuel, water, ice, and hull and engine repairs are available. A marine railway can handle craft up to 40 feet. The head of the harbor is used by boats drawing less than 5 feet which enter by the narrow unmarked channel southward of **Goose Island.**

(231)   **Hay Harbor,** at the west end of Fishers Island, is used by small craft.

(232)   **Silver Eel Cove (Silver Eel Pond)** is on the west side of Fishers Island, 0.6 mile northeastward of Race Point. The entrance, about 75 feet wide and jettied, is marked by a private light and has a depth of about 13 feet, with similar depths inside. Submerged fender pilings are reported on both sides of the entrance. Dolphins are on the northeast side of the cove, and the channel is clear between them and the wharves on the southwest side. Vessels must go to the wharves as there is no room for anchorage. There is very little dockage available. The entrance is difficult with northwesterly or westerly winds. A lighted bell buoy is about 450 yards off the entrance. A ferry which operates between Fishers Island and New London lands here. During the summer,

a Coast Guard unit is stationed inside the entrance to the cove.

(233) On the north side of Fishers Island Sound are: Little Narragansett Bay, and Pawcatuck River leading to the towns of Westerly and Pawcatuck; Stonington Harbor and the town of Stonington; and Mystic Harbor leading to the towns of Noank and Mystic.

(234) **Napatree Beach**, 1.3 miles long between Watch Hill Point and **Napatree Point**, is bare. **Sandy Point**, about 1.4 miles north-northwestward of Napatree Point, is at the northwestern end of a long and narrow sand island in Little Narragansett Bay. An extensive sandspit makes off from the northeasterly and southwesterly sides of the island; give these areas a good berth. The island is subject to continual change; caution is advised.

(235) **Napatree Point Ledge**, a boulder reef with little depth, extends nearly 0.4 mile southward of the point. It is marked by a lighted bell buoy. A sunken wreck is about 0.3 mile eastward of the ledge in about 41°18′N., 71°53′W.

(236) The west side of Napatree Point should not be approached closer than 175 yards to avoid a stone jetty which is covered at high water. Between Napatree Point and the Stonington outer breakwater is an extensive flat on which the depths are 3 to 10 feet, rocky bottom. **Middle Ground**, the western part of the flat, is marked by the outer breakwater, which has a light at its western end. A fog signal is at the light.

(237) A depth of 17 feet can be taken to an anchorage inside this breakwater, giving the light on the breakwater a berth of more than 250 yards. In anchoring, give the inside of the breakwater a berth of over 300 yards to avoid shoals and fishweirs. This anchorage provides good shelter except in southwesterly and westerly winds, although it is seldom used.

(238) **Little Narragansett Bay**, at the eastern end of Fishers Island Sound, is entered at its extreme western end southward of Stonington Point. The channel, with dredged sections, extends generally southeasterly across the bay into Pawcatuck River to Westerly. In December 1989, the controlling depth was 4½ feet from the entrance to Little Narragansett Bay to the entrance to Pawcatuck River, except for shoaling to bare in the middle of the dredged channel section near the turn opposite Little Narragansett Bay Entrance Lighted Buoy 3. Deep water is available, with local knowledge, north of the channel opposite the shoal. In March-April 1983, the controlling depth was 8 feet (10 feet at midchannel) to Certain Draw Point (41°20′33″N., 71°49′52″W.), thence 4 feet (7 feet at midchannel) for about 1.7 miles to a point in about 41°22.1′N., 71°50.1′W., thence 3½ feet at midchannel to Westerly. The channel is well marked.

(239) Caution should be exercised in entering Little Narragansett Bay. Shoal water extends for about 200 yards off **Stonington Point**, and the shoal area north of **Sandy Point** is subject to continual change. Strangers are advised to obtain local information before entering because of rocks and shoal water near the edges of the channel.

(240) In the dredged channel northward of Sandy Point, the currents have a velocity of 1.3 knots. The flood sets eastward and the ebb westward. (See the Tidal Current Tables for predictions and Tidal Current Charts, Block Island Sound and Eastern Long Island Sound, for hourly velocities and directions.)

(241) **Watch Hill Cove**, in the southeastern part of Little Narragansett Bay, is used by small craft. In September-October 1978, the buoyed dredged channel leading to the cove had a controlling depth of 7½ feet (9 feet at midchannel). Depths of 5½ to 10 feet are inside the cove and at the

wharves. A **special anchorage** is in the cove. (See **110.1 and 110.47**, chapter 2, for limits and regulations.)

(242) A yacht club and town dock are in Watch Hill Cove; berths, guest moorings, electricity, diesel fuel, and water are available. In July 1981, a depth of 10 feet was reported at the face of the town dock.

(243) **Pawcatuck River**, entered just south of **Pawcatuck Point**, extends about 4 miles to Westerly.

(244) About 1 mile above the entrance to Pawcatuck River the **tidal current** has a velocity of 0.6 knot on flood, and 0.5 knot on the ebb. The river is generally closed by **ice** from January to March.

(245) **Colonel Willie Cove**, 0.5 mile above Pawcatuck Point, has a boatyard with a marine railway that can handle craft up to 45 feet for hull and engine repairs. Berths, electricity, gasoline, water, ice, launching ramp, storage facilities, marine supplies, and a 20-ton crane are also available. In July 1981, a reported depth of 4 feet could be carried in the cove to the boatyard.

(246) A **special anchorage** is in **Thompson Cove**, 2 miles above Pawcatuck Point. (See **110.1** and **110.48**, chapter 2, for limits and regulations.) A yacht club pier is in the cove. Private seasonal buoys mark the approach to the pier.

(247) **Westerly**, 4 miles above Pawcatuck Point, is an important manufacturing town.

(248) There are numerous small-craft facilities along both sides of the Pawcatuck River and at the head at Westerly and Pawcatuck, just across the river. The largest marine railway in the area is at Avondale and it can handle craft to 55 feet. Berths, electricity, gasoline, diesel fuel, water, ice, storage facilities, launching ramps, lifts, and marine supplies are available. Depths of 7 to 9 feet are reported at the town dock at Pawcatuck.

(249) **Wequetequock Cove** is a shallow cove at the northern end of Little Narrangansett Bay. A narrow unmarked channel leads eastward of **Elihu Island** into the cove. A depth of about 4 feet can be taken as far as **Goat Island**, about a mile above Sandy Point. A fixed railroad bridge with a clearance of 6 feet crosses the cove about 0.2 mile above Goat Island. A small-craft facility is on the west side of the cove near the head. Berths, gasoline, storage facilities, launching ramp, 4-ton forklift, marine supplies, and hull and engine repairs are available. In July 1981, a reported depth of 2 feet could be carried to the facility.

(250) **Stonington Harbor**, 3 miles northwestward of Watch Hill Point, is protected by breakwaters on each side. Each of the breakwaters is marked at its seaward end by a light. The controlling depth to the inner harbor is about 11 feet. Anchorage can be selected inside the west breakwater in depths of 15 to 18 feet, taking care to keep the south end of Wamphassuc Point bearing northward of 270°. Vessels drawing up to 8 feet can find anchorage in the inner harbor. A rock that bares at low water is about 50 yards southward of the fishing wharf and is marked by a private buoy. **Special anchorages** are in Stonington Harbor. (See **110.1** and **110.50**, chapter 2, for limits and regulations.)

(251) Stonington Harbor is approached from southeastward and westward. Vessels with local knowledge sometimes cross Noyes Shoal from southwestward. The southeastern approach is best, with fewer dangers, and the navigational aids serve as excellent guides to avoid them. In daytime with clear weather, no difficulty should be experienced in entering any of the approaches.

(252) From southeastward, the course from south of Napatree Point Ledge should be west-northwestward until off the buoy at the southwest end of Middle Ground, from which a northerly course can be shaped past the breakwater lights and into the harbor.

(253) From southwestward, a northeasterly course can be shaped from the lighted bell buoy south of Ram Island Reef to south of White Rock, and thence eastward past the north side of Noyes Rock to the harbor.

(254) The inner breakwater, about 400 yards northward of Stonington Point on the east side of the entrance, extends westward about 250 yards and is marked by a light.

(255) **Stonington** is on the east side of the harbor. Traffic is mostly fishing and recreational craft. The wharves have depths of 7 to 12 feet alongside. Following southerly weather, a surge is felt by vessels tied to the southern side of the seaward pier.

(256) A boatyard is in the northeast part of the harbor. Berths, electricity, gasoline, diesel fuel, water, ice, storage, 40-ton lift, marine supplies, and hull, engine, and electronic repairs are available. In July 1981, a reported depth of 7 feet could be carried to the yard. A **harbormaster** is at Stonington.

(257) A railroad causeway, with two fixed spans each having a clearance of 4 feet, crosses Stonington Harbor 0.4 mile above Stonington. Overhead power cables at the openings have clearances of 41 feet.

(258) **Noyes Rock**, 0.4 mile southward of **Wamphassuc Point**, has a least depth of 8 feet. **Noyes Shoal**, with 8 to 17 feet over it, is nearly 1.5 miles long in a west-northwesterly direction; it is marked by a bell buoy near its eastern end.

(259) **Latimer Reef**, about 0.6 mile south of Noyes Shoal, is a very broken and rocky area 0.4 mile long. It is marked by a light at its west end and a buoy at its east end. The eastern end of the reef has a least found depth of 6 feet.

(260) **Latimer Reef Light** (41°18.3'N., 71°56.0'W.), 55 feet above the water, is shown from a white conical tower, brown midway of its height, on a brown cylindrical foundation. A fog signal is at the light.

(261) A detached 11-foot spot, marked by a buoy, is about 0.4 mile northeast of Latimer Reef Light.

(262) **Eel Grass Ground**, about 0.8 mile northwestward of Latimer Reef Light, is a shoal with a least depth of 4 feet, marked by buoys. **White Rock**, about 0.8 mile northeastward of Eel Grass Ground, is bare and prominent. **Red Reef**, covered 1 foot, is 0.2 mile north of White Rock and marked by a buoy. **Ellis Reef**, 0.4 mile northwestward of Eel Grass Ground, is marked on its east side by a daybeacon.

(263) **Mason Island**, 2.5 miles west of Stonington Harbor, is joined to the mainland by a fixed bridge with an 18-foot span and a clearance of 3 feet; the sound end of the island is strewn with boulders. A **special anchorage** is on the east side of Mason Island. (See **110.1 and 110.50a**, chapter 2, for limits and regulations.) An anchorage for small craft is on the west side of the south end of Mason Island where depths range from 8 to 11 feet; caution and local knowledge are required to use this anchorage because of the boulders in the area. A dangerous rock is off the east side of **Mason Point**, the southern extremity of Mason Island, in 41°19'21.6" N., 71°58'05.0"W.

(264) **Enders Island**, 0.3 mile eastward of the southern end of Mason Island, is connected to it by a fixed bridge with a 15-foot span and a clearance of 6 feet.

(265) **Ram Island Reef**, 1.8 miles westward of Latimer Reef Light, has two detached parts: the southerly section is covered 6½ feet and marked by a lighted bell buoy, and the northerly section, covered by 1 foot, is marked by a daybeacon. Passage between the reef and island is unsafe because of shoals.

(266) **Ram Island**, about 0.4 mile southwest of Mason Island, is wooded and grass-fringed. A shoal, on which are two rocky islets, extends about 0.2 mile northeastward from

Ram Island. **Ram Island Shoal**, extending nearly 0.5 mile westward from Ram Island, has little water over it and many rocks bare at low water. **Whaleback Rock** and the islet 300 yards northwestward of it are bare.

(267) The narrow but deep channel along the north side of Ram Island Shoal is the easterly entrance to Mystic Harbor. Between the shoal and Groton Long Point is an area of foul ground and several dangerous rocks, including **Whale Rock**, which bares at low water, at the northwesterly end of Ram Island Shoal. This rock is marked by a seasonal lighted buoy. Leading across the shoal is the buoyed channel, good for about 11 feet, which is used by vessels entering Mystic Harbor from westward.

(268) A rock covered 12 feet is 400 yards eastward of Groton Long Point; about 0.5 mile southerly of that rock is **Intrepid Rock**, with 13 feet over it and marked by a buoy, which should be avoided. **Mouse Island**, marked by several dwellings, is 150 yards southwestward of Morgan Point.

(269) In November 1983, a rock, covered about 2 feet, was reported 0.2 mile west of Mouse Island in about 41°18'52"N., 71°59'50"W.

(270) **Morgan Point**, on the west side at the entrance of Mystic Harbor, is marked by an abandoned light tower. A privately maintained and marked channel leading to the piers in **West Cove** at Noank westward of the point had a least depth of 4 feet reported in July 1981.

(271) **Groton Long Point**, on which is a summer settlement, is about 0.9 mile southwestward of Morgan Point. A reef extends nearly 300 yards southwestward from the point and is marked by a buoy. About 0.3 mile to the west a rock awash at low water is 175 yards off the southwest end of Groton Long Point. It is marked by a buoy.

(272) **Mystic Harbor**, about 6 miles westward of Watch Hill Point, is the approach to the towns of Noank and Mystic. A channel with two dredged sections leads from Fishers Island Sound through Mystic Harbor to the Mystic Seaport Museum Wharf, 0.6 mile northward of the highway bridge at Mystic on the Mystic River. In August-October 1987, the midchannel controlling depths were 10 feet to the highway bridge, thence 8 1/2 feet to the head of the Federal project. The channel is marked by buoys and a light. In November 1984, shoaling and timber debris were reported in the channel in the vicinity of the railroad swing bridge below Mystic.

(273) **Special anchorages** are in Mystic Harbor. (See **110.1, 110.50b**, and **110.50d**, chapter 2, for limits and regulations.)

(274) **Routes.**–To enter from eastward, lay a west-northwesterly course from south of the lighted bell buoy marking Napatree Point Ledge for a little over 3 miles to about 400 yards south of the buoy marking the south end of **Cormorant Reef**. From here steer 261° for the abandoned light tower on Morgan Point in range with the north end of the northern rocky islet off the north end of Ram Island until Mason Point is abeam. Then follow the buoyed channel.

(275) From westward, proceed cautiously from about 100 yards or more southward of the buoy southward of Groton Long Point on an easterly course for about 0.5 mile to Mystic Harbor Channel Buoy 1, then steer a northerly course through the buoyed channel into Mystic Harbor, rounding Noank Light 5 at a distance of about 75 yards.

(276) **Noank** is a town on the west side of the channel through Mystic Harbor. The mean range of the tide is about 2.3 feet. There are several small-craft facilities at Noank and in **West Cove**. Berths, electricity, gasoline, diesel fuel, water, ice, storage facilities, launching ramps, 30-ton mobile lift, and marine supplies are available; hull, engine, sail, and electronic repairs can be made. A **harbormaster** is at Noank.

(277) **Mystic River** flows into Mystic Harbor from northward just below Mystic. The river is used by recreational

MYSTIC

West Mystic

Mystic

Andrews
Island

Mystic
Harbor
Channel

Swing
Railway
Bridge

Mason
Island

Enders
Island

Fishers Island Sound

1976

craft, the local fishing fleet, and by transient craft visiting Mystic Seaport. An **anchorage area** with depths of 3½ to 7 feet is in the lower part of the river between Willow Point and Murphy Point. Ice usually closes the river during January and February.

(278)   **Willow Point**, 0.6 mile below Mystic, has several small-craft facilities that can provide berths, electricity, water, ice, some engine parts, and marine supplies. A 12-ton crane and 30-ton mobile hoist are available; hull and engine repairs can be made.

(279)   A channel, privately marked by daybeacons, leads from the vicinity of Willow Point for 0.3 mile in an easterly direction, thence about 0.4 mile northeastward to a marina on the west side of the mouth of **Pequotsepos Brook**, just below the Amtrak railroad bridge. Berths, electricity, water, ice, storage, marine supplies, a 12-ton mobile hoist, and hull and engine repairs are available. In July 1981, a reported depth of 4 feet could be carried in the channel to the marina.

(280)   Several small-craft facilities are on the northern end of Mason Island. Berths, electricity, water, ice, storage facilities, marine supplies, 25-ton mobile hoist, and hull and engine repairs are available. In July 1981, a reported depth of 4 feet could be carried to the facilities.

(281)   The Amtrak railroad bridge over Mystic River below Mystic has a swing span with a clearance of 8 feet. The U.S. Route 1 highway bridge at Mystic has a bascule span with a clearance of 4 feet. (See **117.1 through 117.59 and 117.211**, chapter 2, for drawbridge regulations.) The bridgetenders monitor VHF-FM channel 13; call signs KJA–842 and KXR–912, respectively. In 1983, a railroad swing bridge with a design clearance of 8½ feet was under construction immediately south of the railroad bridge; when completed it will replace the existing bridge.

(282)   **Mystic**, a town about 2 miles above Noank, has several small-craft facilities. Berths, electricity, gasoline, diesel fuel, water, ice, marine supplies, storage facilities, mobile hoists, and marine railways up to 110 feet are available; hull and engine repairs can be made. A **harbormaster** is at Mystic.

(283)   The **Mystic Seaport Museum** is about 0.6 mile above the highway bridge at Mystic. The whaler CHARLES W. MORGAN, full-rigged training ship JOSEPH CONRAD, and Grand Banks fishing schooner L. A. DUNTON are permanently moored at the museum and open to the public. Along the waterfront of the museum property, a mid-19th Century coastal village has been recreated with shops and lofts of that period. Collections of maritime relics are on exhibit in several formal museum buildings.

(284)   Above the Mystic Seaport Museum, the channel is very narrow and is marked by privately maintained seasonal daybeacons; boats of about 5-foot draft can be taken to the **Narrows**, and thence depths are 1 and 2 feet to **Old Mystic**. Twin fixed highway bridges crossing the Narrows have clearances of 25 feet. The stream follows the east bank to the

next narrows and the west bank to a marina in the bight about 0.3 mile below Old Mystic.

(285)   **Charts 13213, 13212, 13214.**–Mumford Cove is entered about 2 miles west of Mystic Harbor. A privately dredged channel leads northward from the entrance to the head of the cove; two spur channels lead eastward from the main channel, about 0.3 mile and 0.6 mile, respectively, above the entrance. The channels are marked by private seasonal buoys and daybeacons. In July 1981, the channels had a reported controlling depth of 2 feet.

(286)   **Special anchorages** are in the cove. (See **110.1 and 110.50c**, chapter 2, for limits and regulations.)

(287)   **Venetian Harbor** is a yacht basin on the east side of the entrance to Mumford Cove. A channel 75 feet wide leads through stone breakwaters into a basin with depths of about 3 to 7 feet. A submerged jetty extends along the channel from the outer end of the east breakwater. The entrance to the harbor is marked by a light on the outer end of the west breakwater.

(288)   **Horseshoe Reef**, 0.5 mile southward of Mumford Cove entrance, is awash at low water, and is marked by a buoy. Broken and rocky grounds extend from the reef to the shore eastward of Mumford Point.

(289)   **Vixen Ledge**, with a depth of 10 feet and marked by a buoy, is about 1 mile west of Horseshoe Reef. **Pine Island** is bluff and grassy, about 1.3 miles west of Mumford Point. It is surrounded by shoal water and rocky bottom, and is marked off the southwest side by a lighted bell buoy. A rock, covered 7 feet, in 41°18′35″ N., 72°03′17″W., is about 0.3 mile northwestward of Vixen Ledge.

(290)   A **special anchorage** is on the north side of Pine Island. (See **110.1 and 110.51**, chapter 2, for limits and regulations.)

(291)   The cove indenting the mainland northward of Pine Island and eastward of **Avery Point**, is entered between Avery Point and westward of Pine Island. The entrance to the cove is marked by two buoys just inside and eastward of Avery Point. Depths shoal from about 10 feet in the entrance to about 1 foot at the head of the cove. A breakwater, marked at its end by a private light, extends southeasterly from the east end of Avery Point. A yacht club, marina, and State launching ramp are in the cove. An unmarked rock awash is about 500 yards 060° from the former lighthouse tower at Avery Point. Berths, guest moorings, gasoline, electricity, water, ice, marine supplies, and a 14-ton mobile hoist are available at the marina; hull and engine repairs can be made. In July 1981, a reported depth of 5 feet could be carried to the marina.

(292)   Special purpose buoys maintained by the City of Groton show a **speed limit** of 5 m.p.h. in the area.

(293)   A **special anchorage** is in the cove. (See **110.1 and 110.51**, chapter 2, for limits and regulations.)

8. EASTERN LONG ISLAND SOUND

(1) This chapter describes the eastern portion of Long Island Sound following the north shore from Thames River to and including the Housatonic River, and then the south shore from Orient Point to and including Port Jefferson. Also described are the Connecticut River; the ports of New London, New Haven, and Northville; and the more important fishing and yachting centers on Niantic River and Bay, and in Westbrook Harbor, Guilford Harbor, Branford Harbor, and Mattituck Inlet.

(2) **COLREGS Demarcation Lines.**–The lines established for Long Island Sound are described in **80.155** chapter 2.

(3) **Chart 12354.**–**Long Island Sound** is a deep navigable waterway lying between the shores of Connecticut and New York and the northern coast of Long Island.

(4) In this region are boulders and broken ground, but little or no natural change in the shoals. The waters are well marked by navigational aids so that strangers should experience no difficulty in navigating them. As all broken ground is liable to be strewn with boulders, vessels should proceed with caution in the broken areas where the charted depths are not more than 6 to 8 feet greater than the draft. All of the more important places are entered by dredged channels; during fog, vessels are advised to anchor until the weather clears before attempting to enter. The numerous oyster grounds in this region are usually marked by stakes and flags. These stakes may become broken off and form obstructions dangerous to small craft. Mariners should proceed with caution especially at night.

(5) **Caution.**–Submarine operating areas are in the approaches to New London Harbor, Connecticut River, and off the northern shore of Long Island. As submarines may be operating submerged in these areas, vessels should proceed with caution.

(6) **Anchorages.**–New London Harbor is the most important of the anchorages sought for shelter in the eastern part of Long Island Sound. Niantic Bay and the approach between Bartlett Reef and Hatchett Reef are used to some extent by small vessels when meeting unfavorable weather or reaching the eastern part of the sound. Small vessels can select anchorage eastward or westward of Kelsey Point Breakwater, also in Duck Island Roads. Off Madison there is anchorage sheltered from northerly winds. New Haven Harbor is an important harbor of refuge.

(7) **Tides.**–The time of tide is nearly simultaneous throughout Long Island Sound, but the range of tide increases from about 2.5 feet at the east end to about 7.3 feet at the west end. Daily predictions of the times and heights of high and low waters for New London, Bridgeport, and Willets Point are given in the Tide Tables.

(8) The effect of strong winds, in combination with the regular tidal action, may at times cause the water to fall several feet below the plane of reference of the charts.

(9) **Currents.**–In the eastern portion of Long Island Sound the current turns from ½ to 1½ hours earlier along the north shore than in the middle of the sound.

(10) Proceeding westward from The Race in the middle of the sound, the velocity of current is 1.8 knots off Cornfield Point, about 1 knot off New Haven, 1 knot off Eatons Neck, 0.4 knot between Peningo Neck and Matinecock Point, and 0.5 knot eastward of Hart Island.

(11) About 1.5 miles east-southeastward of Barlett Reef, the velocity of flood is 1.2 knots and ebb 1.6 knots. The flood current sets 285° and the ebb 062°.

(12) At a point about 3 miles southward of Cornfield Point, the flood current sets 256° with a velocity of 2 knots and the ebb sets 094° with a velocity of 1.7 knots.

(13) About 1 mile north of Stratford Shoal (Middle Ground) Light, the velocity is 1 knot, the flood setting westward and the ebb eastward. (See Tidal Current Tables for predictions.) Current directions and velocities at various places throughout the eastern portion of Long Island Sound for each hour of the tidal cycle are shown on the Tidal Current Charts, Block Island Sound and Eastern Long Island Sound.

(14) **Weather.**–Weather is most favorable from mid-May to mid-October, when the most common hazards are thunderstorms and fog. There is also a rare threat of a tropical cyclone. During June, July and August on the average, there are 20 to 25 days per month with conditions generally considered ideal even for small boaters. Fog is most likely in spring and early summer. Fog, or the lack of it, at inland locations is not a guide to conditions in the Sound or its approaches. Areas along the coast, at the heads of bays and within rivers may be relatively clear, while offshore the fog is thick. For example, on exposed Block Island heavy fog is encountered about 10 to 12 percent of the time from April though August compared to 1 to 3 percent at Westhampton. Thunderstorms on the other hand are more likely over land, but can be viscous in the Sound, especially in a squall line preceding a cold front in spring and early summer. Winter winds are mostly out of the west through north, but gales blow less than 5 percent of the time in these somewhat sheltered waters. Waves are restricted by limited fetch except to the east. However, choppy conditions can create problems.

(15) **Ice.**–In ordinary winters the floating and pack ice in Long Island Sound, while impeding navigation, does not render it absolutely unsafe; but in exceptionally severe winters the reverse is true, none but powerful steamers can make their way.

(16) Drift ice, which is formed principally along the northern shore of the sound under the influence of the prevailing northerly winds, drifts across to the southern side and accumulates there, massing into large fields, and remains until removed by southerly winds, which drive it back to the northerly shore.

(17) In ordinary winters ice generally forms in the western end of the sound as far as Eatons Neck; in exceptionally severe winters ice may extend to Falkner Island and farther eastward.

(18) **Effects of winds on ice.**–In Long Island Sound northerly winds drive the ice to the southern shore of the sound and southerly winds carry it back to the northern shore. Northeasterly winds force the ice westward and cause formations heavy enough to prevent the passage of vessels of every description until the ice is removed by westerly winds. These winds carry the ice eastward and, if of long duration, drive it through The Race into Block Island Sound, thence it goes to sea and disappears.

(19) In New Haven Harbor, the influence of the northerly winds clear the harbor and its approaches unless the local formation is too heavy to be moved. Southerly winds force

the drift ice in from the sound and prevent the local formations from leaving the harbor. Tides have little effect upon the ice. Additional information concerning ice conditions in the waters adjoining Long Island Sound is given under the local descriptions.

(20)   **Vessel Traffic Service (New York),** operated by the U.S. Coast Guard, serves New York Harbor (see **161.501 through 161.580,** chapter 2, for regulations).

(21)   **Pilotage, Long Island Sound.**–Pilotage is compulsary in Long Island Sound for foreign vessels and U.S. vessels under register.

(22)   The pilot boat sets radio guard at least 1 hour before a vessel's ETA.

(23)   Vessels to be boarded should provide a ladder 3 feet above the water on the lee side.

(24)   Pilot services are generally arranged at least 24 hours in advance through ships' agents or directly by shipping companies.

(25)   Pilotage, in the waters of Long Island Sound, is available from, but not limited to:

(26)   Sound Pilots, Inc. (a division of Northeast Marine Pilots, Inc.), 243 Spring Street, Newport RI 02840, telephone 401-847-9050 (24 hours), 800-274-1216, FAX 401-847-9052, Cable RISPILOT, Newport. Pilot boats are RHODE ISLAND PILOT, 35-foot, black hull, white superstructure, word PILOT on sides; NORTHEAST I, 49-foot, black hull, white superstructure, word PILOT on sides; and NORTHEAST II, 49-foot, gray hull, gray superstructure, word PILOT on sides. The boat monitor channels 16, 10, 13, 14; work on 10.

(27)   Connecticut State Pilots (a division of Interport Pilots Agency, Inc.), State Pier, New London, CT 06320, telephone 800-346-4877 or 908-787-5554, FAX 908-787-5538, cable PORTPILOTS. Pilot boats are CONNECTICUT PILOT, 65-foot, with blue hull, white superstructure; CONNECTICUT PILOT II, 47-foot, with blue hull, and white superstructure. The boat monitors channels 16 and 13, works on 11.

(28)   Constitution State Pilots Association, 500 Waterfront Street, New Haven, CT 06512, telephone 800-229-7456 or 203-783-5991, FAX 516-582-6327. The pilot boat CONSTITUTION, is 65-foot, with black hull, white superstructure, and the word PILOT on sides. The boat monitors 16, 13, and 9A; works on 13 or 9A.

(29)   Long Island Sound State Pilots Association, Inc., 1440 Whalley Avenue, Suite 123, New Haven, CT 06515, telephone 203-772-0101, FAX 302-629-9392, Cable LISPILOT, New Haven. The pilot boat LONG ISLAND SOUND PILOT, is 46-foot, with black hull, white superstructure, and the word PILOT in black letters. The boat monitors channel 16; works on 11.

(30)   See Pilotage, New London-Groton (indexed as such), this chapter; Pilotage, New Haven (indexed as such), this chapter; Pilotage, Bridgeport (indexed as such), chapter 9; Pilotage, Offshore Terminal, Northville-Riverhead (indexed as such), this chapter; see Pilotage, Offshore Terminal, Northport (indexed as such), chapter 9.

(31)   **Charts 13213, 13212, 12372.**–New London Harbor, near the east end of Long Island Sound at the mouth of the **Thames River,** is an important harbor of refuge. Vessels of deep draft can find anchorage here in any weather and at all seasons.

(32)   Waterborne commerce in New London Harbor and on the Thames River is chiefly in petroleum products, chemicals, lumber, pulpwood, and general cargo.

(33)   **Security Zones** have been established in New London Harbor. (See **165.1 through 165.7, 165.30, 165.33, and 165.140,** chapter 2, for limits and regulations.)

(34)   **New London** is a city on the west bank of Thames River about 2.5 miles above the mouth. The town of **Groton** on the east bank is connected to New London by a highway bridge and a railroad bridge. The main harbor comprises the lower 3 miles of Thames River from Long Island Sound to the bridges, and includes Shaw Cove, Greens Harbor, and Winthrop Cove. It is approached through the main entrance channel extending from deep water in Long Island Sound to deep water in the upper harbor. The harbor is generally used by vessels drawing 9 to 30 feet; the deepest draft entering is about 36 feet. Petroleum products, molasses, sulfuric acid, woodpulp, hemp fiber, coconut products, and lumber are the principal waterborne products handled at the port.

(35)   **Greens Harbor,** a small-craft shelter just north of the entrance, has general depths of 6 to 17 feet. **Special anchorages** are in the harbor. (See **110.1** and **110.52,** chapter 2, for limits and regulations.)

(36)   **New London Coast Guard Station** is at **Fort Trumbull,** on the west side of main channel northward of Greens Harbor.

(37)   **Shaw Cove** is a dredged basin about 0.8 mile northward of Greens Harbor. In February 1986, the controlling depth was 15 feet in the entrance channel through the south draw of the bridge, thence depths of 11 to 15 feet were available in the basin. The railroad bridge over the entrance has a swing span with clearances of 6½ feet. (See **117.1 through 117.59** and **117.223,** chapter 2, for drawbridge regulations.)

(38)   **Winthrop Cove,** northward of Shaw Cove, is part of the main waterfront channel. The fixed railroad bridge near the head of this cove has a clearance of 4 feet.

(39)   **Prominent features.**–New London Ledge Light (41°18.3′N., 72°04.7′ W.), 58 feet above the water, is shown from a red brick building on a square white pier on the west side of New London Ledge; a fog signal is sounded at the station.

(40)   Other prominent features in approaching New London Harbor are: New London Harbor Light, on the west side of the entrance channel; the training tank at the submarine base; the globular tank at Fort Trumbull; the monument at Fort Griswold; the microwave tower atop a building in downtown New London; the large sheds at the shipyard on the east side of the river opposite Fort Trumbull; and the highway bridge at New London.

(41)   **Channels.**–A U.S. Navy project for New London Harbor provides for a channel 40 feet deep to Fort Trumbull, thence 38 feet to State Pier No. 1, thence 36 feet to the U.S. Navy Submarine Base. A Federal project provides for a channel 23 feet deep in the waterfront channels north of Fort Trumbull and in Winthrop Cove. (See Notice to Mariners and latest editions of the charts for controlling depths.) Lighted and unlighted buoys and a 354° lighted range mark the channel. The range does not mark the center of the lower end of the channel.

(42)   **Pine Island Channel,** northeastward of New London Ledge Light, between Pine Island and Black Ledge, has a rocky and very broken bottom on which the least found depth is 10 feet. It is used some by local vessels between New London Harbor and Fishers Island Sound, but should be avoided by any vessel drawing more than 10 feet.

(43)   **Anchorages.**–General and naval anchorages are in the approaches to, and in, New London Harbor. (See **110.1 and 110.147,** chapter 2, for limits and regulations.) Special anchorages are in Greens Harbor and in the vicinity of the U.S. Coast Guard Academy. (See **110.1 and 110.52,** chapter 2, for limits and regulations.)

NEW LONDON HARBOR

New London

Greens Harbor

Thames River

Groton

Hobs Island

1976

Legend
1 White Rock
2 Powder Island
3 Fort Trumbull
4 Long Dock
5 State Pier
6 Winthrop Point

(44) **Dangers.**–On the west side of the approach to New London Harbor, foul ground extends about 1 mile from shore in the vicinity of **Goshen Point** (chart 13211). The southerly and southeasterly limits of this area are marked by buoys. The area has numerous rocky patches and boulders, some showing above water, and should be avoided by small craft. **Rapid Rock,** marked by a buoy on its southeast side, is about 1.6 miles southwestward of New London Ledge Light. It has a least depth of 11 feet. An unmarked ledge covered 38 feet is about 750 yards southeast of Rapid Rock and is the outermost shoal to the southward. **Sarah Ledge,** 0.7 mile northeastward of Rapid Rock and marked by a buoy, has a least depth of 16 feet and is the easternmost shoal on the west side of the main channel approach.

(45) On the east side of the main channel foul ground extends about 1 mile offshore. **New London Ledge,** marked by New London Ledge Light, has a least depth of 7 feet. **Black Ledge,** just to the northeastward of New London Ledge, has a rocky islet, 2 feet high, on it. Depths are 2 to 16 feet on the ledge. Buoys mark the shoal area.

(46) Broken ground fringes the shore southwestward of New London Harbor Light. Rocks with 2 to 11 feet over them extend about 0.2 mile from shore in the bight just southward of the light.

(47) **White Rock,** an islet in Greens Harbor, is 200 yards from the 18-foot curve on the western edge of the channel. **Hog Back,** a small ledge awash at low water, is 150 yards southwestward of White Rock and about 0.3 mile from the western shore, and is marked by two buoys. Rocks, covered 3 to 6 feet, are in the middle of the northern part of Greens Harbor. **Melton Ledge,** northward of White Rock, with one-half foot over it, is 125 yards eastward of **Powder Island** and is marked by a buoy; a rock awash is close westward of Melton Ledge.

(48) **Bridges.**–Four bridges cross the Thames River below Norwich: three near Winthrop Point and one about 0.2 miles southward of Fort Point. The first is the railroad bridge, which has a bascule span with a clearance of 30 feet. (See **117.1 through 117.59 and 117.224,** chapter 2, for drawbridge regulations.) The bridgetender of the railroad bridge monitors VHF-FM channel 13; call sign KT-5473. Just above it are two high-level fixed bridges with clearances of 135 feet, and 7.9 miles farther up the Thames is a fixed highway bridge with a clearance of 75 feet.

(49) Overhead power cables with a clearance of 160 feet cross the river about 5.5 miles below Norwich.

(50) **Tides and currents.**–The mean range of tide at New London is 2.6 feet. Daily predictions are given in the Tide Tables.

(51) The tidal currents follow the general direction of the channel and usually are not strong. At Winthrop Point, on the west side of the river at New London, the velocity is 0.4 knot, and at Stoddard Hill, about 6.5 miles above New London, 0.7 knot on the flood and 0.4 knot on the ebb. During freshets or when the river is high and the wind is from the north, the current can have considerable southerly set even on the flood. Current directions and velocities at various places on the Thames River for each hour of the tidal cycle are shown on the Tidal Current Charts, Block Island Sound and Eastern Long Island Sound.

(52) **Ice** obstructs navigation about 2 months each year above the naval station, which is some 5 miles above New London Ledge Light, but seldom forms below the station. In extremely severe winters, however, heavy ice from the sound, driven in by winds, has been known to extend about 1.8 miles above the entrance. Between New London and the mouth of the river small vessels may navigate with comparative safety in ordinary winters; and even in severe weather it is rare that navigation for small vessels stops for more than a week. Steamers can nearly always enter and leave with safety. Drift ice sometimes forms a decidedly dangerous obstruction in the approaches through Long Island Sound during severe winters, especially during February and March; and small vessels are much hindered in their movements during January, February, and March.

(53) **Freshets** usually occur in the river in the spring. It is reported that they seldom exceed 2 feet above high water at Norwich.

(54) New London Harbor and Thames River are easy of access by day or night, but local knowledge is required to take drafts greater than 20 feet above the submarine base.

(55) **Pilotage, New London-Groton.**–Pilotage is compulsary in Long Island Sound for foreign vessels and U.S. vessels under register. See Pilotage, Long Island Sound (indexed as such),chapter 8. Pilotage for New London is available from: New London Connecticut Pilots Association (NLCPA), 239 Ocean Avenue, New London, CT 06320, telephone 203-443-4431 or 203-443-2401. Pilot boat JM5, 35-foot, red hull, white superstructure, word PILOT on sides. The boat monitors channel 13; works 18 and 79. A NLCPA pilot boards a ship about 2 miles south of New London Ledge Light. The NLCPA requests a 48-hour advance notice of arrival with updates at 24, 12, and 6 hours.

(56) Pilotage for New London is also available from Constitution State Pilots Association (CSPA), 500 Waterfront Street, New Haven, CT 06512, telephone 800-229-7456 or 203-783-5991, FAX 516-582-6327. Pilot boat CONSTITUTION is 65-foot, with black hull, white superstructure, and the word PILOT on sides. The boat monitors 16, 13, and 9A, works on 13 or 9A. The CSPA pilot will meet a New London bound vessel about 2 miles south of New London Ledge Light; also will meet a vessel off Montauk Point. See Pilotage Pickup Locations Off Montauk Point (indexed as such), chapter 7.

(57) Pilotage for New London is also available from Long Island Sound State Pilots Association, Inc. (LISSPA), 1440 Whalley Avenue, Suite 123, New Haven, CT 06515, telephone 203-772-0101, FAX 302-629-9392, Cable LISPILOT, New Haven. Pilot boat LONG ISLAND SOUND PILOT is 46-foot, with black hull, white superstructure, and the word PILOT in black letters. The boat monitors channel 16; works on 11. Among other locations, the LISSPA pilot will meet a ship off Montauk Point. See Pilotage Pickup Locations Off Montauk Point (indexed as such), chapter 7.

(58) Pilotage for New London is also available from Sound Pilots, Inc. (SPI) (a division of Northeast Marine Pilots, Inc.), 243 Spring Street, Newport, RI 02840, telephone 401-847-9050 (24 hours), 800-274-1216, FAX 401-847-9052, Cable RISPILOT, Newport, RI 02840. The pilot boats are NORTHEAST II, 49-foot, with grey hull and superstructure and the word PILOT on the side; or RHODE ISLAND PILOT, 35-foot, with black hull and white superstructure and the word PILOT on the side; or NORTHEAST I, 49-foot, similiarly marked as the RHODE ISLAND PILOT. The SPI pilots meet a ship bound for a Long Island Sound port, off Point Judith, but will also meet a ship off Montauk Point by prearrangement. See Pilotage, Narragansett Bay and Other Rhode Island Waters (indexed as such), chapter 6, and Pilotage Pickup Locations Off Montauk Point (indexed as such), chapter 7.

(59) **Towage.**–Tugs to 3,200 hp are available at New London. Vessels usually proceed to the upper harbor without assistance, although a tug may be required when entering with a head wind and contrary current. Large vessels normally require tugs for docking and undocking.

(60) New London is a **customs port of entry.**

(61) **Quarantine, customs, immigration, and agricultural quarantine.**–(See chapter 3, Vessel Arrival Inspections, and appendix for addresses.)

(62) **Quarantine** is enforced in accordance with regulations of the U.S. Public Health Service. (See Public Health Service, chapter 1.) New London has several hospitals.

(63) **Coast Guard.**–The **Captain of the Port** maintains an office at the New London Coast Guard Station. (See appendix for address.)

(64) **Harbor regulations** are in force for New London Harbor. The harbormaster has authority to berth vessels, shifting them if necessary, but occasion for doing so seldom arises.

(65) **Wharves.**–New London Harbor has more than 30 wharves and piers. Most of these facilities are used as repair berths, and for mooring recreational craft, fishing vessels, barges, ferries, and government vessels. Depths alongside these facilities range from 10 to 40 feet. Only the deep-draft facilities are described. For a complete description of the port facilities refer to Port Series No. 4, published and sold by the U.S. Army Corps of Engineers. (See appendix for address.) The alongside depths are reported; for information on the latest depths contact the private operator.

(66) **Amerada Hess Corp. Wharf** (41°20′09″N., 72°04′58″W.): on the east side of the river opposite Greens Harbor; T-head pier with 55-foot face, 960 feet of berthing space with dolphins; 40 feet alongside; deck height, 8 feet; pipelines to storage tanks; fresh water connection; railroad and highway connections; receipt and shipment of petroleum products and receipt of molasses; bunkering vessels; owned and operated by Hess Oil and Chemical Division, Amerada Hess Corp.

(67) **State Pier No. 1:** the more easterly of the two long piers southwestward of the Thames River bridges, about 1.3 miles northward of Amerada Hess Corp. Wharf; 200-foot face, 28 to 32 feet alongside; west side 1,000 feet, 28 to 36 feet alongside; east side 1,020 feet, 36 to 38 feet alongside; deck height, 10 feet; 20-ton crane; 153,000 square feet of covered storage, 5 acres open storage; electricity and potable and feed water connections on pier; railroad and highway connections; receipt and shipment of general cargo, woodpulp, copper, hemp, and paper products and mooring naval vessels; owned by State of Connecticut, west side operated by New London Terminal Co., east side and face by U.S. Navy.

(68) **Supplies** of all kinds are available. Gasoline and diesel oil can be obtained from oil companies on 48 hours' notice by tank truck. Water is available at most of the piers, wharves, and marinas.

(69) **Repairs.**–A shipbuilding company at New London can perform all kinds of repairs on steel-hulled vessels. The company has a floating drydock in Winthrop Cove. The drydock has a length of 180 feet, width of 84 feet, and a lifting capacity of 2,000 tons.

(70) Cranes to 70 tons and floating derricks to 25 tons are available at New London.

(71) Several companies in New London are in the business of wrecking, salvage, and marine contracting work. They are equipped with pumps, divers' outfits, floating equipment, and other gear.

(72) **Small-craft facilities.**–There are numerous small-craft facilities in Greens Harbor and Shaw Cove. (See the small-craft facilities tabulation on chart 12372 for services and supplies available.

(73) **Communications.**–New London has good railroad and bus communications. Automobile-passenger ferry service is available to Block Island, Fishers Island, and to Orient Point, Long Island.

(74) Thames River above New London has a dredged channel to Norwich, the head of navigation. In January-June 1978, the controlling depth was 35 feet from above the bridges at New London to the north end of the turning basin opposite Smith Cove, thence in August-September 1974, depths of 16 feet (23 feet at midchannel) to Stoddard Hill, and thence 18 feet to the turning basin at Norwich, and 11 feet in the turning basin. The channel is well marked by navigational aids.

(75) **Caution.**–The dikes along the Thames River from Easter Point (41°28.2′N., 72°04.5′W.) to Norwich are submerged at half tide.

(76) **Pilots** for the river are available at New London.

(77) The **U.S. Coast Guard Academy** is on the west side of Thames River about 1 mile north of the center of New London. The administration building, with its white tower and clock, and the lighted chapel spire are very prominent, but are not visible until almost abeam of the academy. Depths alongside the 410-foot-long academy pier are reported to be 17 feet at the face, 19 feet along the south side, and 15 to 17 feet on the north side.

(78) The **U.S. Naval Submarine Base** is on the east side of the Thames River about 2 miles above New London. The submarine escape training tank at the base, 143 feet high with a flashing white light atop, is prominent.

(79) A **restricted area** is off the U.S. Naval Submarine Base. (See 334.75, chapter 2, for limits and regulations.)

(80) Just below **Gales Ferry**, on the east side about 4 miles above the bridges, are the crew training quarters and boathouses of Harvard and Yale Universities. Opposite Gales Ferry is the town of **Bartlett**, site of a prominent power plant with two tall and conspicuous stacks. A privately dredged channel with depths of about 19 feet leads to the dock and coal tipple.

(81) At **Montville Station**, just above Bartlett, is a dock with a depth of 23 feet at the face. The northeast end of the dock is in ruins. Overhead power cables with a clearance of 160 feet cross the river 0.5 mile above the station near **Kitemaug**.

(82) **Allyn Point**, on the east side about 5 miles above New London, is the site of a large private pier for receiving liquid chemicals, with a reported depth of about 30 feet alongside. It is marked by an elevated water sphere and several small tanks on the pier.

(83) **Fort Point**, on the east side 8 miles above New London, has a long fuel pier marked by privately maintained red lights, and on shore is a building with several stacks. Numerous piles are in the water southward of the pier. The fixed highway bridge crossing the river about 0.2 miles south of Fort Point has a clearance of 75 feet.

(84) The red brick buildings of the Norwich State Hospital are on a bluff just north of Fort Point and are a conspicuous landmark.

(85) At **Thamesville**, on the west side of the river about 1 mile below Norwich, are two finger piers each with breasting dolphins used to receive petroleum products from barges. Depths of 20 to 25 feet are reported alongside the face of the piers.

(86) **Norwich**, a city at the head of navigation on Thames River at its junction with **Shetucket River** and **Yantic River**, is about 11 miles above New London. In 1981, waterborne commerce to Norwich consisted of petroleum products. Small boats generally anchor in Shetucket River just above the fixed bridges at Norwich, which have a minimum clearance of 13 feet.

(87) **Charts 13211, 13212, 12372.**–Bartlett Reef Light (41°16.5′N., 72°08.2′W.), 35 feet above the water and shown

from a skeleton tower with a red and white diamond-shaped daymark, is about 3.3 miles southwestward of New London Ledge Light and marks the south end of **Bartlett Reef.** A fog signal is at the light. The reef, about 1.3 miles long in a general north-south direction and about 0.3 mile wide, is covered 2 to 12 feet and has rocks awash near its northern end. The north end of the reef is marked by a buoy. A lighted bell buoy and an unlighted buoy are about 0.9 mile southward and about 0.3 mile eastward of the light, respectively.

(88)   **A general anchorage** is about 0.8 mile northeastward of Bartlett Reef Light. (See **110.1 and 110.147 (a) (4),** and **(b),** chapter 2, for limits and regulations.)

(89)   **Twotree Island,** small and bare, about 1.4 miles northwestward of Bartlett Reef Light, is surrounded by shoals. A buoy marks rocks awash that extend off the northern end of the island.

(90)   **Twotree Island Channel** leads northward of Bartlett Reef and Twotree Island. With an adverse current in the sound, this channel is used to some extent by light tows and sailboats with a leading wind in the daytime, as the tidal currents turn about 1 hour earlier along the north shore than in the middle of the sound. About 0.3 mile southwestward of **Seaside,** the tidal currents have a velocity of 1.2 knots, and ebb 1.6 knots. Flood sets westerly and the ebb easterly. The channel is buoyed, but strangers are advised to use it with caution and should never attempt to beat through.

(91)   From **Goshen Point** (41°18.0′ N., 72°06.8′W.) westward, there are scattered boulders which extend offshore as much as 0.2 mile in places. **Jordan Cove,** 1.5 miles west of Goshen Point, is foul in its northerly half, and the southerly part is obstructed by **Flat Rock,** bare at low water and marked by a buoy, and **High Rock,** which shows at high water and is marked by a buoy.

(92)   **Millstone Point,** on the east side at the entrance of Niantic Bay, is occupied by the buildings of the Millstone Nuclear Power Station. A 389-foot red and white stack at the station and a radio tower on the point are the most conspicuous landmarks in the area. A cove with depths of 9 to 15 feet is on the west side of the point. A rock with 1 foot over it lies 60 feet off the mouth of the cove. The station maintains channel markers and a range for occasional barge traffic. A dredged area for the power station's water intakes is 0.2 mile northwest of the cove.

(93)   **Charts 13211, 12372.–White Rock** is an islet on the east side of the entrance to Niantic Bay 0.5 mile westward of Millstone Point. **Little Rock,** two rocks partly bare at low water, is 150 yards east of White Rock. A rock over which the least depth is 8 feet is about midway between Little Rock and the cove at Millstone Point. A shoal spot, covered 12 feet, is 200 yards eastward of the rock. A rock, covered 14 feet, is about 300 yards south-southeast of White Rock and is marked by a lighted bell buoy.

(94)   **Niantic Bay,** 4.5 miles westward of New London Harbor, is a good anchorage sheltered from easterly, northerly, and westerly winds. It is a harbor of refuge in northerly gales and can be used by small vessels and tows. The general depth of the bay is about 19 feet; the water shoals gradually northward. The entrance is 1.5 miles wide, and the dangers are marked by buoys or show above water.

(95)   **Niantic** and **Crescent Beach** are summer resorts with railroad communication at the north end and northwest side of the bay.

(96)   The Niantic Bay Yacht Club basin at Crescent Beach is protected on the south, east, and partially on the north side by a U-shaped breakwater; a private seasonal light is near the outer end of the breakwater.

(97)   **A special anchorage** is on the west side of Niantic Bay off Crescent Beach. (See **110.1** and **110.53,** chapter 2, for limits and regulations.)

(98)   **Niantic River** empties into the northeast end of Niantic Bay and is entered through a dredged channel that leads from the bay, thence through a narrow passage at the entrance, and thence to a point about 300 yards northward of the entrance to Smith Cove. In August-October 1988, the controlling depth was 6 feet at midchannel to the highway swing bridge about 0.4 mile above the channel entrance, thence 4½ feet to the head of the channel. The channel is marked by daybeacons and seasonal buoys. Two bridges cross the narrow passage at the entrance. The more southerly is the Amtrak bridge, with a 45-foot bascule span and a clearance of 11 feet; the State Route 156 highway bridge, about 0.1 mile northward, has a swing span with a clearance of 9 feet. (See **117.1 through 117.59 and 117.215,** chapter 2, for drawbridge regulations.) The bridgetender at each bridge monitors VHF-FM channel 13; call signs KGA-511 and KXR–911, respectively. In May 1989, a replacement bascule highway bridge with a design clearance of 30 feet was under construction just south of the existing bascule bridge.

(99)   Strangers attempting to enter Niantic River are cautioned to pass through the bridges either at slack water or against the current.

(100)   Above the head of the dredged channel, small craft can navigate for about another 1.5 miles to **Golden Spur (East Lyme)** with local knowledge. The river from westward of Sandy Point to the stone bulkhead at Golden Spur is deep and clear; vessels generally follow the west bank. **Pine Grove, Sandy Point,** and **Saunders Point** are summer resorts on Niantic River.

(101)   The mean range of **tide** is about 2.7 feet in Niantic Bay.

(102)   The **tidal currents** through the bridges set fair with the channel; the flood velocity is 1.6 knots and the ebb velocity, 0.8 knot. It has been reported that much greater velocities may be expected under storm and freshet conditions. (See Tidal Current Tables for predictions.) Current directions and velocities for the entrance to the Niantic River for each hour of the tidal cycle are shown on the Tidal Current Charts, Block Island Sound and Eastern Long Island Sound.

(103)   **Ice** generally closes the river to navigation for about 3 months during the winter.

(104)   **Smith Cove** is on the west side of Niantic River about 1.5 miles above the channel entrance. A channel, marked by private daybeacons, leads westward from the river channel into the cove. In July 1981, the channel had a reported depth of 5 feet.

(105)   There are several small-craft facilities just above the entrance at Niantic and **Waterford,** on the west side and east side of Niantic River, respectively, and in Smith Cove. (See the small-craft facilities tabulation on chart 12372 for services and supplies available.) **Harbormasters** are at Niantic and Waterford. A 6 mph **speed limit** is enforced on the river.

(106)   **Black Point,** on the west side at the entrance to Niantic Bay, is flat with bluffs at the water and is occupied by many summer cottages. Broken ground with a least found depth of 20 feet extends 0.6 mile south of the southwest side of the point.

(107)   The bight between Black Point and Hatchet Point, about 2.3 miles to the westward, has many rocks showing above high water. **Griswold Island,** on the northeast side of the bight, is high and prominent. Rocks extend 0.35 mile

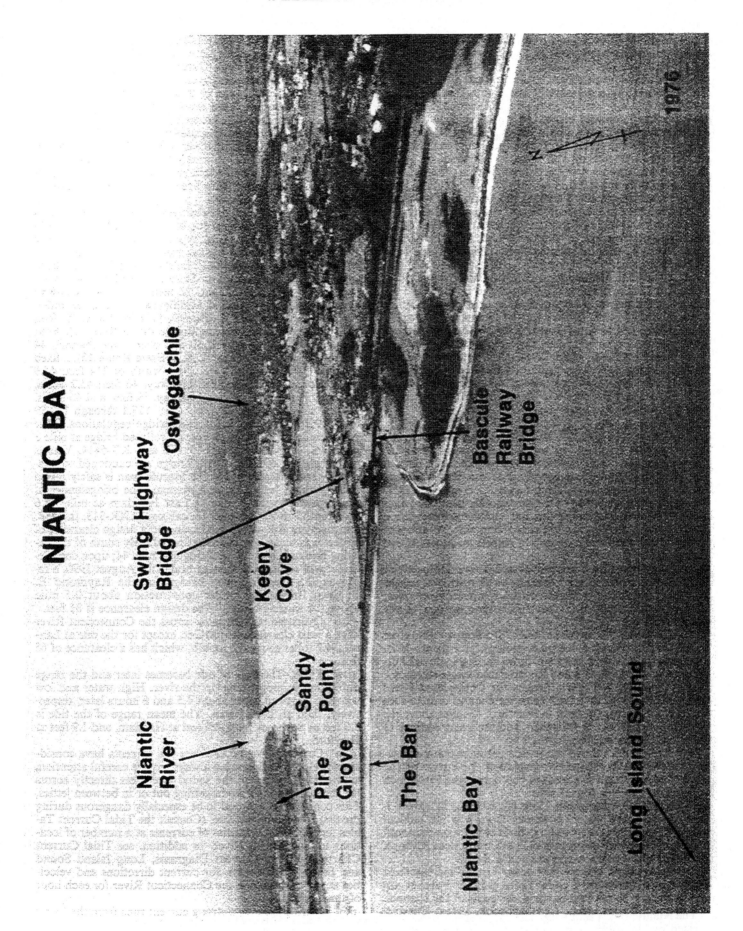

NIANTIC BAY

Oswegatchie

Swing Highway
Bridge

Keeny
Cove

Bascule
Railway
Bridge

Sandy
Point

Niantic
River

Pine
Grove

The Bar

Niantic Bay

Long Island Sound

N

1976

southward and 0.2 mile southwestward of the island. The southwest rocks are marked by a buoy. **South Brother**, in the center, and **North Brother**, in the northwestern part of the bight, are prominent bare rocks. A rock, covered 6 feet, is 250 yards off the west side of Black Point. **Blackboys**, two rocks awash are 0.4 mile southward of Griswold Island. A rock, covered 3 feet and marked by a buoy, is about 0.2 mile southward of Blackboys. **Johns Rock**, covered 5 feet, is 0.3 mile off the northwest side of the bight, about 0.5 mile west-southwestward of South Brother; the range of South Brother well open northward of Griswold Island leads southward of Johns Rock.

(108)   Strangers entering the bight should proceed with caution, as the bottom is broken; the best route is to pass southward and westward of the buoy southward of Blackboys, and pass on either side of South Brother. **Seal Rock**, 160 yards south of the end of **Giants Neck**, is marked by a buoy on the south side.

(109)   A **special anchorage** is east of Giants Neck. (See **110.1** and **110.54**, chapter 2, for limits and regulations.) An unmarked rock is within the anchorage area, about 0.1 mile south of Giants Neck; depth over the rock is not known.

(110)   **Hatchett Point** has several large dwellings. A reef extends about 0.2 mile off the southwest side of the point.

(111)   **Hatchett Reef**, 0.6 to 1 mile south-southwestward of Hatchett Point, has a least depth of 5 feet and is marked by buoys. Close to the southeast side of the reef the depths are 30 to 48 feet. A bar with 10 to 16 feet over it extends westward from Hatchett Reef to Saybrook Bar.

(112)   **Charts 12375, 12377, 12372.**–Connecticut River rises in the extreme northern part of New Hampshire, near the Canadian border, and flows southerly between the States of Vermont and New Hampshire and across Massachusetts and Connecticut to Long Island Sound. It is approximately 375 miles long and is one of the largest and most important rivers in New England. The head of commercial navigation is at Hartford, about 45 miles from the mouth. Waterborne commerce on the river is mostly in petroleum products and chemicals.

(113)   The river water is fresh at and above Deep River. Each year after the spring freshets, shoals with least depths of 10 feet are found in places on bars in the upper river; dredging to remove such shoals is begun as soon as the water subsides.

(114)   Between the entrance and Middletown the river banks are hard and in some places rocky, but between Middletown and Hartford the river flows through alluvial bottom land, where freshets and ice jams may cause shoaling.

(115)   **Channels.**–A Federal project for Connecticut River provides for a 15-foot jettied entrance channel and 15-foot dredged cuts across the bars to Hartford, 45 miles above the entrance. (See Notice to Mariners and the latest editions of the charts for controlling depths.)

(116)   The channel above the jettied entrance channel usually follows the banks on the outside of the curves of the river, except through the dredged cuts across the bars which are marked by navigational aids.

(117)   **Saybrook Breakwater Light** (41°15.8'N., 72°20.6'W.), 58 feet above the water, is shown from a white conical tower, 49 feet high, on a brown cylindrical pier on the south end of the west jetty at the entrance to Connecticut River. A fog signal and a radiobeacon are at the light.

(118)   **Anchorages.**–Secure anchorage can be had eastward or northeastward of Lynde Point Light. Farther up anchorage can be selected in the wider parts of the channel. Special anchorages are at Old Saybrook, Essex, Chester, Lord Island, Eddy Rock Shoal in the vicinity of Connecticut

River Light 45, and Mouse Island Bar vicinity. (See **110.1** and **110.55**, chapter 2, for limits and regulations.)

(119)   **Dangers.**–Saybrook Outer Bar, which obstructs the mouth of the Connecticut River, is shifting, with depths of 4 to 12 feet extending nearly 2 miles off the mouth; it is marked off its southeastern end by a lighted bell buoy.

(120)   In March 1976, obstructions were reported in the channel at the railroad bascule bridge 3 miles above the mouth of the Connecticut River; a least depth of 13 feet is reported in the channel in area 40 to 50 feet from the east abutment of the bridge. Mariners requiring greater depths are advised to avoid this area of the channel during passages.

(121)   **Bridges.**–Several drawbridges and fixed bridges cross Connecticut River between the entrance and Hartford. The distance above the mouth, type, and clearance of each bridge follows: 3 miles, Amtrak railroad with bascule span, 19 feet; 3.5 miles, Raymond E. Baldwin (IS 95) Bridge, fixed highway, 81 feet; 14.6 miles, State Route 82 highway with swing span at East Haddam, 22 feet; 27.8 miles, ConRail railroad with swing span at Middletown, 25 feet; 28 miles, Arrigoni Bridge (State Route 66), fixed highway, 92 feet; 41.2 miles, Wm. H. Putnam Bridge (State Route 3), fixed highway near Wethersfield, 80 feet over main channel; 44 miles, **Charter Oak Bridge (U.S. 5/State Route 15)**, a fixed highway at Hartford, 81 feet for a width of 214 feet; 44.9 miles, Founders Bridge, fixed highway, 46 feet; 45.2 miles, Bulkeley Bridge (I-84), fixed highway, 39 feet; and 46 miles, Conrail fixed railroad, 28 feet. (See **117.1 through 117.59 and 117.205**, chapter 2, for drawbridge regulations.) The bridgetender of the Amtrak bascule railroad bridge at mile 3 monitors VHF-FM channel 13; call sign KT-5414. Vessels requesting the opening of this bridge are cautioned to confirm by radiotelephone that the bascule span is safely raised and stabilized before making passage. The bridgetender of the highway swing bridge at East Haddam at mile 14.6 monitors VHF-FM channel 13; call sign KXR-913. In 1988, a highway bridge with a fixed span and a design clearance of 65 feet was under construction immediately south of the existing bridge (Charter Oak Bridge) at mile 44; upon completion it will replace the existing bridge. In August 1990, a replacement fixed highway bridge for the Raymond E. Baldwin Bridge was under construction about 0.5 mile above the existing bridge. The design clearance is 81 feet.

(122)   Overhead power cables across the Connecticut River have a least clearance of 100 feet, except for the one at **Laurel**, 24.2 miles above the mouth, which has a clearance of 65 feet.

(123)   **Tides.**–The time of tide becomes later and the range diminishes in progressing up the river. High water and low water at Hartford occur about 4.5 and 6 hours later, respectively, than at the entrance. The mean range of the tide is 3.5 feet at Saybrook jetty, 2.5 feet at Haddam, and 1.9 feet at Hartford.

(124)   **Currents.**–At the entrance the currents have considerable velocity at times and always require careful attention, as the tidal current of the sound often sets directly across the direction of the current setting out or in between jetties. This condition is reported to be especially dangerous during the first 3 hours of ebb tide. (Consult the Tidal Current Tables for times and velocities of currents at a number of locations in Connecticut River. In addition, see Tidal Current Charts and Tidal Current Diagrams, Long Island Sound and Block Island Sound, for current directions and velocities at various places in the Connecticut River for each hour of the tidal cycle.)

(125)   During the ebb, a strong current runs from the Lyme Landing toward the center of the railroad bridge. Towboats

with vessels in tow should steer for the east pier of the draw and should not swing out for the draw until almost in it, to avoid being set to the west side of the channel. Because of river discharge, the ebb current usually will be considerably stronger than the flood. Ebb current velocities of 1 knot or more have been observed under normal conditions on the bars in Connecticut River between Higganum and Hartford; the velocities of the flood currents are much less.

(126)   **Freshets** occur principally in the spring, when the snow is melting, although occasional floods have occurred in every month of the year except July and September. At Hartford the usual rise due to spring freshets is between 16 and 24 feet. The highest freshets are generally of short duration, but the period during which the river at Hartford is at the level of 8 feet or more above mean low water averages nearly 2 months of each year. Below Middletown the height of the crest of a freshet decreases rapidly. At the mouth the variation in water level is due to the tides.

(127)   **Ice** closes the river to navigation a part of every winter for wooden hull boats. The duration of closing is about 2 months.

(128)   **Weather.**–Hartford is well inside the northern temperate climatic zone in a prevailing west to east movement of air carrying the majority of weather systems into Connecticut from the west. The average wintertime position of the "Polar Front" boundary between cold dry polar air and warm moist tropical air is just south of New England, which helps to explain the extensive winter storm activity and the day-to-day variability of local weather. In the summer, the "Polar Front" has an average position along the New England-Canada border and Hartford has a warm and pleasant climate.

(129)   The location of Hartford, relative to the continent and ocean, is also significant. Rapid weather changes result when storms move northward along the Mid-Atlantic Coast, frequently producing strong and persistent northeast winds associated with storms known locally as coastals or northeasters. Seasonally, weather characteristics vary from the cold and dry continental-polar air of winter to the warm, maritimes air of summer, the one from Canada, the other from the Gulf of Mexico, Caribbean Sea, or Atlantic Ocean.

(130)   Summer thunderstorms develop in the Berkshire Mountains to the west and northwest, and move over the Connecticut Valley and, when accompanied by wind and hail, sometimes cause considerable damage to crops. During the winter, rain often falls through cold air trapped in the valley and creates extremely hazardous ice conditions. On clear nights in the late summer or early autumn, cool air drainage into the valley and the moisture from the Connecticut River produce steam and/or ground fog which becomes quite dense throughout the valley and temporarily hampers transportation.

(131)   Fog is reported to develop locally in the vicinity of the nuclear power plant's efflux at Haddam Neck and around Gildersleeve Island.

(132)   The National Weather Service office is at Bradley International Airport, northwest of Hartford. (See page T-4 for **Hartford climatological table.**)

(133)   **Routes.**–To enter Connecticut River from eastward, pass southward of Hatchett Reef and Saybrook Bar, until Saybrook Breakwater Light bears 315°. Steer for Saybrook Breakwater Light on this course through the buoyed opening between the south end of Saybrook Bar and the east end of Long Sand Shoal to the entrance channel between the jetties.

(134)   To enter from westward, pass 1 mile southward of Falkner Island Light on course **076°**. This will lead about 0.4 mile northward of the lighted bell buoy on the western end of Long Sand Shoal and about 0.2 mile southward of the lighted bell buoy southward of Cornfield Point. Then steer about **067°**, with Saybrook Breakwater Light a little on the port bow to the entrance channel between the jetties.

(135)   **Pilotage, Connecticut River.**–Pilotage is compulsary in Long Island Sound for foreign vessels and U.S. vessels under register. See Pilotage, Long Island Sound (indexed as such), chapter 8. Pilotage for the Connecticut River is available from Connecticut River Pilots Association (CRPA), 104 Nehantic Trail, Old Saybrook, CT 06475, telephone (203) 388-4167. Pilot boat TRUDEE II is 36-foot, with black hull, white superstructure, and with the word PILOT on the house, forward. The boat monitors channel 16 and 13; works on 13. The CRPA pilot boards vessels abeam of the marina at the south end of Saybrook Point.

(136)   Pilot services are arranged in advance through ships' agents or directly by shipping companies. A 24-hour advance notice is requested.

(137)   Hartford is a **customs port of entry.**

(138)   **Wharves.**–The Connecticut River has more than 20 commercial piers and wharves, most of which handle petroleum products from barges or coastal tankers. Most of the facilities below Rocky Hill, about 34 miles above Saybrook Point, are marginal-type wharves, while those above Rocky Hill are finger-type piers with breasting dolphins. Depths of 11 to 15 feet are reported alongside these facilities.

(139)   **Supplies and repairs.**–Gasoline, diesel fuel, water, ice, and marine supplies are available at the principal towns and landings along the Connecticut River. Boatyards along the river can make engine, hull, and electronic repairs.

(140)   **Charts 12375, 12372.**–**Old Saybrook** is a village on the west side of Connecticut River, about 1.4 miles northward of Saybrook Breakwater Light. There are several small-craft facilities along the west side of the river from Saybrook Point to **Ferry Point**, about 2 miles to the northward. (See the small-craft facilities tabulation on chart 12372 for services and supplies available.)

(141)   A 5 mph **speed limit** is enforced at Old Saybrook between the railroad bridge and the Connecticut Turnpike bridge.

(142)   **North Cove,** a dredged small-boat basin that affords excellent anchorage, is entered through a dredged channel that leads westward from the main channel about 0.4 mile northward of Saybrook Point. In April 1989, the midchannel controlling depth was 4½ feet in the channel with depths of 4 feet in the basin except for lesser depths along the edges. The entrance channel is marked by private buoys.

(143)   From Saybrook Point to Hartford local knowledge is required to carry the best water. Small craft should have no difficulty in following the channel.

(144)   **Lieutenant River,** leading to **Old Lyme,** enters the east side of Connecticut River about 1.4 miles northward of Saybrook Point. Pipe stakes mark the south side of the channel across the bar at the entrance A midchannel depth of about 3 feet can be carried over the bar to about 0.2 mile above the second bridge. A railroad bridge with a 33-foot fixed span and a clearance of 11 feet crosses the river 0.4 mile above the entrance. An overhead power cable with a reported clearance of about 10 feet is on the north side of the bridge. About 0.3 mile above that bridge is a highway bridge with a 24-foot fixed span and a clearance of 6 feet. A **harbormaster** is at Old Lyme.

(145)   The passage to the east and north of **Calves Island,** about 1 mile above the railroad bridge crossing Connecticut River, is used extensively for mooring small craft in the summer. This passage is subject to shoaling, particularly on the north side of Calves Island; caution is advised. A sunken

barge, covered 2 feet and marked by a private seasonal buoy, is close off the east side of Calves Island in 41°19′31″ N., 72°20′37″W. A small-craft facility is on the east side of the passage just above the entrance. Berths, electricity, gasoline, diesel fuel, water, ice, marine supplies, a 25-ton mobile hoist, and a 20-ton crane are available; hull, engine, and electronic reparis can be made. In July 1981, depths of 25 feet were reported at the facility.

(146) **Lord Cove** has its entrance about 300 yards northward of Calves Island. In July 1981, a depth of 3½ feet was available through the unmarked entrance. The marshlands surrounding Lord Cove and the other coves between Essex and the river mouth at Saybrook are frequented by duck hunters in October and November. Because of danger of gunfire, mariners are cautioned not to stray too close to the numerous duck blinds that exist in this area.

(147) The dredged section of the main channel in Connecticut River westward of Calves Island has numerous obstructions and sunken rocks close to its edges; mariners are advised to exercise caution and to avoid the edges of the channel.

(148) **Haydens Point**, about 4.6 miles above Saybrook Point, is marked by a light. Foul ground is between the light and the shore.

(149) **Essex**, a town on the west bank about 5 miles above Saybrook Point, is the scene of considerable small-boat activity. Depths alongside the town landing are about 6 feet. **Essex Cove** is the area off the main river channel skirting the waterfront at Essex. A dredged channel, marked by private buoys, leads from the main channel through the cove, and thence rejoins the main channel to the northward. In 1973–1974, a controlling depth of 6½ feet was available in the buoyed channel.

(150) A 5 mph **speed limit** is enforced.

(151) A privately marked small-boat channel leads westward from near the southerly end of Essex Cove and northward of **Thatchbed Island** to **Middle Cove**. In July 1981, the channel had a reported depth of 6 feet.

(152) Essex has excellent small-craft facilities. (See the small-craft facilities tabulation on chart 12372 for services and supplies available.)

(153) **Special anchorages** are at Essex. (See **110.1** and **110.55 (a), (a-1), (b),** and **(c)**, chapter 2, for limits and regulations.)

(154) **Hamburg Cove** and **Eightmile River**, which empties into the north end of the cove, indent the east side of Connecticut River, 6 miles above Saybrook Point. A dredged channel leads from Connecticut River to a turning basin at **Hamburg**, a village at the head of navigation. In 1977, the controlling depth was 3 feet in the channel with 4 feet in the basin except for shoaling at the north end and along the east edge. There are boulders in places outside the dredged channel, and the entrance channel is outlined by grassy flats on each side. Buoys mark the entrance, and private seasonal buoys and daybeacons mark the remainder of the channel to Hamburg. The center of the turning basin has piles used for moorings. A small-craft facility, on the east side of the basin, has berths, electricity, gasoline, water, ice, and some marine supplies.

(155) **Chart 12377.**–**Eustasia Island,** 8.5 miles above Saybrook Point, divides the Connecticut River into two channels. A light off the southeast end of the island marks the junction of the two channels. The eastern channel crossing **Potash Bar** through a dredged cut is better marked and easier to follow. The western channel leads to **Pratt Creek**, westward of the southerly end of Eustasia Island, and to the landing at **Deep River** and thence crosses **Chester Creek**

Bar through a swash channel to **Chester Creek**. A sand shoal and a rocky reef, both bare at low water, are north of Eustasia Island, between the main channel east of the island and Chester Creek.

(156) In July 1981, it was reported that depths of 15 feet could be carried to the facilities on Pratt Creek and in March 1990, depths to 5 feet were reported to the facilities in Chester Creek. A rock, covered 3 feet, is on the south side of the entrance to Chester Creek in about 41°24′24.1″N., 72°25′46.6″W.

(157) There are several small-craft facilities on Pratt Creek and Chester Creek. Lifts to 25 tons, berths, electricity, gasoline, water, ice, storage, marine supplies, launching ramp, and complete hull and engine repairs are available in the area.

(158) **Special anchorages** are off Chester Creek. (See **110.1** and **110.55 (e–1)** and **(e–2)**, chapter 2, for limits and regulations.)

(159) The Chester-Hadlyme vehicular ferry crosses the river near **Fort Hill**, 2 miles above Eustasia Island. The ferry operates from April through November.

(160) **Special anchorages** are northeastward of Connecticut River Light 45 (41°26.2′ N., 72°27.6′W.), about 12.8 miles above Saybrook Point. (See **110.1** and **110.55 (d)** and **(e)**, chapter 2, for limits and regulations.)

(161) On the east side of the river, the turret of the opera house at **East Haddam**, 13.3 miles above Saybrook Point, is prominent. A marina is on the west side of the river just above the swing bridge between East Haddam and **Tylerville**. Limited guest berths, limited marine supplies, electricity, water, and ice are available. In March 1990, a reported depth of 5 feet was available in the marina basin.

(162) The shoal off the west side of the river, just north of East Haddam, is reported to be increasing.

(163) **Salmon Cove**, on the east side of the river, 1 mile above East Haddam, is reported to be navigable only by small craft at high tide. The entrance to the cove is subject to shoaling. Considerable grass in the channel and cove makes boat operation difficult.

(164) Overhead power cables with a least clearance of 86 feet cross the cove about 1.2 miles above the mouth.

(165) A small-craft facility is on the west side of the river about 1.1 miles above East Haddam. Berths, electricity, water, ice, a 10-ton mobile hoist, and a launching ramp are available; hull and engine repairs can be made. In March 1990, a depth of 6 feet was reported at the facility.

(166) **Haddam Island** divides the Connecticut River about 3.2 miles above East Haddam. The main river channel leads eastward of the island through a dredged cut known as Haddam Island Bar Channel. A pinnacle rock, covered 13 feet, is in the approach to Haddam Island Bar Channel in 41°29′31″N., 72°30′49″ W.

(167) The passage westward of Haddam Island is closed by a bare sand shoal lying between the island's southerly tip and the westerly shore of the river.

(168) The shoal off the east side of the river opposite **Higganum Creek**, 5.5 miles above East Haddam, is extending westward.

(169) A rock breakwater extends southward from the east side of the river, 1 mile above Higganum Creek. In 1969, the shoal, about 200 yards southward of the breakwater, was found to be extending southward.

(170) A boatyard is on the north side of the river at **Cobalt**, about 3.5 miles above Higganum Creek. Storage facilities and a 15-ton hoist are available. In October 1990, a reported depth of 7 feet could be carried to the facility.

(171) After passing through the channel in **Paper Rock Shoal**, 9.7 miles above East Haddam, favor the south side of

the river to about 300 yards southeastward of **Bodkin Rock**, then cross to the north side and pass it close-to.

(172)   About 0.5 mile westward of Bodkin Rock, a dredged section of the channel leads along the southerly shore of Connecticut River and southward of Mouse Island Bar.

(173)   **Special anchorages** are along the north and east sides of the river, between Bodkin Rock and Portland. (See **110.1** and **110.55 (f)** and **(g)**, chapter 2, for limits and regulations.)

(174)   Caution is recommended when rounding the point on the south side of the river, about 1.5 miles above Bodkin Rock, to avoid a submerged crib that extends northward from the point.

(175)   **Portland**, 26.3 miles above Saybrook Point, has several boatyards with marine railways; the largest railway can handle craft to 60 feet for engine and hull repairs. Gasoline, water, berths, ice, storage, marine supplies, sewage pump-out, launching ramps, and lifts to 50 tons are available at Portland. In March 1990, depths of 7 to 9 feet were reported available.

(176)   Berthing and water are available at Harbor Park in **Middletown**, across the river from Portland. Depths of 18 feet are reported to be available along the wharves.

(177)   Two small-craft facilities are on the east side of the river at **Gildersleeve**, about 2.5 miles above Portland. Gasoline, diesel fuel, water, marine supplies, a launching ramp, and 15- and 20-ton mobile hoists are available, and hull and engine repairs can be made.

(178)   From **Belamose**, 6.5 miles above Portland, northward to Hartford, the land is much lower, and the Connecticut River narrows, its curves become more pronounced, and both of its shores have numerous wood-stake-and-rock groins.

(179)   A marina on the east side of the river opposite Belamose has gasoline, berths, electricity, water, ice, marine supplies, and a 15-ton lift; engine and hull repairs can be made. In July 1983, the privately marked channel into the marina basin had a reported controlling depth of 7 feet.

(180)   At **Rocky Hill**, 1 mile above Belamose, a seasonal vehicular ferry crosses the river to South Glastonbury. A small-craft launching ramp is just above the ferry landing.

(181)   The cove at **Crow Point**, on the west side of the river about 5.7 miles above Belamose, is used to obtain land fill. Dredging in the cove is uneven, but the bottom is soft ooze. In July 1981, it was reported that the entrance had shoaled to bare and could be used only by small outboards.

(182)   A rock, covered 5 feet, is on the south side of the dredged channel about 0.8 mile above Crow Point in about 41°42'43.0"N., 72°37'46.5"W.; and a shoal that bares is in 41°43'11"N., 72°38'52"W., on the west side of Connecticut River, about 1.9 miles above Crow Point.

(183)   **Wethersfield Cove**, on the west side of the river 14 miles above Portland, is entered through a narrow dredged channel that leads to a dredged anchorage basin about 0.3 mile above the entrance. In June 1977, the midchannel controlling depth was 3 feet, and depths of 6 feet were available in the basin. The channel is marked by daybeacons and buoys. The Interstate 91 highway bridge over the entrance has a fixed span with a clearance of 38 feet. The speed limit in the channel and cove is 5 knots. Gasoline, water, ice, transient berthing, and some supplies can be obtained at the yacht club on the south side of the cove. A town marina is on the east side of the cove; a launching ramp is available at the facility. The Wethersfield **harbormaster** can be contacted through the local police department or town hall.

(184)   The only remaining commercial docks at **Hartford** are the bulk fuel handling facility of the Hartford Electric Light Company's powerplant on the west side of the river,

about 0.2 mile below the Charter Oak Bridge, and the Hartford Gas Company's barge unloading facilities on the west side of the river, about 0.5 mile above the Charter Oak Bridge. A flood control dike is along the west side of the river from just north of the Charter Oak Bridge to the Bulkeley Bridge.

(185)   Connecticut River above Hartford is practically unimproved, but is navigable about 30 miles to **Holyoke** for boats not exceeding 3-foot draft, when the river is not low. The channel is constantly shifting.

(186)   **Chart 12354.**—**Long Sand Shoal** extends 6 miles westward from off the entrance of Connecticut River and has a greatest width of nearly 0.3 mile. The general depths on the shoal are 4 to 15 feet; bottom is hard and lumpy. Shoaling is abrupt on both sides, but especially on the south side, where the 5-fathom curve is only 100 yards from it in places. The shoal is marked at its eastern end by a buoy, and on the south side and west end by lighted sound buoys.

(187)   A fairway lighted whistle buoy is 4.5 miles south of Cornfield Point.

(188)   At the western end of Long Sand Shoal and 1 mile southward is an area about 0.6 mile long with rocky and broken bottom, and with a least found depth of 22 feet.

(189)   **Sixmile Reef**, about 3 miles southwestward of Long Sand Shoal, is an area of broken ground about 2.5 miles long in a west-northwesterly direction with depths of 19 to 30 feet. The bottom is rocky and shoaling is abrupt in places. A lighted bell buoy is off the southerly edge of this reef. With extreme low tides, due to northerly and westerly winds, this shoal may be dangerous to vessels with 15-foot draft. Tide rips occur on the reef whenever the direction of the tidal currents is opposed to that of the wind. This is especially true during spring tides and a southwest wind.

(190)   A ridge with depths of 24 to 36 feet is near the middle of Long Island Sound southward of Sixmile Reef and 5 miles north-northwestward of Horton Point Light. It is marked by a lighted buoy.

(191)   **Charts 12375, 12372.**—**Cornfield Point**, 2 miles westward of Saybrook Breakwater Light, is marked by a large red-roofed stone building. Rocky shoals and foul ground extend about 0.5 mile southerly from this point and for about 1.9 miles westerly. **Cornfield Point Shoal**, a small rocky patch covered 3 feet, is about 0.4 mile south of the point. Westward of this shoal are **Hen and Chickens**, bare in spots at low water, and **Crane Reef**, an area of broken ground with a least depth of 3 feet. These dangers are buoyed. About 0.5 mile westward of the point is **Halftide Rock**, surrounded by foul ground and marked by a private daybeacon.

(192)   **Charts 12374, 12372.**—**Westbrook Harbor** is the western part of the open bight between Cornfield Point and Menunketesuck Island. It has many unmarked submerged rocks and is seldom used as an anchorage; the anchorage in Duck Island Roads is better. The bight is characterized by boulders.

(193)   **Westbrook**, a town on the north side of Westbrook Harbor, is marked on its east side by an elevated tank. A **harbormaster** is at Westbrook and can be contacted through the town hall.

(194)   **Menunketesuck Island** is the outermost of several low narrow islands connected to the mainland at low water on the west side of Westbrook Harbor. It has boulders at the south end. A boulder reef extends nearly 0.5 mile south-southeastward from the point to the 18-foot curve. Tide rips frequently occur on this reef. A private seasonal buoy is about 0.3 mile southeastward of Menunketesuck Island.

(195) Between Menunketesuck Island and Hammonasset Point, about 4 miles westward, broken ground extends about 1.5 miles offshore. A boulder reef extends 0.5 mile southward from Duck Island to the 18-foot curve and is marked by a buoy. A rock with 1 foot over it is on this reef about 300 yards south of Duck Island. Tide rips have been reported to extend from the vicinity of these rocks to the buoy. During strong flood currents and a southwest wind, tide rips extend from the shoal water southwest of Duck Island to the vicinity of **Southwest Reef** over 1 mile southwestward. Caution is advised when navigating small boats in this vicinity during these conditions.

(196) **Duck Island Roads,** between Menunketesuck Island and **Kelsey Point,** is a harbor of refuge protected by breakwaters 1,100 feet northward and nearly 0.5 mile westward from **Duck Island,** with the added protection of Kelsey Point Breakwater on Stone Island Reef. A prominent landmark on Duck Island is a stone chimney. Both breakwaters extending from Duck Island are marked by lights.

(197) The dredged anchorage enclosed by the breakwaters extending northward and westward from Duck Island is subject to shoaling. General depths of 4 to 7 feet are in the protected area, and 8 to 15 feet in the western end. In addition to the area inside the breakwaters, a small area northward and northeastward of Duck Island North Breakwater Light can be used as an anchorage in southwesterly weather.

(198) The western entrance of Duck Island Roads is easy of access and should be used by vessels with greater draft than 8 feet.

(199) **Routes.**–Pass southward of Duck Island and keep the light on the end of Kelsey Point Breakwater bearing northward of 264° until Duck Island West Breakwater Light 2DI bears 010°, then steer northward. Approaching from westward, the only dangers are the two 16-foot spots south-southwestward of Kelsey Point Breakwater Light, the southerly of which is marked by a buoy.

(200) The eastern entrance of Duck Island Roads is obstructed by a sand shoal with a least depth of 8 feet about 0.3 mile eastward of Duck Island, and by boulder reefs which extend about 0.2 mile off the western side of Menunketesuck Island. This entrance is easy of access for vessels drawing up to 8 feet.

(201) Anchorage in 18 to 24 feet, bottom generally sticky, can be had between the Duck Island West Breakwater Light 2DI and the 17-foot rocky patches southeastward of Kelsey Point. This anchorage is exposed to winds southward of east and west.

(202) **Patchogue River,** used chiefly by fishing and recreational craft, empties into Duck Island Roads just west of Menunketesuck Island. A channel leads from deep water in Duck Island Roads to the first fixed highway bridge, about 0.6 mile above the mouth. The approach channel is marked by buoys, and the river channel is marked by private aids. A light is on the outer end of the breakwater on the west side of the river mouth. In January 1990, the midchannel controlling depth was 7 feet from the entrance to the first turn near Menunketesuck River, thence 5½ feet in the western half of the channel to a point just above Buoy 6, thence a midchannel controlling depth of 6½ feet to the head of the project. The anchorage basin had depths of 4½ to 8 feet, except for shoaling to about 1 foot near the southeast corner.

(203) In May 1991, shoaling to bare was reported near the channel edge between Buoy 3 and Light 3A.

(204) Several **small-craft facilities** are on the river. (See the small-craft facilities tabulation on chart 12372 for services and supplies available.)

(205) **Menunketesuck River,** sharing the same entrance channel as Patchogue River, is a shallow stream westward

of Patchogue River. In July 1981, a depth of about 8 feet was reported to the first fixed highway bridge crossing the river above which depths of less than 1 foot are reported. A shoal was reported extending south from shore at the junction of Patchogue and Menunketesuck Rivers; caution is advised. The junction is marked by a private seasonal buoy. Small-craft facilities on the river can provide berths, electricity, gasoline, diesel fuel, water, ice, storage, marine supplies, and engine and hull repairs; a 12-ton mobile hoist is available. The privately maintained channel in the river is reported to be marked by seasonal private aids; local knowledge is advised.

(206) A 6 mph **speed limit** is enforced on both rivers.

(207) **Kelsey Point Breakwater** extends on **Stone Island Reef** over 0.6 mile south-southeastward from Stone Island and is marked by a light. The least depth on the rocky broken ground southwestward of the light is 16 feet. The outer spot is marked by a buoy. **Stone Island,** at the north end of the breakwater, is mostly covered at high water. Some rocks bare at low water are between the island and the shore. Tide rips frequently occur in the area southwestward from the end of the breakwater to the bell buoy. Depths of 18 feet or less near Kelsey Point Breakwater indicate areas of broken rocky bottom which should be avoided in anchoring. The broken ground east of the breakwater includes depths of 12 feet close to it; the 18-foot patch 0.2 mile east-northeast of the end of the breakwater; **East Ledge** with depths of 2 to 17 feet, which extends 0.4 mile southward from Kelsey Point; and the broken ground with depths of 8 to 17 feet which extends over 0.4 mile southeastward from Kelsey Point.

(208) The bight at the entrance of Clinton Harbor and westward of Kelsey Point Breakwater affords anchorage, but is exposed to southeasterly and southwesterly winds.

(209) **Clinton Harbor,** the bight westward of Kelsey Point Breakwater, is the entrance to **Hammonasset River,** a stream used chiefly by fishing and recreational craft. **Wheeler Rock,** with 1 foot over it, just outside the bar, is marked by a lighted buoy. The channel is marked by buoys to Cedar Island and thence by seasonal private buoys to the anchorage basin at **Clinton.** A radiobeacon is on the east side of the harbor about 0.55 mile north of **Hammock Point.** In July-August 1989, the midchannel controlling depth was 5½ feet to Buoy 11A, thence 7 feet in the north half of the channel to the head of the project, thence depths of 4½ to 8 feet were available in the anchorage basin on the northeast side of the channel east of the wharves at Clinton. From opposite the basin to the upstream limit of the Federal project, the southwest and south side of the channel is obstructed by a series of pilings. Boats may be moored between the pilings, caution is advised. Above the dredged channel, the midchannel controlling depth is about 2 feet in the Hammonasset River to the overhead pipeline and bridge crossing about 2 miles above Clinton. Private daybeacons mark this section of the channel.

(210) Several boatyards and marinas are in the harbor. (See the small-craft facilities tabulation on chart 12372 for services and supplies available.) Mooring facilities are available by arrangement with the town **dockmaster** who can be contacted through the town hall or police department. A 6 mph **speed limit** is enforced in the harbor. The town maintains a fireboat at Clinton Harbor. The vessel can be contacted through the Clinton Police Department or the Coast Guard.

(211) Northeastward of **Cedar Island** in Clinton Harbor are two narrow crooked channels close together, with depths of about 1 foot. The eastern one is usually marked by bush stakes; it leads to a marina and boatyard just inside the mouth of **Hammock River.** The western channel, marked by a private range, leads to a boatyard on **Indian River.**

(212) **Hammonasset Point**, on the southwest side of Clinton Harbor, is a low marshy area with many wooded knolls. The end of the point is a rocky knoll. **Hammonasset State Park** is marked by a conspicuous flagstaff and the buildings at the recreational center. In the summer it is an active resort. Broken ground with rocky irregular bottom and least depths of 10 to 11 feet extends 0.5 mile southward of Hammonasset Point.

(213) **West Rock** is the outermost of the bare rocks which extend a short distance off the east end of Hammonasset Point. A reef, with two bare rocks and a groin on its inner part, extends 0.3 mile southwestward from the point and is marked by a buoy, northeastward of which tide rips frequently occur. When rounding the point, vessels should not pass between the buoy and Hammonasset Point.

(214) **Madison Reef**, over 2 miles westward of Hammonasset Point, extends over a mile east and west. This reef consists of several rocky patches with depths of 4 to 17 feet, with deeper water between them. **Charles Reef**, with a least depth of 7 feet, is about 0.5 mile southwest of Madison Reef and marked by a buoy.

(215) **Kimberly Reef**, about 1.9 miles southward of Charles Reef, is an area of broken ground with a least depth of 12 feet. An isolated 27-foot spot, marked by a lighted horn buoy, is about 0.2 mile south of the shoal. A bank with depths of 14 to 28 feet extends about 1.5 miles west of Kimberly Reef to Falkner Island.

(216) Vessels of 10-foot draft can anchor northward of Madison Reef, but should proceed with caution to avoid the rocky patches at lesser depths.

(217) **Tuxis Island**, northward of Madison Reef and 0.2 mile south of **Middle Beach**, is high and rocky. Between the island and the shore the water is shallow and the ground foul. Rocks awash are 200 to 600 yards eastward of the island, and an islet is 100 yards westward of the island. A steel bulkhead in ruins, the top of which is awash at high water, extends from shore to **Gull Rock**, a high bare ledge about 300 yards east-northeastward of Tuxis Island.

(218) **Madison**, a town on the railroad, has one landing which bares alongside at low water and is in disrepair. A few small craft moor in the cove on its north side. Rocks, bare at low water, are 100 yards eastward of the landing. A beach club building, with a small stone landing, is northward of Tuxis Island. A church with a prominent tower and gilded dome is 0.8 mile northward of Tuxis Island.

(219) **Charts 12373, 12372.**—**Guilford Harbor**, a bight 5.5 miles westward of Hammonasset Point, is used only by small craft. **East River** and **Sluice Creek** empty into Guilford Harbor from the northward. The approach to the harbor is obstructed by rocks and foul ground. The outermost dangers are: **Half Acre Rock**, about 0.8 mile southeastward of the entrance channel, which shows at high water; scattered rocks, some bare at low water and others with 7 to 16 feet over them, extending about a mile eastward from Half Acre Rock; **Outer White Top**, about 0.6 mile southwestward of Half Acre Rock, and several rocks northward of it bare at low water; and **Indian Reef**, extending about 1 mile southwestward of Outer White Top, the highest part of which is covered at high water. Indian Reef is marked on its south and southwestern sides by buoys. Stakes and fish traps may exist northward of **Riding Rock**, 0.6 mile northwestward of Half Acre Rock.

(220) The approach channel to Guilford Harbor, marked by buoys, leads along the southeasterly side of Indian Reef, thence westward of Half Acre Rock to a dredged channel about 0.5 mile northwestward of Half Acre Rock. The dredged channel leads northward through the harbor and eastward of **Guilford Point** to a junction with Sluice Creek and East River, about 0.6 mile above the channel entrance. At the junction, the dredged channel leads northwesterly into Sluice Creek for about 0.1 mile and northeasterly into East River for about 0.4 mile to an anchorage basin. Buoys and a private range mark the dredged channel to the junction. In 1985, the reported midchannel controlling depth in the dredged channel was 4 feet to the junction of East River and Sluice Creek, thence in 1981-1982, the midchannel controlling depths were 4 feet in Sluice Creek, thence 5½ feet in East River to the anchorage basin, with 5 to 6 feet in the basin except for shoaling to bare toward the north limit.

(221) In May 1988, a submerged obstruction was reported about 0.3 mile southwest of Half Acre Rock in about 41°51.1'N., 72°39.6'W.

(222) At high water and with local knowledge, small boats can go above the anchorage basin in East River to the fixed railway bridge, about 1.3 miles above the basin. The bridge has a clearance of 4 feet. An overhead power cable with a clearance of 45 feet is about 0.3 miles below the bridge. A town marina, just above the entrance to Sluice Creek, has berths, electricity, water, and a launching ramp. In July 1981, depths of 1 to 2 feet were reported alongside the marina.

(223) A 5 mph **speed limit** is enforced in the harbor.

(224) **West River** empties into the western side of Guilford Harbor 0.2 mile westward of Guilford Point. A railroad bridge about 0.7 mile above the mouth has a clearance of 6 feet. **Guilford** is the town above the railroad bridge. In September 1988-July 1989, a depth of 4½ feet was reported in West River entrance channel; the channel is marked by buoys and a **321° lighted range**.

(225) There are two boatyards with several marinas and marine railways on West River. The largest marine railway can handle craft up to 40 feet; limited supplies, a 12-ton mobile crane, and complete engine and hull repairs are available.

(226) **Falkner Island** and **Goose Islands**, with **Stony Island** to the southward, are about 3 miles south of Guilford Harbor. Each is surrounded by reefs and rocks that bare at low water. A depth of about 16 feet can be carried between Goose Islands and Falkner Island by staying in the middle of the passage and avoiding the 8-foot and 11-foot spots, about 0.35 mile 244° and 0.4 mile 300° from the light on Falkner Island, respectively, and the shoals and reefs extending from the islands. **Falkner Island Light** (41°12.7'N., 72°39.2'W.), 94 feet above the water, is shown from a 46-foot white octagonal tower near the center of Falkner Island. A lighted gong buoy marks the shoal off the northern end of Falkner Island, and a lighted bell buoy is off the southern end of Stony Island.

(227) From Indian Reef westward are rocky shoals and islets extending from 0.2 to 0.7 mile off **Vineyard Point** and **Sachem Head**. **Chimney Corner Reef**, about 0.3 mile south of Sachem Head and marked by a buoy, is a rocky broken area on which the least depth is 9 feet. Westward of it are **Goose Rocks Shoals**, on which are **Goose Rocks**, the northerly of which is bare and the southerly one covered at high water. The outer limit of Goose Rocks Shoals is marked by a lighted bell buoy. To ensure clearing the westerly end of Goose Rocks Shoals, care must be taken not to round the buoy too closely.

(228) **Sachem Head Harbor**, an anchorage for small craft on the southwest side of Sachem Head, is 0.3 mile long and 0.1 mile wide, and has depths of 3 to 8 feet at the floats and in the moorings; it is sheltered except from westerly winds. The island forming the south point at the entrance is connected with the shore by a bridge. A yacht clubhouse is on

the island. From the north point of the island a breakwater extends 100 yards in a northwesterly direction; a rock awash, marked by a private seasonal light, is off the end of the breakwater. A rock covered at half tide is 50 yards off the southeast side of the harbor, about 350 yards eastward of the end of the breakwater.

(229) The approach to Sachem Head Harbor for small craft from eastward is along the south side of the rocks making off from the south side of Sachem Head. Approaching eastward of Goose Rocks, give the rocks a berth of over 300 yards. The approach from westward is clear between Goose Rocks and Leetes Rocks.

(230) **Joshua Point**, the western extremity of Sachem Head, is marked by a rocky islet on its west side and a privately maintained seasonal light. Just northward of the islet a stone jetty with a bulkhead on its north side extends about 100 yards in a northwesterly direction from the shore. Vessels can anchor in the angle near the shore where the depth is about 4½ feet.

(231) **Joshua Cove**, northwestward of Sachem Head, is little used, but affords good anchorage in its entrance for small vessels in northerly or easterly winds in 6 to 10 feet, soft bottom. The approach from southwestward is clear between Goose Rocks and Leetes Rocks.

(232) **Leetes Rocks**, midway between Sachem Head and the north end of The Thimbles, are two rocks bare at low water, with an area of broken ground around them. A 9-foot spot is about 200 yards southward of the southerly rock, and a 3-foot spot is 0.3 mile northeast of the southerly rock.

(233) **Leetes Island Quarry** is a prominent feature on the south side of **Hoadley Point**; on the north side of the cove eastward of the point are the ruins of an old dock.

(234) **The Thimbles**, about 1.6 miles west of Sachem Head, comprise many islands, islets, and rocks that bare. All of the area, extending over 2 miles from Hoadley Point southwestward to **East Reef**, is foul with rocky bottom and many shoals. To lesser extent, the area from East Reef for 2 miles westward and northwestward to Branford Harbor entrance is dotted with islets and rocks. The whole area is suitable only for small pleasure craft, which are very active here in summer. Many oyster stakes are encountered; these do not mark channels and caution should be used to avoid fouling them. Caution also is advised to avoid fouling the pipelines and cables in the area.

(235) The outermost of The Thimbles proper is **Outer Island**, marked by a house chimney. A boat landing protected by a stone jetty is on the northeast side of this island, and an unmarked rock, bare at lowest tides, is 200 yards eastward. The reefs southwestward of Outer Island, to and including East Reef and **Browns Reef**, are buoyed.

(236) From eastward a buoyed channel leads through The Thimbles. The channel passes between **Wayland Island** and a buoy marking the foul area southward of **Cat Island**. The channel extends between **Davis Island** and **Dogfish Island**, thence north of **East Crib** and **West Crib** into the more open water westward of The Thimbles; it is good for about 13 feet.

(237) **Stony Creek**, a village on the railroad, extends southward to **Flying Point** (41°15.5'N., 72°45.1'W.). A dredged channel west of Flying Point leads north to a turning basin at Stony Creek. The channel is marked by private buoys. In December 1988, the midchannel controlling depths were 3 feet in the channel with 1 to 4 feet in the basin. Rocks were reported in the northwest corner of the basin. Gasoline, marine supplies, inside storage, and a small-craft launching ramp are available at marinas eastward of the turning basin; small craft can be hauled out on a flatbed trailer for hull and engine repairs. The village dock is on the southeast side of the turning basin.

(238) Between the rocks westward of **Rogers Island** and **Blackstone Rocks**, a privately dredged channel, 0.9 mile westward of Flying Point, leads northeastward to a quarry wharf on the west side of a dredged basin. In 1980, the channel and basin had a reported controlling depth of 13 feet. The entrance channel is marked by a private 028° range consisting of a front and middle light and a rear daybeacon.

(239) **Thimble Island Harbor**, in the western part of The Thimbles, affords good shelter for small craft between **Pot Island** and **Money Island** on the east and **High Island** and **West Crib** on the west. Although open southwestward, the sea from that direction loses much of its force before reaching the inner harbor. A rock with 3 feet over it and marked by a buoy is 80 yards off the east side of High Island, just above its south end. Vessels sometimes anchor near midchannel, between this rock and the north end of Pot Island in depths of 13 to 18 feet, soft bottom, but care should be taken to avoid the cables in the area. The harbor is easy of access between Outer Island and Inner Reef.

(240) **Pine Orchard**, about 3 miles westward of Sachem Head, is a summer resort extending northward and westward of **Brown Point**. A breakwater extending about 300 yards southeastward from Brown Point protects a yacht basin entered through a privately dredged channel that leads from southward of **St. Helena Island** north-northwestward to the basin. In 1978, the entrance channel and basin had reported depths of 7 feet. The basin approach northward of St. Helena Island has depths of 3 to 5 feet. Gasoline, diesel fuel, ice, and water may be obtained at the yacht club landing.

(241) From Brown Point to Branford Harbor, 2.5 miles westward, bare rocks and shoals extend up to about 2 miles offshore. A seawall extends westward from Brown Point, and the shore is thickly settled. A rock bare at half tide is 600 yards westward of Brown Point and 300 yards from shore.

(242) Rocks bare at low water are eastward of **Haycock Point**, and rocks that bare at half tide are off the southeast side and southwest end of **Green Island**. The foul ground extends about 0.6 mile south-southwestward from Haycock Point, including **Foot Rocks** which are partly above water.

(243) **Branford Reef**, about 1.8 miles southward of Indian Neck and 5 miles eastward of New Haven entrance, is marked by a light. This reef is surrounded by shoal water for a distance of 150 to 450 yards from the light.

(244) Deep water is between Branford Reef and **Negro Heads**, a reef bare in one place at low water about 0.9 mile northward. Shoreward of Negro Heads are **Spectacle Island**, **Sumac Island**, and **Clam Island**, together with numerous rocks bare and covered.

(245) A private boat landing is on the northwest side of Clam Island. Small craft can enter **Maltby Cove** between the bare rocks off the southwest end of Clam Island and **Jeffrey Rock**, favoring the northwest side of Clam Island. Private markers are sometimes at the entrance. The northwest side of the cove is foul, the principal danger being a rock bare at low water near the middle, northwestward of Clam Island; the rock is sometimes marked by a seasonal private spindle.

(246) **Jeffrey Point**, the eastern point at the entrance of Branford Harbor, has a bare rock close to its western end.

(247) **Branford Harbor** is a shallow cove between Jeffrey Point and Johnson Point. Vessels up to 10-foot draft can select anchorage in the harbor southward of the Mermaids in 10 to 14 feet, protected against all but southerly and southwesterly winds. Boats up to 5-foot draft can select a well-

sheltered anchorage in the upper part of the harbor above the Mermaids. The harbor is used chiefly for recreational boating and by the small local lobster fishing fleet.

(248) The dangers in the approach and entrance to Branford Harbor either show above water or are marked by buoys. **Cow and Calf**, 1.3 miles southwestward of Jeffrey Point, are two boulders close together bare at low water. Boulders, reported covered 10 feet, are about 0.2 mile northward of Cow and Calf. **Five Foot Rock**, 0.5 mile northeastward of Cow and Calf, has 5 feet over it. **Taunton Rock**, 0.9 mile northeastward of Cow and Calf near the middle of the entrance to Branford Harbor, is large but low and bare. **Blyn Rock**, midway between Johnson Point and Taunton Rock, is covered at extreme high tide. **Bird Rock**, 0.2 mile northward of Blyn Rock, has 5 feet over it.

(249) **Little Mermaid**, showing a little above high water, and **Big Mermaid**, a high rock marked by a light, are near the middle of Branford Harbor. Two bare rocks are near the head of the harbor. A rock, bare at low water and usually marked by stakes, is about 100 feet north-northeastward of the north end of **Lovers Island**.

(250) **Routes.**—To enter Branford Harbor from eastward, pass southward of the lighted buoy marking Negro Heads, steer about **306°** heading for Taunton Rock, and enter between Taunton and Jeffrey Rocks; or a **333°** course with Branford Reef Light astern will lead into the harbor between Jeffrey and Taunton Rocks. From westward, pass southward and over 100 yards eastward of the lighted bell buoy marking Cow and Calf, thence westward of the buoys marking Blyn Rock and Bird Rock to the buoyed channel in the harbor.

(251) Local craft pass northwestward of Cow and Calf Shoal and midway between Johnson Point and Blyn Rock.

(252) **Branford River**, narrow and crooked, extends northeasterly from Branford Harbor. In February-March 1990, the controlling depths in the dredged channel were 8 feet from Branford Harbor to a point about 0.2 mile above **Branford Point**, thence 6½ feet at midchannel to the upstream limit of the dredged channel. In 1981, the wharves at Branford were in disrepair.

(253) At low water the channel above Branford Point is defined by bare shoals on each side. During the summer numerous stakes used as moorings mark both sides of the channel. A privately dredged channel and basin at a marina 0.5 mile east of Branford Point had reported depths of 7 feet in July 1981.

(254) The principal waterborne commerce at Branford is in petroleum products. There are several marinas and boatyards on the river. (See the small-craft facilities tabulation on chart 12372 for services and supplies available.)

(255) A 5 mph **speed limit** is enforced on the river.

(256) The **harbormaster** at Branford controls all moorings and anchoring; he can be contacted through the small-craft facilities.

(257) **Johnson Point** is the western entrance point to Branford Harbor; a rock covered 2 feet is about 100 yards off its south side. A small privately dredged basin on the southwest side of the point is well protected in all but southerly winds. In 1971, it was reported that 4 feet could be carried to and in the basin.

(258) **Gull Rocks**, about 0.3 mile westward of Johnson Point, consist of small islets and submerged rocks that extend about 0.5 mile southwestward from shore on the easterly side of the entrance to a large cove. A rock, bare at half tide, is in the northwestern part of the cove about 350 yards southward of **Short Beach**. The northwest end of the cove has a yacht club landing with a reported depth of 2 feet alongside.

(259) **Farm River Gut**, a small bight on the west side of the cove, is a good anchorage for small craft. Depths range from 4 to 5 feet in the eastern part of the gut with shoaling to bare in the northern and western parts. Two rocks awash are on the north side of the gut about 125 yards inside the entrance. The gut offers good protection from all but easterly winds, mud bottom. A marine railway at a boatyard on the north side of the gut can handle boats to 40 feet for engine and hull repairs. The yard can be reached only at high tide. **Old Clump** is a bare rock about 400 yards south of the bight.

(260) **Farm River**, locally known as East Haven River, about 1.5 miles westward of Branford Harbor, is used by local craft. In July 1981, it was reported that depths of 3 feet could be carried in the river to the fixed bridge with a clearance of 4 feet about 1 mile above the mouth. Several boatyards on the river provide gasoline, berths, electricity, water, storage, and limited marine supplies; diesel fuel can be delivered by truck. A 10-ton mobile hoist and a 12-ton crane can handle vessels for complete engine and hull repairs.

(261) **East Indies Rocks**, about 0.4 mile south of the entrance to Farm River, cover at half tide and are marked by a buoy to the eastward; a rocky shoal with a least depth of 5 feet is 0.2 mile to the eastward. A small ledge, bare at low water, is midway between East Indies Rocks and the south side of Mansfield Point, the western entrance point to Farm River. **Darrow Rocks**, a group of bare rocks, are on the east side of the entrance to the river. The westernmost rocky knoll is marked by a flagstaff. A ledge, bare at low water, with a buoy off its southern end, is 200 yards south of the flagstaff.

(262) **Mansfield Point** and the shore westward of the entrance to Farm River are thickly settled. Bus communication is available to New Haven.

(263) **Charts 12371, 12372.**—**New Haven Harbor**, an important harbor of refuge, is about 68 miles from New York, 179 miles from Boston via Cape Cod Canal, and 171 miles from Nantucket Shoals Lighted Horn Buoy N (LNB). It comprises all the tidewater northward of the breakwaters constructed across the mouth of the bay, including the navigable portions of the West, Mill, and Quinnipiac Rivers. It is about 2 miles wide. The inner harbor, northward of Sandy Point and Fort Hale, is shallow for the most part, except where the depths have been increased by dredging. The main entrance channel, between Middle Breakwater and the East Breakwater, leads northward to Tomlinson Bridge at New Haven. Anchorage basins for medium draft vessels are on the west side of the channel north of Sandy Point. Waterborne commerce in the harbor consists of petroleum products, scrap metal, lumber, automobiles, gypsum, paper and pulp products, steel products, chemicals, rock salt, and general cargo.

(264) **New Haven**, at the head of the harbor, is an important manufacturing city.

(265) **Prominent features.**—On the approach from well offshore in clear weather, the prominent landmarks are: on East Rock (41°19.7′N., 72°54.4′W.), the Soldiers and Sailors Monument; in New Haven, the Knights of Columbus Building, a tall rectangular structure with circular pillars at its corners; the lighted stack of the powerplant on the east side of the harbor opposite City Point; and on the west side of Mill River, a large gas tank with a red and white checkerboard band around the top and the words "New Haven Gas". The lights on the ends of the breakwaters, the aerolight at Tweed-New Haven Airport, and the abandoned tower on Lighthouse Point are also prominent.

NEW HAVEN HARBOR

1976

New Haven

Sandy Point

To Long
Island
Sound

Legend
1 New Haven Long Wharf
2 Tomlinson Bridge
3 Atlantic-Richfield Co. Wharf
4 New Haven Terminal Scrap Metal
  Dock and Pier
5 Exxon Terminal Wharf
6 United Illuminating Co. New Haven
  Harbor Station Pier

(266) **Southwest Ledge Light** (41°14.1'N., 72°54.7'W.), 57 feet above the water, is shown from a white octagonal house on a brown cylindrical pier at the westerly end of East Breakwater. A fog signal is sounded at the light.

(267) **Channels.**–A Federal project for New Haven Harbor provides for an entrance channel 35 feet deep to a point just below the junction of Mill River and Quinnipiac River. The channel is well marked. (See Notice to Mariners and latest editions of the charts for controlling depths.)

(268) **West River,** on the west side of the main channel about 3 miles above Southwest Ledge Light, has a dredged channel marked by buoys to just below the first highway bridge (Kimberly Avenue Bridge), 1.2 miles above the channel entrance. In November 1988-March 1989, the midchannel controlling depth was 9½ feet from the channel entrance to Buoy 18, thence 5½ feet (8 feet at midchannel) to the Connecticut Turnpike Bridge, the head of navigation. An anchorage area is on the south side of the channel about 0.9 mile above the entrance; in 1988-March 1989, the controlling depth was 4½ feet. Principal waterfront facilities are at **City Point.**

(269) **Mill River,** on the west side of **Fair Haven** about 4 miles above Southwest Ledge Light, is entered from the main channel through a dredged entrance channel that branches into an east and west fork to the Grand Avenue Bridge, 0.6 mile above the mouth. In June 1982, the controlling depths were 6½ feet (11 feet at midchannel) to the Chapel Street Bridge about 0.25 mile above the entrance, thence 9 feet through the east bridge opening and 3½ feet through the west opening, thence 6½ feet to the junction with the east and west forks, thence 9½ feet at midchannel for about 250 yards in the east fork, thence in 1980, 1 foot at midchannel to the head of the channel, and in 1980-June 1982, 5½ feet at midchannel for about 225 yards in the west fork, thence in 1980, 1½ feet at midchannel to the head of the channel.

(270) **Quinnipiac River,** on the east side of Fair Haven about 4 miles above Southwest Ledge Light, has a dredged channel to Grand Avenue Bridge, about 1 mile above the mouth. In October 1982, the controlling depth was 15 feet at midchannel to the Ferry Street Bridge about 0.5 mile above the mouth, thence in 1977, 8 feet through the bridge, thence in 1980-October 1982, 10 feet to the Grand Avenue Bridge except for shoaling along the edges.

(271) **Anchorages.**–Inside West Breakwater and the southwest half of Middle Breakwater, anchorage is available for vessels up to 20-foot draft. Caution should be exercised to avoid the fish stakes in this area.

(272) Vessels may anchor northward of Southwest Ledge Light in depths of 18 to 20 feet, soft bottom in places. Care should be taken to avoid the ledges northward of the East Breakwater. Deep-draft vessels awaiting berthing assignments can anchor about 1 mile southward of the sea buoy; holding ground is excellent.

(273) **Morris Cove,** on the east side of the main channel just above Lighthouse Point, affords good anchorage and is used by yachts, but is rough in westerly and southerly winds. In July 1981, isolated, uncharted 40-foot spots were reported in the cove. Caution is advised when anchoring. **New Haven Coast Guard Station** is on the north side of the jutting point, about 1.5 miles northward of Lighthouse Point.

(274) An anchorage basin on the west side of the main channel southward of New Haven Long Wharf is sometimes used, but considerable shoaling is gradually extending into the anchorage from westward. A sunken barge with 5 feet over it is in this anchorage about 550 yards southward of New Haven Long Wharf. In February-March 1985, depths of 10 to 5 feet were available in the anchorage basin with lesser depths along the edges.

(275) An anchorage area, sometimes used by small craft and scows, is northward of the New Haven Long Wharf (Naval Reserve Pier) in the northwest side of the main channel where depths range from about 5 to 6 feet.

(276) No special regulations prescribe the limits within which vessels must anchor, except that the dredged channels must be kept clear.

(277) **Dangers.–Townshend Ledge,** 2.7 miles southeastward of Southwest Ledge Light, has a least depth of 18 feet and is marked by a lighted bell buoy.

(278) **Stony Islet,** 2.2 miles eastward of Southwest Ledge Light, is low, bare, and surrounded by ledges bare at low water to a distance of about 100 yards. A partly bare ledge is about 0.2 mile north-northwestward of Stony Islet. From this ledge and Stony Islet westward to the entrance of New Haven Harbor, an area of foul ground with many rocks bare at low water extends about 0.5 mile offshore. This area should be avoided.

(279) Shoals with 16 to 18 feet over them extend over 0.5 mile southeastward from the breakwaters on both sides of the dredged entrance channel. A spoil area with reported depths of 15 feet is on the eastern side of the entrance channel. An 18-foot spot is on the east side of the main channel, at the first turn westward of Southwest Ledge Light.

(280) The bights on the west shore of New Haven Harbor from Pond Point northward are shoal with bare rocks and foul ground in most of them. The shore is rocky at **Woodmont,** about 2 miles northeastward of Pond Point.

(281) **Black Rock,** bare at low water and marked by a seasonal buoy, is 0.2 mile off the north end of Morris Cove. Opposite, on the west side, is a breakwater, partly covered, extending from **Sandy Point** and marked by a light. **Shag Bank,** a flat extending about 0.5 mile northward from Sandy Point, has a sand tip about 0.1 mile long.

(282) **Bridges.**–Tomlinson Bridge, at the head of the main harbor at the confluence of Mill and Quinnipiac Rivers, has a double bascule span with a clearance of 60 feet. Just above this bridge is a fixed highway bridge with a clearance of 60 feet. The bridgetender of the Tomlinson Bridge monitors VHF-FM channel 13; call sign KXJ-688. An overhead power cable with a clearance of 91 feet crosses the channel just above the fixed highway bridge.

(283) A **regulated navigation area** is at Tomlinson Bridge. (See **165.1 through 165.13, and 165.304,** chapter 2, for limits and regulations.)

(284) Over Mill River, about 0.3 mile above the entrance, is the Chapel Street Bridge with a swing span having clearance of 7 feet. In April 1990, a replacement bridge with a design clearance of 7½ feet was under construction. The fixed highway bridge at Grand Avenue has a clearance of 6 feet over the east fork and a clearance of 2 feet over the west fork. Bridges above this point have minimum clearance of 2 feet. Small unmasted boats go as far as the bridge at State Street, 0.5 mile above Grand Avenue. Overhead power cables crossing the west fork have a minimum clearance of 80 feet.

(285) The Ferry Street Bridge over Quinnipiac River, 0.6 mile above the Tomlinson Bridge, has a bascule span with a clearance of 25 feet. The Grand Avenue Bridge, 0.5 mile farther upstream, has a center-pier swing span with a clearance of 9 feet. Above this are several fixed bridges and trestles.

(286) Kimberly Avenue Bridge over West River has a fixed span with a clearance of 23 feet.

(287) (See **117.1 through 117.59 and 117.213,** chapter 2, for drawbridge regulations.)

(288)   **Tides.**–The mean range of tide is 6.2 feet. Extreme tides have been recorded as reaching more than 2.5 feet below the plane of mean low water and more than 8 feet above the same datum.

(289)   **Currents.**–In the entrance between the breakwaters, the tidal current has a velocity on flood of 1.4 knots, and ebb 0.9 knot. The flood sets 319° and the ebb 152°. In the draw of Tomlinson Bridge, the velocity is 0.4 knot. The flood sets 015° and the ebb 215°. Ebb velocities are increased by freshets. (Consult the Tidal Current Tables for predicted times and velocities of currents.)

(290)   **Ice** generally obstructs navigation to some extent for low-powered vessels from December to March and sometimes extends to the mouth of the harbor. During severe winters the accumulation of ice is local. Except in severe weather, powered vessels can always enter and leave the harbor without much difficulty. In New Haven Harbor northerly winds tend to clear the harbor of ice if the formation is light; southerly winds are apt to force in drift ice from the sound.

(291)   **Weather.**–New Haven's climate is typical of coastal areas of southern New England. It is vigorous without being overly severe. New Haven is located at the widest part of Long Island Sound, and the tempering effect of the water is most pronounced in this vicinity. During the summer season, the sea breeze holds temperatures 5° to 15° lower in the afternoon; during the winter season, minimum temperatures in the southern section of the city are usually 5° to 10° higher than those reported from northern sections. The highest summertime temperatures occur with a moderate northerly wind. The lowest winter readings also occur with a northerly wind.

(292)   Precipitation is quite evenly distributed throughout the year. The elevation of the land increases northward from the station and results in somewhat higher amounts of precipitation in the northern suburbs as well as a few more thunderstorms each year. During the winter, a variety of precipitation is found in most storms. It is common to have rain along the shore, freezing rain and sleet a short distance inland, and snow in the northern parts of the city. Heavy snow is rather uncommon in the immediate coastal area and usually melts in a few days. Farther inland, the snow becomes progressively heavier and a layer of snow coversthe ground most of the winter.

(293)   Prevailing wind direction varies with the seasons. From late spring until fall, winds are predominantly south to southwest due to the effect of the sea breeze. During the winter, the prevailing winds are northerly. Strong southeast winds cause unusually high tides and some local flooding in low-lying coastal areas two or three times a year.

(294)   The National Weather Service maintains an office at the Tweed-New Haven Airport, about 3 miles southeast of the city. (See page T-6 for **New Haven climatological table.**)

(295)   **Routes.**–To enter New Haven Harbor from eastward, it is safer for large vessels to pass southward of Branford Reef and Townshend Ledge to the entrance channel. To enter from westward, pass northward of Stratford Shoal Light at a distance of 1.8 miles and head for the entrance channel.

(296)   The passage eastward of East Breakwater has boulder patches and is very broken, but can be used by small craft drawing less than 6 feet, taking care to avoid the foul ground along the northeast side of the passage. This passage is buoyed, and local vessels of 10- to 12-foot draft use it at high water. Avoid **Quixes Ledge,** which extends about 200 yards southeastward from the eastern end of the breakwater, and pass about 100 yards eastward of the breakwater. The principal danger inside the breakwater is the reef, marked

by a buoy, that extends 300 yards southwestward from **Lighthouse Point. Adams Fall,** a rock with 5 feet over it and marked by a buoy, is 0.4 mile southwestward of Lighthouse Point.

(297)   **Pilotage, New Haven.**–Pilotage is compulsary in Long Island Sound for foreign vessels and U.S. vessels under register. See Pilotage, Long Island Sound (indexed as such), chapter 8.

(298)   Pilotage for New Haven is available from New Haven Bridgeport Pilots Association (NHBPA), 60 Appletree Lane, Hamden, CT 06518, telephone 203-878-8667.

(299)   Pilot boats (rented) utilized by NHBPA pilots are SUSY II, 42-foot, blue hull, white superstructure, word PILOT on side; and GALE, 42-foot, white hull, white superstructure, word PILOT on side. The boat monitors channel 16, 13 and 77; works on 77 and 09. Pilots board about 1 mile south of New Haven Harbor Lighted Whistle Buoy NH.

(300)   Pilotage for New Haven is also available from Constitution State Pilots Association (CSPA), 500 Waterfront Street, New Haven, CT 06512, telephone 800-229-7456 or 203-783-5991, FAX 516-582-6327. Pilots of CSPA board vessels from a launch or the tug, at New Haven Harbor Lighted Whistle Buoy NH.

(301)   Pilotage for New Haven is also available from Long Island Sound State Pilots Association, Inc. (LISSPA), 1440 Whalley Avenue, Suite 123, New Haven, CT 06515, telephone 203-772-0101, FAX 302-629-9392, Cable LISPILOT, New Haven. Pilot boat LONG ISLAND SOUND PILOT is 46-foot, with black hull, white superstructure, and the word PILOT in black letters. The boat monitors channel 16; works on 11. Among other locations, the LISSPA pilot will meet a ship off Montauk Point. See Pilotage Pickup Locations Off Montauk Point (indexed as such), chapter 7.

(302)   Pilotage for New Haven is also available from Sound Pilots, Inc. (SPI) (a division of Northeast Marine Pilots, Inc.), 243 Spring Street, Newport, RI 02840, telephone 401-847-9050 (24 hours), 800-274-1216, FAX 401-847-9052, Cable RISPILOT, Newport, RI 02840. The pilot boats are NORTHEAST II, 49-foot, with grey hull and superstructure and the word PILOT on the side; or RHODE ISLAND PILOT, 35-foot, with black hull and white superstructure and the word PILOT on the side; or NORTHEAST I, 49-foot, similarily marked as the RHODE ISLAND PILOT. The SPI pilots meet a ship bound for a Long Island Sound port, off Point Judith, but will also meet a ship off Montauk Point, by prearrangement. See Pilotage, Narragansett Bay and Other Rhode Island Waters (indexed as such), chapter 6, and Pilotage Pickup Locations Off Montauk Point (indexed as such), chapter 7.

(303)   Pilot services are arranged in advance through ships' agents or directly by shipping companies.

(304)   **Towage.**–Tugs up to 1,800 hp are available at New Haven, and tugs to 4,000 hp can be obtained by prior arrangement. Vessels usually proceed to the harbor without assistance. Large vessels normally require tugs for docking and undocking. Arrangements for tug service should be made 24 hours in advance, usually through ships' agents or directly by shipping companies. The tugs monitor VHF-FM channels 13 and 16 and use channel 19A as a working frequency; call sign KEE-234.

(305)   Launch service to ships at anchor is available. Launches monitor VHF-FM channel 16 (156.80 MHz) and use channel 19A (156.95 MHz) as a working frequency.

(306)   New Haven is a **customs port of entry.**

(307)   **Quarantine, customs, immigration, and agricultural quarantine.**–(See chapter 3, Vessel Arrival Inspections, and appendix for addresses.)

(308)   **Quarantine** is enforced in accordance with regulations of the U.S. Public Health Service. (See Public Health Service, chapter 1.)

(309)   New Haven has many public and private hospitals.

(310)   **Coast Guard.**–The **Captain of the Port** maintains an office in New Haven. The nearest **vessel documentation** office is in Bridgeport, Conn. (See appendix for addresses.)

(311)   The **harbormaster** at New Haven has charge of the anchoring of vessels; he can be contacted through the local police department.

(312)   The city police maintain a harbor patrol during the summer.

(313)   **Wharves.**–The deep-draft facilities at the Port of New Haven are along the north and east sides of the inner portion of New Haven Harbor. Facilities for smaller vessels and barges are along the sides of the harbor and in Mill, Quinnipiac, and West Rivers. Depths alongside the facilities in Quinnipiac River range from about 5 to 15 feet; Mill River, 12 to 13 feet; and West River about 12 to 18 feet. Only the deep-draft facilities are described. For a complete description of the port facilities refer to Port Series No. 4, published and sold by the U.S. Army Corps of Engineers. (See appendix for address.) The alongside depths for the facilities described are reported; for information on the latest depths contact the private operator. All the facilities have direct highway connections, and most have railroad connections. Water and electrical shore power connections are available at most piers and wharves.

(314)   General cargo at the port is usually handled by ship's tackle; special handling equipment, if available, is mentioned in the description of the particular facility. Cranes up to 250 tons and warehouses and cold storage facilities adjacent to the waterfront are available.

(315)   **Wyatt Light Oil Pier:** north end of harbor 0.35 mile northeastward of New Haven Long Wharf; 150-foot face, 715 feet of berthing space with dolphins, 38 feet alongside; deck height, 11 feet; receipt and shipment of petroleum products; owned and operated by Wyatt, Inc.

(316)   **Wyatt Heavy Oil Wharf:** 50 yards east of Wyatt Light Oil Pier; west side 210 feet, 480 feet of berthing space with dolphins; 30 feet alongside; deck height, 11 feet; receipt and shipment of petroleum products, receipt of asphalt; owned and operated by Wyatt, Inc.

(317)   **Gulf Refining and Marketing Co. Wharf:** on each side of harbor, 200 yards south of Tomlinson Bridge; 60-foot face, 735 feet of berthing space with dolphins; 35 feet alongside; deck height, 13 feet; vessels normally moor starboardside-to; receipt and shipment of petroleum products; owned and operated by Gulf Oil Refining and Marketing Co.

(318)   **Gulf Refining and Marketing Co. Pier:** 100 yards southward of Gulf Refining and Marketing Co. Wharf; north side 400 feet, 25 feet alongside; south side 380 feet, 25 feet alongside; deck height, 10 feet; receipt and shipment of petroleum products; owned and operated by Gulf Refining and Marketing Co.

(319)   **ARCO Petroleum Products Co. Wharf:** 300 yards southwestward of Gulf Refining and Marketing Co. Pier; 110-foot face, 760 feet with dolphins; 35 feet alongside; deck height, 15 feet; vessels normally moor starboardside-to; receipt and shipment of petroleum products; owned and operated by ARCO Petroleum Products Co.

(320)   **New Haven Terminal, Scrap Metal Dock:** 275 yards southward of ARCO Petroleum Products Co. Wharf; 640-foot face; 35 feet alongside; deck height, 14 feet; two 30-ton traveling gantry cranes, crawler cranes to 250 tons; receipt and shipment of general and containerized cargo and steel products, shipment of scrap metal, receipt of copper, zinc, and lumber; owned and operated by New Haven Terminal, Inc.

(321)   **New Haven Terminal Pier:** 50 yards southward of Scrap Metal Dock; north and south sides, 650 feet usable, can accommodate tankers up to 700 feet; 35 and 39 feet alongside, north and south sides, respectively; deck height, 13 feet; cranes up to 50 tons; 36,000 square feet covered storage; receipt and shipment of general cargo, receipt of petroleum products, petrochemicals, chemicals, copper, zinc, lumber, and steel products; owned and operated by New Haven Terminal, Inc.

(322)   **Exxon Co. Terminal Wharf:** 175 yards southward of New Haven Terminal Pier; 80-foot face, 700 feet with dolphins; 35 feet alongside; deck height, 13 feet; vessels normally moor starboardside-to; receipt and shipment of petroleum products; owned and operated by Exxon Co., U.S.A.

(323)   **Supplies.**–Oil bunkering terminals at New Haven are maintained by the major oil companies. Fuel oil and diesel oil in the usual commercial grades are obtainable. Barges are available for bunkering in the anchorages outside the breakwaters or at the piers; 24-hour advance notice is required, and arrangements should be made through ships' agents. Water, provisions, and marine supplies can be procured.

(324)   **Repairs.**–New Haven has no facilities for making major repairs or for drydocking deep-draft vessels; the nearest such facilities are at Boston, Mass., and New York. Machine shops in the area can make limited repairs to machinery and boilers, and fabricate shafts and other pieces of equipment.

(325)   **Small-craft facilities.**–There are excellent facilities on the east and west sides of the harbor and on West and Quinnipiac Rivers. (See the small-craft facilities tabulation on chart 12372 for services and supplies available.)

(326)   **Charts 12370, 12364.**–**Pond Point,** about 5 miles southwestward of the New Haven Harbor entrance, has a rocky shoal with little depth over the greater part of it that extends about 0.3 mile southward. It is marked by a buoy. A prominent white mast is on the point.

(327)   **Welches Point,** 0.8 mile westward of Pond Point, forms the east side of the entrance of The Gulf. A reef extends 0.3 mile southward from the point and is marked by a buoy.

(328)   **The Gulf,** a bight between Welches Point and Charles Island, about 6.5 miles westward of New Haven Harbor entrance, affords anchorage in 6 to 15 feet and is sheltered in all but southerly and southeasterly winds. The entrance is clear. The shoaling is gradual, and soundings are the best guide on the northwest side of the bight; the western side of Welches Point and the reefs around Charles Island extending to the mainland should be approached with caution, as the shoaling is abrupt. The mean range of **tide** is about 6.6 feet.

(329)   **Milford Harbor,** comprising the lower portion of the **Wepawaug River,** is entered at the mouth of the river between two jetties at the head of The Gulf. The westerly jetty extends southward from **Burns Point,** and the easterly jetty is marked by Milford Harbor Light 10. The harbor is used chiefly for recreational boating, and occasionally for the receipt of shellfish and fish. The National Marine Fisheries Service, U.S. Department of Commerce, maintains a laboratory and research vessel base on the west side of the harbor, about 0.2 mile northward of Burns Point.

(330)   A dredged channel leads from The Gulf through the jettied entrance to a point about 400 feet above the town wharf, 0.6 mile above Burns Point. In June 1988, the reported controlling depth was 9½ feet to Burns Point, thence

8 feet to the head of the channel. In March 1986, depths of 3½ to 6 feet were available in the anchorage basin along the southwest side of the channel except for shoaling to 1 foot near the north end. The channel is marked by a lighted buoy and an unlighted buoy to the jettied entrance. An obstruction, a pile, is in the anchorage basin, about 0.2 mile northwestward of Burns Point.

(331) Milford Harbor has several small-craft facilities. (See the small-craft facilities tabulation on chart 12364 for services and supplies available.)

(332) A 5 mph **speed limit** is enforced in the harbor.

(333) **Charles Island,** on the southwest side at the entrance to The Gulf, is low and partly covered with trees. A white flagpole, barely visible over the trees, is on the island. The island is connected to the mainland by **The Bar,** a narrow neck about 0.5 mile long and surrounded by rocks awash and shoals. A buoy marks the end of a shoal that extends 250 yards east-northeastward from the island, and a lighted bell buoy marks the end of a rocky area that extends 0.4 mile southward from the island. Northward of Charles Island is a good anchorage in 10 to 16 feet, sheltered from southerly to southwesterly winds.

(334) Between Charles Island and **Stratford Point,** about 3 miles southwestward, several summer resorts are along the shore and the Housatonic River empties into Long Island Sound just above the point. The shoals which extend southward from Stratford Point toward Stratford Shoal Light (see chart 12354) consist of narrow ridges of hard sand with deeper water between, and have oyster beds marked with stakes. Depths of 12 feet or less extend 1 mile offshore.

(335) **Stratford Point Light** (41°09.1'N., 73°06.2'W.), 52 feet above the water, is shown from a white conical tower, with brown band midway of its height, from the southerly part of the point; a radiobeacon and a fog signal are at the light.

(336) **Chart 12370.**–**Housatonic River** rises in the Berkshire Hills of western Massachusetts and Connecticut, and empties into Long Island Sound about 10 miles southwestward of the New Haven Harbor entrance. The river is joined by the nonnavigable **Naugatuck River** in the vicinity of Derby, conn. Housatonic River is navigable to a point about 1 mile above Shelton, Conn., where it is closed by a power dam. The head of navigation for all practical purposes is at the towns of Derby and Shelton, 11.5 miles above the entrance. Small vessels can anchor in the river abreast of Stratford, where the channel has an available width of about 500 feet. The waterborne commerce on the river is principally in barge shipments of aggregate, fuel oil to the power plant at Devon, and seasonal commercial shellfishing. Navigation above Devon is limited to recreational boating.

(337) On the east side of the entrance to Housatonic River, a breakwater extends out from **Milford Point** across the bar and is marked at its south end by Housatonic River Breakwater Light 2A. The inner section of the breakwater is awash at high water.

(338) **Channels.**–A Federal project provides for an 18-foot dredged channel from Long Island Sound between the breakwater on the east and Stratford Point on the west upriver for about 4.3 miles to the lower end of Culver Bar. (See Notice to Mariners and the latest editions of the charts for controlling depths.) Above the lower end of Culver Bar, the river channel extends through several dredged sections across river bars to the towns of Derby and Shelton about 11.5 miles above the river entrance. In 1976-1978, the controlling depth was 5 feet (5½ feet at midchannel) to Camp Meeting Bar, 7.1 miles above the channel entrance, thence 2 feet to Twomile Island Bar, thence 1 foot (5½ feet at midchannel) across the bar, and thence 3 feet (5½ feet at midchannel) to Derby and Shelton. In September 1978, shoaling to 3 feet was reported in the channel across Mill Bar. The channel is marked to a point about 2.5 miles below Derby and Shelton.

(339) **Stratford** is a town on the west side of the river 2.3 miles above the entrance. The principal wharf has a depth of about 9 feet at its end. The **harbormaster** at Stratford controls anchorages and moorings, and has jurisdiction from the entrance of the river to the Shelton town line. Harbor regulations may be obtained from the harbormaster who may be contacted through the Stratford police or at the Town Hall.

(340) Stratford has several small-craft facilities. (See the small-craft facilities tabulation on chart 12364 for services and supplies available.)

(341) **Devon** is on the east side about 1 mile above Stratford. Local small craft anchor near the east bank of the river, just north of the highway bridge, in depths up to 10 feet. A 40-foot marine railway at a small–craft facility at Devon can haul out craft for engine and hull repairs; gasoline, water, ice, marine supplies, and storage are available. In July 1981, depths of 4 feet were reported alongside the facility.

(342) **Shelton,** a town on the west side of the river about 11.5 miles above the entrance is connected to **Derby** by two bridges; the town has several important factories. In 1971, the wharves at Derby and Shelton were in ruins and unsuitable for craft of any size.

(343) **Bridges.**–About 1 mile above Stratford is U.S. Route 1 highway bridge with a bascule span having a clearance of 32 feet. Two bridges cross the river about 0.3 mile farther up: the first, Interstate Route 95 fixed highway bridge, has a clearance of 65 feet, and the second, a railroad bridge with a bascule span, has a clearance of 19 feet. The bridgetenders of the U.S. Route 1 bridge and the railroad bridge monitor VHF-FM channel 13; call signs KXJ-695 and KU-6035, respectively. An overhead power cable with a clearance of 135 feet crosses at the railroad bridge. Other cables, near **Pecks Mill,** 1.5 miles above, have minimum clearance of 79 feet.

(344) The fixed highway bridge about 3.7 miles above Stratford has a clearance of 85 feet. At Shelton, two fixed highway bridges and a fixed railroad bridge have a least clearance of 17 feet. In April 1983, the railroad bridge suffered severe structural damage. The area should be avoided, but if transit is necessary, extreme caution should be exercised.

(345) (See 117.1 through 117.59 and 117.207, chapter 2, for drawbridge regulations.)

(346) **Tides.**–The mean range of tide is 5.5 feet at Stratford and 5 feet at Shelton. The time of the tide becomes later and the range diminishes in progressing up the river. At Stratford the tide is about 0.8 hour later than at the entrance whereas at Shelton high water is about 1.8 hours later and low water about 2.8 hours later than at the entrance. The river water is fresh about 6 miles above the entrance.

(347) **Currents.**–At the entrance near the end of the breakwater the flood has a strong westerly set. Between Milford Point and **Crimbo Point,** flood and ebb have a velocity of about 1.2 knots. The flood sets about 330° and the ebb 135°. Just north of the draw of the railroad bridge above Stratford, the velocity of flood is 1.1 knots and of ebb, 1.3 knots. In the openings of the bridge the flood current has some easterly set, but the ebb sets fair with the openings. Between that bridge and Shelton the tidal current has a velocity of about 1 knot. Because of the drainage flow of the river, the

(348) ebb is usually greater and the flood less than 1 knot. (Consult the Tidal Current Tables for current predictions and further details.)

(348)   Spring **freshets** at Shelton rise 10 feet or more above mean high tide.

(349)   **Ice** closes the river above Stratford during the winter and sometimes extends to the entrance.

(350)   **Routes.**–The channel in Housatonic River is narrow and crooked, with little depth on either side, and across the bars in the channel are dredged cuts 100 feet wide. The tidal currents are strong, especially in the lower part of the river, and strangers are advised to take a pilot. Small craft, without a pilot, should proceed with caution and preferably on a rising tide.

(351)   When entering the river during a flood current, care must be taken to avoid being set on the shoals on the west side by strong westerly currents. In the vicinity of Milford Point care should be exercised to avoid a shoal that reportedly extends from Milford Point to the eastern edge of the channel. Care should also be exercised off the extreme northern end of Nells Island as a shoal is reported to have encroached into the channel. By steering a midchannel course no difficulty should be encountered.

(352)   **Pilots** and **tugs** can be obtained at New Haven.

(353)   A 5 mph **speed limit** is enforced on the river near anchorage and mooring areas and near boat slips.

(354)   **Chart 12354.**–**Stratford Shoal Middle Ground**, 5.4 miles south of Stratford Point and covered 4½ to 18 feet, is marked by **Stratford Shoal (Middle Ground) Light** (41°03.6′ N., 73°06.1′W.), 60 feet above the water and shown from a gray granite octagonal tower projecting from a house on a pier, and by buoys that mark the outer ends of shoal areas extending 1 mile north, 0.9 mile northeast, and 0.5 mile south of the light. A fog signal is at the light.

(355)   **North Shore of Long Island.**–From Orient Point (41°09.6′N., 72°14.0′W.), for about 11 miles to Horton Point, the south shore of Long Island Sound is generally bluff and rocky. The 10-fathom curve is from 0.3 to 0.8 mile from shore, and the shoaling is generally abrupt. The outlying dangers are Orient Shoal and the rocky patch northward of Horton Point.

(356)   The prominent features are Browns Hills, a tower at Rocky Point, a tank and television tower at Greenport, and Horton Point Light.

(357)   Several rocky shoals, including **Orient Shoal** with a least depth of 7 feet, are offshore in the vicinity of **Rocky Point**, about 5 miles westward of Orient Point. The north end of Orient Shoal is marked by a buoy.

(358)   **Horton Point Light** (41°05.1′ N., 72°26.8′W.), 103 feet above the water, is shown from a white square tower attached to a dwelling on the northwest part of the point. A radiobeacon is 72 yards south-southeastward of the light. The former lighthouse tower is close by, southwestward of the present light.

(359)   A rocky shoal with a least found depth of 26 feet is 1.6 miles northward of Horton Point. The shoal is a ridge having a northeast-southwest direction, with abrupt shoaling on its northwest and southeast sides.

(360)   From Horton Point for about 32 miles to Old Field Point, the shore is fringed with shoals that extend off a greatest distance of 1.5 miles and rise abruptly from the deep water of Long Island Sound. Boulders are found near the shore on the shoals which extend off 0.5 mile in places. A sand shoal, about 0.5 mile in extent with a least depth of 26 feet, is about 1.1 miles northwestward of Duck Pond Point.

(361)   The bluffs begin about 1 mile westward of Goldsmith Inlet and reach their greatest elevation just eastward of **Duck Pond Point**. A valley, formed by a break in the bluffs, is just westward of the point; a bathing pavilion is on the beach. Boulders that bare at low water are on the shoals that fringe the shore between Duck Pond Point and Mattituck Inlet.

(362)   **Chart 12358.**–**Mattituck Inlet**, 6.7 miles southwestward of Horton Point Light, is entered between two short jetties. The inlet is marked by a long break in the bluffs, and numerous storage tanks inside the inlet are prominent. The outer end of the west jetty is marked by a light. A gong buoy about 1 mile north of the jetty light marks the entrance of the inlet. The sides of the channel are sandy, and, although shoaling is liable to occur at the entrance, strangers can enter the inlet without great danger. In September 1987, the controlling depth was 4 feet (6 feet at midchannel) from the entrance for about 1.8 miles to the turning basin at Mattituck with 7 feet available in the basin. The channel is marked by buoys and private markers. The overhead power cable about 1 mile above the entrance has a clearance of 78 feet.

(363)   The **tidal currents** have an estimated velocity of about 3 knots in the narrow parts of the entrance of Mattituck Inlet. Slack waters occur possibly 1 hour after the time of high and low water. With northerly and westerly winds, the sea is rough in the entrance. The mean range of **tide** is 5.2 feet at the entrance. The inlet is sometimes closed by **ice** during portions of cold winters.

(364)   Several marinas and a boatyard are inside the inlet. A 50-ton mobile hoist at the boatyard can haul out craft for engine, hull, and radio repairs. Marine supplies, gasoline, diesel fuel, water, and covered and wet storage can be obtained. A transient dock, operated by the Mattituck Park Commission, is at the head of the inlet; depths of about 6 feet are at the dock. A **dockmaster** is at the dock; water is available.

(365)   **Mattituck** is a village on the railroad at the head of the inlet. Provisions can be obtained.

(366)   **Jacobs Point** is about 11 miles southwestward of Horton Point Light. An aquaculture site, marked by private buoys, is about 1.4 miles west-northwest of Jacobs Point.

(367)   **Offshore Terminal, Northville-Riverhead.**–An offshore platform for the delivery and receipt of petroleum products is in open roadstead, off Northville, NY (and Riverhead, NY), about 1.2 miles northward of Jacobs Point. It is owned and operated by Northville Industries Corporation, Riverhead, NY.

(368)   A safety zone surrounds the offshore facility. (See **166.155**, chapter 2, for limits and regulations.

(369)   The facility consists of a 45- by 100-foot steel platform structure with breasting dolphins and mooring dolphins providing two berths; one on the north side and one on the south side. The deck height is 24.5 feet. The north berth has depths alongside of 64 feet, and can accomodate tankers up to 225,000 DWT and up to 1,150-foot length, of 62-foot maximum draft.

(370)   The south berth has depths alongside of 50 feet, and can accomodate tankers of up to 42,000 DWT and up to 6,00-foot length, of 42-foot maximum draft. Barges mooring in this berth must be at least 220 feet long.

(371)   A private fog signal is on the platform and private lights mark the four corners.

(372)   **Wharf.**–An 800-foot barge pier is just east of Jacobs Point and southward of the platform. In May 1991, only the

west side of the pier was used for the transhipment of petroleum products. Barges to 30,000 barrel capacity are received. Depth alongside is 16 feet. However, depths of 13 feet surround the area and a 11-foot shoal marked by a private buoy, must be cleared on the recommended southwest approach to, and northwest departure from the west pier berth. Vessels with draft greater than 12 feet should exercise caution when approaching the pier and should endeavor to arrive or depart at high water.

(373)   **Prominent feature.**–The numerous light green oil storage tanks on Jacobs Point are prominent.

(374)   **Communications.**–Vessels transitting Long Island Sound or approaching the facility may do so through a VHF-FM marine operator. Available marine operator stations' name and channel are:

(375)   Riverhead   28
(376)   New Bedford   26
(377)   New London   26
(378)   Bridgeport   24.

(379)   Upon the approach of an incoming vessel, the platform, voice call "Northville Industries Offshore Platform", or "Northville-Riverhead Platform", or "Northville-Riverhead Terminal", or "Northville-Riverhead Dock", monitors VHF-FM channels 16, 13 and 19A; works channel 19A.

(380)   Vessels calling at the platform are moored at any time, weather conditions permitting. The tidal current periods are substantially the same as at The Race. Strong winds from the north and northwest are experienced during the winter and spring. Tidal currents during maximum ebb and flood may reach 3 knots. The mean range of tide is 5.4 feet.

(381)   Vessels awaiting berth at the platform will normally anchor north of the platform. A vessel drawing more than 50 feet of water may wish to anchor in deeper water northwest of the platform. Pilots are familiar with the best anchorages. Holding ground is good and a scope of 8 shots (120 feet) is considered adequate.

(382)   **Pilotage, Offshore Terminal, Northville-Riverhead.**–Pilotage is compulsary in Long Island Sound for foreign vessels and U.S. vessels under register. For these vessels, pilotage to this terminal is available from:

(383)   Sound Pilots, Inc. (a division of Northeast Marine Pilots, Inc.).

(384)   For U.S. enrolled vessels in the coastwise trade, pilotage to this terminal is available from

(385)   Connecticut State Pilots (a division of Interport Pilots Agency, Inc.),

(386)   Constitution State Pilots Association,

(387)   Long Island Sound State Pilots Association, Inc., and

(388)   Sound Pilots, Inc. (a division of Northeast Marine Pilots, Inc.).

(389)   See Pilotage, Long Island Sound (indexed as such), early this chapter, and Pilotage, New York Harbor and Approaches, (indexed as such), chapter 11.

(390)   The pilot serves as docking master and remains on board on standby while the vessel is moored at the platform. Pilot services are arranged in advance through ships' agents or directly by shipping companies.

(391)   **Tugs.**–Tug service is available from New Haven, Providence, Brooklyn, or Staten Island on advance notice. Normally two or three tugs are used for docking and one or two tugs for undocking.

(392)   **Launch service.**–J & H Launch Service, Port Jefferson (516-331-5336), provides transfer service for vessels at anchor or alongside the platform.

(393)   **Supplies.**–Fueling of a ship alongside the platform is not permitted. A ship may fuel while at anchor from a barge. Water is not available from this facility. Stores may

be brought on board via launch while alongside or at anchor.

(394)   New York City is the **quarantine, customs, immigration,** and **agricultural quarantine** port of entry for Northville. Officials are stationed in New York City. (See appendix for addresses.) Arrangements for such inspections must be made by ships' agents in advance, usually not less than 24 hours Monday through Friday and 48 hours on Saturday and Sunday. Officials will board vessels in the anchorage prior to arrival within the vicinity of the offshore mooring facility.

(395)   **Chart 12354.**–Between Mattituck Inlet and Port Jefferson the shore is fringed with rock shoals extending in places 1.5 miles offshore. The outer ends of the shoals are marked by buoys.

(396)   **Horse in Bank,** 7.3 miles westward of Mattituck Inlet, is an area of white patches in the brush-covered bluff at **Friars Head.** The feature is at the western end of **Roanoke Point Shoal** and 14 miles westward of Horton Point Light.

(397)   The valley of **Wading River,** about 20 miles westward of Horton Point Light, forms a broad break in the high bluffs. The entrance to Wading River is protected by a short jetty on the west side. In July 1981, a reported depth of about 3 feet could be carried in the river to a town launching ramp 0.1 mile above the entrance. A small canal, about 350 yards westward of the entrance to Wading River, leads southward to the site of a nuclear power station. The canal, closed to general navigation, had a reported depth of about 12 feet in June 1989.

(398)   **Tuttles White Bank** is a high white bluff 0.6 mile westward of Wading River.

(399)   **Charts 12362, 12364.**–Mount Sinai Harbor, 22.5 miles westward of Mattituck Inlet, is marked by a low break in the beach nearly 1 mile long. The approach to the harbor is marked by a buoy. The entrance is protected by two jetties, the outer parts of which are awash at high water. Caution should be exercised when rounding them. A private light and a private daybeacon mark the outer ends of the east and west jetties, respectively. In June 1981, a depth of about 8 feet was reported available through the entrance. The northern part of the harbor has general depths of 10 to 20 feet. A channel marked by private buoys leads eastward from the entrance to small-craft facilities on the north shore of the harbor. The southern part of the harbor is shoal; the chart is the guide. Several **small-craft facilities** are in the harbor. (See the small-craft facilities tabulation on chart 12364 for services and supplies available.) A **speed limit** of 6 mph is enforced in the harbor by the Suffolk County Police.

(400)   **Mount Misery,** 180 feet high, between Mount Sinai Harbor and Port Jefferson, slopes off gradually toward the sound where the bluffs are about 60 feet high and very prominent. Sand banks dug out by sand and gravel companies are very conspicuous.

(401)   **Port Jefferson Harbor,** on the south shore of Long Island Sound eastward of Old Field Point, is entered through a dredged channel that leads between two jetties to a docking area near the southwestern end of the harbor; the jetties are each marked by a light. The approach is marked by a lighted whistle buoy, about 1.1 miles northwest of the entrance. Three stacks on the west side near the head of the harbor are conspicuous landmarks. A 12 mph **speed limit** is enforced in the main entrance channel, and a 5 mph **speed limit** is enforced at the head of the harbor in the vicinity of the mooring areas and wharves.

(402)   A **121°-301° measured nautical mile** is westward of the entrance to Port Jefferson Harbor on Old Field Beach.

The front markers are orange posts about 8 feet high; the rear markers are rectangles mounted on legs about 12 feet high, painted red with a 6-inch black vertical stripe in the middle.

(403)   The approach to Port Jefferson Harbor is clear, taking care to avoid **Mount Misery Shoal** with depths of 7 to 12 feet, about 0.8 mile north-northeast of the east jetty light.

(404)   In November 1990, the controlling depth was 23 feet (26 feet at midchannel) in the dredged channel through Port Jefferson Harbor to the docking area off an oil wharf at the southern end. Shoaling to 10 feet is near the southwest corner of the southern limit of the project. The channel is marked by lighted and unlighted buoys and a **146°** lighted range. In September 1982, it was reported that due to the closeness of the range lights it may be difficult to determine when they are in line. It was further reported that the range may be obscured by vessels tied up at the oil wharf on the west side of the harbor.

(405)   Shoals with little depth are on both sides of the channel from the entrance to Port Jefferson to Lighted Bell Buoy 5 inside the entrance. The ground from the east jetty to the lighted bell buoy is broken, with shoals covered 4 to 11 feet. The lighted bell buoy cannot be seen over the breakwater at low tide by small vessels approaching the harbor.

(406)   The mean range of **tide** is 6.6 feet.

(407)   **Currents.**–In the channel between the jetties the velocity of the tidal currents is 2.6 knots on flood and 1.9 on ebb; flood sets 151° and the ebb 323°. It is reported that on the ebb there is a current with a velocity of 1 to 2 knots across the entrance to the harbor.

(408)   Ice forms over the entire harbor and interrupts navigation in very cold weather, but does not endanger shipping in the harbor.

(409)   **Pilotage, Port Jefferson.**–Pilotage is compulsary in Long Island Sound for foreign vessels and U.S. vessels under register. For these vessels, pilotage is available from:

(410)   Sound Pilots, Inc. (a division of Northeast Marine Pilots, Inc.).

(411)   For U.S. enrolled vessels in the coastwise trade, pilotage is available from:

(412)   Connecticut State Pilots (a division of Interport Pilots Agency, Inc.),

(413)   Constitution State Pilots Association,

(414)   Long Island Sound State Pilots Association, Inc., and

(415)   Sound Pilots, Inc. (a division of Northeast Marine Pilots, Inc.).

(416)   See Pilotage, Long Island Sound (indexed as such), early this chapter, and Pilotage, New York Harbor and Approaches, (indexed as such), chapter 11.

(417)   Pilot services are arranged in advance through ships' agents or directly by shipping companies.

(418)   **Tugs.**–Tug service is available from New Haven, Providence, Brooklyn, or Staten Island on advance notice. Normally, two tugs are used for docking and one for undocking.

(419)   **Port Jefferson** is a town at the southern end of the harbor. The principal industries of the port are the shipping of sand and gravel and the distribution of petroleum products. There are small-craft facilities at the head of the harbor. (See the small-craft facilities tabulation on chart 12364 for services and supplies available.) A launching ramp is at the head of the harbor.

(420)   **Wharves.**–Depths ranging from 16 feet to bare are reported alongside the small commercial wharves and piers at the head of the harbor. In June 1983, the depths were 31 feet alongside the oil wharf on the west side of the harbor about 400 yards from the head. The powerplant wharf about 150 yards to the northwestward had depths of 25 to 28 feet alongside in June 1983.

(421)   **Communications.**–Port Jefferson is served by railroad and bus. A ferry operates to Bridgeport, Conn.

(422)   **Conscience Bay** is entered through a long, narrow channel at the northwest end of Port Jefferson Harbor. The bay and entrance have depths of 1 to 2 feet. Strangers should not attempt to enter as there are many rocks at the entrance.

(423)   **Setauket Harbor**, on the western side of Port Jefferson Harbor, has a narrow crooked channel. In June 1981, a reported depth of about 2½ feet was available in the channel to the boatyard at Setauket. The entrance from Port Jefferson is marked by private seasonal buoys. Gasoline, moorings, and limited marine supplies are available at the boatyard; a flatbed trailer can haul out craft to 32 feet long.

(424)   **Setauket** is a village on the south shore of Setauket Harbor about 1 mile above the entrance.

9. WESTERN LONG ISLAND SOUND

(1)   This chapter describes the western part of Long Island Sound along the north shore from Bridgeport to Throgs Neck, the south shore from Old Field Point to Willets Point, and the East and Harlem Rivers. Also described are the many bays and their tributaries that make into this part of the sound including Bridgeport Harbor, Stamford Harbor, Captain Harbor, Mamaroneck Harbor, Norwalk Harbor, Eastchester Bay, Huntington Bay, Oyster Bay, Hempstead Harbor, Manhasset Bay, Flushing Bay, and New Rochelle Harbor, and the commercial and small-craft facilities found in these waters.

(2)   **COLREGS Demarcation Lines.**–The lines established for Long Island Sound are described in **80.155**, chapter 2.

(3)   **Chart 12363.**–Western Long Island Sound is that portion of the deep navigable waterway between the shores of Connecticut and New York and the northern coast of Long Island westward of the line between Bridgeport and Old Field Point.

(4)   This region has boulders and broken ground, with little or no natural change in the shoals. the waters are well marked by navigational aids so that strangers should experience no difficulty in navigating them. As all broken ground is liable to be strewn with boulders, vessels should proceed with caution when in the vicinity of broken areas where the charted depths are less than 6 to 8 feet greater than the draft. All of the more important places are entered through dredged channels. During fog, vessels are advised to anchor until the weather clears before attempting to enter. The numerous oyster grounds in this region are usually marked by stakes and flags. These stakes may become broken off and form obstructions dangerous to small craft which, especially at night, should proceed with caution when crossing oyster areas.

(5)   **Anchorages.**–There is anchorage for large vessels in the bight outside Bridgeport Harbor Light. Cockenoe Harbor is sometimes used by small vessels, but Sheffield Island Harbor is preferred and is sometimes used by tows. Westward of Norwalk Islands, seagoing vessels can anchor toward the north shore and, with good ground tackle, hold on in northerly winds. Captain Harbor affords good shelter, but is rarely used except by local vessels. On the south shore, Huntington Bay and Hempstead Harbor are available for large vessels; Oyster Bay is also used, and Manhasset Bay is available for light-draft vessels. City Island Harbor is a fine resort for coasters.

(6)   **Tides.**–The time of tide is nearly simultaneous throughout Long Island Sound, but the range of tide increases from about 2.5 feet at the east end to about 7.3 feet at the west end. Daily predictions of the times and heights of high and low waters for New London, Bridgeport, and Willets Point are given in the Tide Tables.

(7)   The effect of strong winds, in combination with the regular tidal action, may at times cause the water to fall several feet below the plane of reference of the charts.

(8)   **Currents.**–About 1.3 miles northward of Eatons Neck Light the ebb runs about 5 hours longer than the flood. The current has a velocity of 1.4 knots; the flood sets 283° and the ebb sets 075°.

(9)   The direction and velocity of the currents are affected by strong winds which may increase or diminish the periods of flood or ebb. Directions and velocities from Point Judith

to Throgs Neck for each hour of the tidal cycle will be found in Tidal Current Charts, Long Island Sound and Block Island Sound. Currents in East River are described in the latter part of this chapter.

(10)   **Weather.**–These waters are more protected than the eastern Sound resulting in fewer gales. However, winters are colder and summers warmer due to this sheltering effect. Fog is not so frequent either and tends to burn off quicker than farther east. Winter winds of 16 knots or more are likely about 12 to 15 percent of the time and are predominantly from the west through northwest. Harbors such as Cold Spring, Oyster Bay, Hempstead and Manhasset offer additional shelter. In summer thunderstorms may develop on 4 to 5 days per month. These are most likely during the afternoon or evening.

(11)   In Long Island Sound the north and south shores are equally subject to fog, except that on spring and summer mornings, when there is little or no wind, fog will often hang along the Connecticut shore while it is clear offshore and southward.

(12)   In the western end of Long Island Sound, although fogs are liable to occur at any time, they are not encountered so often nor do they generally last so long as farther eastward.

(13)   **Ice.**–In ordinary winters the floating and pack ice in Long Island Sound, while impeding navigation, does not render it absolutely unsafe, but in exceptionally severe winters the reverse is true; then only the powerful steamers can make their way.

(14)   Drift ice, which is formed principally along the northern shore of the sound under the influence of the prevailing northerly winds, drifts across to the southern side and accumulates there, massing into large fields, and remains until removed by southerly winds which drive it back to the northerly shore.

(15)   In ordinary winters ice generally forms in the western end of the sound as far as Eatons Neck; in exceptionally severe winters ice may extend to Falkner Island and farther eastward.

(16)   **Effects of winds on ice.**–In Long Island Sound northerly winds drive the ice to the southern shore of the sound and southerly winds carry it back to the northern shore. Northeasterly winds force the ice westward and cause formations heavy enough to prevent the passage of vessels of every description until the ice is removed by westerly winds. These winds carry the ice eastward and, if of long enough duration, drive it through The Race into Block Island Sound, from where it goes to sea and disappears.

(17)   In Bridgeport Harbor winds from north to northwest clear the harbor of drift ice, and those from southeast through south to southwest force the ice into the harbor from the sound. The outer buoys may be carried out of position by heavy ice during severe winters.

(18)   Additional information concerning ice conditions in the waters adjoining Long Island Sound is given under the local descriptions.

(19)   **Vessel Traffic Service (New York),** operated by the U.S. Coast Guard, serves New York Harbor (see **161.501 through 161.580,** chapter 2, for regulations).

(20)   **Pilotage, Western Long Island Sound.**–Pilotage is compulsary in Long Island Sound for foreign vessels and U.S. vessels under register. For vessels entering Long Island

APPENDIX

(1) **Sales Information.**–National Ocean Service publications and nautical charts are sold by NOS and its authorized sales agents in many U.S. ports and in some foreign ports. Mail orders should be addressed to:

(2) National Ocean Service,

(3) Distribution Branch (N/CG33),

(4) 6501 Lafayette Avenue,

(5) Riverdale, MD 20737-1199.

(6) Orders should be accompanied by a check or money order payable to NOS, Department of Commerce. Remittance from outside the United States should be made either by an International Money Order or by a check payable on a U.S. bank. Chart catalogs, which include a listing of authorized sales agents, are free upon request. The National Ocean Service maintains over-the-counter cash sales offices at Distribution Branch, Riverdale (see address above), and at 701 C Street, Box 38, Anchorage, AK 99513.

(7) **National Ocean Service Offices**

(8) **Washington, DC** (Headquarters): Assistant Administrator, National Ocean Service, NOAA, Herbert C. Hoover Bldg., 14th Street and Constitution Avenue, NW., Room 5805, Washington, DC 20230-0001.

(9) **Rockville:** Director, Coast and Geodetic Survey, National Ocean Service, NOAA, 6001 Executive Boulevard, Rockville, MD 20852-3806.

(10) **Norfolk:** Director, Atlantic Marine Center, National Ocean Service, NOAA, 439 West York Street, Norfolk, VA 23510-1114.

(11) **Seattle:** Director, Pacific Marine Center, National Ocean Service, NOAA, 1801 Fairview Avenue East, Seattle, WA 98102-3767.

(12) **Charts and Publications-National Ocean Service**

(13) **Nautical Charts** (See Chart Catalogs)

(14) United States Coastal and Intracoastal Waters, and possessions.

(15) Great Lakes, Lake Champlain, New York State Canals, and the St. Lawrence River-St. Regis to Cornwall, Canada.

(16) **Publications** (See Chart Catalogs for latest editions and prices)

(17) **Coast Pilots**

(18) U. S. Coast Pilot 1, Atlantic Coast, Eastport to Cape Cod.

(19) U. S. Coast Pilot 2, Atlantic Coast, Cape Cod to Sandy Hook.

(20) U. S. Coast Pilot 3, Atlantic Coast, Sandy Hook to Cape Henry.

(21) U. S. Coast Pilot 4, Atlantic Coast, Cape Henry to Key West.

(22) U. S. Coast Pilot 5, Atlantic Coast–Gulf of Mexico, Puerto Rico, and Virgin Islands.

(23) U.S. Coast Pilot 6, Great Lakes, Lakes Ontario, Erie, Huron, Michigan, and Superior and St. Lawrence River.

(24) U.S. Coast Pilot 7, Pacific Coast, California, Oregon, Washington, and Hawaii.

(25) U.S. Coast Pilot 8, Pacific Coast Alaska, Dixon Entrance to Cape Spencer.

(26) U.S. Coast Pilot 9, Pacific and Arctic Coasts, Alaska–Cape Spencer to Beaufort Sea.

(27) **Distance Tables**

(28) Distances Between United States Ports.

(29) **Tide Tables**

(30) Europe and West Coast of Africa.

(31) East Coast, North and South America.

(32) West Coast, North and South America.

(33) Central and Western Pacific Ocean and Indian Ocean.

(34) Supplemental Tidal Predictions-Anchorage, Nikiski, Seldovia, and Valdez, Alaska.

(35) **Tidal Current Tables**

(36) Atlantic Coast, North America.

(37) Pacific Coast, North America and Asia.

(38) **Tidal Current Charts/Atlas**

(39) Boston Harbor.

(40) Narragansett Bay to Nantucket Sound.

(41) Narragansett Bay.

(42) Long Island Sound and Block Island Sound.

(43) Delaware Bay and River Atlas.

(44) Upper Chesapeake Bay.

(45) Charleston Harbor, S.C.

(46) Tampa Bay.

(47) Puget Sound, Northern Part.

(48) Puget Sound, Southern Part.

(49) **Tidal Current Diagrams**

(50) Boston Harbor.

(51) Long Island Sound and Block Island Sound.

(52) New York Harbor.

(53) **Regional Tide and Tidal Current Table.**

(54) New York to Chesapeake Bay.

(55) **Charts and Publications-Other U.S. Government Agencies**

(56) A partial list of publications and charts considered of navigational value is included for the ready reference of the mariner. In addition to the agents located in the principal seaports handling publication sales, certain libraries have been designated by the Congress of the United States to receive the publications as issued for public review.

(57) **Government Printing Office.**–Publications of the U.S. Government Printing Office may be ordered from Superintendent of Documents, U.S. Government Printing Office, Washington, DC 20402-9325. Orders may be charged to Visa, Mastercard, or Choice by calling (202) 783-3238 during normal business hours.

(58) **Defense Mapping Agency Procurement Information.**-Publications and charts of the Defense Mapping Agency Hydrographic/Topographic Center are available from Defense Mapping Agency Combat Support Center (Code DDCP), Washington, DC 20315-0020 and its sales agents.

(59) **Nautical Charts**

(60) U.S. Waters:

(61) Apalachicola, Chattahoochee and Flint Rivers Navigation Charts, Alabama River Charts, and Black Warrior-Tombigbee Rivers River Charts: Published and for sale by U.S. Army Engineer District Mobile, P.O. Box 2288, 109 St. Joseph Street, Mobile, Ala. 36628-0001.

(62) Flood Control and Navigation Maps of the Mississippi River, Cairo, Ill. to the Gulf of Mexico: Published by Mississippi River Commission and for sale by U.S. Army Engineer District Vicksburg, P.O. Box 60, U.S. Post Office and Courthouse, Vicksburg, Miss. 39180-0060.

(63) Upper Mississippi River Navigation Charts (Mississippi River, Cairo, Ill. to Minneapolis, Minn.): Published by U.S. Army Engineer North Central Division and for sale by

U.S. Army Engineer District St. Louis, 210 N. Tucker Boulevard, St. Louis, Mo. 63101-1986.

(64)   Charts of the Illinois Waterway, from Mississippi River at Grafton, Ill. to Lake Michigan at Chicago and Calumet Harbors: Published and for sale by U.S. Army Engineer District Rock Island, Clock Tower Bldg., Rock Island, Ill. 61201-2004.

(65)   Foreign Waters: Published by Defense Mapping Agency Hydrographic/Topographic Center (see Defense Mapping Agency Procurement Information above).

(66)   **Marine Weather Service Charts:** Published by the National Weather Service; for sale by NOS Distribution Branch (see Sales Information above).

(67)   **Publications**

(68)   **Notices to Mariners:**

(69)   The Local Notice to Mariners is available without charge upon application to the appropriate Coast Guard District Commander (see address further on). The Defense Mapping Agency Notice to Mariners is available without charge by operators of ocean-going vessels (see Defense Mapping Agency Procurement Information above).

(70)   **Special Notice to Mariners** are published annually in Defense Mapping Agency Notice to Mariners 1. These notices contain important information of considerable interest to all mariners. Interested parties are advised to read these notices.

(71)   **Light Lists (United States and Possessions):** Published by U.S. Coast Guard; for sale by the Government Printing Office. (See Government Printing Office, early this appendix.)

(72)   **List of Lights (Foreign Countries):** Published by Defense Mapping Agency Hydrographic/Topographic Center (see Defense Mapping Agency Procurement Information above).

(73)   **Sailing Directions (Foreign Countries):** Published by Defense Mapping Agency Hydrographic/Topographic Center (see Defense Mapping Agency Procurement Information above).

(74)   **Radio Navigational Aids,** Pub. 117: Published by Defense Mapping Agency Hydrographic/Topographic Center (see Defense Mapping Agency Procurement Information above).

(75)   The **Nautical Almanac,** the **Air Almanac,** and **Astronomical Almanac:** Published by U.S. Naval Observatory; for sale by Government Printing Office. (see Government Printing Office, early this appendix.)

(76)   **American Practical Navigator (Bowditch) (Pub. 9):** Published by Defense Mapping Agency Hydrographic/Topographic Center (see Defense Mapping Agency Procurement Information above).

(77)   **International Code of Signals (Pub. 102):** Published by Defense Mapping Hydrographic/Topographic Center (see Defense Mapping Agency Procurement Information above).

(78)   **Selected Worldwide Marine Weather Broadcasts:** Published by National Weather Service; for sale by the Government Printing Office. (See Government Printing Office, early this appendix.)

(79)   **Navigation Rules:** Navigation Rules, International-Inland (COMDTINST M16672.2 series): Published by the U.S. Coast Guard; for sale by Government Printing Office. (see Government Printing Office, early this appendix.)

(80)   **Federal Requirements for Recreational Boats:** Published by U.S. Coast Guard; available without charge by contacting the toll free Boating Safety Hotline (telephone, 800-368-5647).

(81)   **Port Series of the United States:** Published and sold by Corps of Engineers, U.S. Army, Water Resources Support Center, Port Facilities Branch, Casey Building, Fort Belvoir, VA 22060-5586.

(82)   **Maritime Radio User Handbook:** Published and sold by Radio Technical Commission for Maritime Services, 655 Fifteenth Street, N.W., Suite 300, Washington, DC 20005-5701.

(83)   **Corps of Engineers Offices**

(84)   **New England Division Office:** 424 Trapelo Road, Waltham, MA 02254-9149.

(85)   The New England Division, an operating division with both district and division functions, covers all of New England except western Vermont and small portions of Massachusetts and Connecticut along their western boundaries, and includes small portions of southeastern New York, all embraced in the drainage basins tributary to Long Island Sound and the Atlantic Ocean east of the New York-Connecticut State line. It also includes Fishers Island, N.Y.

(86)   **New York District Office:** 26 Federal Plaza, New York, NY 10278-0090.

(87)   The New York District includes western Vermont, small portions of western Massachusetts and Connecticut, eastern and south-central New York, including Long Island, and northeastern New Jersey embraced in the drainage basins tributary to Lake Champlain and the St. Lawrence River system east thereof and to the Atlantic Ocean from New York-Connecticut State line to, but not including, Manasquan Inlet, N.J.

(88)   It exercises jurisdiction, however, over all matters pertaining to the improvement of the Great Lakes to Hudson River waterway. Under the direction of the Secretary of the Army, the district engineer, as Supervisor of New York Harbor, also exercises jurisdiction under the laws enacted for the preservation of the tidal waters of New York Harbor, its adjacent or tributary waters, and the waters of Long Island Sound.

(89)   **Environmental Protection Agency (EPA) Offices.**—Regional offices and States in the EPA coastal regions:

(90)   **Region I** (New Hampshire, Vermont, Maine, Massachusetts, Connecticut, Rhode Island): J. F. Kennedy Federal Bldg., Boston, Mass. 02203.

(91)   **Region II** (New Jersey, New York, Puerto Rico, Virgin Islands): 26 Federal Plaza, New York, N.Y. 10278.

(92)   **Region III** (Delaware, Maryland, Virginia, District of Columbia, Pennsylvania): 841 Chestnut Street, Philadelphia, PA 19107.

(93)   **Region IV** (Alabama, Florida, Georgia, Mississippi, South Carolina, North Carolina): 345 Courtland Street, N.E., Atlanta, Ga. 30365.

(94)   **Region V** (Illinois, Indiana, Michigan, Minnesota, Ohio, Wisconsin): 230 South Dearborn Street, Chicago, Ill. 60604.

(95)   **Region VI** (Louisiana, Texas): First International Bldg., 1201 Elm Street, Dallas, Tex. 75270.

(96)   **Region IX** (California, Hawaii, Guam): 215 Fremont Street, San Francisco, Calif. 94105.

(97)   **Region X** (Alaska, Oregon, Washington): 1200 Sixth Avenue, Seattle, Wash. 98101.

(98)   **Coast Guard District Offices**

(99)   Commander, First Coast Guard District, 408 Atlantic Avenue, Boston, MA 02210-3350. Maine; New Hampshire; Vermont; Massachusetts; Rhode Island; Connecticut; New York except that part north of latitude 42°N. and west

of longitude 74°39'W; that part of New Jersey north of 39°57'N. (about the mouth of Toms River), east of 74°27'W. and northeast of a line from 39°57'N. 74°27'W. north west to the New York, New Jersey, and Pennsylvania boundaries at Tristate.

(100) **Note:** A Marine Safety Office combines the functions of the Captain of the Port and Marine Inspection Office.

(101) The symbol (D) preceding an office indicates that a Documentation Office is at the same address.

(102) **Coast Guard Marine Safety Offices**

(103) (D) Boston, MA: 447 Commercial Street 02109-1045.

(104) Portland ME: 312 Fore Street 04112-0108.

(105) Providence, RI: John O. Pastore Federal Building 02903-1790.

(106) **Coast Guard Captains of the Port**

(107) Long Island Sound Captain of the Port, 120 Woodward Avenue, New Haven, CT 06512-3698.

(108) New York Captain of the Port, Governors Island, New York, NY 10004-5098.

(109) **Coast Guard Marine Inspection Offices**

(110) (D) New York, N.Y.: Battery Park Bldg. 10004-1466.

(111) **Coast Guard Stations.**—The stations listed are in the area covered by this Coast Pilot. They have search and rescue capabilities and may provide lookout, communication, and/or patrol functions to assist vessels in distress. The National VHF-FM Distress System provides continuous coastal radio coverage outwards to 20 miles on channel 16. After contact on channel 16, communications with the Coast Guard should be on channel 22. If channel 22 is not available to the mariner, communications may be made on channel 12. Selected stations guard the International Radiotelephone Distress, Safety and Calling Frequencies.

(112) **Massachusetts:**

(113) Cape Cod Canal (41°46.4'N., 70°30.0'W.). East entrance to the canal, near Sandwich, Mass.

(114) Cape Cod Coast Guard Air Station (41°37.5'N., 70°31.5'W.). On Cape Cod at Otis Air Force Base.

(115) Provincetown (42°02.7'N., 70°11.6'W.). On southwest side of harbor, about 0.4 mile southwest of town pier.

(116) Chatham (41°40.3'N., 69°57.0'W.). Southeastern Cape Cod, near Chatham Light.

(117) Woods Hole (41°31.2'N., 70°40.0'W.). On west side of Little Harbor, about 450 yards northward of Juniper Point.

(118) Brant Point (41°17.4'N., 70°05.5'W.). On west side of entrance to Nantucket Harbor, near Brant Point Light.

(119) Menemsha (41°21.0'N., 70°45.9'W.). West end of Martha's Vineyard, near Menemsha Light.

(120) **Rhode Island:**

(121) Castle Hill (41°27.7'N., 71°21.5'W.). On west shore of Newport Neck, near Castle Hill Light.

(122) Point Judith (41°21.7'N., 71°28.9'W.). On Point Judith, near Point Judith Light, 0.5 mile east of Point Judith Harbor of Refuge.

(123) **Connecticut:**

(124) New London (41°20.7'N., 72°05.7'W.). At Fort Trumbull, on west side of main channel northward of Greens Harbor.

(125) New Haven (41°16.4'N., 72°54.2'W.). On the north side of the jutting point, about 1.5 miles northward of Lighthouse Point.

(126) **New York:**

(127) Fishers Island (41°15.4'N., 72°01.9'W.). In Silver Eel Pond, on west end of island (manned during summer months only).

(128) Eatons Neck (40°57.3'N., 73°23.9'W.). Near Eatons Neck Light, north shore of Long Island, east side of entrance to Huntington Bay.

(129) Montauk Point (41°04.3'N., 71°56.1'W.). In Montauk Harbor, Long Island.

(130) Shinnecock (40°51.0'N., 72°30.3'W.). East side of Ponquogue Point, 1.3 miles northwest of Shinnecock Inlet.

(131) Fire Island (40°37.5'N., 73°15.6'W.). Near west end of island, 0.2 mile northeast of Fire Island Light.

(132) Rockaway (40°34.1'N., 73°53.1'W.). On Rockaway Beach, 2.5 miles east of Rockaway Point.

(133) Coast Guard Air Station Brooklyn, Floyd Bennett Field (40°35.3'N., 73°53.5'W.). On Barren Island.

(134) Fort Totten (40°47.6'N., 73°46.9'W.). On the east side of Little Bay.

(135) New York (40°41.5'N., 74°01.0'W.). On Governors Island.

(136) **New Jersey:**

(137) Sandy Hook (40°28.2'N., 74°00.8'W.). On the Bay side, 0.5 mile south of the northern extremity of Sandy Hook.

(138) **Coast Guard Radio Broadcasts.**—Urgent, safety, and scheduled marine information broadcasts are made by Coast Guard radio stations. In general, these broadcasts provide information vital to vessels operating in the approaches and coastal waters of the United States including Puerto Rico and U.S. Virgin Islands. Transmissions are as follows:

(139) **Urgent and safety broadcasts:**

(140) (1) **By radiotelegraph:** (a) Upon receipt, except within 10 minutes of the next silent period, for urgent messages only; (b) during the last 15 seconds of the first silent period after receipt: (c) repeated at the end of the first silent period which occurs during the working hours of one-operator ships unless the original warning has been cancelled or superseded by a later warning message.

(141) (2) **By radiotelephone:** (a) upon receipt; (b) repeated 15 minutes later (for urgent messages only); (c) text only on the first scheduled broadcast unless cancelled; (d) additional broadcasts at the discretion of the originator.

(142) (3) Urgent broadcasts are preceded by the urgent signal; XXX for radiotelegraph; PAN for radiotelephone. Both the urgent signal and message are transmitted on 500 kHz, 2182 kHz, and channel 16. Safety broadcasts are preceded by the safety signal: TTT for radiotelegraph; SECURITY for radiotelephone. After the preliminary signal on 500 kHz and 2182 kHz, the station shifts to its assigned working medium frequency for the radiotelegraph broadcast and 2670 kHz for the radiotelephone transmission. Those stations broadcasting on VHF will announce on channel 16, shifting to channel 22.

(143) **Scheduled broadcasts.**—The following Coast Guard radio stations make scheduled broadcasts, preceded by a preliminary call on 500 kHz, 2182 kHz, and VHF-FM channel 16, at the times and frequencies indicated:

(144) **Radiotelegraph**

(145) NMF, Boston, Mass., 472 kHz, 0950 and 1900 e.s.t.

(146) **Radiotelephone**

(147) NMF, Boston, 2670 kHz, 1140 and 2340 e.s.t.

(148) NMF-7, Boston, channel 22a 0535 and 1735 e.s.t., antennas: Boston Bank Building, Boston (42°21.5'N., 71°03.5'W.), Eastern Point, Gloucester (42°34.8'N., 70°39.9'W.).

(149) NMF-2, Woods Hold, MA, channel 22A, 0505 and 1705 e.s.t., antennas: Pilgrim Monument, Provincetown (42°03'N., 70°11'W.), Nobska Point, Woods Hole (41°31'N., 70°39.5'W.), Brant Point, Nantucket Harbor (41°17.5'N., 70°06'W.).

(150) NMY-41, East Moriches, Long Island, 2670 kHz, 0710 and 1910 e.s.t., antenna: 1.5 miles north of Moriches Inlet (40°47.3'N., 72°44.9'W.).

(151)   Channel 22A, 0710 and 1910 e.s.t., antennas: atop Montauk Point Light, 1.2 miles northwest of Shinnecock Inlet (40°50.9'N., 72°30.2'W.), and Fire Island CG Station (40°37.3'N., 73°15.7'W.).

(152)   **NMK**, Cape May, 2670 kHz, 0603 and 1803 e.s.t., antenna: Cape May.

(153)   Channel 22A, 0603 and 1803 e.s.t., antennas: Atlantic City, Cape May, Fortescue, and Indian River.

(154)   **Customs Ports of Entry and Stations**

(155)   Vessels may be entered and cleared at any port of entry or customs station, but at the latter only with advance authorization from the Customs Service district director.

(156)   **Northeast Region**

(157)   Boston District:

(158)   Ports of Entry: New Bedford and Fall River, Mass.; New London, Hartford, New Haven, and Bridgeport, Conn.

(159)   Customs Station: Provincetown, Mass. (supervised by Plymouth port of entry).

(160)   Providence District:

(161)   Ports of Entry: Newport and Providence, R.I.

(162)   **New York Region**

(163)   New York District:

(164)   Ports of Entry: Albany and New York, N.Y.; Perth Amboy, N. J.

(165)   **National Weather Service Offices.**–The following offices will provide forecasts and climatological data or arrange to obtain these services from other offices. They will also check barometers in their offices or by telephone; refer to the local telephone directory for numbers:

(166)   Bridgeport, CT: Sikorsky Memorial Airport, Stratford, CT 06497;

(167)   Hartford, CT: Bradley International Airport, Windsor Locks, CT 06096.

(168)   Newark, NJ: Newark International Airport, Building 51, Room 421, 07114.

(169)   New York, NY: 30 Rockefeller Plaza, Mezzanine Floor, Room 9, 10112.

(170)   Providence, RI: T.F. Green Airport, 562 Airport Road, Warwick, RI 02886.

(171)   **Radio Weather Broadcasts.**–Taped or direct broadcasts of marine weather forecasts and storm warnings are made by commercial and Coast Guard radio stations in the area covered by this Coast Pilot. The Coast Guard broadcast coastal and offshore marine weather forecasts of the times and frequencies indicated:

(172)   **NMN**, Portsmouth, Va.:

(173)   4426.0 kHz, 0030, 0500, and 2300 e.s.t.

(174)   6501.0 kHz, 0030, 0500, 0630, 1100, 1700, 1830, and 2300 e.s.t.

(175)   8764.0 kHz, 0030, 0500, 0630, 1100, 1230, 1700, 1830, and 2300 e.s.t.

(176)   13089.0 kHz, 0630, 1100, 1230, 1700, and 1830 e.s.t.

(177)   17314.0 kHz, 1230 e.s.t.

(178)   Marine Weather Services Charts are available for the following areas covered by this Coast Pilot:

(179)   Eastport, ME to Montauk Point, NY.

(180)   Montauk Point, NY to Manasquan, NJ.

(181)   VHF-FM weather broadcast schedules of Coast Guard radio stations are also listed in the description of Coast Guard Radio Broadcasts found elsewhere in this appendix.

(182)   **NOAA Weather Radio.**–National Weather Service VHF-FM radio stations provide mariners with continuous FM broadcasts of weather warnings, forecasts, radar reports, and surface weather observations. These stations usually transmit on 162.55, 162.475, or 162.40 MHz. Reception range is up to 40 miles from the antenna site, depending on the terrain, type of receiver, and antenna used. The following VHF-FM radio stations with location of antenna are in or near the area covered by this Coast Pilot:

(183)   KHB-35, Boston, Mass. (42°12'N., 71°06'W.), 162.475 MHz.

(184)   KEC-73, Hyannis, Mass. (41°41'N., 70°20'W.), 162.55 MHz.

(185)   WXJ-39, Providence, R.I. (41°48'N., 71°28'W.), 162.40 MHz.

(186)   WXJ-42, Meriden, Conn. (41°33'N., 72°50'W.), 162.40 MHz.

(187)   KHB-47, New London, Conn. (41°26'N., 72°08'W.), 162.55 MHz.

(188)   WXM-80, Riverhead, NY (40°53'N., 72°43'W.), 162.475 MHz.

(189)   KWO-35, New York, N. Y. (40°45'N., 73°58'W.), 162.55 MHz.

(190)   **National Weather Service Forecast Offices (WSFOs).**–Scheduled coastal marine forecasts are issued four times daily by Weather Service Forecast Offices. (See National Weather Service, chapter 1, for further details.) Individual WSFO's and their specific areas of broadcast coverage are as follows:

(191)   Boston, MA: From New Hampshire-Massachusetts border to Watch Hill, RI, out 25 miles.

(192)   New York, N.Y.: (1) From Watch Hill to Montauk Point, to and including Manasquan, N.J., out 20 miles; (2) Long Island Sound; (3) New York Harbor.

(193)   **National Weather Service Port Meteorological Officers (PMOs).**–Port Meteorological Officers provide assistance on matters of weather chart interpretation, instruments, marine weather communication, and requirements affecting ship operations. (See National Weather Service, chapter 1, for further details.) PMO offices in the area covered by this Coast Pilot are as follows:

(194)   New York, N.Y.: 30 Rockefeller Plaza 10112.

(195)   Newark, N.J.: Newark International Airport, Bldg. 51, 07114.

(196)   **Public Health Service Quarantine Stations.**–Stations where quarantine examinations are performed:

(197)   Boston: U.S. Quarantine Station. Logan International Airport, East Boston, Mass. 02128.

(198)   New York: U.S. Quarantine Station, International Arrivals Bldg., J.F. Kennedy International Airport, Jamaica, NY 11430-1081.

(199)   At other ports, quarantine and/or medical examinations are usually performed by Public Health Service contract personnel or by quarantine inspectors from the nearest quarantine station. Inquiries concerning quarantine matters should be directed to the nearest quarantine station.

(200)   **Food and Drug Administration (FDA) Regional Offices**

(201)   **Northeast Region** (New York, Maine, Connecticut, New Hampshire, Vermont, Rhode Island): 830 Third Avenue, Brooklyn, NY 11232.

(202)   **Mid-atlantic Region** (Delaware, Pennsylvania, Virginia, Maryland, Ohio, New Jersey): U.S. Customhouse, 2nd and Chestnut Streets, Philadelphia, PA 19106.

(203)   **Southeast Region** (South Carolina, North Carolina, Georgia, Alabama, Louisiana, Mississippi, Florida, Puerto Rico): 60 Eighth Street, N.E., Atlanta, GA 30309.

(204)   **Midwest Region** (Illinois, Indiana, Michigan, Wisconsin): 20 N. Michigan Avenue, Chicago, IL 60602.

(205)   **Southwest Region** (Texas): 3032 Bryan Street, Dallas, TX 75204.

(206) **Pacific Region** (California, Hawaii, Alaska, Washington, Oregon): 50 U.N. Plaza, San Francisco, CA 94102

(207) **Department of Agriculture, Animal and Plant Health Inspection Service (APHIS) Offices.**Department of, Animal and Plant Health Inspection Service (APHIS) Offices' > (APHIS)' > –Listed below are ports covered by this volume where APHIS inspectors are available to inspect plants, and plant and animal products, and locations of Animal Import Centers where livestock and birds are inspected.

(208) Information on importation of plants, animals, and plant and animal products is available from APHIS, Department of Agriculture, Federal Building, 6505 Belcrest Road, Hyattsville, Md. 20782. The specific offices to contact are as follows: for plants, including fruits and vegetables, and plant products, Plant Protection and Quarantine, Room 635, telephone 301-436-6799; for animal products, Import-Export Animals and Products Staff, Room 756A, telephone 301-436-7885; and for live ruminants, swine, equines, and poultry and other birds, Veterinary Services, Import-Export Animals and Products Staff, Room 764, telephone 301-436-8590.

(209) **Connecticut:**
(210) Wallingford: Federal Bldg., P.O. Box 631, 06492.
(211) **Massachusetts:**
(212) Boston: U.S. Custom House 02109; Logan International Airport, East Boston 02128.
(213) **New Jersey:**
(214) Hoboken: 209 River Street 07030.
(215) **New York:**
(216) Albany: 80 Wolf Road, Suite 503, 12205.
(217) New York: 26 Federal Plaza 10007.
(218) New York: John F. Kennedy International Airport, International Arrivals Bldg., Jamaica 11430.
(219) **Rhode Island:**
(220) Warwick: 48 Quaker Lane, West Warwick 02893.
(221) **Animal Import Centers:**
(222) Honolulu, Hawaii: P.O. Box 50001, 96850.
(223) Miami, Fla.: 8120 NW 53rd Street 33166.
(224) Rock Tavern, N.Y.: New York Animal Import Center, Stewart Airport Rural Route 1, Box 74, 12575.

(225) **Immigration and Naturalization Service Offices**
(226) **Connecticut:**
(227) Hartford: Ribicoff Federal Bldg., 450 Main Street 06103-3060.
(228) **Massachusetts:**
(229) Boston: John F. Kennedy Federal Bldg., Government Center 02203.
(230) **New Jersey:**
(231) Newark: Federal Bldg., 970 Broad Street 07102.

(232) **New York:**
(233) Albany: U.S. Post Office and Courthouse, 445 Broadway 12207.
(234) Flushing: Flushing Federal Savings Bldg., 136–21 Roosevelt Avenue 11354.
(235) New York: 26 Federal Plaza 10278.
(236) **Rhode Island:**
(237) Providence: John O. Pastore Federal Bldg.-U.S. Post Office, Exchange Terrace 02903.

(238) **Federal Communications Commission Offices**
(239) **District field offices:**
(240) Boston, Massachusetts: U.S. Customhouse, 165 State Street 02109.
(241) New York, N.Y., 201 Varick Street 10014.

(242) **Canadian Government Agencies.**–Hydrographic Chart Distribution Office, Department of Fisheries and Oceans, P.O. Box 8080, 1675 Russell Road, Ottawa, Ontario, KIG 3H6 Canada.
(243) Superintendent, Quebec Canals, Parks, Canada, 200 Churchill Boulevard, Greenfield Park, Quebec, J4V 2M4, Canada.

(244) **Radio shore stations providing medical advice.**–Messages to shore stations may be transmitted in code groups or plain language; messages should be signed by the master and be prefixed: "DH MEDICO". The following stations maintain a continuous guard on 500 kHz. (See Medical advice, chapter 1.)
(245) NMF, Sandwich, Cape Cod, Mass., U.S. Coast Guard.
(246) WCC, Chatham, Cape Cod, Mass., RCA Global Communications, Inc.

(247) **Measured Courses.**–The positions of measured courses are shown on the chart and their description is included in the Coast Pilots when information is reported to the National Ocean Service. Courses are located in the following places covered by this Coast Pilot.
(248) Beach Channel, along south shore of Jamaica Bay 12350.
(249) Captain Harbor, on south side of Great Captain Island 12367.
(250) Eatons Neck, on west side of Eatons Neck 12365.
(251) Port Jefferson, off Port Jefferson Harbor 12362.
(252) West Gilgo Beach, along State Boat Channel 12352.
(253) Sandy Hook Bay, on south side of Sandy Hook Bay off Municipal Yacht Basin 12327.
(254) The pages in the text describing the courses can be obtained by referring to the index for the geographic places; chart numbers follow the names.

COASTAL WARNING DISPLAYS

DAYTIME SIGNALS

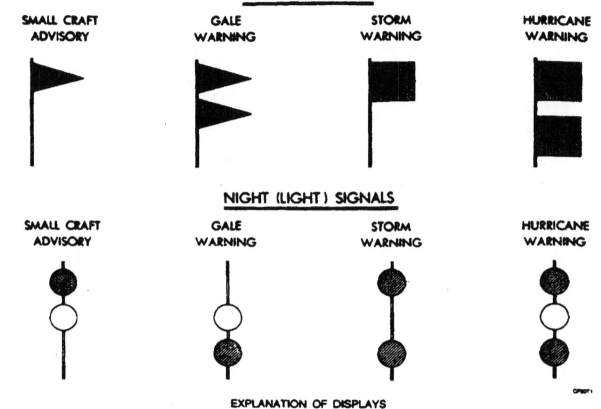

| SMALL CRAFT ADVISORY | GALE WARNING | STORM WARNING | HURRICANE WARNING |

NIGHT (LIGHT) SIGNALS

| SMALL CRAFT ADVISORY | GALE WARNING | STORM WARNING | HURRICANE WARNING |

CP80T1

EXPLANATION OF DISPLAYS

Small Craft Advisory: One RED pennant displayed by day and a RED light ABOVE a WHITE light at night, to alert mariners to sustained (more than two hours) weather or sea conditions, either present or forecast, that might be hazardous to small boats. Mariners learning of a Small Craft Advisory are urged to determine immediately the reason by tuning their radios to the latest marine broadcasts. Decision as to the degree of hazard will be left up to the boatman, based on his experience and size and type of boat. The threshold conditions for the Small Craft Advisory are usually 18 knots of wind (less than 18 knots in some dangerous waters) or hazardous wave conditions.

Gale Warning: Two RED pennants displayed by day and a WHITE light ABOVE a RED light at night to indicate that winds within the range 34 to 47 knots are forecast for the area.

Storm Warning: A single square RED flag with a BLACK center displayed during daytime and two RED lights at night to indicate that winds 48 knots and above, no matter how high the speed, are forecast for the area. However, if the winds are associated with a tropical cyclone (hurricane) the STORM WARNING display indicates that winds within the range 48 to 63 knots are forecast.

Hurricane Warning: Displayed only in connection with a tropical cyclone (hurricane). Two square RED flags with BLACK centers displayed by day and a WHITE light between two RED lights at night to indicate that winds 64 knots and above are forecast for the area.

Note: A "HURRICANE WATCH" is an announcement issued by the National Weather Service via press and radio and television broadcasts whenever a tropical storm or hurricane becomes a threat to a coastal area. The "Hurricane Watch" announcement is not a warning, rather it indicates that the hurricane is near enough that everyone in the area covered by the "Watch" should listen to their radios for subsequent advisories and be ready to take precautionary action in case hurricane warnings are issued.

Note: As of 1 February 1989 the National Weather Service discontinued its operation of the above visual system. Some local organizations, however, continued this program using information from a NOAA Weather Radio or some similar source for activating or ending their display. A SPECIAL MARINE WARNING BULLETIN is issued whenever a severe local storm or strong wind of brief duration is imminent and is not covered by existing warnings or advisories. Boaters will be able to receive these special warnings by keeping tuned to a NOAA VHF-FM radio station or to Coast Guard and commercial radio stations that transmit marine weather information.

ATLANTIC OCEAN DISTANCES
MONTREAL, CANADA, TO PANAMA CANAL ZONE
(Nautical Miles)

Figure at intersection of columns opposite ports in question is the nautical mileage between the two. Example: New York, N. Y., is 1399 nautical miles from San Juan, P. R.

MONTREAL, CANADA* (St. Lambert Lock)	Cabot Strait 47°07.0'N., 60°17.0'W.	Gut of Canso (Lock) 45°39.0'N., 61°25.0'W.	Portland, Maine 43°39.4'N., 70°14.7'W.	Boston, Mass. 42°22.0'N., 71°03.0'W.	NANTUCKET SHOALS 40°30.0'N., 69°25.0'W.	NEW YORK, N.Y. 40°42.0'N., 74°01.0'W.	Philadelphia, Pa. 39°56.6'N., 75°08.3'W.	Baltimore, Md. 39°16.0'N., 76°34.5'W.	CHESAPEAKE BAY ENT. 36°56.3'N., 75°58.6'W.	Norfolk, Va. 36°50.9'N., 76°17.9'W.	DIAMOND SHOALS 35°08.0'N., 75°15.0'W.	Wilmington, N.C. 34°14.0'N., 77°57.0'W.	Charleston, S.C. 32°47.2'N., 79°55.2'W.	Savannah, Ga. 32°05.0'N., 81°05.7'W.	Jacksonville, Fla. 30°19.2'N., 81°39.0'W.	Key West, Fla. 24°33.7'N., 81°48.5'W.	STRAITS OF FLORIDA 24°25.0'N., 83°00.0'W.	Tampa, Fla. 27°36.5'N., 82°26.7'W.	Pensacola, Fla. 30°24.0'N., 87°13.0'W.	Mobile, Ala. 30°42.5'N., 88°02.5'W.	NEW ORLEANS, La. (via SW Pass) 29°57.0'N., 90°03.7'W.	Port Arthur, Tex. 29°49.5'N., 93°57.6'W.	Galveston, Tex. 29°19.0'N., 94°47.0'W.	Corpus Christi, Tex. 27°48.6'N., 97°24.0'W.	San Juan, P.R. 18°27.8'N., 66°06.7'W.	YUCATAN CHANNEL 21°50.0'N., 85°03.0'W.	Panama Canal (Atlantic Ent.) 9°23.5'N., 79°55.3'W.	PANAMA CANAL (Pacific Ent.) 8°53.0'N., 79°31.0'W.
681																												
717	120																											
1276	595	484																										
1318	637	526	100																									
1311	630	519	203	163																								
1534	853	742	426	386	223																							
1682	1001	890	575	535	372	240																						
1838	1157	1046	734	694	531	417	392																					
1669	1006	896	584	544	381	267	242	150																				
1716	1035	923	611	571	408	294	269	173	27																			
1729	1048	936	628	588	425	345	322	267	117	144																		
1948	1267	1155	847	807	644	564	541	486	336	363	219																	
2014	1333	1221	913	873	710	630	607	552	402	429	285	151																
2068	1407	1295	987	947	784	704	681	626	476	503	359	227	102															
2172	1491	1379	1071	1031	868	788	765	710	560	587	443	315	197	145														
2479	1798	1690	1387	1347	1184	1109	1086	1031	881	908	764	667	572	543	462													
2540	1859	1751	1448	1408	1245	1170	1147	1092	942	969	825	728	633	604	523	73												
2772	2091	1983	1680	1640	1477	1402	1379	1324	1174	1201	1057	960	865	836	755	305	232											
2977	2296	2188	1885	1845	1682	1607	1584	1529	1379	1406	1262	1165	1070	1041	960	510	437	347										
3011	2330	2222	1919	1879	1716	1641	1618	1563	1413	1440	1296	1199	1104	1075	994	544	471	389	89									
3080	2399	2291	1988	1948	1785	1710	1687	1632	1482	1509	1365	1268	1173	1144	1063	613	540	502	288	269								
3240	2559	2451	2148	2108	1945	1870	1847	1792	1642	1669	1525	1428	1333	1304	1223	700	697	504	491	441								
3242	2561	2453	2150	2110	1947	1872	1849	1794	1644	1671	1527	1430	1335	1306	1225	775	702	703	509	496	446	89						
3347	2666	2558	2255	2215	2052	1977	1954	1899	1749	1776	1632	1535	1440	1411	1330	880	807	810	618	605	555	249	207					
2445	1764	1669	1531	1486	1334	1399	1395	1375	1225	1252	1114	1153	1138	1156	1121	966	1017	1249	1448	1448	1557	1717	1719	1824				
2730	2049	1937	1629	1589	1426	1346	1323	1268	1118	1145	1001	904	809	780	699	251	192	404	533	562	587	691	696	769	1111			
3203	2522	2419	2189	2149	1986	1972	1955	1904	1754	1781	1637	1609	1563	1564	1513	1060	1001	1213	1342	1371	1396	1487	1493	1549	990	809		
3249	2568	2465	2235	2195	2032	2018	2001	1950	1800	1827	1683	1655	1609	1610	1559	1106	1047	1259	1380	1417	1442	1533	1539	1595	1036	855	46	

*Quebec, Canada · SUBTRACT 139 miles

All tabular distances are by outside routes which can be used by the deepest-draft vessel that the listed ports can accommodate. Lighter-draft vessels can save considerable mileage by transiting Canso Lock (Canada), the Cape Cod Canal (Massachusetts), and the Chesapeake and Delaware Canal (Delaware-Maryland); see the detailed tables. Gulf of Mexico distances are through the Shipping Safety Fairways.

COASTWISE DISTANCES
CAPE COD, MASS., TO NEW YORK, N.Y.
(Nautical Miles)

Figure at intersection of columns opposite ports in question is the nautical mileage between the two. Example: New Bedford, Mass., to New London, Conn., is 74 nautical miles from New London, Conn.

Ports (with coordinates), listed along the diagonal:

- Port Newark, N. J. — 40°41. 8'N., 74°08. 0'W.
- Elizabethport, N. J. — 40°38. 8'N., 74°11. 2'W.
- Perth Amboy, N. J. — 40°30. 3'N., 74°15. 7'W.
- NEW YORK, N. Y. — 40°42. 0'N., 74°01. 0'W.
- MONTAUK POINT, N. Y. — 41°01. 7'N., 71°47. 3'W.
- Port Jefferson, N. Y. — 40°57. 0'N., 73°04. 5'W.
- Greenport, N. Y. — 41°06. 0'N., 72°21. 5'W.
- Sag Harbor, N. Y. — 41°00. 2'N., 72°17. 7'W.
- Montauk, N. Y. — 41°02. 6'N., 71°57. 5'W.
- Stamford, Conn. — 41°01. 8'N., 73°32. 3'W.
- South Norwalk, Conn. — 41°05. 7'N., 73°24. 7'W.
- Bridgeport, Conn. — 41°10. 3'N., 73°10. 8'W.
- Stratford, Conn. — 41°11. 3'N., 73°07. 3'W.
- New Haven, Conn. — 41°17. 4'N., 72°54. 5'W.
- Hartford, Conn. — 41°45. 0'N., 72°39. 0'W.
- New London, Conn. — 41°21. 4'N., 72°05. 4'W.
- Stonington, Conn. — 41°19. 9'N., 71°54. 6'W.
- Great Salt Pond, R. I. — 41°11. 1'N., 71°34. 9'W.
- Providence, R. I. — 41°48. 5'N., 71°24. 0'W.
- Fall River, Mass. — 41°42. 4'N., 71°09. 8'W.
- Newport, R. I. — 41°29. 8'N., 71°19. 8'W.
- New Bedford, Mass. — 41°38. 1'N., 70°55. 1'W.
- Woods Hole, Mass. — 41°31. 4'N., 70°40. 4'W.
- Vineyard Haven, Mass. — 41°27. 3'N., 70°35. 8'W.
- Nantucket, Mass. — 41°17. 2'N., 70°05. 7'W.
- NANTUCKET SHOALS — 40°30. 0'N., 69°25. 0'W.
- CAPE COD CANAL E ENT. — 41°46. 8'N., 70°29. 0'W.

Distance values (nautical miles), read as the vertical column of figures appearing beneath each diagonal port heading (top of chart toward bottom):

Port heading	Figures (top → bottom)
Port Newark, N. J.	5
Elizabethport, N. J.	10, 15
Perth Amboy, N. J.	20, 10, 12
NEW YORK, N. Y.	122, 123, 124, 126
MONTAUK POINT, N. Y.	68, 52, 72, 62, 64
Port Jefferson, N. Y.	54, 30, 102, 122, 112, 114
Greenport, N. Y.	11, 56, 32, 103, 123, 113, 115
Sag Harbor, N. Y.	21, 22, 58, 16, 105, 125, 115, 117
Montauk, N. Y.	76, 74, 72, 24, 85, 33, 53, 43, 45
Stamford, Conn.	11, 75, 73, 71, 23, 84, 40, 53, 50, 52
South Norwalk, Conn.	21, 22, 62, 60, 58, 15, 74, 52, 60, 62, 64
Bridgeport, Conn.	10, 26, 27, 56, 54, 52, 15, 65, 57, 67, 67, 69
Stratford, Conn.	15, 25, 36, 37, 51, 49, 47, 23, 62, 68, 78, 78, 80
New Haven, Conn.	74, 81, 86, 101, 102, 66, 64, 62, 84, 75, 131, 141, 143
Hartford, Conn.	62, 49, 54, 60, 64, 20, 27, 25, 56, 28, 104, 124, 114, 116
New London, Conn.	12, 66, 52, 59, 77, 77, 18, 29, 28, 61, 19, 129, 119, 121
Stonington, Conn.	19, 29, 80, 65, 72, 91, 92, 23, 39, 37, 74, 121, 109, 131, 133
Great Salt Pond, R. I.	43, 55, 68, 118, 105, 110, 115, 129, 130, 63, 77, 76, 112, 159, 179, 169, 171
Providence, R. I.	21, 38, 49, 63, 113, 100, 105, 124, 125, 58, 72, 71, 107, 154, 174, 164, 166
Fall River, Mass.	16, 21, 23, 34, 48, 98, 84, 90, 108, 109, 42, 57, 56, 91, 51, 139, 159, 149, 151
Newport, R. I.	38, 54, 58, 48, 58, 74, 124, 111, 113, 122, 135, 136, 66, 81, 60, 118, 35, 166, 186, 176, 178
New Bedford, Mass.	15, 38, 44, 57, 50, 61, 72, 125, 109, 117, 123, 135, 136, 69, 83, 62, 118, 59, 166, 186, 176, 178
Woods Hole, Mass.	7, 28, 45, 51, 65, 54, 67, 77, 129, 114, 121, 127, 140, 141, 74, 86, 87, 123, 63, 171, 191, 181, 183
Vineyard Haven, Mass.	29, 33, 53, 71, 77, 91, 80, 92, 103, 155, 140, 153, 166, 167, 99, 114, 113, 149, 89, 196, 216, 206, 208
Nantucket, Mass.	85, 88, 92, 111, 111, 126, 131, 114, 126, 136, 187, 171, 176, 182, 195, 196, 127, 143, 142, 149, 113, 223, 223, 225, 227
CAPE COD CANAL E ENT.	144, 69, 43, 22, 31, 54, 69, 74, 66, 77, 89, 140, 127, 132, 138, 151, 152, 85, 100, 99, 134, 76, 182, 202, 191, 193

Ambrose Light (40°27. 5'N., 73°49. 8'W.) to New York (The Battery), 20.7 miles.

INSIDE-ROUTE DISTANCES

SOUTH SIDE OF LONG ISLAND
GREENPORT, N.Y., TO EAST ROCKAWAY INLET, N.Y.
(Nautical Miles)

Figure at intersection of columns opposite ports in question is the nautical mileage between the two. Example: Freeport is 61 nautical miles from Shinnecock Canal North End.

Ports (with positions):

- Manasquan Inlet, N. J. • — 40°06. 1'N., 74°01. 9'W.
- NEW YORK (The Battery) • — 40°42. 0'N., 74°01. 0'W.
- Rockaway Point • — 40°34. 9'N., 73°45. 4'W.
- East Rockaway Inlet — 40°35. 7'N., 73°39. 4'W.
- Long Beach — 40°37. 6'N., 73°34. 9'W.
- Freeport — 40°34. 4'N., 73°34. 9'W.
- Jones Inlet — 40°36. 2'N., 73°30. 8'W.
- Jones Beach — 40°39. 6'N., 73°24. 8'W.
- Amityville — 40°41. 2'N., 73°18. 9'W.
- Babylon — 40°37. 8'N., 73°18. 6'W.
- Fire Island Inlet — 40°42. 8'N., 73°14. 2'W.
- Bay Shore — 40°45. 5'N., 73°01. 2'W.
- Patchogue — 40°45. 1'N., 72°56. 0'W.
- Bellport — 40°45. 8'N., 72°45. 3'W.
- Moriches Inlet — 40°48. 2'N., 72°38. 4'W.
- Westhampton Beach — 40°50. 3'N., 72°28. 6'W.
- Shinnecock Inlet — 40°53. 9'N., 72°30. 3'W.
- Shinnecock Canal, N. End — 40°55. 0'N., 72°39. 4'W.
- Riverside — 41°00. 2'N., 72°17. 7'W.
- Sag Harbor — 41°06. 0'N., 72°21. 5'W.
- Greenport

From \ To	Greenport	Sag Harbor	Riverside	Shinnecock Canal, N. End	Shinnecock Inlet	Westhampton Beach	Moriches Inlet	Bellport	Patchogue	Bay Shore	Fire Island Inlet	Babylon	Amityville	Jones Beach	Jones Inlet	Freeport	Long Beach	East Rockaway Inlet	Rockaway Point	New York (The Battery)	Manasquan Inlet
Greenport		11	21	16	21	28	34	42	48	57	62	61	66	72	76	77	80	85	94	107	116
Sag Harbor			22	17	22	29	35	43	49	58	63	62	67	73	77	78	81	86	95	108	117
Riverside				8	13	20	26	34	40	49	54	53	58	64	68	69	72	77	86	99	108
Shinnecock Canal, N. End					5	12	18	26	32	41	46	45	50	56	60	61	64	69	78	91	100
Shinnecock Inlet						9	15	23	29	39	44	42	47	54	58	58	61	66	75	88	97
Westhampton Beach							7	15	21	30	35	34	39	45	49	49	53	58	67	80	89
Moriches Inlet									11	17	27	32	30	35	45	46	49	54	63	76	85
Bellport									6	16	21	19	24	31	35	35	38	44	53	66	75
Patchogue										13	18	17	22	28	32	32	36	41	50	63	72
Bay Shore											9	5	10	17	21	21	24	29	38	51	60
Fire Island Inlet												8	12	16	20	21	24	29	38	51	60
Babylon													6	13	17	18	21	26	35	48	57
Amityville														7	11	12	15	20	29	42	51
Jones Beach															4	4	8	13	22	35	44
Jones Inlet																4	5	10	19	32	41
Freeport																	6	11	20	33	42
Long Beach																		5	14	27	36
East Rockaway Inlet																			9	22	31
Rockaway Point																				13	27
New York (The Battery)																					40
Manasquan Inlet																					

* Outside distances westward of East Rockaway Inlet.

DISTANCES ON HUDSON RIVER

NEW YORK, N.Y. TO TROY LOCK, N.Y.
(Nautical Miles)

Figure at intersection of columns opposite ports in question is the nautical mileage between the two. Example: Poughkeepsie, N.Y., is 60 nautical miles from Albany, N.Y.

Ports (with coordinates):

- Troy Lock — 41°45.1'N, 73°41.1'W
- Watervliet — 42°43.7'N, 73°41.9'W
- Troy — 42°43.7'N, 73°41.8'W
- Rensselaer — 42°37.9'N, 73°45.1'W
- Albany — 42°37.9'N, 73°45.3'W
- Coeymans — 42°28.5'N, 73°47.4'W
- Coxsackie — 42°21.0'N, 73°47.6'W
- Athens — 42°15.6'N, 73°48.5'W
- Hudson — 42°15.3'N, 73°48.1'W
- Catskill — 42°13.0'N, 73°52.1'W
- Saugerties — 42°04.4'N, 73°56.7'W
- Kingston — 41°55.1'N, 73°59.0'W
- Hyde Park — 41°47.3'N, 73°56.9'W
- Poughkeepsie — 41°42.3'N, 73°56.5'W
- Newburgh — 41°30.1'N, 74°00.3'W
- West Point — 41°23.1'N, 73°57.3'W
- Peekskill — 41°17.3'N, 73°56.0'W
- Haverstraw — 41°11.8'N, 73°57.5'W
- Ossining — 41°08.6'N, 73°52.3'W
- Nyack — 41°05.4'N, 73°54.9'W
- Tarrytown — 41°04.7'N, 73°52.2'W
- Yonkers — 40°56.1'N, 73°54.3'W
- NEW YORK (The Battery) — 40°42.0'N, 74°01.0'W

Distance matrix (nautical miles), read left-to-right from each port:

From \\ to	Watervliet	Troy	Rensselaer	Albany	Coeymans	Coxsackie	Athens	Hudson	Catskill	Saugerties	Kingston	Hyde Park	Poughkeepsie	Newburgh	West Point	Peekskill	Haverstraw	Ossining	Nyack	Tarrytown	Yonkers	New York
Troy	2																					
Rensselaer	0	2																				
Albany	6	6	8																			
Coeymans	0	6	6	8																		
Coxsackie	10	10	16	16	18																	
Athens	7	18	18	24	24	26																
Hudson	6	14	24	24	30	30	32															
Catskill	1	7	14	24	24	30	30	32														
Saugerties	5	5	11	19	29	29	35	35	37													
Kingston	11	14	14	21	28	38	38	44	44	46												
Hyde Park	12	21	24	24	30	38	48	48	54	54	56											
Poughkeepsie	9	19	28	31	31	37	44	55	55	61	61	63										
Newburgh	5	14	24	33	36	36	42	49	60	60	66	66	68									
West Point	13	18	27	37	46	49	49	55	62	73	73	79	79	81								
Peekskill	8	21	26	35	45	54	57	57	63	70	81	81	87	87	89							
Haverstraw	6	15	29	34	43	52	61	64	64	71	78	88	88	94	94	96						
Ossining	6	13	21	34	39	48	58	67	70	70	76	84	94	94	100	100	102					
Nyack	5	11	17	25	38	43	52	62	71	74	74	80	88	98	98	104	104	106				
Tarrytown	6	10	15	22	29	43	48	57	66	75	78	78	85	92	102	102	108	108	110			
Yonkers	2	6	9	15	21	29	42	47	56	66	75	78	78	85	92	102	102	108	108	110		
New York	9	10	14	18	23	29	37	50	55	64	74	83	86	86	93	100	110	110	116	116	118	
New York (Battery)	16	24	25	29	33	38	45	53	66	71	80	89	99	102	102	108	115	126	126	132	132	134

INDEX

The numbers of the largest scale charts on which the names appear follow the indexed items. Some geographic names are indexed more than once when more than one place has the same geographic name. Charts published by the Defense Mapping Agency Hydrographic/Topographic Service are indicated by an asterisk.

PART 2 - SECTION A

LIGHT LIST

Volume II - Atlantic Coast

covering

CHESAPEAKE BAY ENTRANCE and approaches

for

general information refer to PART 1, SECTION A

DEPARTMENT OF TRANSPORTATION, U.S. COAST GUARD

LIGHT LIST

Volume II

ATLANTIC COAST

TOMS RIVER, NEW JERSEY TO
LITTLE RIVER, SOUTH CAROLINA

IMPORTANT

THIS PUBLICATION SHOULD BE CORRECTED
EACH WEEK FROM THE LOCAL NOTICE TO MARINERS
OR NOTICE TO MARINERS AS APPROPRIATE.

COMDTPUB P16502.2

U.S. GOVERNMENT PRINTING OFFICE
WASHINGTON, DC:

For sale by Superintende   Documer   S. Government Printing Office, Washington, DC 20402
Stock number: 050-012-00321-1

United States Coast Guard
RADIOBEACON SYSTEM ATLANTIC COAST
VOLUME 2   EDITION

SERVICE RANGE is shown in nautical miles (M).

CHARACTERISTIC IDENTIFICATION consists of a combination of dots and dashes. The characteristic signal of all beacons is superimposed on a continuous carrier when they are transmitting. The last ten seconds of the minute are devoted to a long dash for maximum bearing accuracy using manual operation.

The FREQUENCY in kilohertz is indicated on the chart in Arabic numerals following the characteristic identification.

BARNEGAT INLET 20M
322

ATLANTIC CITY 15M
316

CAPE MAY 10M
325

PA

NJ

DE

MD

VA

MD

VA

CAPE HENLOPEN 125M
298

OCEAN CITY INLET 10M
293

INDIAN RIVER INLET 10M
308

COVE POINT 20M
314

SMITH POINT 20M
310

VA

NC

WACHAPREAGUE INLET 10M
324

CAPE HENRY 150M
289

OREGON INLET 50M
314

HATTERAS INLET 30M
306

FORT MACON 125M
294

OAK ISLAND 70M
303

RADIOBEACON SYSTEM – ATLANTIC COAST
CONTINUOUS – By Frequency

Freq kHz	Station	Characteristic	Range (n.m.)	Lat. (N) ° ' "	Long. (W) ° ' "
289	CAPE HENRY	CB (−.−. −...)	150	36 55 35	76 00 27
293	OCEAN CITY INLET	OC (−−− −.−.)	10	38 19 30	75 05 18
294	FORT MACON	CL (−.−. .−..)	150	34 41 53	76 41 00
298	CAPE HENLOPEN	HL (.... .−..)	125	38 47 39	75 05 26
303	OAK ISLAND	OA (−−− .−)	70	33 53 33	78 02 06
308	INDIAN RIVER INLET	IR (.. .−.)	10	38 36 35	75 04 06
309	HATTERAS INLET STATION	HI (.... ..)	30	35 12 27	75 42 21
310	SMITH POINT	SP (... .−−.)	20	37 52 47	76 11 03
314	COVE POINT	CP (−.−. .−−.)	20	38 23 10	76 22 55
314	OREGON INLET	OI (−−− ..)	50	35 47 48	75 33 01
316	ATLANTIC CITY	AC (.− −.−.)	15	39 21 57	74 24 37
322	BARNEGAT INLET	BI (−... ..)	20	39 45 28	74 06 21
324	WATCHAPREAGUE INLET	WI (.−− ..)	10	37 34 24	75 37 30
325	CAPE MAY	CM (−.−. −−)	10	38 56 38	74 52 20

GEOGRAPHIC RANGE TABLE

The following table gives the approximate geographic range of visibility for an object which may be seen by an observer at sea level. It is necessary to add to the distance for the height of any object the distance corresponding to the height of the observer's eye above sea level.

Distances of visibility for objects of various elevations above sea level.

Height Feet	Height Meters	Distance Nautical Miles (NM)	Height Feet	Height Meters	Distance Nautical Miles (NM)	Height Feet	Height Meters	Distance Nautical Miles (NM)
5	1.5	2.6	70	21.3	9.8	250	76.2	18.5
10	3.1	3.7	75	22.9	10.1	300	91.4	20.3
15	4.6	4.5	80	24.4	10.5	350	106.7	21.9
20	6.1	5.2	85	25.9	10.8	400	121.9	23.4
25	7.6	5.9	90	27.4	11.1	450	137.2	24.8
30	9.1	6.4	95	29.0	11.4	500	152.4	26.2
35	10.7	6.9	100	30.5	11.7	550	167.6	27.4
40	12.2	7.4	110	33.5	12.3	600	182.9	28.7
45	13.7	7.8	120	36.6	12.8	650	198.1	29.8
50	15.2	8.3	130	39.6	13.3	700	213.4	31.0
55	16.8	8.7	140	42.7	13.8	800	243.8	33.1
60	18.3	9.1	150	45.7	14.3	900	274.3	35.1
65	19.8	9.4	200	61.0	19.0	1000	304.8	37.0

Example: Determine the geographic visibility of an object, with a height above water of 65 feet, for an observer with a height of eye of 35 feet. Enter above table;

Height of object	65 feet	9.4 NM
Height of observer	35 feet	6.9 NM
Computed geographic visibility		16.3 NM

LUMINOUS RANGE DIAGRAM

The nominal range given in this Light List is the maximum distance a given light can be seen when the meteorological visibility is 10 nautical miles. If the existing visibility is less than 10 miles, the range at which the light can be seen will be reduced below its nominal range. And, if the visibility is greater than 10 miles, the light can be seen at greater distances. The distance at which a light may be expected to be seen in the prevailing visibility is called its luminous range.

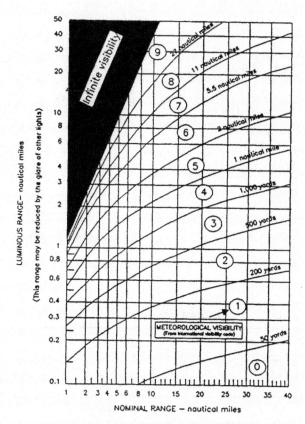

METEORLOGICAL VISIBILITY		
(From International Visibility code)		
Code	Metric	Nautical (approximate)
0	Less than 50 meters	Less than 50 yards
1	50—200 meters	50—200 yards
2	200—500 meters	200—500 yards
3	500—1,000 meters	500—1,000 yards
4	1—2 kilometers	1,000—2,000 yards
5	2—4 kilometers	1—2 nautical miles
6	4—10 kilometers	2—5.5 nautical miles
7	10—20 kilometers	5.5—11 nautical miles
8	20—50 kilometers	11—27 nautical miles
9	Greater than 50 km	Greater than 27 nm

This diagram enables the mariner to determine the approximate luminous range of a light when the nominal range and the prevailing meteorological visibility are known. The diagram is entered from the bottom border using the nominal range listed in column 6 of this book. The intersection of the nominal range with the appropriate visibility curve (or, more often, a point between two curves) yields, by moving horizontally to the left border, the luminous range.

CAUTION: When using this diagram is must be remembered that:
1. The ranges obtained are approximate.
2. The transparency of the atmosphere may vary between the observer and the light.
3. Glare from background lighting will considerably reduce the range at which lights are sighted.
4. The rolling motion of the mariner and/or of a lighted aid to navigation may reduce the distance at which lights can be detected and identified.

(1) No.	(2) Name and location	(3) Position	(4) Characteristic	(5) Height	(6) Range	(7) Structure	(8) Remarks

CAPE MAY TO FENWICK ISLAND (Chart 12214)

(1)	(2)	(3)	(4)	(5)	(6)	(7)	(8)
		N/W					
190 1275	*Hen and Chickens Shoal* *Lighted Gong Buoy* *1 HC* *Off southeast end of* *shoal.*	38 42.4 75 00.0	Fl G 2.5ˢ		4	Green.	
195 4125	*Indian River Inlet* *Lighted Gong Buoy 1*	38 36.6 75 02.8	Fl G 2.5ˢ		5	Green.	
200 4135	**Indian River Inlet** **Radiobeacon**	38 36.6 75 04.1	IR (•• •—•)	80	10	Whip antenna.	FREQ: 308 kHz.

FENWICK ISLAND TO CHINCOTEAGUE ISLAND
(Chart 12211)

(1)	(2)	(3)	(4)	(5)	(6)	(7)	(8)
205	FENWICK ISLAND LIGHT	38 27.1 75 03.3	Oc W 13ˢ 7.5ˢ fl 5.5ˢ ec	83	8	White tower. 87	Private aid.
210	*Fenwick Shoal Lighted* *Gong Buoy 1 FIS* *On west side of shoal.*	38 26.8 74 57.4	Fl G 4ˢ		5	Green.	
215	*Isle of Wight Shoal* *Buoy IWS*	38 23.5 74 56.0				Green and red bands; can.	
220	*Great Gull Bank Lighted* *Whistle Buoy 4*	38 16.4 75 00.4	Fl R 4ˢ		5	Red.	

CAPE SABLE TO CAPE HATTERAS (Chart 13003)

(1)	(2)	(3)	(4)	(5)	(6)	(7)	(8)
225	*NOAA Data Lighted* *Buoy 44004 (ODAS)*	38 32.2 70 43.3	Fl (4) Y 20ˢ			Yellow boat-shaped buoy.	

OCEAN CITY INLET TO CAPE HATTERAS
(Chart 12200)

(1)	(2)	(3)	(4)	(5)	(6)	(7)	(8)
230 4485	OCEAN CITY INLET JETTY LIGHT	38 19.5 75 05.1	Iso W 6ˢ	28	9	NB on skeleton tower.	HORN: 1 blast ev 15ˢ (2ˢ bl).
235 4490	**Ocean City Inlet** **Radiobeacon**	38 19.5 75 05.3	OC (——— —•—•)		10		FREQ: 293 kHz. Antenna located on Ocean City Inlet Jetty Light.
240	*Ocean City Lighted* *Research Buoy*	38 20.1 75 01.0	Fl Y 20ˢ			Yellow.	Maintained by US Army Corps of Engineers.
245 4495	*Ocean City Inlet* *Lighted Bell Buoy 2*	38 19.5 75 04.1	Fl R 4ˢ		3	Red.	
250	Ocean City Warning Buoy	38 18.9 75 05.1				White with orange bands worded, DANGER SUBMERGED OBJECT; can.	
255	Little Gull Bank Buoy LG	38 16.9 75 04.3				Green and red bands; can.	
260	Sugar Point Buoy 4A	38 04.8 75 00.4				Red nun.	
265	Jack Spot Buoy 2JS	38 05.3 74 45.1				Red nun.	

(1) No.	(2) Name and location	(3) Position	(4) Characteristic	(5) Height	(6) Range	(7) Structure	(8) Remarks

(1) No.	(2) Name and location	(3) Position	(4) Characteristic	(5) Height	(6) Range	(7) Structure	(8) Remarks
	OCEAN CITY INLET TO CAPE HATTERAS (Chart 12200)	N/W					
270	Winter Quarter Shoal Buoy 5	37 58.3 75 09.2				Green can.	
275	Winter Quarter Shoal Lighted Buoy 6	37 59.7 75 01.4	Fl R 6s		4	Red.	
280	**Assateague Light**	37 54.7 75 21.4	Fl (2) W 5s 0.1sfl 1.0s ec. 0.1sfl 3.8s ec.	154	22	Conical tower with red and white bands. 142	
285	Ship Shoal Buoy SS	37 50.9 75 19.9				Red and white stripes; nun.	
290	Blackfish Bank Buoy 8A	37 50.4 75 15.9				Red.	
295	Blackfish Bank Lighted Whistle Buoy 8 East of 24 foot spot.	37 50.6 75 12.1	Fl R 2.5s		4	Red.	
300	Turners Lump Buoy 2	37 48.9 75 19.5				Red nun.	
305	Turners Lump Lighted Bell Buoy 2TL	37 48.9 75 22.5	Fl R 4s		5	Red.	
310 6210	Wachapreague Inlet Lighted Whistle Buoy A	37 35.0 75 33.7	Mo (A) W		6	Red and white stripes with red spherical topmark.	
315 6250	**Wachapreague Inlet Radiobeacon**	37 34.4 75 37.1	WI (•—— ••)		10	Lookout tower.	FREQ: 324 kHz.
320	Parramore Bank Lighted Gong Buoy 10	37 32.0 75 25.9	Fl R 4s		5	Red.	
325 6305	Quinby Inlet Lighted Buoy Q	37 28.1 75 36.1	Mo (A) W		6	Red and white stripes.	
330 6335	QUINBY INLET ENTRANCE LIGHT	37 27.8 75 40.2	Fl W 4s	28	8	NB on skeleton tower on structure.	
332 6400	Great Machipongo Inlet Lighted Whistle Buoy GM		Mo (A) W		5	Red and white stripes with red spherical topmark.	
335	Hog Island Lighted Bell Buoy 12	37 17.7 75 34.7	Fl R 2.5s		5	Red.	
340	Cape Charles Lighted Bell Buoy 14	37 07.4 75 41.0	Fl R 2.5s		5	Red.	
345	**Cape Charles Light**	37 07.4 75 54.4	Fl W 5s	180	24	Octagonal, pyramidal skeleton tower, upper part black, lower part white. 191	Operates 24 hours.
350	Surface Gunnery Area 7 Lighted Buoy GA	37 00.0 75 21.5	Fl Y 6s		6	Yellow.	
355	**Chesapeake Light**	36 54.3 75 42.8	Fl (2) W 15s 0.1sfl 2.9s ec. 0.1sfl 11.9s ec.	117	24	Blue tower on white square superstructure on four black piles, CHESAPEAKE on sides.	Emergency light of lower intensity will be displayed when main light is inoperative. RACON: N (—•). HORN: 1 blast ev 30s (3s bl). Operates continuously.
360	Navy SESEF Lighted Buoy A	36 55.0 75 38.3	Fl Y 2.5s		5	Yellow.	

(1) No.	(2) Name and location	(3) Position	(4) Characteristic	(5) Height	(6) Range	(7) Structure	(8) Remarks

OCEAN CITY INLET TO CAPE HATTERAS
(Chart 12200)

		N/W					
365	**Cape Henry Light**	36 55.6 76 00.4	Mo (U) W 20^s (R sector) 1^s fl 2^s ec. 1^s fl 2^s ec. 7^s fl 7^s ec.	164	W 17 R 15	Octagonal pyramidal tower, upper and lower half of each face alternately black and white. 163	Red from 154° to 233°, covers shoals outside Cape Charles and Middle Ground inside bay. Emergency light of lower intensity will be displayed when main light is extinguished.
366	**Cape Henry Radiobeacon**		CB (— • — • — • • •)		150		FREQ: 289 kHz. Antenna 80 yards, 326° from Cape Henry Light.
370	Middle Ground South End Lighted Bell Buoy 4A	37 00.3 75 55.8	Fl R 4^s		4	Red.	
375	North Chesapeake Entrance Lighted Whistle Buoy NCA	36 58.7 75 48.6	Fl Y 2.5^s		6	Yellow.	
380	North Chesapeake Entrance Lighted Gong Buoy NCB	36 58.0 75 50.8	Fl Y 6^s		7	Yellow.	
385	North Chesapeake Entrance Lighted Bell Buoy NCC	36 57.4 75 53.0	Fl Y 4^s		6	Yellow.	
390	North Chesapeake Entrance Lighted Gong Buoy NCD	36 56.8 75 55.1	Fl Y 2.5^s		6	Yellow.	
395	Chesapeake Bay Entrance Junction Lighted Gong Buoy CBJ	36 56.1 75 57.5	Fl (2+1) G 6^s		5	Green and red bands.	

Chesapeake Bay Southern Approach

400	– Lighted Whistle Buoy CB	36 49.0 75 45.6	Mo (A) W		6	Red and white stripes with red spherical topmark.	RACON: K(— • —).
401	– Lighted Buoy 1	36 49.5 75 46.9	Fl G 2.5^s		4	Green.	
402	– Lighted Buoy 2	36 49.7 75 46.7	Fl R 2.5^s		4	Red.	
403	– Lighted Buoy 3	36 50.2 75 48.3	Fl G 4^s		4	Green.	
404	– Lighted Buoy 4	36 50.3 75 48.1	Fl R 4^s		4	Red.	
405	– Lighted Buoy 5	36 50.9 75 49.6	Fl G 4^s		4	Green.	
406	– Lighted Buoy 6	36 51.0 75 49.5	Fl R 4^s		4	Red.	
407	– Lighted Buoy 7	36 51.5 75 50.9	Fl G 2.5^s		4	Green.	
408	– Lighted Buoy 8	36 51.7 75 50.8	Fl R 2.5^s		4	Red.	
409	– Lighted Buoy 9	36 52.2 75 52.3	Q G		4	Green.	

(1) No.	(2) Name and location	(3) Position	(4) Characteristic	(5) Height	(6) Range	(7) Structure	(8) Remarks
			SEACOAST (Virginia) – Fifth District				
		N/W					
	OCEAN CITY INLET TO CAPE HATTERAS (Chart 12200)						
	Chesapeake Bay Southern Approach						
410	– Lighted Buoy 10	36 52.4 75 52.1	Q R		4	Red.	
411	– Lighted Buoy 11	36 53.1 75 53.3	Fl G 2.5s		4	Green.	
412	– Lighted Buoy 12	36 53.3 75 53.1	Fl R 2.5s		4	Red.	
413	– Lighted Buoy 13	36 54.0 75 54.3	Fl G 4s		4	Green.	
414	– Lighted Buoy 14	36 54.2 75 54.2	Fl R 4s		4	Red.	
415	– Lighted Buoy 15	36 55.0 75 55.4	Q G		4	Green.	
416	– Lighted Buoy 16	36 55.1 75 55.2	Q R		4	Red.	
420	Navy SESEF Lighted Buoy B	36 55.0 75 45.5	Fl Y 4s		5	Yellow.	
425	Rudee Inlet Lighted Whistle Buoy RI	36 50.0 75 56.8	Mo (A) W		5	Red and white stripes.	
430	RUDEE INLET JETTY LIGHT 2	36 49.8 75 58.0	Fl R 2.5s	22	3	TR on pile.	
435	RUDEE INLET JETTY LIGHT 1	36 49.8 75 58.0	Fl G 4s	21	4	SG on pile.	
440	Dam Neck Disposal Area Lighted Buoy A		Fl Y 2.5s		4	Yellow.	Position changed frequently for dredging.
442	Dam Neck Disposal Area Lighted Buoy B		Fl Y 4s		4	Yellow.	Position changed frequently for dredging.
444	Dam Neck Disposal Area Lighted Buoy C		Fl Y 6s		4	Yellow.	Position changed frequently for dredging.
452	Dam Neck Firing Zone Lighted Buoy A	36 49.5 75 51.1	Fl Y 2.5s		5	Yellow.	
455	Virginia Beach Wreck Lighted Bell Buoy WR2V Marks wreck of TIGER.	36 46.1 75 46.1	Q R		4	Red.	
457	Dam Neck Firing Zone Lighted Buoy B	36 43.8 75 54.4	Fl Y 4s		5	Yellow.	
460	False Cape Lighted Buoy 4A	36 35.6 75 44.0	Fl R 2.5s		5	Red.	
462	NOAA Data Lighted Buoy 44014 (ODAS)	36 35.0 74 50.0	Fl (4) Y 20s			Yellow disc-shaped hull.	
			SEACOAST (North Carolina) – Fifth District				
	OCEAN CITY INLET TO CAPE HATTERAS (Chart 12200)						
465	**Currituck Beach Light**	36 22.6 75 49.8	Fl W 20s	158	18	Red conical tower. 163	

(1) No.	(2) Name and location	(3) Position	(4) Characteristic	(5) Height	(6) Range	(7) Structure	(8) Remarks
	VIRGINIA – Fifth District						
		N/W					
	CHINCOTEAGUE INLET TO GREAT MACHIPONGO INLET (Chart 12210)						
	Virginia Inside Passage						
6465 5900	– Daybeacon 187					SG on pile.	
6470 5895	– LIGHT 186		Fl R 4ˢ	16	3	TR on dolphin.	
	Great Machipongo Channel						
6474	– Buoy 1					Green can.	
6475	– LIGHT 1A	37 27.8 75 47.1	Fl G 4ˢ	15	4	SG on dolphin.	Light equipment removed when endangered by ice.
6480	– Daybeacon 3					SG on pile.	
6481	– Daybeacon 3A					SG on pile.	
6482	– Daybeacon 3B					SG on pile.	
6485	– LIGHT 4		Q R	15	4	TR on pile.	Light equipment remove when endangered by ice.
6490	– LIGHT 6	37 27.8 75 48.4	Fl R 4ˢ	15	4	TR on pile.	Light equipment removed when endangered by ice.
6500	– LIGHT 8	37 28.4 75 48.4	Fl R 4ˢ	15	3	TR on pile.	Light equipment removed when endangered by ice.
6505	– Daybeacon 10	37 29.0 75 48.0				TR on pile.	
6510	– LIGHT 11	37 29.4 75 47.7	Fl G 4ˢ	15	4	SG on pile.	Light equipment removed when endangered by ice.
6515	– LIGHT 12	37 29.9 75 47.7	Fl R 4ˢ	15	3	TR on pile.	Light equipment removed when endangered by ice.
6520	– LIGHT 13	37 30.2 75 47.6	Fl G 4ˢ	15	4	SG on dolphin.	
6525	– Daybeacon 15	37 30.3 75 48.2				SG on pile.	
6530	– Daybeacon 17					SG on pile.	
6535	– Daybeacon 18					TR on pile.	
	CHESAPEAKE BAY ENTRANCE (Chart 12221)						
6540	RAMSHORN CHANNEL LIGHT 2	37 23.4 75 51.2	Fl R 4ˢ	18	4	TR on pile.	Light equipment removed from Dec 1. to Mar. 15.
	Sand Shoal Inlet						
	Positions of buoys frequently shifted with changing conditions.						
6545	– *Lighted Bell Buoy A*	37 17.8 75 42.9	Mo (A) W		6	Red and white stripes with red spherical topmark.	
6550	– *Lighted Buoy 1*		Fl G 4ˢ		4	Green.	
6555	– *Lighted Buoy 3*		Fl G 4ˢ		4	Green.	
6560	– Buoy 5					Green can.	
6565	– *Lighted Buoy 6*		Fl R 4ˢ		4	Red.	

(1) No.	(2) Name and location	(3) Position	(4) Characteristic	(5) Height	(6) Range	(7) Structure	(8) Remarks

VIRGINIA – Fifth District

CHESAPEAKE BAY ENTRANCE (Chart 12221)

N/W

Sand Shoal Inlet

Positions of buoys frequently shifted with changing conditions.

6570	– SOUTH LIGHT	37 17.9 75 48.2	Fl W 4s	15	5	NB on dolphin.	
6575 6065	OYSTER CHANNEL JUNCTION LIGHT OC	37 17.4 75 53.7	Fl (2+1) R 6s	15	6	JR on slatted pile structure.	
6580	– Daybeacon 2					TR on pile.	
6585	– LIGHT 3		Fl G 2.5s	16	5	SG on dolphin.	
6590	– Daybeacon 5 Marks encroaching shoal.					SG on pile.	
6595	– LIGHT 6		Fl R 4s	16	3	TR on dolphin.	
6600	– LIGHT 8		Fl R 4s	16	3	TR on dolphin.	
6605	– LIGHT 10		Fl R 4s	16	3	TR on dolphin.	

CHESAPEAKE BAY (Virginia) – Fifth District

CHESAPEAKE BAY ENTRANCE (Chart 12221)

Chesapeake Channel

6610	Cape Henry Buoy 1	36 55.0 75 58.0				Green can.	
6615	– Lighted Bell Buoy 2C	36 57.3 75 58.4	Fl R 2.5s		4	Red.	
6620	Cape Henry Wreck Lighted Buoy 2CH 250 yards, 225° from last reported position of wreck. Marks wreck of CHILORE.	36 57.6 76 00.8	Q R		4	Red.	
6625	– Lighted Buoy 3 75 feet outside channel limit.		Fl G 4s		4	Green.	
6630	– Lighted Buoy 4 75 feet outside channel limit.		Fl R 4s		4	Red.	
6635	– Lighted Bell Buoy 5 75 feet outside channel limit.		Fl G 2.5s		4	Green.	
6640	– Lighted Buoy 6 75 feet outside channel limit.		Q R		4	Red.	
6645	Tail Of The Horseshoe Shoal Lighted Bell Buoy 2T		Fl R 4s		4	Red.	

Fish net buoys in Chesapeake Bay and tributary waters are not listed; however, they are shown on the nautical charts. Fish net buoys are painted yellow and are maintained for the Corps of Engineers to mark boundaries of fishing areas where fish nets and traps are permitted as prescribed by the Corps of Engineers.

(1) No.	(2) Name and location	(3) Position	(4) Characteristic	(5) Height	(6) Range	(7) Structure	(8) Remarks

CHESAPEAKE BAY (Virginia) – Fifth District

CHESAPEAKE BAY ENTRANCE (Chart 12221)   N/W

Chesapeake Channel

6650	– Lighted Buoy 7 75 feet outside channel limit.		Q G		4	Green.	
6660	– Lighted Buoy 9		Fl G 4s		4	Green.	
6665	– Lighted Buoy 10		Fl R 4s		4	Red.	
6667	– Lighted Buoy 11		Q G		4	Green.	
6669	– Lighted Bell Buoy 12		Q R		4	Red.	
6670	– TUNNEL SOUTH LIGHT		F G	22	6	Mounted atop wall on centerline.	BELL: 1 stroke ev 10s Operates during periods of low visibility only. Ra ref. Private aid.
6675	– TUNNEL NORTH LIGHT		F R	22	6	Mounted atop wall on centerline.	HORN: 1 blast ev 20s (2s bl). Operates during periods of low visibility only. Private aid.
6677	– Lighted Buoy 13		Fl G 4s		4	Green.	
6679	– Lighted Buoy 14		Fl R 4s		4	Red.	
6680	– Lighted Bell Buoy 15 75 feet outside channel limit.		Q G		4	Green.	
6685	– Lighted Buoy 16 75 feet outside channel limit.		Q R		4	Red.	
6688	–Lighted Buoy 18		Fl R 2.5s		5	Red.	
6690	– Junction Lighted Gong Buoy CY 75 feet outside channel limit.		Fl (2+1) G 6s		5	Green and red bands.	
6695	– Lighted Buoy 19 75 feet outside channel limit.		Fl G 4s		4	Green.	
6700	– Lighted Buoy 20 75 feet outside channel limit.		Fl R 4s		4	Red.	
6705	– Lighted Bell Buoy 22 75 feet outside channel limit.		Q R		4	Red.	
6710	– Lighted Buoy 23 75 feet outside channel limit.		Q G		4	Green.	
6715	– Lighted Buoy 24 75 feet outside channel limit.		Fl R 2.5s		4	Red.	

Fish net buoys in Chesapeake Bay and tributary waters are not listed; however, they are shown on the nautical charts.
Fish net buoys are painted yellow and are maintained for the Corps of Engineers to mark boundaries of fishing areas
where fish nets and traps are permitted as prescribed by the Corps of Engineers.

(1) No.	(2) Name and location	(3) Position	(4) Characteristic	(5) Height	(6) Range	(7) Structure	(8) Remarks

CHESAPEAKE BAY ENTRANCE (Chart 12221) N/W

Chesapeake Channel

6720	– *Lighted Buoy 25* 75 feet outside channel limit.		Fl G 4s		4	Green.	
6725	– *Lighted Buoy 26* 75 feet outside channel limit.		Fl R 4s		4	Red.	
6730	– *Lighted Buoy 28* 75 feet outside channel limit.		Q R		4	Red.	
6735	– *Lighted Buoy 29* 75 feet outside channel limit.		Q G		4	Green.	
6740	– *Lighted Buoy 30* 75 feet outside channel limit.		Fl R 2.5s		4	Red.	
6745	– *Lighted Buoy 31* 75 feet outside channel limit.		Fl G 4s		4	Green.	
6750	– *Lighted Buoy 32* 75 feet outside channel limit.		Fl R 4s		4	Red.	
6755	– Calibration Buoy	37 12.3 76 08.5				White with green band.	Maintained by U.S. Army Corps of Engineers.
6770	– *Lighted Buoy 33* 75 feet outside channel limit.		Fl G 6s		4	Green.	
6775	– *Lighted Buoy 34* 75 feet outside channel limit.		Fl R 6s		4	Red.	
6780	– *Lighted Buoy 35* 75 feet outside channel limit.		Fl G 4s		4	Green.	
6785	– *Lighted Buoy 36* 75 feet outside channel limit.		Fl R 4s		4	Red.	
6787	– *Lighted Buoy 37* 75 feet outside channel limit.		Fl G 2.5s		5	Green.	
6788	– *Lighted Buoy 38* 75 feet outside channel limit.		Fl R 2.5s		5	Red.	
6789	– *Lighted Buoy 40*		Fl R 4s		5	Red.	Replaced by nun when endangered by ice.
6790 19585	OLD PLANTATION FLATS LIGHT	37 13.8 76 02.8	Fl W 4s	39	7	NB on pile.	Higher intensity beam toward 200°.

Fish net buoys in Chesapeake Bay and tributary waters are not listed; however, they are shown on the nautical charts. Fish net buoys are painted yellow and are maintained for the Corps of Engineers to mark boundaries of fishing areas where fish nets and traps are permitted as prescribed by the Corps of Engineers.

(1) No.	(2) Name and location	(3) Position	(4) Characteristic	(5) Height	(6) Range	(7) Structure	(8) Remarks
			CHESAPEAKE BAY (Virginia) – Fifth District				
	WOLF TRAP TO SMITH POINT (Chart 12225)	N/W					
	Chesapeake Channel						
6800	**Wolf Trap Light**	37 23.4 76 11.4	Fl W 15s	52	11	Octagonal red brick dwelling, square tower on brown cylinder.	
6805	*Wolf Trap Degaussing Lighted Bell Buoy WT2 150 yards west of obstruction.*	37 24.2 76 03.7	Q R		3	Red.	
6808	*- Lighted Buoy 41*		Fl G 4s		4	Green.	
6810	*- Lighted Gong Buoy 42*	37 25.6 76 05.1	Fl R 4s		5	Red.	
6820	*- Mid Channel Lighted Whistle Buoy CB*	37 30.0 76 02.6	Mo (A) W		6	Red and white stripes.	Replaced by nun when endangered by ice.
6821	RAPPAHANNOCK SHOAL CHANNEL SOUTH RANGE FRONT LIGHT	37 32.3 76 00.9	F W	31		Red monopod with white equipment hut on top.	
6821.1	RAPPAHANNOCK SHOAL CHANNEL SOUTH RANGE REAR LIGHT 7,300 yards. 140° from front light.		F W	220		Skeleton tower on caisson.	
6822	*- Lighted Buoy 43*		Fl G 2.5s		5	Green.	Replaced by can when endangered by ice.
6823	*- Lighted Buoy 44*		Fl R 2.6s		5	Red.	Replaced by nun when endangered by ice.
6823.5	*- Lighted Buoy 45*		Fl G 2.5s		4	Green.	Replaced by can when endangered by ice.
6824	*- Lighted Bell Buoy 46*		Q R		4	Red.	Replaced by nun when endangered by ice.
6824.5	*- Lighted Buoy 47*		Q G		4	Green.	Replaced by can when endangered by ice.
6825	STINGRAY POINT LIGHT	37 33.7 76 16.2	Fl W 4s	34	8	NG on pile.	
6830	WINDMILL POINT LIGHT	37 35.8 76 14.2	Fl W 6s (2 R sectors)	31	W 8 R 6	NR on pile.	Red from 293° to 082° and from 091.5° to 113°.
6835 13475	*Rappahannock River Junction Lighted Bell Buoy R*	37 33.6 76 10.3	Fl (2+1) G 6s		4	Green and red bands.	
6836	*Rappahannock Dumping Ground Lighted Buoy A*		Fl Y 4s			Yellow.	
6837	*Rappahannock Dumping Ground Lighted Buoy B*		Fl Y 2.5s			Yellow.	
6838	*Rappahannock Dumping Ground Lighted Buoy C*		Fl Y 6s			Yellow.	

Fish net buoys in Chesapeake Bay and tributary waters are not listed; however, they are shown on the nautical charts. Fish net buoys are painted yellow and are maintained for the Corps of Engineers to mark boundaries of fishing areas where fish nets and traps are permitted as prescribed by the Corps of Engineers.

(1) No.	(2) Name and location	(3) Position	(4) Characteristic	(5) Height	(6) Range	(7) Structure	(8) Remarks

CHESAPEAKE BAY (Maryland) – Fifth District

SANDY POINT TO SUSQUEHANNA RIVER (Chart 12273) N/W

Harbor North Channel

Aberdeen Restricted Area

8295	– Buoy 5					Green can.	Maintained from Apr. 1 to Nov. 15. Private aid.
8300	– Buoy 6					Red nun.	Maintained from Apr. 1 to Nov. 15. Private aid.
8305	– Buoy 7					Green can.	Maintained from Apr. 1 to Nov. 15. Private aid.
8310	– Buoy 8					Red nun.	Maintained from Apr. 1 to Nov. 15. Private aid.

Elk River Channel

8313	– Lighted Buoy 21		Fl G 4s		4	Green.	Replaced by LIB of lower intensity from Dec. 1 to Mar. 15.
8315	– Lighted Buoy 22 75 feet outside channel limit.		Fl R 4s		4	Red.	Replaced by LIB of lower intensity from Dec. 1 to Mar. 15.
8317	BOHEMIA RIVER LIGHT 2	39 28.5 75 53.2	Fl R 4s	15	4	TR on pile.	
8318	Bohemia River Daybeacon 4					TR on pile.	
8319	Bohemia River Daybeacon 6					TR on pile.	

Back Creek Channel

8325	– Lighted Buoy 24		Fl R 2.5s		4	Red.	Replaced by LIB of lower intensity from Dec. 1 to Mar. 15.
8330	– LIGHT 25		Fl G 2.5s	25	4	SG on pile.	
8335	– LIGHT 26		Fl R 4s	25	4	TR on pile.	
8337	– Lighted Buoy 27 30 feet outside channel limit.		Fl G 4s		5	Green.	Replaced by LIB of lower intensity from Dec. 1 to Mar. 15.
8339	– Lighted Buoy 28		Fl R 2.5s		5	Red.	Replaced by LIB of lower intensity from Dec. 1 to Mar. 15.

CHESAPEAKE BAY (Virginia) – Fifth District

CAPE HENRY TO THIMBLE SHOAL LIGHT (Chart 12254)

Thimble Shoal Channel

Vessels drawing less than 25 feet are not permitted to use this channel.

8340	– Lighted Bell Buoy 1TS	36 56.9 76 01.4	Fl G 2.5s		4	Green.	

Fish net buoys in Chesapeake Bay and tributary waters are not listed; however, they are shown on the nautical charts. Fish net buoys are painted yellow and are maintained for the Corps of Engineers to mark boundaries of fishing areas where fish nets and traps are permitted as prescribed by the Corps of Engineers.

CHESAPEAKE BAY (Virginia) – Fifth District

CAPE HENRY TO THIMBLE SHOAL LIGHT
N/W
(Chart 12254)

Thimble Shoal Channel

Vessels drawing less than 25 feet are not permitted to use this channel.

No.	Name and location	Characteristic	Height	Range	Structure	Remarks
8345	– Lighted Buoy 2	Fl R 2.5s		4	Red.	
8350	– Lighted Buoy 3	Fl G 4s		4	Green.	
8355	– Lighted Gong Buoy 4	Fl R 4		4	Red.	
8360	– Lighted Bell Buoy 5	Fl G 6s		4	Green.	
8365	– Lighted Buoy 6	Fl R 6s		4	Red.	
8370	– Lighted Buoy 7	Fl G 2.5s		4	Green.	
8375	– Lighted Gong Buoy 8	Fl R 2.5s		4	Red.	
8380	THIMBLE SHOAL TUNNEL SOUTH LIGHT	F G	32		On wall.	BELL: 1 stroke ev 10s. Operates during periods of low visibility only. Private aid.
8385	THIMBLE SHOAL TUNNEL NORTH LIGHT	F R	32		On wall.	HORN: 1 blast ev 20s (2s bl). Operates during periods of low visibility only. Private aid.
8390	– Lighted Bell Buoy 9	Fl G 4s		4	Green.	
8395	– Lighted Buoy 10	Fl R 4s		4	Red.	
8400	– Lighted Buoy 11	Fl G 6s		4	Green.	
8405	– Lighted Gong Buoy 12	Fl R 6s		4	Red.	
8410	– Lighted Bell Buoy 13	Fl G 2.5s		4	Green.	
8415	– Lighted Buoy 14	Fl R 2.5s		4	Red.	
8420	– Lighted Buoy 15	Fl G 4s		4	Green.	
8425	– Lighted Gong Buoy 16	Fl R 4s		4	Red.	

CHESAPEAKE BAY - THIMBLE SHOAL CHANNEL
(Chart 12245)

Thimble Shoal Channel

Vessels drawing less than 25 feet are not permitted to use this channel.

No.	Name and location	Characteristic	Height	Range	Structure	Remarks
8430	– Lighted Gong Buoy 17	Fl G 2.5s		4	Green.	
8435	– Lighted Buoy 18	Q R		4	Red.	
8440	– Lighted Buoy 19	Q G		4	Green.	

Fish net buoys in Chesapeake Bay and tributary waters are not listed; however, they are shown on the nautical charts.
Fish net buoys are painted yellow and are maintained for the Corps of Engineers to mark boundaries of fishing areas
where fish nets and traps are permitted as prescribed by the Corps of Engineers.

(1) No.	(2) Name and location	(3) Position	(4) Characteristic	(5) Height	(6) Range	(7) Structure	(8) Remarks

N/W
CHESAPEAKE BAY - THIMBLE SHOAL CHANNEL
(Chart 12245)

Thimble Shoal Channel

Vessels drawing less than 25 feet are not permitted to use this channel.

No.	Name and location	Position	Characteristic	Height	Range	Structure	Remarks
8450	**Thimble Shoal Light**	37 00.9 76 14.4	Iso W 6s	55	13	Red conical tower on brown cylindrical pier.	HORN: 1 blast ev 30s (3s bl). Operates continuously.
8455	– Lighted Bell Buoy 21		Q G		4	Green.	
8460	– Lighted Buoy 22	37 00.1 76 17.9	Q R		4	Red.	

Naval Ordnance

No.	Name and location	Position	Characteristic	Height	Range	Structure	Remarks
8475	– Buoy F					Orange and white bands; sphere.	Maintained by U.S. Navy.
8480	– Buoy G					Orange and white bands; sphere.	Maintained by US. Navy.
8485	– Buoy H					Orange and white bands; sphere.	Maintained by U.S Navy
8490	– Buoy K					Orange and white bands; sphere.	Maintained by U.S. Navy.
8495	– Buoy L					Orange and white bands; sphere.	Maintained by U.S. Navy.
8500	– Buoy M					Orange and white bands; sphere.	Maintained by U.S. Navy.
8505	– Lighted Buoy P	37 00.3 76 17.0	Fl Y 4s		6	Yellow.	
8510	– Lighted Buoy R		Fl Y 4s		6	Yellow.	
8515	– Lighted Buoy T		Fl Y 4s		6	Yellow.	
8517	NORFOLK ENTRANCE REACH RANGE FRONT LIGHT	37 00.7 76 17.1	Occ W 4s	20		On platform on four pile structure.	Lighted throughout 24 hours.
8518	NORFOLK ENTRANCE REACH RANGE REAR LIGHT 960 yards, 045° from front light.		F W	58		On platform on four pile structure.	Lighted throughout 24 hours.

HAMPTON ROADS (Chart 12245)

Hampton Bar

No.	Name and location	Position	Characteristic	Height	Range	Structure	Remarks
8520	**Old Point Comfort Light**	37 00.1 76 18.4	Fl (2) R 12s (W sector) 2s fl 2s ec 2s fl 6s ec	54	W 16 R 14	White tower.	White from 265° to 038°. Emergency light of reduced intensity will be displayed when main light is inoperative.
8525	FORT WOOL LIGHT	36 59.2 76 18.2	Fl W 4s	25	8	On small gray house.	
8530	– Buoy 14					Red nun.	

Fish net buoys in Chesapeake Bay and tributary waters are not listed; however, they are shown on the nautical charts. Fish net buoys are painted yellow and are maintained for the Corps of Engineers to mark boundaries of fishing areas where fish nets and traps are permitted as prescribed by the Corps of Engineers.

(1) No.	(2) Name and location	(3) Position	(4) Characteristic	(5) Height	(6) Range	(7) Structure	(8) Remarks

JAMESTOWN ISLAND TO JORDAN POINT (Chart 12251)

N/W

James River

(1) No.	(2) Name and location	(3) Position	(4) Characteristic	(5) Height	(6) Range	(7) Structure	(8) Remarks
11400	– CHANNEL LIGHT 124 190 feet outside channel limit.	37 20.0 77 16.4	Fl R 4^s	18	4	TR on dolphin.	
11405	– *Channel Lighted Buoy 126*	37 20.4 77 16.2	Fl R 4^s		4	Red.	
11410	– LIGHT 127		Fl G 2.5^s	15	3	SG on pile.	
11415	– *Lighted Buoy 128* 300 feet outside channel limit.	37 20.7 77 16.1	Fl R 4^s		4	Red.	
11420	– LIGHT 132	37 21.2 77 16.5	Fl R 4^s	24	3	TR on pile.	
11425	– LIGHT 133		Fl G 4^s	20	4	SG on pile.	
11430	– OBSTRUCTION LIGHT A	37 21.1 77 17.1	F W	15		On dolphin.	Private aid.
11435	– LIGHT 135		Fl G 2.5^s	16	3	SG on pile.	
11440	– LIGHT 137		Fl G 4^s	18	4	SG on pile.	
11445	– *Channel Lighted Buoy 138*	37 21.8 77 18.4	Fl R 4^s		3	Red.	
11450	– LIGHT 139		Fl G 6^s	18	4	SG on pile.	
11455	– *Channel Lighted Buoy 140*	37 22.1 77 18.5	Fl R 4^s		3	Red.	
11460	– LIGHT 143		Fl G 4^s	16	4	SG on pile.	
11465	– LIGHT 144		Fl R 4^s	16	3	TR on dolphin.	
11470	– LIGHT 146		Fl R 4^s	15	3	TR on pile.	
11475	– LIGHT 147		Fl G 4^s	16	4	SG on pile.	
11480	– LIGHT 150		Fl R 4^s	18	3	TR on pile.	
11485	DUTCH GAP LIGHT	37 22.5 77 21.5	Q W			On dolphin.	Private aid.
11490	– LIGHT 151		Q G	15	3	SG on pile.	
11495	– LIGHT 152	37 22.7 77 21.7	Fl R 4^s	19	3	TR on pile.	
11497	– LIGHT 152A		Fl R 2.5^s	18	3	TR on pile.	
11500	– LIGHT 154		Fl R 4^s	15	3	TR on dolphin.	
11505	VIRGINIA POWER WHARF LIGHT	37 22.9 77 22.7	Fl G 11^s	11		On wharf.	Private aid.
11510	Virginia Power Turning Basin Daybeacon					On black and white striped pile.	Private aid.
11515	– LIGHT 155		Q G	18	3	SG on pile.	

Fish net buoys in Chesapeake Bay and tributary waters are not listed; however, they are shown on the nautical charts. Fish net buoys are painted yellow and are maintained for the Corps of Engineers to mark boundaries of fishing areas where fish nets and traps are permitted as prescribed by the Corps of Engineers.

CHESAPEAKE BAY (Virginia) – Fifth District

N/W
JAMESTOWN ISLAND TO JORDAN POINT (Chart 12251)

James River

11517	– LIGHT 155A		Fl G 2.5s	18	3	SG on pile.	
11520	– LIGHT 156		Q R	18	3	TR on pile.	
11525	– LIGHT 157		Fl G 4s	18	4	SG on pile.	
11530	– LIGHT 158		Fl R 4s	18	3	TR on pile.	
11535	– LIGHT 160		Q R	18	3	TR on pile.	
11540	– LIGHT 161		Fl G 4s	18	3	SG on pile.	
11545	– *Channel Lighted Buoy 162*	37 25.3 77 25.1	Fl R 2.5s		4	Red.	
11550	EXXON PIER LIGHTS	37 25.4 77 25.5	(3) F G	12		On pile.	Private aids.
11555	– LIGHT 163		Fl G 4s	18	4	SG on pile.	
11560	– LIGHT 165	37 26.2 77 25.7	Fl G 4s	20	4	SG on pile.	
11565	– LIGHT 166		Fl R 4s	18	3	TR on pile.	
11570	– LIGHT 168		Fl R 4s	18	3	TR on pile.	
11575	– *Channel Buoy 169*					Green can.	
11580	– *Channel Buoy 171*					Green can.	
11585	– *Channel Buoy 172*					Red nun.	
11590	– LIGHT 173		Fl G 4s	15	4	SG on pile.	

CAPE CHARLES TO NORFOLK HARBOR (Chart 12222)

Chesapeake Bay

11595	*Horseshoe Crossing Lighted Bell Buoy HC*	37 01.3 76 08.9	Mo (A) W		6	Red and white stripes with red spherical topmark.	
11600	BUCKROE BEACH FISHING PIER LIGHT	37 02.3 76 17.3	F W	16		White circular daymark on white structure.	Private aid.

Salt Ponds

11610	– Buoy 1					Green can.	Private aid.
11615	– Daybeacon 2					TR on pile.	Private aid.
11620	– Daybeacon 3					SG on pile.	Private aid.
11625	– Daybeacon 4					TR on pile.	Private aid.
11630	– Daybeacon 5					SG on pile.	Private aid.
11635	– LIGHT 6	37 03.7 76 16.7	Fl R 4s	19		TR on pile.	Private aid.
11640	– LIGHT 7	37 03.8 76 17.0	Fl G 2.5s			SG on pile.	Private aid.

Fish net buoys in Chesapeake Bay and tributary waters are not listed; however, they are shown on the nautical charts. Fish net buoys are painted yellow and are maintained for the Corps of Engineers to mark boundaries of fishing areas where fish nets and traps are permitted as prescribed by the Corps of Engineers.

(1) No.	(2) Name and location	(3) Position	(4) Characteristic	(5) Height	(6) Range	(7) Structure	(8) Remarks

CAPE CHARLES TO NORFOLK HARBOR (Chart 12222) N/W

Salt Ponds

(1) No.	(2) Name and location	(3) Position	(4) Characteristic	(5) Height	(6) Range	(7) Structure	(8) Remarks
11645	– Daybeacon 8					TR on pile.	Private aid.
11650	– Daybeacon 10					TR on pile.	Private aid.
11655	– Daybeacon 12					TR on pile.	Private aid.
11660	– Daybeacon 14					TR on pile.	Private aid.
11665	– Daybeacon 16					TR on pile.	Private aid.
11670	GRAND VIEW FISHING PIER LIGHT	37 04.4 76 16.6	F W	22			Private aid.

MOBJACK BAY AND YORK RIVER ENTRANCE
(Chart 12238)

Back River

(1) No.	(2) Name and location	(3) Position	(4) Characteristic	(5) Height	(6) Range	(7) Structure	(8) Remarks
11675	– Entrance Lighted Bell Buoy 1	37 05.6 76 15.0	Fl G 4s		4	Green.	
11680	– Channel Daybeacon 2					TR on pile.	
11685	– CHANNEL LIGHT 4		Fl R 4s	17	3	TR on pile.	
11690	– CHANNEL LIGHT 5		Fl G 4s	19	4	SG on pile.	
11695	– Channel Daybeacon 6					TR on pile.	
11700	– CHANNEL LIGHT 7		Fl G 4s	15	4	SG on pile.	
11705	– CHANNEL LIGHT 8		Fl R 4s	14	3	TR on pile.	Light equipment removed from Dec. 1 to Mar. 15.
11710	– CHANNEL LIGHT 9	37 06.6 76 17.6	Fl G 4s	19	4	SG on pile.	
11715	– South Channel Daybeacon 1					SG on pile.	
11720	– South Channel Daybeacon 3					SG on pile.	

Dandy Haven Marina Entrance

(1) No.	(2) Name and location	(3) Position	(4) Characteristic	(5) Height	(6) Range	(7) Structure	(8) Remarks
11725	– Daybeacon 1	37 06.0 76 18.1				SB on pile.	Private aid.
11730	– Daybeacon 2					TR on pile.	Private aid.
11735	– Daybeacon 3					SB on pile.	Private aid.
11740	– Daybeacon 4					TR on pile.	Private aid.
11745	– Daybeacon 5					SB on pile.	Private aid.
11750	– Daybeacon 6					TR on pile.	Private aid.
11755	– Daybeacon 7					SB on pile.	Private aid.
11760	– Daybeacon 8					TR on pile.	Private aid.
11765	– Daybeacon 9					SB on pile.	Private aid.

Fish net buoys in Chesapeake Bay and tributary waters are not listed; however, they are shown on the nautical charts.
Fish net buoys are painted yellow and are maintained for the Corps of Engineers to mark boundaries of fishing areas
where fish nets and traps are permitted as prescribed by the Corps of Engineers.

CHESAPEAKE BAY (Virginia) – Fifth District

MOBJACK BAY AND YORK RIVER ENTRANCE N/W
(Chart 12238)

Back River

Dandy Haven Marina Entrance

No.	Name and location	Position	Characteristic	Height	Range	Structure	Remarks
11770	– Daybeacon 10					TR on pile.	Private aid.
11775	– Daybeacon 11					SB on pile.	Private aid.
11780	– Daybeacon 12					TR on pile.	Private aid.

Back River

No.	Name and location	Position	Characteristic	Height	Range	Structure	Remarks
11785	– Channel Daybeacon 10					TR on pile.	
11790	– Channel Daybeacon 12					TR on pile.	
11795	– CHANNEL LIGHT 13		Fl G 4s	15	4	SG on pile.	
11800	– Channel Daybeacon 14					TR on pile.	
11805	– Channel Daybeacon 16					TR on pile.	

Harris River Approach

No.	Name and location	Position	Characteristic	Height	Range	Structure	Remarks
11810	– Daybeacon 2	37 06.1 76 19.0				TR on pile.	Private aid.
11815	– Daybeacon 3					SB on pile.	Private aid.
11820	– Daybeacon 4					TR on pile.	Private aid.
11825	– Daybeacon 5					SB on pile.	Private aid.
11830	– Daybeacon 6					TR on pile.	Private aid.
11835	– Daybeacon 8					TR on pile.	Private aid.

Back River

No.	Name and location	Position	Characteristic	Height	Range	Structure	Remarks
11840	– CHANNEL LIGHT 17		Fl G 2.5s	14	3	SG on pile.	Light equipment removed from Dec. 1 to Mar. 15.
11845	– CHANNEL LIGHT 18		Q R	14	4	TR on pile.	
11850	– Channel Daybeacon 20					TR on pile.	
11855	– CHANNEL LIGHT 21		Fl G 4s	14	4	SG on pile.	
11860	– CHANNEL LIGHT 22		Fl R 4s	14	3	TR on pile.	Light equipment removed from Dec. 1 to Mar. 15.
11865	– CHANNEL LIGHT 25		Fl G 2.5s	15	4	SG on pile.	
11870	– CHANNEL LIGHT 27		Fl G 4s	12	4	SG on pile.	Light equipment removed from Dec. 1 to Mar. 15.
11875	Langley Yacht Club Buoy A	37 04.8 76 20.5				White can with orange bands and orange circle worded NO WAKE.	Private aid.
11880	Langley Yacht Club Buoy B					White can with orange bands and orange circle worded NO WAKE.	Private aid.

Fish net buoys in Chesapeake Bay and tributary waters are not listed; however, they are shown on the nautical charts. Fish net buoys are painted yellow and are maintained for the Corps of Engineers to mark boundaries of fishing areas where fish nets and traps are permitted as prescribed by the Corps of Engineers.

(1) No.	(2) Name and location	(3) Position	(4) Characteristic	(5) Height	(6) Range	(7) Structure	(8) Remarks
			CHESAPEAKE BAY (Virginia) – Fifth District				
	N/W **MOBJACK BAY AND YORK RIVER ENTRANCE** (Chart 12238)						
	Back River						
11885	– NORTHWEST BRANCH LIGHT 1		Fl G 2.5ˢ	14	3	SG on pile.	Light equipment removed when endangered by ice.
11890	– NORTHWEST BRANCH LIGHT 3		Fl G 4ˢ	14	4	SG on pile.	Light equipment removed when endangered by ice.
11895	– Northwest Branch Daybeacon 4					TR on pile.	
11900	– Northwest Branch Daybeacon 5					SG on pile.	
11905	– Northwest Branch Daybeacon 6					TR on pile.	
	Poquoson River						
11910	– Entrance Lighted Buoy 2	37 13.5 76 19.5	Fl R 4ˢ		3	Red.	
11915	– Entrance Buoy 4					Red nun.	
11920	– Entrance Lighted Buoy 6		Fl R 4ˢ		4	Red.	
11925	– Entrance Buoy 8					Red nun.	
11930	– Entrance Lighted Buoy 10		Fl R 2.5ˢ		3	Red.	
11935	– ENTRANCE LIGHT 11		Fl G 4ˢ	15	4	SG on dolphin.	
11940	– Daybeacon 13					SG on pile.	
11945	– LIGHT 14		Fl R 4ˢ	16	4	TR on pile.	Light equipment removed from Dec. 1 to Mar. 15.
11950	Chisman Creek Daybeacon 2					TR on pile.	
11955	Chisman Creek Daybeacon 4	37 10.8 76 24.5				TR on pile.	
11960	Chisman Creek Daybeacon 5					SG on pile.	
11965	GOOSE CREEK JUNCTION LIGHT GC	37 11.1 76 25.4	Fl (2+1) R 6ˢ	15	4	JR on pile.	Light equipment removed from Dec. 1 to Mar. 15.
11970	Chisman Creek Daybeacon 6					TR on pile.	
11975	Goose Creek Daybeacon 2					TR on pile.	
11980	– LIGHT 15		Fl G 2.5ˢ	15	4	SG on pile.	Light equipment removed from Dec. 1 to Mar. 15.
11985	– Daybeacon 16					TR on pile.	
11990	– Daybeacon 17					SG on pile.	
11995	Quarter March Creek Entrance Daybeacon 2					TR on pile.	

Fish net buoys in Chesapeake Bay and tributary waters are not listed; however, they are shown on the nautical charts.
Fish net buoys are painted yellow and are maintained for the Corps of Engineers to mark boundaries of fishing areas
where fish nets and traps are permitted as prescribed by the Corps of Engineers.

(1) No.	(2) Name and location	(3) Position	(4) Characteristic	(5) Height	(6) Range	(7) Structure	(8) Remarks

CHESAPEAKE BAY (Virginia) – Fifth District

N/W

MOBJACK BAY AND YORK RIVER ENTRANCE
(Chart 12238)

Poquoson River

(1) No.	(2) Name and location	(3) Position	(4) Characteristic	(5) Height	(6) Range	(7) Structure	(8) Remarks
12000	Quarter March Creek Daybeacon 4					TR on pile.	
	Bennett Creek						
12005	– Daybeacon 1	37 09.7 76 22.8				SG on pile.	
12010	– LIGHT 2		Fl R 4s	15	4	TR on pile.	Light equipment removed from Dec. 1 to Mar. 15.
12015	– Daybeacon 4					TR on pile.	
12020	– Daybeacon 6					TR on pile.	
12025	– Daybeacon 8					TR on pile.	
12030	– LIGHT 10		Fl R 4s	19	4	TR on pile.	
12035	White House Cove Daybeacon 1	37 08.7 76 22.4				SG on pile.	
12040	White House Cove Daybeacon 1A	37 08.6 76 22.6		15		SG on pile.	
12045	White House Cove Daybeacon 2					TR on pile.	
12050	POQUOSON RIVER MARINA PIER LIGHTS	37 08.5 76 22.8	(3) F W	8			Private aids.
	Goodwin Thorofare						
12055	– LIGHT 2	37 12.3 76 22.9	Fl R 2.5s	18	4	TR on pile.	Light equipment removed when endangered by ice.
12060	– LIGHT 3	37 12.6 76 23.4	Fl G 4s	18	4	SG on dolphin.	
12065	– LIGHT 4		Fl R 4s	18	3	TR on dolphin.	
12070	– Daybeacon 5					SG on pile.	
12075	– Daybeacon 7					SG on pile.	
12080	– Daybeacon 8					TR on pile.	
12085	– CHANNEL LIGHT 10		Fl R 4s	19	4	TR on pile.	
12090	– CHANNEL LIGHT 12		Fl R 4s	15	3	TR on pile.	
12095	– CHANNEL LIGHT 13		Fl G 4s	15	4	SG on pile.	
12100	– Channel Daybeacon 14					TR on pile.	
12105	– Channel Daybeacon 15					SG on pile.	
12110	– CHANNEL LIGHT 16		Fl R 4s	14	4	TR on pile.	Light equipment removed when endangered by ice.

Fish net buoys in Chesapeake Bay and tributary waters are not listed; however, they are shown on the nautical charts. Fish net buoys are painted yellow and are maintained for the Corps of Engineers to mark boundaries of fishing areas where fish nets and traps are permitted as prescribed by the Corps of Engineers.

(1) No.	(2) Name and location	(3) Position	(4) Characteristic	(5) Height	(6) Range	(7) Structure	(8) Remarks

CHESAPEAKE BAY (Virginia) – Fifth District

N/W
MOBJACK BAY AND YORK RIVER ENTRANCE
(Chart 12238)

Back Creek

12115	– Daybeacon 1	37 12.6 76 24.8				SG on pile.	
12120	– Daybeacon 2					TR on pile.	
12125	– Daybeacon 3					SG on pile.	

CHESAPEAKE BAY ENTRANCE (Chart 12221)

York River

Entrance channel buoys located 75 feet outside channel limit.

12130	– Entrance Channel Lighted Gong Buoy 2	37 07.4 76 09.2	Fl R 4s		4	Red.	
12135	– Entrance Channel Lighted Buoy 1YR		Fl G 4s		4	Green.	
12140	– Entrance Channel Buoy 3					Green can.	
12145	– Entrance Channel Buoy 4					Red nun.	
12150	– Entrance Channel Lighted Buoy 5		Fl G 4s		4	Green.	
12155	– Entrance Channel Lighted Buoy 6		Fl R 4s		4	Red.	
12160	– Entrance Channel Buoy 7					Green can.	
12165	– Entrance Channel Buoy 8					Red nun.	
12170	– Entrance Channel Lighted Buoy 9	37 10.3 76 13.9	Fl G 4s		4	Green.	
12175	– Entrance Channel Lighted Buoy 10		Fl R 4s		4	Red.	
12180	– Entrance Channel Buoy 11					Green can.	
12185	– Entrance Channel Buoy 12					Red nun.	
12190	YORK SPIT LIGHT	37 12.6 76 15.3	Fl W 6s	30	8	NR on pile.	
12195	– Entrance Channel Lighted Buoy 13		Fl G 4s		4	Green.	
12200	– Entrance Channel Lighted Buoy 14		Fl R 4s		4	Red.	
12205	– Entrance Channel Buoy 15					Green can.	

Fish net buoys in Chesapeake Bay and tributary waters are not listed; however, they are shown on the nautical charts. Fish net buoys are painted yellow and are maintained for the Corps of Engineers to mark boundaries of fishing areas where fish nets and traps are permitted as prescribed by the Corps of Engineers.

(1) No.	(2) Name and location	(3) Position	(4) Characteristic	(5) Height	(6) Range	(7) Structure	(8) Remarks

CHESAPEAKE BAY ENTRANCE (Chart 12221) N/W

York River

Entrance channel buoys located 75 feet outside channel limit.

(1) No.	(2) Name and location	(3) Position	(4) Characteristic	(5) Height	(6) Range	(7) Structure	(8) Remarks
12210	– Entrance Channel Buoy 16					Red nun.	
12215	– *Entrance Channel Lighted Buoy 17*		Fl G 4s		4	Green.	
12220	– *Entrance Channel Lighted Gong Buoy 18*		Q R		4	Red.	
12225	York Spit Warning Daybeacon					NW on pile worded DANGER SHOAL.	

YORK RIVER - YORKTOWN AND VICINITY (Chart 12241)

York River

(1) No.	(2) Name and location	(3) Position	(4) Characteristic	(5) Height	(6) Range	(7) Structure	(8) Remarks
12230	– *Lighted Bell Buoy 21*		Fl G 4s		4	Green.	Replaced by can when endangered by ice.
12235	– *Lighted Bell Buoy 22*		Q R		4	Red.	
12240	TUE MARSHES LIGHT	37 14.1 76 23.2	Fl W 6s	41	8	NG on pile.	

Perrin River

(1) No.	(2) Name and location	(3) Position	(4) Characteristic	(5) Height	(6) Range	(7) Structure	(8) Remarks
12245	– *Junction Lighted Buoy PR*	37 14.8 76 23.5	Fl (2+1) R 6s		3	Red and green bands.	
12250	– Entrance Buoy 2					Red nun.	
12255	– ENTRANCE LIGHT 4		Fl R 4s	19	3	TR on pile.	
12260	– Entrance Daybeacon 6					TR on pile.	
12265	– ENTRANCE LIGHT 7		Fl G 4s	19	4	SG on pile.	
12270	– ENTRANCE LIGHT 8	37 15.6 76 25.2	Fl R 4s	19	3	TR on pile.	
12275	– Entrance Daybeacon 9					SG on pile.	
12280	– Daybeacon 11					SG on pile.	

York River

(1) No.	(2) Name and location	(3) Position	(4) Characteristic	(5) Height	(6) Range	(7) Structure	(8) Remarks
12285	– RANGE FRONT LIGHT	37 13.6 76 29.3	Q W	11		KRG on small white house on pile structure.	
12290	– RANGE REAR LIGHT 575 yards, 258° from front light.		Iso W 6s	65	13	KRG on skeleton tower.	
12295	– Buoy 24					Red nun.	
12300	– Buoy 23					Green can.	

Fish net buoys in Chesapeake Bay and tributary waters are not listed; however, they are shown on the nautical charts. Fish net buoys are painted yellow and are maintained for the Corps of Engineers to mark boundaries of fishing areas where fish nets and traps are permitted as prescribed by the Corps of Engineers.

(1) No.	(2) Name and location	(3) Position	(4) Characteristic	(5) Height	(6) Range	(7) Structure	(8) Remarks

YORKTOWN TO WEST POINT (Chart 12243) N/W

York River

Queen Creek

(1) No.	(2) Name and location	(3) Position	(4) Characteristic	(5) Height	(6) Range	(7) Structure
12520	– Daybeacon 7					SG on pile.
12525	– Daybeacon 8					TR on pile.
12530	– Daybeacon 10					TR on pile.
12535	– Daybeacon 11					SG on pile.
12538	– Daybeacon 12					TR on pile.
12540	– Daybeacon 13					SG on pile.
12543	– Daybeacon 14					TR on pile.
12544	– Daybeacon 15					SG on pile.
12545	– Daybeacon 15A					SG on pile.
12550	– Daybeacon 16					TR on pile.
12555	– Daybeacon 18					TR on pile.
12560	– Daybeacon 20					TR on pile.

York River

12565	Cedarbush Creek Daybeacon 2	37 18.6 76 33.9				TR on pile.
12570	PAGES ROCK LIGHT Off rock.	37 18.7 76 35.2	Fl W 6ˢ	43	8	NR on skeleton tower.
12575	– Channel Buoy 35					Green can.

Aberdeen Creek

12580	– ENTRANCE LIGHT 2	37 20.1 76 36.1	Fl R 4ˢ	15	5	TR on pile.
12585	– LIGHT 3		Fl G 4ˢ	15	4	SG on pile.
12590	– Daybeacon 5					SG on pile.
12595	– Daybeacon 7					SG on pile.
12600	– Daybeacon 9					SG on pile.
12605	– Daybeacon 11					SG on pile.

York River

12610	– Channel Buoy 37					Green can.
12615	Carter Creek Entrance Daybeacon 2					TR on pile.
12620	– LIGHT 39		Fl G 4ˢ	14	5	SG on pile.
12625	– Channel Buoy 41					Green can.
12630	– LIGHT 42		Fl R 4ˢ	15	5	TR on pile.

Fish net buoys in Chesapeake Bay and tributary waters are not listed; however, they are shown on the nautical charts. Fish net buoys are painted yellow and are maintained for the Corps of Engineers to mark boundaries of fishing areas where fish nets and traps are permitted as prescribed by the Corps of Engineers.

(1) No.	(2) Name and location	(3) Position	(4) Characteristic	(5) Height	(6) Range	(7) Structure	(8) Remarks
		N/W				CHESAPEAKE BAY (Virginia) – Fifth District	

YORKTOWN TO WEST POINT (Chart 12243)

York River

(1) No.	(2) Name and location	(3) Position	(4) Characteristic	(5) Height	(6) Range	(7) Structure	(8) Remarks
12635	– Channel Buoy 43					Green can.	
12640	– Channel Buoy 44					Red nun.	

Croaker Landing

12645	– Daybeacon 1	32 25.7 76 43.4				SG on pile.	Private aid.
12650	– Daybeacon 2					TR on pile.	Private aid,
12655	– Daybeacon 3					SG on pile.	Private aid.
12660	– Daybeacon 4					TR on pile.	Private aid.

York River

12665	– LIGHT 46		Fl R 4s	15	5	TR on pile.	
12670	– Channel Buoy 47					Green can.	
12675	BELLS ROCK LIGHT		Fl W 4s (R sector)	40	W 8 R 6	NR on white skeleton tower on piles.	Red from 120° to 329°.
12680	– Channel Buoy 49					Green can.	
12685	– Channel Buoy 50					Red nun.	
12690	– LIGHT 51		Fl G 4s	14	5	SG on pile.	
12695	– Channel Buoy 53					Green can.	
12700	– Channel Buoy 54					Red nun.	
12705	– Channel Buoy 55					Green can.	
12710	– Channel Buoy 57					Green can.	
12715	West Point Spit Junction Buoy					Red and green bands; nun.	
12720	– Channel Buoy 59					Green can.	
12725	– Channel Buoy 61					Green can.	

MOBJACK BAY AND YORK RIVER ENTRANCE (Chart 12238)

Mobjack Bay

12730	NEW POINT COMFORT SPIT LIGHT 2		Fl R 2.5s	18	4	TR on pile.	Light equipment removed when endangered by ice.
12735	NEW POINT COMFORT SPIT LIGHT 4		Fl R 4s	15	5	TR on dolphin.	

York Spit Swash Channel

12740	– Daybeacon 1					SG on pile.	
12745	– Daybeacon 2					TR on pile.	

Fish net buoys in Chesapeake Bay and tributary waters are not listed; however, they are shown on the nautical charts.
Fish net buoys are painted yellow and are maintained for the Corps of Engineers to mark boundaries of fishing areas where fish nets and traps are permitted as prescribed by the Corps of Engineers.

CHESAPEAKE BAY (Virginia) – Fifth District

(1) No.	(2) Name and location	(3) Position	(4) Characteristic	(5) Height	(6) Range	(7) Structure	(8) Remarks
	N/W **MOBJACK BAY AND YORK RIVER ENTRANCE** (Chart 12238)						
	Mobjack Bay						
	York Spit Swash Channel						
12750	– LIGHT 3	37 15.7 76 20.0	Fl G 4s	15	4	SG on pile.	
12755	– Daybeacon 5					SG on pile.	
12760	DUTCHMAN POINT LIGHT 6		Fl R 4s	15	5	TR on dolphin.	
	Davis Creek						
12765	– CHANNEL LIGHT 1	37 19.2 76 18.0	Fl G 4s	15	4	SG on dolphin.	
12770	– CHANNEL LIGHT 2		Fl R 4s	14	3	TR on dolphin.	
12775	– Channel Daybeacon 4					TR on pile.	
12780	– CHANNEL LIGHT 6		Fl R 4s	15	3	TR on dolphin.	
12785	– CHANNEL LIGHT 8		Q R	15	3	TR on pile.	
12790	– CHANNEL LIGHT 10		Fl R 4s	14	4	TR on pile.	
12795	Pepper Creek Daybeacon 1	37 20.0 76 19.6				SG on pile.	
12800	Pepper Creek Daybeacon 2					TR on pile.	
	East River						
12805	– ENTRANCE LIGHT 1 On south end of shoal.	37 21.3 76 21.1	Fl G 4s	15	4	SG on dolphin.	Light equipment removed when endangered by ice.
12810	– Daybeacon 2					TR on pile.	
12815	– LIGHT 3		Fl G 4s	16	3	SG on slatted pile structure.	
12820	Mobjack Marina Channel Daybeacon 1	37 22.7 76 20.6				SG on pile.	
12825	Mobjack Marina Channel Daybeacon 3	37 22.7 76 20.7				SG on pile.	
12830	– LIGHT 5		Q G	15	4	SG on pile.	
12835	– LIGHT 9		Fl G 4s	15	4	SG on pile.	Obscured from 120° to 180°.
12840	– Daybeacon 7					SG on pile.	
12845	– Daybeacon 11					SG on pile.	
12850	– Daybeacon 13					SG on pile.	
12855	– Daybeacon 15					SG on pile.	
12860	– Daybeacon 17					SG on pile.	
12865	– Daybeacon 18					TR on pile.	

Fish net buoys in Chesapeake Bay and tributary waters are not listed; however, they are shown on the nautical charts.
Fish net buoys are painted yellow and are maintained for the Corps of Engineers to mark boundaries of fishing areas
where fish nets and traps are permitted as prescribed by the Corps of Engineers.

(1) No.	(2) Name and location	(3) Position	(4) Characteristic	(5) Height	(6) Range	(7) Structure	(8) Remarks
			CHESAPEAKE BAY (Virginia) – Fifth District				
	MOBJACK BAY AND YORK RIVER ENTRANCE (Chart 12238)	N/W					
	Mobjack Bay						
	Browns Bay						
12870	– LIGHT 1	37 18.1 76 22.9	Fl G 4s	16	4	SG on slatted pile structure.	Light equipment removed when endangered by ice.
12875	– Entrance Daybeacon 2					TR on pile.	
12880	– LIGHT 3		Fl G 4s	12	4	SG on pile.	Light equipment removed from Dec. 1 to Mar. 15.
12885	– LIGHT 4		Fl R 4s	12	3	TR on pile.	
	Severn River						
12890	– JUNCTION LIGHT SR	37 20.2 76 23.7	Fl (2+1) R 6s	16	4	JR on pile.	
12895	– LIGHT 1		Fl G 4s	16	4	SG on pile.	Light equipment removed when endangered by ice.
12897	– Daybeacon 2					TR on pile.	
12900	– LIGHT 3		Fl G 4s	16	4	SG on slatted pile structure.	
12905	– Daybeacon 5					SG on pile.	
	Southwest Branch						
12910	– Daybeacon 1					SG on pile.	
12915	– Daybeacon 2					TR on pile.	
12920	– Daybeacon 3					SG on pile.	
12925	– Daybeacon 4					TR on pile.	
12930	Rowes Creek Daybeacon 2					TR on pile.	Private aid.
12935	Rowes Creek Daybeacon 3					SG on pile.	Private aid.
12940	Rowes Creek Range Marker					KRW on pile.	Private aid.
	Ware River						
12945	– Daybeacon 2					TR on pile.	
12950	– LIGHT 3		Fl G 2.5s	15	4	SG on pile.	
12955	– Daybeacon 5					SG on pile.	
12960	– LIGHT 6		Q R	16	4	TR on dolphin.	
12965	– Daybeacon 7					SG on pile.	
12970	– LIGHT 9		Fl G 6s	15	4	SG on pile.	
12975	– Daybeacon 10					TR on pile.	
12980	– Daybeacon 11					SG on pile.	
12985	– Daybeacon 12					TR on pile.	

Fish net buoys in Chesapeake Bay and tributary waters are not listed; however, they are shown on the nautical charts.
Fish net buoys are painted yellow and are maintained for the Corps of Engineers to mark boundaries of fishing areas
where fish nets and traps are permitted as prescribed by the Corps of Engineers.

(1) No.	(2) Name and location	(3) Position	(4) Characteristic	(5) Height	(6) Range	(7) Structure	(8) Remarks

N/W

MOBJACK BAY AND YORK RIVER ENTRANCE
(Chart 12238)

Mobjack Bay

North River

No.	Name and location	Position	Characteristic	Height	Range	Structure	Remarks
12990	– ENTRANCE LIGHT 1	37 22.1 76 23.6	Fl G 4s	16	5	SG on dolphin.	
12995	BLACKWATER CREEK LIGHT 2		Fl R 2.5s		3	TR on pile.	
12996	Blackwater Creek Daybeacon 3					SG on pile.	
13000	– Daybeacon 3					SG on pile.	
13005	Green Mansion Cove Junction Daybeacon					JR on pile.	
13010	– LIGHT 5		Fl G 4s	16	3	SG on slatted pile structure.	
13015	– LIGHT 6		Fl R 4s	16	3	TR on slatted pile structure.	
13020	– Daybeacon 7					SG on pile.	
13025	Green Mansion Cove Daybeacon 2					TR on pile.	Private aid.
13030	Green Mansion Cove Daybeacon 3					SG on pile.	Private aid.

Horn Harbor

No.	Name and location	Position	Characteristic	Height	Range	Structure	Remarks
13035	– ENTRANCE LIGHT HH	37 20.2 76 15.1	Mo (A) W	19	5	MR on pile.	
13040	– LIGHT 2		Fl R 4s	15	3	TR on house on cylindrical base.	
13045	– LIGHT 3		Fl G 2.5s	15	3	SG on pile.	
13052	– Daybeacon 4					TR on pile.	
13053	– LIGHT 5		Q G	14	3	SG on pile.	
13054	– Daybeacon 6					TR on pile.	
13055	– LIGHT 7		Fl G 4s	14	3	SG on pile.	
13060	– Daybeacon 7A					SG on pile.	
13065	– LIGHT 8		Fl R 6s	16	4	TR on dolphin.	
13070	– LIGHT 10		Fl R 2.5s	15	. 3	TR on dolphin.	
13075	– LIGHT 12		Fl R 4s	15	3	TR on pile.	
13080	– Daybeacon 14					TR on pile.	
13085	– LIGHT 16		Fl R 6s	15	4	TR on pile.	
13090	– Daybeacon 17					SG on pile.	
13095	– Daybeacon 18					TR on pile.	

Fish net buoys in Chesapeake Bay and tributary waters are not listed; however, they are shown on the nautical charts.
Fish net buoys are painted yellow and are maintained for the Corps of Engineers to mark boundaries of fishing areas
where fish nets and traps are permitted as prescribed by the Corps of Engineers.

(1) No.	(2) Name and location	(3) Position	(4) Characteristic	(5) Height	(6) Range	(7) Structure	(8) Remarks

N/W

MOBJACK BAY AND YORK RIVER ENTRANCE
(Chart 12238)

Horn Harbor

13100	– Daybeacon 19					SG on pile.	

Winter Harbor

13105	– CHANNEL LIGHT 1		Fl G 2.5s	15	3	SG on pile.	
13110	– Channel Daybeacon 1A					SG on pile.	
13115	– CHANNEL LIGHT 3		Fl G 4s	15	4	SG on pile.	
13120	– Channel Daybeacon 4					TR on pile.	
13125	– Channel Daybeacon 4A					TR on pile.	
13130	– Channel Daybeacon 6					TR on pile.	
13135	– Channel Daybeacon 8					TR on pile.	
13140	– Channel Daybeacon 10					TR on pile.	
13145	– Channel Daybeacon 12					TR on pile.	
13150	– Channel Daybeacon 14					TR on pile.	
13155	– Channel Daybeacon 16					TR on pile.	

RAPPAHANNOCK RIVER ENTRANCE (Chart 12235)

Milford Haven

13160	– East Lighted Buoy 1		Fl G 4s		4	Green.	Remove from station when endangered by ice.
13165	– EAST LIGHT 3	37 27.2 76 12.7	Fl G 2.5s	15	4	SG on pile.	Light equipment removed when endangered by ice.
13170	– EAST LIGHT 5		Fl G 4s	15	5	SG on pile.	Light equipment removed when endangered by ice.
13175	– EAST LIGHT 6		Fl R 4s	15	4	TR on pile.	
13180	– EAST LIGHT 8		Fl R 2.5s	15	4	TR on pile.	
13185	– EAST LIGHT 9		Fl G 4s	12	4	SG on pile.	Light equipment removed when endangered by ice.
13190	– EAST LIGHT 11		Fl G 2.5s	12	4	SG on pile.	
13195	– East Daybeacon 12					TR on pile.	
13200	– EAST LIGHT 14		Q R	15	4	TR on pile.	
13202	– East Daybeacon 16					TR on pile.	

Stutts Creek

13205	– Entrance Daybeacon 1					SG on pile.	
13210	– Entrance Daybeacon 2					TR on pile.	
13215	– Daybeacon 3					SG on pile.	

Fish net buoys in Chesapeake Bay and tributary waters are not listed; however, they are shown on the nautical charts.
Fish net buoys are painted yellow and are maintained for the Corps of Engineers to mark boundaries of fishing areas
where fish nets and traps are permitted as prescribed by the Corps of Engineers.

(1) No.	(2) Name and location	(3) Position	(4) Characteristic	(5) Height	(6) Range	(7) Structure	(8) Remarks

CHESAPEAKE BAY (Maryland) – Fifth District

N/W

APPROACHES TO BALTIMORE HARBOR (Chart 12278)

Patapsco River

Spring Garden Channel

19450	– Daybeacon 2	39 15.6 76 37.1				TR on pile.	
19455	– Daybeacon 4					TR on pile.	
19460	– Daybeacon 6					TR on pile.	

Port Covington Basin

19465	– Buoy 1					Green can.	
19470	PORT COVINGTON MOORING PLATFORM LIGHT	39 15.5 76 36.3	F R		12	On 20′ X 30′ mooring platform.	Private aid.
19475	– Buoy 3					Green can.	
19480	Elevator Channel Buoy 2					Red nun.	
19485	Elevator Channel Buoy 4					Red nun.	

Northwest Harbor

19489	– Lighted Buoy 2NH 75 feet outside channel limit.		Q R		4	Red.	Replaced by nun when endangered by ice.
19495	– Lighted Buoy 3 75 feet outside channel limit.		Q G		3	Green.	Replaced by can when endangered by ice.
19496	– Lighted Buoy 5		Fl G 4ˢ		4	Green.	
19498	– Lighted Buoy 7		Q G		4	Green.	
19500	Navy Reserve Pier Buoy					Orange sphere.	Maintained by U.S. Navy.
19505	HUMBLE OIL COMPANY OBSTRUCTION LIGHT	39 16.5 76 34.5	F W		12	On dolphin.	Private aid.
19510	– Junction Lighted Buoy NH		Fl (2+1) R 6ˢ		4	Red and green bands.	

CHESAPEAKE BAY (Virginia) – Fifth District

CHESAPEAKE BAY ENTRANCE (Chart 12221)

North Channel

19515	– Entrance Buoy 2	37 01.3 75 54.1				Red nun.	
19520	– Buoy 4					Red nun.	
19525	– Buoy 6					Red nun.	
19530	– Buoy 8					Red nun.	
19535	– Buoy 10					Red nun.	
19540	– Buoy 11					Green can.	

Fish net buoys in Chesapeake Bay and tributary waters are not listed; however, they are shown on the nautical charts.
Fish net buoys are painted yellow and are maintained for the Corps of Engineers to mark boundaries of fishing areas
where fish nets and traps are permitted as prescribed by the Corps of Engineers.

CHESAPEAKE BAY (Virginia) – Fifth District

CHESAPEAKE BAY ENTRANCE (Chart 12221)

N/W

North Channel

19545	**North Channel Bridge** **Fog Signals**	37 05.3 75 59.2					HORN: 1 blast ev 20s (2s bl). Continuous. Private aid.

CAPE CHARLES TO WOLF TRAP (Chart 12224)

Beach Channel

19550	– Buoy 13					Green can.	
19555	Latimer Shoal Junction Buoy					Red and black bands; nun.	
19560	– Buoy 16					Red nun.	
19565 6205	VIRGINIA INSIDE PASSAGE LIGHT 270		Fl R 2.5s	18	4	TR on pile.	Light equipment removed from Dec. 1 to Mar. 15.

Kiptopeke Beach

19570	– BREAKWATER SOUTH OBSTRUCTION LIGHT		Fl W 5s	14		Black skeleton tower.	Private aid.
19575	– BREAKWATER NORTH OBSTRUCTION LIGHT		Fl W 5s	14		Black skeleton tower.	Private aid.
19580	CHERRYSTONE CHANNEL LIGHT 2	37 12.1 76 01.6	Fl R 2.5s	18	4	TR on pile.	Higher intensity toward North Channel and up Cherrystone Channel. Light equipment removed from Dec. 1 to Mar. 15.
19585 6790	OLD PLANTATION FLATS LIGHT	37 13.8 76 02.8	Fl W 4s	39	7	NB on pile.	Higher intensity beam toward 200°.
19595	CAPE CHARLES CITY RANGE A FRONT LIGHT	37 14.8 76 01.5	Q W	19		KRW on slatted pile structure.	Visible on rangeline only.
19600	CAPE CHARLES CITY RANGE A REAR LIGHT 400 yards, 054° from front light.		Iso W 6s	33		KRW on skeleton tower.	Visible on rangeline only.

Cape Charles City

19605	– Lighted Buoy 1		Fl G 4s		4	Green.	
19610	– Lighted Buoy 2		Q R		3	Red.	
19615	– RANGE B FRONT LIGHT 8	37 15.8 76 01.7	Q R	16		KRW and TR on upstream side of pile.	Visible all around; higher intensity on rangeline. Ra ref.
19620	– RANGE B REAR LIGHT 520 yards, 020.3° from front light.		Iso R 6s	41		KRW on white skeleton tower.	
19625	– Lighted Buoy 4		Fl R 4s		3	Red.	
19630	– APPROACH LIGHT C	37 15.4 76 01.9	Fl W 4s	30	5	NB on skeleton tower on caisson.	
19635	– Buoy 5					Green can.	

Fish net buoys in Chesapeake Bay and tributary waters are not listed; however, they are shown on the nautical charts.
Fish net buoys are painted yellow and are maintained for the Corps of Engineers to mark boundaries of fishing areas
where fish nets and traps are permitted as prescribed by the Corps of Engineers.

(1) No.	(2) Name and location	(3) Position	(4) Characteristic	(5) Height	(6) Range	(7) Structure	(8) Remarks

CHESAPEAKE BAY (Virginia) – Fifth District

CAPE CHARLES TO WOLF TRAP (Chart 12224) N/W

Cape Charles City

19640	– Buoy 6					Red nun.	
19645	– LIGHT 7		Fl G 4s	14	4	SG on pile.	Light equipment removed from Dec. 1 to Mar. 15.
19650	– JETTY LIGHT		Q W	18	5	NR on red skeleton tower.	
19655	– LIGHT 11		Fl G 2.5s	15	3	SG on dolphin.	Light equipment removed from Dec. 1 to Mar. 15.
19660	**Cape Charles Railroad Terminal Fog Signal**	37 15.9 76 01.3				On pile.	SIREN: 1 blast ev 25s (5s bl). Operates continuously. Private aid.
19665	Mud Creek Channel Daybeacon 1 10 feet outside channel limit.					SG on pile.	
19670	Mud Creek Channel Daybeacon 2 10 feet outside channel limit.					TR on pile.	

Kings Creek

19675	– LIGHT 1		Fl G 4s	16	4	SG on dolphin.	Light equipment removed when endangered by ice.
19680	– LIGHT 3		Fl G 4s	15	3	SG on dolphin.	Light equipment removed from Dec. 1 to Mar. 15.
19685	– JUNTION LIGHT KC	37 16.9 76 01.4	Fl (2+1) G 6s	14	3	JG on pile.	
19690	– LIGHT 6		Fl R 2.5s	15	4	TR on pile.	Light equipment removed when endangered by ice.
19695	– Daybeacon 7					SG on pile.	
19700	– LIGHT 8		Fl R 4s	15	4	TR on pile.	Light equipment removed from Dec. 1 to Mar. 15.
19705	– LIGHT 9		Fl G 4s	15	3	SG on pile.	
19710	– Daybeacon 10					TR on pile.	
19715	– LIGHT 11		Fl G 4s	15	4	SG on pile.	
19720	– Daybeacon 12					TR on pile.	
19725	– LIGHT 15		Fl G 4s	15	4	SG on pile.	
19730	– Daybeacon 14					TR on pile.	

WOLF TRAP TO PUNGOTEAGUE CREEK (Chart 12226)

Mattawoman Creek

19735	– LIGHT 1	37 23.4 75 59.7	Fl W 4s	15	5	SG on pile.	Light equipment removed from Dec. 1 to Mar. 15.

Fish net buoys in Chesapeake Bay and tributary waters are not listed; however, they are shown on the nautical charts.
Fish net buoys are painted yellow and are maintained for the Corps of Engineers to mark boundaries of fishing areas
where fish nets and traps are permitted as prescribed by the Corps of Engineers.

	CHESAPEAKE BAY (Virginia) – Fifth District						
	WOLF TRAP TO PUNGOTEAGUE CREEK (Chart 12226)	N/W					
	Mattawoman Creek						
19740	– LIGHT 2		Fl R 4ˢ	15	3	TR on pile.	Light equipment removed from Dec. 1 to Mar. 15.
19745	– LIGHT 3		Fl G	10	4	SG on pile.	Light equipment removed from Dec. 1 to Mar. 15.
19750	– Daybeacon 5					SG on pile.	
19755	– LIGHT 6		Fl R 4ˢ	10	3	TR on pile.	Light equipment removed from Dec. 1 to Mar. 15.
	Hungar Creek						
19760	– Daybeacon 2	37 24.4 75 58.5				TR on pile.	
19765	– Daybeacon 3					SG on pile.	
19770	– Daybeacon 5					SG on pile.	
19775	– Daybeacon 7					SG on pile.	
19780	– Daybeacon 9					SG on pile.	
	Nassawadox Creek						
19785	– LIGHT 2	37 27.9 75 58.4	Fl R 2.5ˢ	15	4	TR on pile.	Light equipment removed from Dec. 1 to Mar. 15.
19790	– Daybeacon 3					SG on pile.	
19793	– Daybeacon 5	37 28.2 75 57.9				SG on pile.	
19795	– Daybeacon 6					TR on pile.	
19800	– Daybeacon 7					SG on pile.	
19805	– Buoy 8					Red nun.	Removed from station Dec. 1 to Mar. 15.
19810	– Daybeacon 10					TR on pile.	
19815	– Daybeacon 12					TR on pile.	
19820	– Daybeacon 14					TR on pile.	
19825	– Daybeacon 15					SG on pile.	
19830	– Daybeacon 16					TR on pile.	
	Occohannock Creek						
19835	– ENTRANCE LIGHT 1	37 32.5 75 57.8	Fl G 4ˢ	15	4	SG on pile.	Light equipment removed from Dec. 1 to Mar. 15.
19840	– LIGHT 3		Fl G 4ˢ	15	3	SG on pile.	Light equipment removed from Dec. 1 to Mar. 15.
19845	– Daybeacon 5					SG on pile.	
19850	– Daybeacon 6					TR on pile.	

Fish net buoys in Chesapeake Bay and tributary waters are not listed; however, they are shown on the nautical charts. Fish net buoys are painted yellow and are maintained for the Corps of Engineers to mark boundaries of fishing areas where fish nets and traps are permitted as prescribed by the Corps of Engineers.

PART 2 - SECTION B

COAST PILOT 3

Atlantic Coast

covering

CHESAPEAKE BAY ENTRANCE and approaches

for

general information refer to PART 1, SECTION B

contents found on page vii

United States Coast Pilot

3

Atlantic Coast: Sandy Hook to Cape Henry

U.S. DEPARTMENT OF COMMERCE
Barbara Hackman Franklin, Secretary

National Oceanic and Atmospheric Administration (NOAA)
Dr. John A. Knauss, Under Secretary of Commerce for Oceans
and Atmosphere, and Administrator, NOAA

National Ocean Service
W. Stanley Wilson, Assistant Administrator for Ocean Services
and Coastal Zone Management

Washington, DC:
For sale by the National Ocean Service and its sales agents.

LIMITS OF UNITED STATES COAST PILOTS

Atlantic Coast

1 Eastport to Cape Cod
2 Cape Cod to Sandy Hook
3 Sandy Hook to Cape Henry
4 Cape Henry to Key West
5 Gulf of Mexico, Puerto Rico, and Virgin Islands

Pacific Coast

7 California, Oregon, Washington, and Hawaii
8 Alaska - - Dixon Entrance to Cape Spencer
9 Alaska - - Cape Spencer to Beaufort Sea

Great Lakes

6 The Lakes and their Connecting Waterways

Preface

The United States Coast Pilot is published by the National Ocean Service (NOS), Charting and Geodetic Services (C&GS), National Oceanic and Atmospheric Administration (NOAA), pursuant to the Act of 6 August 1947 (33 U.S.C. 883a and b), and the Act of 22 October 1968 (44 U.S.C. 1310).

The Coast Pilot supplements the navigational information shown on the nautical charts. The sources for updating the Coast Pilot include but are not limited to field inspections conducted by NOAA, information published in Notices to Mariners, reports from NOAA Hydrographic vessels and field parties, information from other Government agencies, State and local governments, maritime and pilotage associations, port authorities, and mariners.

This volume of Coast Pilot 3, Atlantic Coast, Sandy Hook to Cape Henry, cancels the 1991 (28th) Edition.

Notice.–Amendments are issued to this publication through U.S. Coast Guard Local Notices to Mariners. A subscription to the Local Notice to Mariners is available upon application to the appropriate Coast Guard District Commander (Aids to Navigation Branch). Consult appendix for address. All amendments are also issued in Defense Mapping Agency Notices to Mariners.

Mariners and others are urged to report promptly to the National Ocean Service errors, omissions, or any conditions found to differ from or to be additional to those published in the Coast Pilot or shown on the charts in order that they may be fully investigated and proper corrections made. A Coast Pilot Report form is included in the back of this book and a Marine Information Report form is published in the Defense Mapping Agency Hydrographic/Topographic Center Notice to Mariners for your convenience. These reports and/or suggestions for increasing the usefulness of the Coast Pilot should be sent to

Director,
Coast and Geodetic Survey (N/CG2211),
National Ocean Service, NOAA,
Rockville, MD 20852-3806.

COAST PILOT 3 – GRAPHIC CHAPTER INDEX

IV

Contents

(184) (b) The regulations. This anchorage is reserved for the exclusive use of naval vessels and except in cases of emergency, no other vessel shall anchor therein without permission from the local naval authorities, obtained through the Captain of the Port, Norfolk, Virginia. Movement of vessels through the anchorage will not be restricted.

(185) §110.168 Hampton Roads, Virginia, and adjacent waters.

(186) (a) Anchorage Grounds–(1) Cape Henry Anchorage. Anchorage A (Naval Anchorage). The waters bounded by the shoreline and a line connecting the following points:

(187) 36°55'33.0"N., 76°02'47.0"W.
(188) 36°57'02.8"N., 76°03'02.6"W.
(189) 36°56'45.0"N., 76°01'30.0"W.
(190) 36°55'54.0"N., 76°01'37.0"W.

(191) (2) Chesapeake Bay, Thimble Shoals Channel Anchorages–(i) Anchorage B (Naval Anchorage). The waters bounded by a line connecting the following points:

(192) 36°57'58.0"N., 76°06'07.0"W.
(193) 36°57'11.0"N., 76°03'02.1"W.
(194) 36°55'48.8"N., 76°03'14.0"W.
(195) 36°56'31.8"N., 76°06'07.0"W.
(196) 36°57'04.0"N., 76°06'07.0"W.
(197) 36°57'08.5"N., 76°06'24.5"W.

(198) (ii) Anchorage C (Naval Anchorage). The waters bounded by a line connecting the following points:

(199) 36°58'54.8"N., 76°09'41.5"W.
(200) 36°58'18.8"N., 76°07'18.0"W.
(201) 36°57'27.0"N., 76°07'37.5"W.
(202) 36°58'04.0"N., 76°10'00.0"W.

(203) (iii) Anchorage D (Naval Anchorage). The waters bounded by the shoreline and a line connecting the following points:

(204) 36°55'49.0"N., 76°10'32.8"W.
(205) 36°58'04.0"N., 76°10'02.1"W.
(206) 36°57'31.2"N., 76°07'54.8"W.
(207) 36°55'24.1"N., 76°08'28.8"W.

(208) (iv) Anchorage E (Commercial Explosive Anchorage). The waters bounded by a line connecting the following points:

(209) 36°59'58.7"N., 76°13'47.0"W.
(210) 36°59'08.2"N., 76°10'33.8"W.
(211) 36°58'13.0"N., 76°10'51.8"W.
(212) 36°59'02.0"N., 76°14'10.2"W.

(213) (A) Explosive Handling Berth E-1: (Explosives Anchorage Berth): The waters bounded by the arc of a circle with a radius of 500 yards and with the center located at:
(214) 36°59'05.0"N., 76°11'23.0"W.

(215) (3) Hampton Roads Anchorages–(i) Anchorage F, Hampton Bar. The waters bounded by a line connecting the following points:

(216) 36°59'51.6"N., 76°19'12.0"W.
(217) 36°59'25.2"N., 76°18'48.5"W.
(218) 36°58'49.1"N., 76°19'33.8"W.
(219) 36°59'25.0"N., 76°20'07.0"W.

(220) (A) Anchorage Berth F-1. The waters bounded by the arc of a circle with a radius of 400 yards and with the center located at:
(221) 36°59'16.7"N., 76°19'39.0"W.

(222) (B) Anchorage Berth F-2. The waters bounded by the arc of a circle with a radius of 400 yards and with the center located at:
(223) 36°59'31.8"N., 76°19'16.0"W.

(224) (ii) Anchorage G, Hampton Flats (Naval Explosives Anchorage). The waters bounded by a line connecting the following points:
(225) 36°59'25.0"N., 76°20'07.0"W.
(226) 36°58'49.1"N., 76°19'33.8"W.

(227) 36°57'41.4"N., 76°21'07.7"W.
(228) 36°57'34.6"N., 76°21'26.7"W.
(229) 36°57'31.1"N., 76°22'01.9"W.
(230) 36°57'07.0"N., 76°22'03.0"W.
(231) 36°58'54.8"N., 76°21'42.6"W.

(232) (A) Explosives Handling Berth G-1. The waters bounded by the arc of a circle with a radius of 500 yards and with the center located at:
(233) 36°57'50.0"N., 76°21'37.0"W.

(234) (B) Explosives Handling Berth G-2. The waters bounded by the arc of a circle with a radius of 500 yards and with the center located at:
(235) 36°58'14.0"N., 76°21'01.5"W.

(236) (C) Explosives Handling Berth G-3. The waters bounded by the arc of a circle with a radius of 500 yards and with the center located at:
(237) 36°58'34.5"N., 76°20'31.0"W.

(238) (D) Explosives Handling Berth G-4. The waters bounded by the arc of a circle with a radius of 500 yards and with the center located at:
(239) 36°58'53.4"N., 76°20'05.0"W.

(240) (iii) Anchorage H, Newport New Bar. The waters bounded by a line connecting the following points:
(241) 36°58'07.0"N., 76°22'03.0"W.
(242) 36°57'31.1"N., 76°22'01.9"W.
(243) 36°57'18.0"N., 76°24'11.2"W.
(244) 36°57'38.3"N., 76°24'20.0"W.
(245) 36°57'51.8"N., 76°22'31.0"W.

(246) (4) James River Anchorage–(i) Anchorage I, Newport News. The waters bounded by a line connecting the following points:
(247) 36°57'06.7"N., 76°24'44.3"W.
(248) 36°56'22.6"N., 76°24'28.0"W.
(249) 36°56'03.0"N., 76°24'37.0"W.
(250) 36°57'53.7"N., 76°26'41.5"W.
(251) 36°58'23.0"N., 76°27'11.0"W.
(252) 36°58'48.5"N., 76°27'11.0"W.
(253) 36°58'35.4"N., 76°26'38.4"W.
(254) 36°57'51.7"N., 76°26'02.8"W.
(255) 36°57'30.6"N., 76°25'34.5"W.

(256) (A) Anchorage Berth I-1. The waters bounded by the arc of a circle with a radius of 400 yards and with the center located at:
(257) 36°57'08.5"N., 76°25'21.6"W.

(258) (B) Anchorage Berth I-2. The waters bounded by the arc of a circle with a radius of 400 yards and with the center located at:
(259) 36°57'22.4"N., 76°25'47.7"W.

(260) (ii) Anchorage J, Newport News Middle Ground. The waters bounded by a line connecting the following points:
(261) 36°57'21.0"N., 76°22'22.1"W.
(262) 36°56'46.5"N., 76°22'39.3"W.
(263) 36°56'25.3"N., 76°23'48.0"W.
(264) 36°57'10.2"N., 76°24'09.9"W.

(265) (iii) Anchorage K, Newport News Middle Ground. The waters bounded by a line connecting the following points:
(266) 36°57'55.8"N., 76°20'20.1"W.
(267) 36°57'07.9"N., 76°20'32.2"W.
(268) 36°56'48.8"N., 76°20'32.2"W.
(269) 36°55'59.9"N., 76°22'11.7"W.
(270) 36°55'59.9"N., 76°24'00.0"W.
(271) 36°56'25.3"N., 76°23'48.0"W.
(272) 36°56'46.5"N., 76°22'39.3"W.
(273) 36°57'21.0"N., 76°22'22.1"W.
(274) 36°57'28.1"N., 76°21'11.7"W.

Subpart B-Regulated Navigation Areas

(1113)   §165.10 Regulated navigation area.

(1114)   A regulated navigation area is a water area within a defined boundary for which regulations for vessels navigating within the area have been established under this part.

(1115)   §165.11 Vessel operating requirements (regulations).

(1116)   Each District Commander may control vessel traffic in an area which is determined to have hazardous conditions, by issuing regulations—

(1117)   (a) Specifying times of vessel entry, movement, or departure to, from, within, or through ports, harbors, or other waters;

(1118)   (b) Establishing vessel size, speed, draft limitations, and operating conditions; and

(1119)   (c) Restricting vessel operation, in a hazardous area or under hazardous conditions, to vessels which have particular operating characteristics or capabilities which are considered necessary for safe operation under the circumstances.

(1120)   §165.13 General regulations.

(1121)   (a) The master of a vessel in a regulated navigation area shall operate the vessel in accordance with the regulations contained in Subpart F.

(1122)   (b) No person may cause or authorize the operation of a vessel in a regulated navigation area contrary to the regulations in this Part.

Subpart C-Safety Zones

(1123)   §165.20 Safety zones.

(1124)   A Safety Zone is a water area, shore area, or water and shore area to which, for safety or environmental purposes, access is limited to authorized persons, vehicles, or vessels. It may be stationary and described by fixed limits or it may be described as a zone around a vessel in motion.

(1125)   §165.23 General regulations.

(1126)   Unless otherwise provided in this part—

(1127)   (a) No person may enter a safety zone unless authorized by the COTP or the District Commander;

(1128)   (b) No person may bring or cause to be brought into a safety zone any vehicle, vessel, or object unless authorized by the COTP or the District Commander;

(1129)   (c) No person may remain in a safety zone or allow any vehicle, vessel, or object to remain in a safety zone unless authorized by the COTP or the District Commander; and

(1130)   (d) Each person in a safety zone who has notice of a lawful order or direction shall obey the order or direction of the COTP or District Commander issued to carry out the purposes of this subpart.

Subpart D-Security Zones

(1131)   §165.30 Security zones.

(1132)   (a) A security zone is an area of land, water, or land and water which is so designated by the Captain of the Port or District Commander for such time as is necessary to prevent damage or injury to any vessel or waterfront facility, to safeguard ports, harbors, territories, or waters of the United States or to secure the observance of the rights and obligations of the United States.

(1133)   (b) The purpose of a security zone is to safeguard from destruction, loss, or injury from sabotage or other subversive acts, accidents, or other causes of a similar nature—

(1134)   (1) Vessels,

(1135)   (2) Harbors,

(1136)   (3) Ports and

(1137)   (4) Waterfront facilities— in the United States and all territory and water, continental or insular, that is subject to the jurisdiction of the United States.

(1138)   §165.33 General regulations.

(1139)   Unless otherwise provided in the special regulations in Subpart F of this part—

(1140)   (a) No person or vessel may enter or remain in a security zone without the permission of the Captain of the Port;

(1141)   (b) Each person and vessel in a security zone shall obey any direction or order of the Captain of the Port;

(1142)   (c) The Captain of the Port may take possession and control of any vessel in the security zone;

(1143)   (d) The Captain of the Port may remove any person, vessel, article, or thing from a security zone;

(1144)   (e) No person may board, or take or place any article or thing on board, any vessel in a security zone without the permission of the Captain of the Port; and

(1145)   (f) No person may take or place any article or thing upon any waterfront facility in a security zone without the permission of the Captain of the Port.

Subpart E-Restricted Waterfront Areas

(1146)   §165.40 Restricted Waterfront Areas.

(1147)   The Commandant, may direct the COTP to prevent access to waterfront facilities, and port and harbor areas, including vessels and harbor craft therein. This section may apply to persons who do not possess the credentials outlined in 33 CFR 125.09 when certain shipping activities are conducted that are outlined in 33 CFR 125.15.

Subpart F-Specific Regulated Navigation Areas and Limited Access Areas

(1148)   §165.501 Chesapeake Bay Entrance and Hampton Roads, Virginia and Adjacent Waters-Regulated Navigation Area.

(1149)   (a) Regulated Navigation Area. The waters enclosed by the shoreline and the following lines are a Regulated Navigation Area:

(1150)   (1) A line drawn across the entrance to Chesapeake Bay between Wise Point and Cape Charles Light, and then continuing to Cape Henry Light.

(1151)   (2) A line drawn across the Chesapeake Bay between Old Point Comfort Light and Cape Charles City Range "A" Rear Light.

(1152)   (3) A line drawn across the James River along the eastern side of the U.S. Route 17 highway bridge, between Newport News and Isle of Wight County, Virginia.

(1153)   (4) A line drawn across Chuckatuck Creek along the northern side of the north span of the U.S. Route 17 highway bridge, between Isle of Wight County and Suffolk, Virginia.

(1154)   (5) A line drawn across the Nansemond River along the northern side of the Mills Godwin (U.S. Route 17) Bridge, Suffolk, Virginia.

(1155)   (6) A line drawn across the mouth of Bennetts Creek, Suffolk, Virginia.

(1156)   (7) A line drawn across the Western Branch of the Elizabeth River along the eastern side of the West Norfolk Bridge, Portsmouth, Virginia.

(1157)   (8) A line drawn across the Southern Branch of the Elizabeth River along the northern side of the I-64 highway bridge, Chesapeake, Virginia.

(1158)   (9) A line drawn across the Eastern Branch of the Elizabeth River along the western side of the west span of the Campostella Bridge, Norfolk, Virginia.

(1159)   (10) A line drawn across the Lafayette River along the western side of the Hampton Boulevard Bridge, Norfolk, Virginia.

(1160) (11) A line drawn across Little Creek along the eastern side of the Ocean View Avenue (U.S. Route 60) Bridge, Norfolk, Virginia.

(1161) (12) A line drawn across Lynnhaven Inlet along the northern side of the Shore Drive (U.S. Route 60) Bridge, Virginia Beach, Virginia.

(1162) (b) Definitions. In this section:

(1163) (1) "CBBT" means the Chesapeake Bay Bridge Tunnel.

(1164) (2) "Thimble Shoal Channel" consists of the waters bounded by a line connecting Thimble Shoal Channel Lighted Bell Buoy 1TS, thence to Lighted Gong Buoy 17, thence to Lighted Buoy 19, thence to Lighted Buoy 21, thence to Lighted Buoy 22, thence to Lighted Buoy 18, thence to Lighted Buoy 2, thence to the beginning.

(1165) (3) "Thimble Shoal North Auxiliary Channel" consists of the waters in a rectangular area 450 feet wide adjacent to the north side of Thimble Shoal Channel, the southern boundary of which extends from Thimble Shoal Channel Lighted Buoy 2 to Lighted Buoy 18.

(1166) (4) "Thimble Shoal South Auxiliary Channel" consists of the waters in a rectangular area 450 feet wide adjacent to the south side of the Thimble Shoal Channel, the northern boundary of which extends from Thimble Shoal Channel Lighted Bell Buoy 1TS, thence to Lighted Gong Buoy 17 thence to Lighted Buoy 19, thence to Lighted Buoy 21.

(1167) (c) Applicability. This section applies to all vessels operating within the Regulated Navigation Area, including naval and public vessels, except vessels that are engaged in the following operations:

(1168) (1) Law Enforcement

(1169) (2) Servicing aids to navigation

(1170) (3) Surveying, maintenance, or improvement of waters in the Regulated Navigation Area.

(1171) (d) Regulations.-(1) Anchoring restrictions.

(1172) (i) No vessel over 65 feet long may anchor or moor in this Regulated Navigation Area outside an anchorage designated in §110.168 of this title, unless:

(1173) (A) The vessel has the permission of the Captain of the Port.

(1174) (B) The vessel is carrying explosives for use on river or harbor works or on other work under a permit issued by the District Engineer, Corps of Engineers, and the vessel is anchored in or near the vicinity of the work site. The District Engineer shall prescribe the quantities of explosives allowed on the vessel and the conditions under which the vessel may store or handle explosives. The vessel may not anchor unless a copy of the permit and instructions relating to the carriage and handling of explosives from the Corps of Engineers to the vessel or contractor are provided to the Captain of the Port before the vessel anchors.

(1175) (ii) A vessel may anchor in a channel with the permission of the Captain of the Port, if the vessel is authorized by the District Engineer to engage in recovery of sunken property, to lay or repair a legally established pipeline or cable, or to engage in dredging operations.

(1176) (iii) A vessel engaged in river and harbor improvement work under the supervision of the District Engineer may anchor in a channel, if the District Engineer notifies the Captain of the Port in advance of the start of the work.

(1177) (iv) Except as provided in paragraphs (d)(1)(ii) and (iii) of this section, a vessel may not anchor in a channel unless it is unable to proceed without endangering the safety of persons, property, or the environment.

(1178) (v) A vessel that is anchored in a channel because it is unable to proceed without endangering the safety of persons, property or the environment, shall:

(1179) (A) Not anchor, if possible, within a cable or pipeline area.

(1180) (B) Not obstruct or endanger the passage of any vessel.

(1181) (C) Anchor near the edge of the channel, if possible.

(1182) (D) Not interfere with the free navigation of any channel.

(1183) (E) Not obstruct the approach to any pier.

(1184) (F) Not obstruct aids to navigation or interfere with range lights.

(1185) (G) Move to a designated anchorage or get underway as soon as possible or when directed by the Captain of the Port.

(1186) (vi) A vessel may not anchor within the confines of Little Creek Harbor, Desert Cove, or Little Creek Cove without the permission of the Captain of the Port. The Captain of the Port shall consult with the Commander, Naval Amphibious Base Little Creek, before granting permission to anchor within this area.

(1187) (2) Secondary Towing Rig Requirements. (i) A vessel over 100 gross tons may not be towed in this Regulated Navigation Area unless it is equipped with a secondary towing rig, in addition to its primary towing rig, that:

(1188) (A) Is of sufficient strength for towing the vessel.

(1189) (B) Has a connecting device that can receive a shackle pin of at least two inches in diameter.

(1190) (C) Is fitted with a recovery pickup line led outboard of the vessel's hull.

(1191) (ii) A tow consisting of two or more vessels, each of which is less than 100 gross tons, that has a total gross tonnage that is over 100 gross tons, shall be equipped with a secondary towing rig between each vessel in tow, in addition to its primary towing rigs, while the tow is operating within this Regulated Navigation Area. The secondary towing rig must:

(1192) (A) Be of sufficient strength for towing the vessels.

(1193) (B) Have connecting devices that can receive a shackle pin of at least two inches in diameter.

(1194) (C) Be fitted with recovery pickup lines led outboard of the vessels' hulls.

(1195) (3) Anchoring Detail Requirements. A self-propelled vessel over 100 gross tons, which is equipped with an anchor or anchors (other than a tugboat equipped with bow fenderwork of a type of construction that prevents an anchor being rigged for quick release), that is underway within two nautical miles of the CBBT or the I-664 Bridge Tunnel shall station its personnel at locations on the vessel without delay in an emergency.

(1196) (4) Draft Limitations. A vessel drawing less than 25 feet may not enter the Thimble Shoal Channel, unless the vessel is crossing the channel. Channel crossings shall be made as perpendicular to the channel axis as possible.

(1197) (5) Traffic Directions. (i) Except when crossing the channel, a vessel in the Thimble Shoal North Auxiliary Channel shall proceed in a westbound direction.

(1198) (ii) Except when crossing the channel, a vessel in the Thimble Shoal South Auxiliary Channel shall proceed in an eastbound direction.

(1199) (6) Restrictions of Vessels With Impaired Maneuverability.-(i) Before entry. A vessel over 100 gross tons whose ability to maneuver is impaired by hazardous weather, defective steering equipment, defective main propulsion machinery, or other damage, may not enter the Regulated Navigation Area without the permission of the Captain of the Port, unless the vessel is attended by one or more tugboats with sufficient total power to ensure the vessel's safe passage through the Regulated Navigation Area.

(1200) (ii) After entry. The master of a vessel over 100 gross tons, which is underway in the Regulated Navigation Area, shall, as soon as possible, do the following, if the vessel's ability to maneuver becomes impaired for any reason:

(1201) (A) Report the impairment to the Captain of the Port.

(1202) (B) Unless the Captain of the Port waives this requirement, have one or more tugboats with sufficient total power to ensure the vessel's safe passage through the Regulated Navigation Area, attend the vessel.

(1203) (7) Requirements for Navigation Charts, Radars, and Pilots. No vessel over 100 gross tons may enter the Regulated Navigation Area, unless it has on board:

(1204) (i) Corrected charts of the Regulated Navigation Area.

(1205) (ii) An operative radar during periods of reduced visibility; or

(1206) (iii) A pilot or other person on board with previous experience navigating vessel on the waters of the Regulated Navigation Area.

(1207) (8) Emergency Procedures. (i) Except as provided in paragraphs (d)(8)(ii) and (iii) of this section, in an emergency any vessel may deviate from the regulations in this section to the extent necessary to avoid endangering the safety of persons, property, or the environment.

(1208) (ii) A vessel over 100 gross tons with an emergency that is located within two nautical miles of the CBBT or I-664 Bridge Tunnel (other than a self-propelled vessel that is capable of getting underway in 30 minutes, has sufficient power to avoid any bridge, tunnel island, or vessel, and whose maneuverability is not impaired by a steering equipment or main propulsion defect):

(1209) (A) Shall notify the Captain of the Port of its location and the nature of the emergency, as soon as possible.

(1210) (B) May not anchor outside an anchorage designated in §110.168 of this title, unless the vessel is unable to proceed to an anchorage without endangering the safety of persons, property, or the environment.

(1211) (C) Shall make arrangements for one or more vessels to attend the vessel, with sufficient power to keep the vessel in position.

(1212) (iii) If a vessel over 100 gross tons must anchor outside an anchorage because the vessel is unable to proceed without endangering the safety of persons, property, or the environment, the vessel shall:

(1213) (A) Not anchor, if possible, within a cable or pipeline area.

(1214) (B) Not obstruct or endanger the passage of any vessel.

(1215) (C) Not interfere with the free navigation of any channel.

(1216) (D) Not obstruct the approach to any pier.

(1217) (E) Not obstruct aids to navigation or interfere with range lights.

(1218) (F) Move to a designated anchorage or get underway as soon as possible or when directed by the Captain of the Port.

(1219) (9) Vessel Speed Limits on Little Creek. A vessel may not proceed at a speed over five knots between the Route 60 bridge and the mouth of Fishermans Cove (Northwest Branch of Little Creek).

(1220) (10) Vessel Speed Limits on the Southern Branch of the Elizabeth River. A vessel may not proceed at a speed over six knots between the junction of the Southern and Eastern Branches of the Elizabeth River and the Norfolk and Portsmouth Belt Line Railroad Bridge between Chesapeake and Portsmouth, Virginia.

(1221) (11) Restrictions on Vessel Operations During Aircraft Carrier and Other Large Naval Vessel Transits of the Elizabeth River. (i) Except for a vessel that is moored at a marina, wharf, or pier or that is anchored, no vessel may, without the permission of the Captain of the Port, come within or remain within 500 yards from a naval aircraft carrier or other large naval vessel, which is restricted in its ability to maneuver in the confined waters, while the aircraft carrier or large naval vessel is transiting the Elizabeth River between the Norfolk Naval Base, Norfolk, Virginia, and the Norfolk Naval Shipyard, Portsmouth, Virginia.

(1222) (ii) The permission required by paragraph (d)(11)(i) of this section may be obtained from a designated representative of the Captain of the Port, including the duty officer at the Coast Guard Marine Safety Office, Hampton Roads, or from the Coast Guard patrol commander.

(1223) (iii) The Captain of the Port issues a Broadcast Notice to Mariners to inform the marine community of scheduled vessel movements that are covered by paragraph (d)(11) of this section.

(1224) (iv) Notwithstanding paragraph (d)(11)(i) of this section, a vessel may not remain moored at the Elizabeth River Ferry dock at the foot of High Street in Portsmouth, Virginia, when the dock is within a safety zone for a naval aircraft carrier or other large naval vessel.

(1225) (12) Restrictions on Vessel Operations During Liquefied Petroleum Gas Carrier Movements on the Chesapeake Bay and Elizabeth River. (i) Except for a vessel that is moored at a marina, wharf, or pier or that is anchored, and which remains moored or at anchor, no vessel may, without the permission of the Captain of the Port, come within or remain within 250 feet from the port and starboard sides and 300 feet from the bow and stern of a vessel that is carrying liquefied petroleum gas in bulk as cargo, while the gas carrier transits between Thimble Shoal Lighted Buoy 3 and the Atlantic Energy Terminal on the Southern Branch of the Elizabeth River.

(1226) (ii) The permission required by paragraph (d)(12)(i) of this section may be obtained from a designated representative of the Captain of the Port, including the duty officer at the Coast Guard Marine Safety Office, Hampton Roads, or from the Coast Guard patrol commander.

(1227) (iii) A vessel that has carried liquefied petroleum gas in a tank is carrying the liquefied petroleum gas as cargo for the purposes of paragraph (d)(12)(i) of this section, unless the tank has been gas freed since liquefied petroleum gas was last carried as cargo.

(1228) (iv) The Captain of the Port issues a Broadcast Notice to Mariners to inform the marine community of scheduled vessel movements that are covered by paragraph (d)(12) of this section.

(1229) (v) Notwithstanding paragraph (d)(12)(i) of this section, a vessel may not remain moored at the Elizabeth River Ferry dock at the foot of High Street in Portsmouth, Virginia, when the dock is within a safety zone for a liquefied petroleum gas carrier.

(1230) (13) Restrictions on the Use of the Elizabeth River Ferry Dock at the Foot of High Street, Portsmouth, Virginia.

(1231) (i) No vessels, other than those being operated as ferries for the Tidewater Transportation District Commission, may embark or disembark passengers or otherwise moor at the Elizabeth River Ferry dock at the foot of High Street, Portsmouth, Virginia.

(1232) (ii) Any vessel being operated for the Tidewater Transportation District Commission may not moor at the dock longer than necessary to embark passengers awaiting area (prohibited). A rectangular area surrounding Piers 1 and 2, Naval Weapons Station, and extending upstream therefrom, beginning at a point on the shore line at latitude 37°15′25″ N., longitude 76°32′32″ W.; thence to latitude 37°15′42″ N., longitude 76°32′06″ W.; thence to latitude 37°15′27″ N., longitude 76°31′48″ W.; thence to latitude 37°15′05″ N., longitude 76°31′27″ W.; thence to a point on the shore line at latitude 37°14′51″ N., longitude 76°31′50″ W.; and thence along the shore line to the point of beginning.

(1623)   (2) Naval mine service-testing area (restrict ed). A rectangular area adjacent to the northeast boundary of the prohibited area described in subparagraph (1) of this paragraph, beginning at latitude 37°16′00″ N., longitude 76°32′29″ W.; thence to latitude 37°16′23″ N., longitude 76°32′00″ W.; thence to latitude 37°15′27″ N., longitude 76°30′54″ W.; thence to latitude 37°15′05″ N., longitude 76°31′27″ W.; thence to latitude 37°15′27″ N., longitude 76°31′48″ W.; thence to latitude 37°15′42″ N., longitude 76°32′06″ W.; thence to latitude 37°15′40″ N., longitude 76°32′09″ W.; and thence to the point of beginning.

(1624)   (3) Explosives-Handling Berth (Naval). A circular area of 600 yards radius with its center at latitude 37°13′56″ N., longitude 76°28′48″ W.

(1625)   (b) The regulations. (1) All persons and all vessels other than naval craft are forbidden to enter the prohibited area described in paragraph (a)(1) of this section.

(1626)   (2) Trawling, dragging, and net-fishing are prohibited, and no permanent obstructions may at any time be placed in the area described in paragraph (a) (2) of this section. Upon official notification, any vessel anchored in the area and any person in the area will be required to vacate the area during the actual mine-laying operation. Persons and vessels entering the area during mine-laying operations by aircraft must proceed directly through the area without delay, except in case of emergency. Naval authorities are required to publish advance notice of mine-laying and/or retrieving operations scheduled to be carried on in the area, and during such published periods of operation, fishing or other aquatic activities are forbidden in the area. No vessel will be denied passage through the area at any time during either mine-laying or retrieving operations.

(1627)   (3) The Explosives-Handling Berth (Naval) described in paragraph (a)(3) of this section is reserved for the exclusive use of naval vessels and except in cases of emergency no other vessel shall anchor therein without the permission of local naval authorities, obtained through the Captain of the Port, U.S. Coast Guard, Norfolk, Va. There shall be no restriction on the movement of vessels through the Explosive-Handling Berth.

(1628)   (4) Vessels shall not be anchored, nor shall persons in the water approach within 300 yards of the perimeter of the Explosives-Handling Berth when that berth is occupied by a vessel handling explosives.

(1629)   (5) The regulations of this section shall be enforced by the Commander, Naval Base, Norfolk, Virginia, and such agencies as he may designate.

(1630)   §334.270 York River adjacent to Cheatham Annex Depot, Naval Supply Center, Williamsburg, Virginia; restricted area. (a) The area. The waters of York River bounded as follows: Beginning at a point on shore at Cheatham Annex Depot at latitude 37°17′14″ N., longitude 76°35′38″ W.; thence to a point offshore at latitude 37°17′52″ N., longitude 76°35′20″ W.; thence approximately parallel to the shore to a point at latitude 37°17′23″ N., longitude 76°34′39″ W.; thence to the shore at latitude 37°16′58″ N., longitude 76°35′03″ W.; and thence along the shore at Cheatham Annex Depot to the point of beginning.

(1631)   (b) The regulations. (1) No loitering will be permitted within the area. Oystermen may work their own leaseholds or public bottom within the area, provided they obtain special permission from the Officer in Charge, Cheatham Annex Depot, Naval Supply Center, Williamsburg, Virginia.

(1632)   (2) The regulations in this section shall be enforced by the Officer in Charge, Cheatham Annex Depot, U.S. Naval Supply Center, Williamsburg, Virginia.

(1633)   §334.280 James River between the entrance to Skiffes Creek and Mulberry Point, Va.; Army training and small craft testing area. (a) The restricted area. Beginning on the shore at latitude 37°09′54″N., longitude 76°36′25″W.; thence westerly to latitude 37°09′50″N., longitude 76°37′45.5″W.; thence southerly to latitude 37°09′00″N., longitude 76°38′05″W.; thence southerly to latitude 37°08′22″N., longitude 76°37′55″W.; thence due east to the shore at latitude 37°08′22″N., longitude 76°37′22″W.; thence northerly along the shore to the point of beginning.

(1634)   (b) The regulations. (1) No vessels other than Department of the Army vessels, and no persons other than persons embarked in such vessels shall remain in or enter the restricted area except as provided in paragraph (b)(2) of this section.

(1635)   (2) Nothing in the regulations of this section shall prevent the harvesting and cultivation of oyster beds or the setting of fish traps within the restricted area under regulations of the Department of the Army, nor will the passage of fishing vessels to or from authorized traps be unreasonably interfered with or restricted.

(1636)   (3) Vessels anchored in the area shall be so anchored as not to obstruct the arc of visibility of Deepwater Shoals Light.

(1637)   (4) The Commanding General, Fort Eustis, Va., will, to the extent possible give public notice from time to time through local news media and the Coast Guard's Local Notice to Mariners of the schedule of intended Army use of the restricted area.

(1638)   (5) The continuation of the restricted area for more than 3 years after the date of its establishment shall be dependent upon the outcome of the consideration of a request for its continuance submitted to the District Engineer, U.S. Army Engineer District, Norfolk, Virginia, by the using agency at least 3 months prior to the expiration of the 3 years.

(1639)   (6) The regulations in this section shall be enforced by the Commanding General, Fort Eustis, Va., and such agencies as he may designate.

(1640)   §334.290 Elizabeth River, Southern Branch, Va., naval restricted areas. (a) The areas–(1) St. Helena Annex Area. Beginning at a point at St. Helena Annex of the Norfolk Naval Shipyard, on the eastern shore of Southern Branch of Elizabeth River, at latitude 36°49′43″, longitude 76°17′26.5″; thence in a southwesterly direction to a point on the eastern boundary of Norfolk Harbor 40-foot channel at latitude 36°49′42″, longitude 76°17′33″; thence in a southerly direction along the eastern boundary of Norfolk Harbor 40-foot channel to latitude 36°49′28″, longitude 76°17′27″; thence easterly to the shore at latitude 36°49′28″, longitude 76°17′22″; and thence, northerly along the shore to the point of beginning.

(1641)   (2) Norfolk Naval Shipyard Area. Beginning at a point on the shore at the northeast corner of the Norfolk Naval Shipyard, at latitude 36°49′43.5″, longitude 76°17′41.5″; thence due east approximately 100 feet to the western boundary of Elizabeth River channel; thence in a southerly direction along the western boundary of the channel to the point where it passes through the draw of the

Norfolk and Portsmouth Belt Line Railroad bridge, thence in a southwesterly direction along the northerly side of the bridge to the western shore of Southern Branch of Elizabeth River; and thence along the shore in a northerly direction to the point of beginning.

(1642)   (3) Southgate Terminal Area. Beginning at a point at the northeast corner of Southgate Terminal Annex of Norfolk Naval Shipyard, at latitude 36°48′23″, longitude 76°17′39″; thence east to latitude 36°48′23″, longitude 76°17′29″; thence southerly along the western boundary of Norfolk Harbor 35-foot channel to latitude 36°48′04″, longitude 76°17′33″; thence west to latitude 36°48′04″, longitude 76°17′41″; and thence along the shore in a northerly direction to the point of beginning.

(1643)   (b) The regulations. (1) No vessels other than Naval vessels and other vessels authorized to move to and from piers at the Norfolk Naval Shipyard and its two annexes described in paragraph (a) (1) and (3) of this section, and no person other than persons embarked in such vessels, shall enter the restricted areas.

(1644)   (2) This section shall be enforced by the Commander, Norfolk Naval Shipyard, Portsmouth, Va., and such agencies as he may designate.

(1645)   §334.300 Hampton Roads and Willoughby Bay, off Norfolk Naval Base; naval restricted area. (a) The area. (1) Beginning at a point on shore at the Destroyer Submarine Piers at latitude 36°56′00″N., longitude 76°19′30″W.; thence westerly to 36°55′59″N., 76°20′08.5″W.; thence northerly along the eastern limit of Norfolk Harbor Channel to 36°57′52″N., 76°20′00″W.; thence easterly to 36°57′52″N., 76°19′35″W.; thence to 36°57′47.7″N., 76°18′57″W.; thence southeasterly to 36°57′26″N., 76°18′42″W.; thence easterly to 36°57′26.2″N., 76°17′55.2″W.; thence southerly to 36°57′05″N., 76°17′52″W.; thence southeasterly to 36°56′56.2″N., 76°17′27″W.; thence northeasterly to 36°57′10″N., 76°16′29″W.; and thence to the shoreline at 36°57′18.8″N., 76°16′22″W.; at the Naval Air Station.

(1646)   (2) Beginning at a point on the Naval Station shore at latitude 36°56′37.5″N., longitude 76°19′44″W.; thence westerly and northerly along the breakwater to its extremity at latitude 36°56′41.5″N., longitude 76°19′54″W.; thence westerly to a point on the eastern limit of Norfolk Harbor Channel at latitude 36°56′41.5″N., longitude 76°20′05.5″W.; thence northerly along the eastern limit of Norfolk Harbor Channel to latitude 36°57′52″N., longitude 76°20′00″W.; thence easterly to latitude 36°57′52″N., longitude 76°19′35″W.; thence to latitude 36°57′47.7″N., longitude 76°18′57″W.; thence southeasterly to latitude 36°57′26″N., longitude 76°18′42″W.; thence easterly to latitude 36°57′26.2″N., longitude 76°17′55.2″W.; thence southerly to latitude 36°57′05″N.; longitude 76°17′52″W.; thence southeasterly to latitude 36°56′56.2″N.; longitude 76°17′27″W.; thence northeasterly to latitude 36°57′10″N., longitude 76°16′29″W.; and thence to the shoreline at latitude 36°57′18.8″N., longitude 76°16′22″W.; at the Naval Air Station.

(1647)   (b) The regulations. (1) No vessels other than Naval vessels and other vessels authorized to move to and from piers at the Norfolk Naval Base, and no person other than persons embarked in such vessels, shall enter the restricted areas.

(1648)   (2) This section shall be enforced by the Commander, Naval Base, Norfolk, Virginia, and such agencies as he/she may designate.

(1649)   §334.310 Chesapeake Bay, Lynnhaven Roads; Navy amphibious training area. (a) The restricted area. Beginning at latitude 36°55′47″, longitude 76°11′04.5″; thence to latitude 36°59′04″, longitude 76°10′11″; thence to latitude

36°58′28.5″, longitude 76°07′54″; thence to latitude 36°55′27.5″, longitude 76°08′42″; thence westerly along the shore and across the mouth of Little Creek to the point of beginning.

(1650)   (b) The regulations. (1) No fishpound stakes or structures shall be allowed in the restricted area.

(1651)   (2) No vessel shall approach within 300 yards of any naval vessel or within 600 yards of any vessel displaying the red "baker" burgee.

(1652)   (3) This section shall be enforced by the Commandant, Fifth Naval District, and such agencies as he may designate.

(1653)   §334.320 Chesapeake Bay entrance; naval restricted area. (a) The area. Beginning at a point on the south shore of Chesapeake Bay at longitude 76°03′06″; thence to latitude 37°01′18″, longitude 76°02′06″; thence to latitude 37°00′18″, longitude 75°55′54″; thence to latitude 36°58′00″, longitude 75°48′24″; thence to latitude 36°51′48″, longitude 75°51′00″; thence to the shore at longitude 75°58′48″, and thence northwesterly and southwesterly along the shore at Cape Henry to the point of beginning.

(1654)   (b) The regulations. (1) Anchoring, trawling, crabbing, fishing, and dragging in the area are prohibited, and no object attached to a vessel or otherwise shall be placed on or near the bottom.

(1655)   (2) This section shall be enforced by the Commandant, Fifth Naval District, Norfolk, Va.

(1656)   §334.330 Atlantic Ocean and connecting waters in vicinity of Myrtle Island, Va.; Air Force practice bombing, rocket firing, and gunnery range. (a) The danger zone. The waters of the Atlantic Ocean and connecting waters within an area described as follows: Beginning at

(1657)   37°12′18″, 75°46′00″; thence southwesterly to

(1658)   37°08′21″, 75°50′00″; thence northwesterly along the arc of a circle having a radius of three nautical miles and centered at

(1659)   37°11′16″, 75°49′29″, to

(1660)   37°10′14″, 75°52′57″; thence northeasterly to

(1661)   37°14′30″, 75°48′32″; thence southeasterly to

(1662)   37°13′38″, 75°46′18″; and thence southeasterly to the point of beginning.

(1663)   (b) The regulations. (1) No vessel shall enter or remain in the danger zone except during intervals specified and publicized from time to time in local newspapers or by radio announcement.

(1664)   (2) This section shall be enforced by the Commanding General, Tactical Air Command, Langley Air Force Base, Virginia, and such agencies as he may designate.

(1665)   §334.340 Chesapeake Bay off Plumtree Island, Hampton, Va.; Air Force precision test area. (a) The danger zone. The waters of Chesapeake Bay and connecting waters within an area bounded as follows: Beginning at latitude 37°08′12″, longitude 76°19′30″, which is a point on the circumference of a circle of 10,000-foot radius with its center on Plumtree Point at latitude 37°07′30″, longitude 76°17′36″; thence clockwise along the circumference of the circle to latitude 37°09′06″, longitude 76°18′00″; thence southeasterly to latitude 37°08′12″, longitude 76°17′48″; thence clockwise along the circumference of a circle of 4,000-foot radius (with its center at latitude 37°07′30″, longitude 76°17′36″ to latitude 37°07′48″, longitude 76°18′24″; thence northwesterly to the point of beginning.

(1666)   (b) The regulations. (1) The danger zone will be in use not more than a total of 4 hours per month, which hours shall be during not more than any 2 days per month.

(1667)   (2) No vessel shall enter or remain in the danger zone during periods of firing or bombing or when the zone is otherwise in use.

(1668)   (3) The Commander, Tactical Air Command, Langley Air Force Base, Va., shall be responsible for publicizing in advance through the Coast Guard's "Local Notice to Mariners," in the local press, and by radio from time to time the schedule of use of the area, and shall station patrol boats to warn vessels during periods of use.

(1669)   (4) This section shall be enforced by the Commander, Tactical Air Command, Langley Air Force Base, Va., or such agency as he may designate.

(1670)   (c) Disestablishment of danger zone. The danger zone will be disestablished not later than December 31, 1967, unless written application for its continuance shall have been made to and approved by the Secretary of the Army prior to that date.

(1671)   §334.350 Chesapeake Bay off Fort Monroe, Va.; firing range danger zone. (a) The danger zone. All of the water area lying within a section extending seaward a distance of 4,600 yards between radial lines bearing 83° True and 115° True, respectively, from a point on shore at latitude 37°01′30″ N., longitude 76°17′54″ W.

(1672)   (b) The regulations. (1) No weapon having a greater range than the 30-calibre carbine is to be fired into the firing range danger zone.

(1673)   (2) During periods when firing is in progress, red flags will be displayed at conspicuous locations on the beach. Observers will be on duty and firing will be suspended as long as any vessel is within the danger zone.

(1674)   (3) Passage of vessels through the area will not be prohibited at any time, nor will commercial fishermen be prohibited from working fish nets within the area. No loitering or anchoring for other purposes will be permitted during announced firing periods.

(1675)   (4) No firing will be done during hours of darkness or low visibility.

(1676)   (5) The Commander, Fort Monroe, Va., is responsible for furnishing in advance the firing schedule to the Commander, 5th Coast Guard District, for publication in his "Local Notice to Mariners" and to the local press at Norfolk and Newport News, Va.

(1677)   (c) The regulations in this section shall be enforced by the Commanding Officer, Fort Monroe, Va., and such agencies as he may designate.

(1678)   §334.360 Chesapeake Bay off Fort Monroe, Virginia; restricted area, U.S. Naval Base and Naval Surface Weapon Center.

(1679)   (a) The area. Beginning at

(1680)   37°00′30″N., 76°18′05″W.; thence to

(1681)   37°00′38″N., 76°17′42″W.; thence to

(1682)   37°00′39″N., 76°16′11″W.; thence to

(1683)   36°59′18″N., 76°17′52″W.; thence to

(1684)   37°00′05″N., 76°18′17″W.; and thence north along the seawall to the point of beginning.

(1685)   (b) The regulations. (1) Anchoring, trawling, fishing, and dragging are prohibited in the danger zone, and no object, either attached to a vessel or otherwise, shall be placed on or near the bottom.

(1686)   (2) This section shall be enforced by the Commander, Naval Base, Norfolk, Virginia, and such agencies as he may designate.

(1687)   §334.370 Chesapeake Bay, Lynnhaven Roads; danger zones, U.S. Naval Amphibious Base. (a) Underwater demolitions area (prohibited)–(1) The area. A portion of the restricted area for Navy amphibious training operations described in §207.157, along the south shore of Chesapeake Bay, bounded as follows: Beginning at a point on the mean low-water line at longitude 76°08′59″; thence 200 yards to latitude 36°55′36″, longitude 76°08′57″; thence 400 yards to latitude 36°55′34″, longitude 76°08′43″; thence 200 yards to a point on the mean low-water line at longitude 76°08′45″; and thence approximately 400 yards along the mean low-water line to the point of beginning. The area will be marked by range poles set on shore on the prolongation of the lines forming its eastern and western boundaries.

(1688)   (2) The regulations. Vessels other than those owned and operated by the United States shall not enter the prohibited area at any time unless authorized to do so by the enforcing agency.

(1689)   (b) Small-arms firing range–(1) The Area. Beginning at a point on the shore line at

(1690)   36°55′27″N., 76°08′38″W.; thence to

(1691)   36°55′50″N., 76°08′37″W.; thence to

(1692)   36°57′11″N., 76°08′11″W.; thence to

(1693)   36°56′53″N., 76°07′18″W.; thence to

(1694)   36°55′39″N., 76°07′46″W.; thence to

(1695)   36°55′22″N., 76°08′17″W.; thence along the shore line to the point of beginning.

(1696)   (2) The regulations. (i) Passage of vessels through the area will not be prohibited at any time, nor will commercial fishermen be prohibited from working fish nets within the area. No loitering or anchoring for other purposes will be permitted.

(1697)   (ii) A large red warning flag will be flown on shore during periods when firing is in progress. Observers will be on duty and firing will be suspended for the passage of vessels and for the placing and maintenance of fish nets within the area.

(1698)   (c) This section shall be enforced by the Commanding Officer, U.S. Naval Amphibious Base, Little Creek, Norfolk, Virginia.

3. SANDY HOOK TO CAPE HENRY

(1) Between New York Bay and Delaware Bay is the New Jersey coast with its many resorts, its inlets, and its Intracoastal Waterway. Delaware Bay is the approach to Wilmington, Chester, Philadelphia, Camden, and Trenton; below Wilmington is the Delaware River entrance to the Chesapeake and Delaware Canal, the deep inside link between Chesapeake and Delaware Bays. The Delaware-Maryland-Virginia coast has relatively few resorts; the numerous inlets are backed by a shallow inside passage that extends all the way from Delaware Bay to Chesapeake Bay. The last seven chapters, nearly half of this book, are required to describe Chesapeake Bay to Norfolk and Newport News, to Washington and Baltimore, and to Susquehanna River 170 miles north of the Virginia Capes.

(2) A vessel approaching this coast from seaward will be made aware of its nearness by the number of vessels passing up and down in the coastal trade. The coast of New Jersey is studded with large hotels, prominent standpipes, and elevated tanks. South of Delaware Bay, the principal landmarks are the lighthouses and Coast Guard stations.

(3) The general tendency along this mostly sandy coast is for the ocean beaches and the points on the north sides of the entrances to wash away and for the points on the south sides of the entrances to build out. Protective works have done much to stabilize the New Jersey coast, but several lighthouses have been abandoned between Delaware Bay and Chesapeake Bay because of erosion.

(4) The shores of Delaware Bay and Delaware River are mostly low and have few conspicuous marks, other than lights, below the industrial centers along the river. The shores of Chesapeake Bay are low as far north as Patuxent River, then rise to considerable heights at the head of the bay.

(5) **Disposal Sites** and **Dumping Grounds.**–These areas are rarely mentioned in the Coast Pilot, but are shown on the nautical charts. (See Disposal Sites and Dumping Grounds, chapter 1, and charts for limits.)

(6) **Aids to navigation.**–Lights are numerous along the section of the coast covered by this Coast Pilot. Radiobeacons and fog signals are at most of the principal light stations. Marker radiobeacons, low-powered and for local use only, are at the entrances to many of the inlets. Many coastal and harbor buoys are equipped with radar reflectors, which greatly increase the range at which the buoys may be detected on the radarscope. The critical dangers are marked.

(7) **Loran.**–Loran C stations provide the mariner with good navigation coverage along this section of the coast.

(8) **Radar,** though always a valuable navigational aid, is generally of less assistance in navigation along this coast due to the relatively low relief; the accuracy of radar ranges to the beach cannot be relied upon. Coastal buoys equipped with radar reflectors are of help in this regard. It is sometimes possible to obtain a usable radar return from the larger lighthouses, but positive target identification is usually difficult. Radar is of particular importance in detecting other traffic and in the prevention of collisions during periods of inclement weather, and in fog and low visibility.

(9) **COLREGS Demarcation Lines.**–Lines have been established to delineate those waters upon which mariners must comply with the International Regulations for Preventing Collisions at Sea, 1972 (72 COLREGS) and those waters upon which mariners must comply with the Inland Navigational Rules Act of 1980 (Inland Rules). The waters inside of the lines are **Inland Rules Waters,** and the waters outside of the lines are **COLREGS Waters.** (See Part 80, chapter 2, for specific lines of demarcation.)

(10) **Ports and Waterways Safety.**–(See Part 160, chapter 2, for regulations governing vessel operations and requirements for notification of arrivals, departures, hazardous conditions, and certain dangerous cargoes to the Captain of the Port.)

(11) **Harbor and Inlet Entrances.**–The channels into Delaware and Chesapeake Bays are broad and deep. The entrances to the inlets are comparatively shallow and are more or less obstructed by shifting sandbars. Some of the inlets have been improved by dredging and by the construction of jetties. On many of the bars the buoys are moved from time to time to mark the shifting channels. The best time to enter most of the inlets is on a rising tide with a smooth sea. Strangers should not attempt to enter the inlets without assistance when the seas are breaking on the bars. The tidal currents have considerable velocity in all of the entrances, and their direction is affected by the force and direction of the wind.

(12) **Traffic Separation Schemes (Traffic Lanes)** have been established at the entrances to New York Harbor, Delaware Bay and Chesapeake Bay, and in the main channel of Chesapeake Bay off Smith Point just south of the entrance to the Potomac River. (See chapters 4, 6, 9, and 12, respectively, for details.)

(13) **Anchorages.**–The only protected anchorage for deep-draft vessels between New York Bay and Chesapeake Bay is outside the channel limits in Delaware Bay according to draft. Absecon Inlet, Cape May Inlet, and some of the others can accommodate light-draft vessels such as trawlers and small yachts, but not medium or deep drafts. Small local craft often seek shelter inside the shallower inlets, but entrance is difficult in heavy weather, and the unimproved inlets are often difficult even in good weather, particularly for strangers.

(14) A number of anchorage areas have been established by Federal Regulations within the area of this Coast Pilot. (See Part 110, chapter 2, for limits and regulations.)

(15) **Dangers.**–The principal dangers along this coast are the outlying sand shoals, the fogs, and the doubtful direction and velocity of the currents after heavy gales. Depths of 7½ fathoms are found as far as 20 miles from shore. There are many wrecks along this coast, but most of them have been blasted off or cleared to safe navigational depths; the others are marked by obstruction buoys.

(16) Gales from northeast to southeast cause heavy breakers on the beaches and outlying shoals; the sea breaks in 4 to 5 fathoms of water, and shoals of that depth or less usually are marked during easterly gales. The bars across the inlets are then impassable and are defined by breakers even in comparatively smooth water with a light swell. The heaviest surf on the beach is on a rising tide near high-water springs; the least surf is encountered on a falling tide near low water. A very heavy surf makes on the beaches after a southeasterly gale followed by a sudden shift of wind to northwest.

(17) **Danger zones** have been established within the area of this Coast Pilot. (See Part 334, chapter 2, for limits and regulations.)

(18) **Fishweirs** are numerous along the outside coast and in Chesapeake Bay and tributaries. The stakes often become broken off and form a hazard to navigation, especially at

swing span with a clearance of 15 feet over the main channel. (See **117.1** through **117.49**, chapter 2, for drawbridge regulations.) The town is principally a shellfish and fishing center, but pleasure craft operate from here during the summer. The wharves and piers along the waterfront have depths of 3 to 10 feet alongside. There are small-craft facilities at Chincoteague that can provide gasoline, diesel fuel, water, berths, and limited marine supplies. Hull and engine repairs can be made; a 40-ton marine railway at Chincoteague can handle craft up to 80 feet.

(79) A boat basin is at the extreme southwest end of Chincoteague Island. In May 1988, the dredged entrance channel, marked by a light, had a midchannel controlling depth of 7 feet with 7 to 8 feet in basin.

(80) **Chincoteague Coast Guard Station** is on the east side of Chincoteague Channel, 0.3 mile south of the highway bridge.

(81) **Chart 12210.**–The 35-mile stretch of coast between Chincoteague Inlet and Great Machipongo Inlet is formed by six islands of about equal length. The islands are separated from each other by narrow inlets and from the mainland by marsh and flats through which are numerous sloughs and channels.

(82) **Wallops Island,** northernmost of the six, is on the southwest side of Chincoteague Inlet.

(83) A **danger zone** extends for about 5 miles off the coast of Wallops Island and covers the entrance to Chincoteague Inlet. A strobe light is displayed at night from a tower in about 37°15'16"N., 75°29'06"W., about 30 minutes prior to the commencement of and during rocket launching operations. (See **334.130** chapter 2, for limits and regulations.)

(84) **Assawoman Inlet,** the ocean entrance between **Wallops Island** and **Assawoman Island,** is very shallow and is not used. **Gargathy Inlet,** the ocean inlet separating Assawoman Island and **Metompkin Islands,** is not used.

(85) **Metompkin Inlet,** the ocean entrance between Metompkin Islands and **Cedar Island,** is used by some small local fishing and oyster boats. The changeable entrance channel is unmarked and should not be entered without local knowledge.

(86) **Porpoise Banks,** 10 miles offshore from Metompkin Inlet, have irregular bottom with depths of 34 to 40 feet.

(87) **Wachapreague Inlet,** between Cedar Island and **Parramore Island,** is 20 miles south-southwestward of Chincoteague Inlet. The entrance is marked by a lighted bell buoy and unlighted buoys that are shifted in position with changing channel conditions. The controlling depth is about 5 feet through the inlet, which is used by many fishing boats and by some boats seeking shelter, but should be entered only with local knowledge. The best anchorage is in **Horseshoe Lead,** southwest of the entrance, where there are depths of 20 to 30 feet west of the middle ground. **Parramore Beach Coast Guard Station** is on the inner side of Parramore Island 0.5 mile south of the inlet. A radiobeacon is atop the lookout tower at the Coast Guard station.

(88) **Parramore Banks** extend about 8 miles offshore from Wachapreague Inlet. The area is lumpy and has numerous depths of 18 to 30 feet. A lighted gong buoy is east of the banks.

(89) Two fish havens are about 2.6 miles and 7.5 miles east-southeast, respectively, from Wachapreague Inlet. The fish haven nearer to shore is marked by buoys.

(90) **Wachapreague,** a town on the mainland about 4 miles west-northwest of Wachapreague Inlet, is an oystering and fishing center, and is a base for some pleasure boats during the summer. A depth of about 4 feet can be carried from Wachapreague Inlet through **Hummock Channel** and **Wachapreague Channel,** marked by lights, to the wharves and marinas at the town. Gasoline, diesel fuel, berths, and some marine supplies can be obtained. Hull and engine repairs can be made; largest marine railway, 50 feet.

(91) **Quinby Inlet,** the ocean entrance between Parramore Island and Hog Island, has a fan of breakers across the bar at the entrance. The buoys marking the inlet are frequently shifted and not charted. In 1982, a draft of 5 feet could be carried through the inlet. The inlet should not be used without local knowledge.

(92) **Quinby** is a village on the mainland about 6 miles north-northwest of Quinby Inlet. A channel to the village, marked by lights, follows **Sandy Island Channel** to **Upshur Bay,** thence through a slough in the mudflats to a dredged channel leading to a basin that has a public landing; gasoline, diesel fuel, berths, some marine supplies, and a pump-out station are available. In May 1988, the midchannel controlling depth was 5 feet in the dredged channel with 5 to 6½ feet in the basin. A no-wake **speed limit** is enforced.

(93) **Great Machipongo Inlet,** the ocean entrance between Hog Island and **Cobb Island,** has breakers that form on the shoals on either side of the entrance at all times, but on the bar only in heavy weather. The inlet is marked by buoys that are shifted in position with changing channel conditions. The controlling depth is about 12 feet over the bar.

(94) **Great Machipongo Channel** extends northwestward through Hog Island Bay from the inlet to the mainland where it continues as **Machipongo River. Willis Wharf,** on the west bank of **Parting Creek** 1 mile above the junction with Machipongo River, is a base for shellfish and fishing boats. Gasoline and diesel fuel are available. A marine railway here can handle craft up to 60 feet for do-it-yourself repairs. In January 1989, the dredged channel in Parting Creek had a midchannel controlling depth of 7 feet from the junction with Machipongo River to Willis Wharf.

(95) A state-owned boat harbor is just below Willis Wharf on the west side of Parting Creek between Daybeacons 17 and 18. An area with about 41 slips is available for commercial fishing boats. The harbor has electricity, water, and a launching ramp.

(96) **Chart 12224.**–**Sand Shoal Inlet,** the ocean entrance between Cobb Island and **Wreck Island,** may be entered through three channels. **Northeast Channel,** protected by extensive shoaling to northward and marked by buoys shifted in position with changing channel conditions, leads along the south end of Cobb Island; the controlling depth is about 10 feet over the bar. **Southeast Channel** is straight, but the bar breaks in heavy weather; the controlling depth is about 10 feet over the bar. **South Channel,** east of Wreck Island, has a controlling depth of about 8 feet. The latter two channels are not marked and should not be used by strangers.

(97) A good fair-weather anchorage is in the channel near the discontinued Coast Guard station east of **Little Cobb Island** for boats able to cross the entrance bar with 3 feet over it.

(98) **Sand Shoal Channel,** marked by lights and daybeacons, extends westward from Sand Shoal Inlet for 6 miles where it joins a marked dredged channel leading to the wharves and public bulkhead at **Oyster** on the mainland. In June 1984, the controlling depth was 6 feet in the dredged channel and in the basin at Oyster. Public piers and a launching ramp are on the northern side of the basin. Numerous wrecks are reported near these facilities; caution is advised.

(99) Oyster is the shipping point for large amounts of clams and oysters. Gasoline, diesel fuel, and some marine supplies are available.

(100) **Ship Shoal Inlet,** the ocean entrance between Ship Shoal Island and **Myrtle Island,** is shallow and unmarked; it is used only by local oyster boats. There is deep water back of the inlet, but the channels to the inside passages are shallow and tortuous.

(101) The **danger zone** of a bombing and gunnery range is centered on Myrtle Island, 6 miles northeastward of Cape Charles Light. (See **334.330,** chapter 2, for limits and regulations.)

(102) **Little Inlet,** between Myrtle Island and Smith Island, is shallow and is little used. Small boats can connect with the inside passage at high water.

(103) **Cape Charles** and the islands on the north side of the entrance to Chesapeake Bay are described in chapter 9.

(104) **Smith Island Inlet,** between Smith Island and Fishermans Island, is fairly wide, but the narrow, changeable channel lies between sandbars and breakers. The inlet is used by many local boats with drafts of 3 to 4 feet, but it is unmarked and should not be used by strangers. The controlling depth over the bar is said to be 1½ feet.

(105) **Charts 12211, 12210, 12221.–Virginia Inside Passage** is between the barrier beach along the Atlantic Ocean on the east and the Virginia portion of the mainland peninsula on the west. The passage extends 74 miles from the south end of Chincoteague Bay through creeks, thorofares, marshy cuts, and bays to enter Chesapeake Bay at Cape Charles. The route is marked with lights and daybeacons which have daymarks with white reflector borders to distinguish them from aids to navigation marking other waterways. Buoys are temporarily established from time to time to mark destroyed aids or critical places.

(106) The Federal project depth is 6 feet for the waterway. Maintenance dredging is performed to provide a 6-foot controlling depth, but due to continuous shoaling 3 feet or less may be found in places, particularly inside the ocean inlets. The overhead clearance is limited only by the 40-foot fixed bridge across Cat Creek, 8 miles southward of Chincoteague, the 50-foot clearance of the power cable over Longboat Creek inshore from Metompkin Inlet, 22 miles southward of Chincoteague, and the 40-foot fixed bridge at Cape Charles.

(107) The mean range of tide varies from 2.5 to 4.5 feet in the inlets along the Virginia coast; greater fluctuations in the water level in the inside waters are caused by high winds and storms.

(108) Gasoline, diesel fuel, and some marine supplies are available at Wachapreague, 29 miles south of Chincoteague; at Quinby, 33 miles south of Chincoteague; at Willis Wharf, 37 miles south of Chincoteague; and at Oyster, 60 miles south of Chincoteague and 12 miles north of Cape Charles. Hull and engine repairs can be made at Wachapreague.

(109) From Chincoteague, the Virginia Inside Passage follows Chincoteague Channel across Chincoteague Inlet to **Walker Point,** thence through **Balfast Narrows, Island Hole Narrows,** the dredged cut in **Bogues Bay,** and **Cat Creek** to the sloughs marked by lights and daybeacons back of Assawoman Inlet, 10 miles southwestward of Chincoteague. The fixed highway bridge over Cat Creek has a clearance of 40 feet. The overhead power cable just north of the bridge has a clearance of 60 feet.

(110) From 1 mile back of Assawoman Inlet, the inside passage continues through **Northam Narrows,** thence through dredged cuts in **Kegotank Bay** and back of Gargathy Inlet to **Wire Passage,** 15 miles southwestward of Chincoteague.

(111) From Gargathy Inlet, the inside passage goes through Wire Passage into a dredged cut in **Metompkin Bay,** and enters Folly Creek westward of Metompkin Inlet. A dredged channel with a controlling depth of 5 feet in February 1991, extends about 0.8 mile up **Parker Creek** from Virginia Inside Passage Light 80. The channel is marked by daybeacons. **Folly Creek,** which leads westward from the south end of Metompkin Bay, has a depth of 1 foot to the landing at its head, 3 miles above the mouth. A launching ramp and a pier are on the south side of Folly Creek about 1 mile west of Light 87.

(112) The passage continues through a dredged cut from Folly Creek into **Longboat Creek,** which has a power cable over its northern part with a clearance of 50 feet, thence through cuts in **Cedar Island Bay, Teagles Ditch,** and **Burtons Bay** into Wachapreague Channel which leads to Wachapreague, 29 miles southward of Chincoteague. Supplies and repair facilities are available at Wachapreague. (Refer to previous description in this chapter.)

(113) From Wachapreague Channel, the passage continues through a cut in **Bradford Bay,** a part of **Millstone Creek,** a cut in **Swash Bay,** a part of The Swash, and **Little Sloop Channel** to Sandy Island Channel, 3 miles inside Quinby Inlet and 36 miles southward of Chincoteague.

(114) The passage southward of Quinby Inlet follows **Sloop Channel** and a dredged cut into **Cunjer Channel,** thence westward in **North Channel** at the north end of **Hog Island Bay** to Great Machipongo Channel, 43 miles southward of Chincoteague.

(115) After passing through Great Machipongo Channel to a point 2 miles inside Great Machipongo Inlet, the route goes westward through **Gull Marsh Channel,** thence southwestward through a natural channel and cut in **Outlet Bay** and **Spidercrab Bay** to **Eckichy Channel,** thence southeastward to Sand Shoal Channel, 1.5 miles inside Sand Shoal Inlet, 56 miles southward of Chincoteague.

(116) From inside of Sand Shoal Inlet, the passage continues westward through Sand Shoal Channel and southward through **Mockhorn Channel** to Magothy Bay.

(117) **Magothy Bay,** which extends southward from Mockhorn Channel to Smith Island Inlet, is shallow except in the well-marked inside passage which passes through the bay to Cape Charles. **Magotha** is a village on the west side of the bay 3.5 miles northwestward of Cape Charles Light.

(118) From the southern part of Magothy Bay, the passage continues southwestward through a dredged cut across Cape Charles into the deep water in Chesapeake Bay. The fixed highway bridge over the passage from Cape Charles to Fishermans Island has a clearance of 40 feet.

36°51'47"N., 75°51'06"W. The southeasterly approach inbound traffic lane has a controlling depth of about 40 feet, and the outbound lane has a controlling depth of about 47 feet. The route north of Chesapeake Light through the buoyed northeasterly approach traffic lanes has a controlling depth of about 29 feet in the inbound lane and about 34 feet in the outbound lane. Federal project main channel depths are 50 feet from the Virginia Capes to Baltimore and 55 feet from the Capes to Hampton Roads. (See Notice to Mariners and latest editions of charts for controlling depths.)

(38) The well-marked channel to Baltimore is discussed further in chapters 11 to 15.

(39) **Tides.**—The mean range of tide is 2.8 feet at Cape Henry.

(40) **Currents.**—The current velocity is 1.0 knot on the flood and 1.5 knots on the ebb in Chesapeake Bay Entrance. (See the Tidal Current Tables for daily predictions.)

(41) **Pilotage** is compulsory for all foreign vessels and for U.S. vessels under register in the foreign trade. Pilotage is optional for U.S. vessels under enrollment in the coastwise trade if they have on board a pilot licensed by the Federal Government to operate in these waters.

(42) The Association of Maryland Pilots has an office in Baltimore (301–342–6013, 301–276–1337; cable address MARPILOT) and provides service to any port in Maryland. The Virginia Pilots Association has an office in Norfolk (804–496–0995; cable address VAPILOT) and provides service to any port in Virginia. Vessels bound for Washington, D.C. may take a pilot from either association.

(43) A pilot boat from the Association of Maryland Pilots is stationed in the pilot cruising area off Cape Henry. The pilot boat, a 180-foot converted tugboat, has a black hull, white superstructure, and a blue stack with the number "1" in the center. The pilot boat monitors VHF-FM channels 16, 11, and 13. The pilot boat displays the standard day and night signals. The pilots are carried to and from the ships in 35- and 47-foot-long launches with blue hulls, white houses, and the word "PILOT" across the wheelhouses. The pilots carry portable radiotelephones for bridge-to-bridge communications on channel 13. Vessels proceeding from the Virginia Capes to Washington, D.C. or the upper part of Chesapeake Bay and northward, when using Maryland pilots, sometimes transfer pilots at a designated transfer area off Piney Point on the Potomac River or in Chesapeake Bay off the entrance to Patuxent River, depending on the port of call.

(44) The Virginia Pilots Association maintains a pilot station at Cape Henry, just north of Cape Henry Light. The pilots monitor VHF-FM channels 11, 16, and 74. Other channels are used on request. Four pilot boats are stationed in Lynnhaven Inlet; two are in use at any given time. The pilot boats are 50 feet long with orange hulls and gray houses with the word "PILOT" on each side.

(45) The Chesapeake and Interstate Pilots Association offers pilot services to vessels engaged in the coastwise trade and public vessels between Cape Henry and any port or place on the Chesapeake Bay and its tributaries. Arrangements for pilots are made through ships' agents or the pilot office in Norfolk (telephone, 804-855-2733; cable, CINPILOT). Pilots meet vessels day or night aboard the pilot boat "CHESAPEAKE II" which is black with a white house and the word "PILOT" on the sides. At night, the standard pilot lights are displayed. A 12-hour estimated time of arrival (ETA) is requested with any change greater than 1 hour being advised to the pilots. The pilot boat "CHESAPEAKE II" monitors VHF-FM channels 16 and 13 about 1 hour and 30 minutes prior to the vessel's ETA or

Departure and switches to VHF-FM channel 6 for working traffic. The pilot boat call sign is WTR 3711.

(46) Vessels are usually boarded at Chesapeake Bay Entrance Lighted Junction Buoy CBJ, but with prior arrangement and if scheduling permits, vessels can be boarded at other places in the lower Chesapeake Bay.

(47) The Interport Pilots Agency, Inc. offers pilotage to public and U.S. vessels in the coastwise trade transiting to Baltimore, the Chesapeake and Delaware Canal, Philadelphia, New York, Long Island Sound, Cape Cod Canal, and ports in the northeast. Arrangements for any of the above services are made in advance through ships' agents or with their office in Atlantic Highlands, N.J. (telephone 201-291-1310; cable, PORTPILOTS). An updated 12-hour estimated time of arrival (ETA) is requested.

(48) The pilot boat "CHESAPEAKE II" is also used by Interport Pilots Agency,

(49) It has been noted that sometimes considerable differences occur between a vessel's ETA and her actual arrival due to conditions encountered between Cape Hatteras and Cape Henry. Revisions to the ETA of 1 hour or greater should be passed to the pilots especially if the vessel's arrival will be sooner than previously advised.

(50) **Charts 12254, 12222, 12256.**—**Thimble Shoal Channel,** the improved approach to Hampton Roads, begins 2.3 miles northwest of Cape Henry Light and extends 9.5 miles west-northwestward; a Federal project provides for a 55-foot-deep channel with a 32-foot-deep auxiliary channel on each side of the main channel. (See Notice to Mariners and latest editions of the charts for controlling depths.)

(51) **Naval and general anchorages** are south of Thimble Shoal Channel. (See **110.1 and 110.168**, chapter 2, for limits and regulations.)

(52) Thimble Shoal Channel is a **Regulated Navigation Area** and draft limitations apply. A vessel drawing less than 25 feet may not enter the channel, unless the vessel is crossing the channel. (See **165.501**, chapter 2, for limits and regulations.)

(53) **Lynnhaven Roads,** an open bight westward of Cape Henry, is protected from southerly winds and is sometimes used as an anchorage. The former dumping-ground area in the western part of the bight has shoals and obstructions with depths as little as 11 feet; elsewhere, general depths are 20 to 28 feet Eastward of Lynnhaven Inlet, the 18-foot curve is no more than 0.3 mile from shore; westward of the inlet, the shoaling is gradual and depths of 18 feet can be found 0.8 mile from shore.

(54) There are two small-craft openings in the Chesapeake Bay Bridge-Tunnel south of Thimble Shoal Channel. Each fixed span has a clearance of 21 feet.

(55) **Lynnhaven Inlet,** 4 miles westward of Cape Henry Light, is subject to continual change. The inlet is marked by a lighted buoy, daybeacons, and lights. The twin fixed highway bridges over the inlet have a clearance of 35 feet. Overhead power cables close southward of the bridges have clearances of 68 feet. **Lynnhaven Bay,** south of the inlet, has depths of 1 to 10 feet.

(56) A dredged channel marked by a light and daybeacons leads eastward from the south end of the inlet to **Broad Bay.** In May-July 1988, the controlling depths were 5½ feet (8 feet in the midchannel) in the channel leading eastward from the south end of the inlet to Daybeacon 6, thence 7 feet to Light 14 at the west end of Broad Bay. Another dredged channel leads eastward from just south of the bridges around the north side of a small island and connects with the southerly channel southeast of the island near Daybeacon 6. In May-July 1988, the midchannel controlling

depth was 8½ feet in the northerly channel. The Great Neck Road fixed highway bridge over the channel 1.2 miles from the twin bridges over the inlet has a clearance of 35 feet; nearby overhead power and telephone cables have a clearance of 55 feet. In 1987, twin fixed highway bridges with a design clearance of 36 feet were under construction about 0.5 mile east of the Great Neck Road bridge.

(57)   **Caution.**–It is reported that this channel has very heavy boat traffic and is especially congested on summer weekends.

(58)   An alternate route to Broad Bay is through **Long Creek** which branches northeastward from the dredged channel in the vicinity of Daybeacon 11. In June 1988, the controlling depth was 8 feet in Long Creek. The 40-foot span of the Great Neck Road Bridge over Long Creek has a clearance of 20 feet. Nearby overhead cables have a clearance of 37 feet. In 1987, twin fixed highway bridges with a design clearance of 36 feet were under construction about 0.5 mile east of the Great Neck Road bridge.

(59)   Depths are about 7 feet in Broad Bay. A marked channel with a midchannel controlling depth of 5 feet in June 1987, leads southeastward through **The Narrows** to the southern end of **Linkhorn Bay** near Virginia Beach.

(60)   Small-craft facilities are inside Lynnhaven Inlet and in both forks of Linkhorn Bay.

(61)   **Little Creek** is entered between jetties 8 miles westward of Cape Henry Light. Most of the creek comprises the **U. S. Naval Amphibious Base,** but the Virginia and Maryland Railroad operates car floats from the south end terminal to the town of Cape Charles on the Delmarva Peninsula; small craft use the west arm.

(62)   A dredged channel in Little Creek leads to a basin off the railroad terminal, 1.2 miles south of the jetties. In June 1987, the reported controlling depth was 20 feet in the channel and in the basin. The channel is marked by a **177°30′** lighted entrance range and by lights. **Little Creek Coast Guard Station** is eastward of the railroad terminal.

(63)   **Fishermans Cove,** on the west side of Little Creek, has fuel and berthing facilities for small craft. A **speed limit** of 5 knots is prescribed for Fishermans Cove. (See **33 CFR 165.509(d)(9),** chapter 2.)

(64)   Naval **danger zones** and **restricted areas** extend northward from the vicinity of Little Creek to the edge of Thimble Shoal Channel. (See **334.310** and **334.370,** chapter 2, for limits and regulations.)

(65)   **Chart 12245.**–**Hampton Roads,** at the southwest corner of Chesapeake Bay, is entered 16 miles westward of the Virginia Capes. It includes the Port of Norfolk, encompassing the cities of Norfolk, Portsmouth, and Chesapeake, and the Port of Newport News, which takes in the cities of Newport News and Hampton.

(66)   Hampton Roads is the world's foremost bulk cargo harbor. Coal, petroleum products, grain, sand and gravel, tobacco, and fertilizer constitute more than 90 percent of the heavy traffic movement by water, although an increasing amount of general cargo is handled by the Hampton Roads ports.

(67)   **Channels.**–The approach to Hampton Roads is through the 55-foot Thimble Shoal Channel. There are natural depths of 80 to 20 feet in the main part of Hampton Roads, but the harbor shoals to less than 10 feet toward the shores. Dredged channels lead to the principal ports.

(68)   Two main Federal project channels, marked by buoys, lead through Hampton Roads. One channel leads southward along the waterfronts of Norfolk, Portsmouth, and Chesapeake to the first bridge across the Southern Branch of Elizabeth River; project depths are 50 feet

through Entrance Reach; thence 55 feet through Craney Island Reach at Lamberts Point; thence 40 feet to the bridge. The other channel with a 55-foot project depth leads westward to the waterfront at Newport News at the entrance to James River. (See Notice to Mariners and latest editions of the charts for controlling depths.)

(69)   **Anchorages.**–Numerous general, explosives, naval, and small-craft anchorages are in Hampton Roads and Elizabeth River. (See **110.1** and **110.168,** chapter 2, for limits and regulations.) The areas are shown on charts 12245 and 12253.

(70)   **Tides.**–The mean range of tide is 2.5 feet in Hampton Roads. (See Tide Tables for daily predictions of tides at Sewells Point.)

(71)   **Currents.**–Information for several places in Hampton Roads and Elizabeth River is given in the Tidal Current Tables. The currents are influenced considerably by the winds and at times attain velocities in excess of the tabulated values. The current velocity is about 1.0 knot in Hampton Roads and about 0.6 knot in Elizabeth River.

(72)   **Ice.**–Hampton Roads is free of ice. In severe winters the upper part of Southern Branch, Elizabeth River, is sometimes closed for short periods.

(73)   **Weather.**–The National Weather Service maintains an office at Norfolk International Airport; **barometers** in the Hampton Roads area can be compared there or checked by telephone.

(74)   **Pilotage** for Hampton Roads ports. (See Pilotage at the beginning of this chapter and chapter 3.)

(75)   **Towage.**–Vessels usually proceed from Cape Henry to points in the Hampton Roads port area under their own power and without assistance. A large fleet of tugs is available at Norfolk and Newport News to assist in docking or undocking and in shifting within the harbor.

(76)   **Quarantine, customs, immigration, and agricultural quarantine.**–(See chapter 3, Vessel Arrival Inspections, and appendix for addresses.)

(77)   **Quarantine** is enforced in accordance with regulations of the U.S. Public Health Service. (See Public Health Service, chapter 1.) The **quarantine anchorage** is southwestward of Old Point Comfort. The U.S. Naval Hospital is in Portsmouth.

(78)   Hampton Roads is a **customs port of entry.**

(79)   **Coast Guard.**–A **Marine Safety Office** is in Norfolk. (See appendix for address.)

(80)   **Harbor regulations.**–Port regulations are principally concerned with grain, coal handling, port charges, and pilotage and stevedoring rates. Copies of these regulations may be obtained from the Hampton Roads Maritime Association, 236 East Plume Street, P.O. Box 3528, Norfolk, Va. 23514.

(81)   **Anchorage regulations** are given in **110.1** and **110.168,** chapter 2.

(82)   **Wharves.**–The Hampton Roads area has more than 200 piers and wharves along more than 30 miles of improved waterfront; only the major deepwater facilities are described. Included are coal piers; containerized-cargo berths; oil storage and bunkering facilities; general-cargo, grain, and ore piers; and marine railways and drydocks. Available depths are 22 to 42 feet at the general-cargo, ore, and grain piers; 36 to 45 feet at the coal piers; and 20 to 42 feet. at the oil-storage and bunkering facilities. A 350-ton floating crane is available.

(83)   **Supplies.**–The principal coal-handling and bunkering piers are those of the Norfolk and Western Railway at Lamberts Point, Norfolk, and of the Chesapeake and Ohio Railway at Newport News. Bunker oil is available at Sewells

Point, in Southern Branch of Elizabeth River, and at Newport News, or it can be delivered from barges in the stream. Freshwater is available on the principal piers and can be supplied from barges. The area also has numerous ship chandlers and marine suppliers.

(84) **Repairs.**—Hampton Roads has extensive facilities for drydocking and making major repairs to large deep-draft vessels. The largest floating drydock at Norfolk has a capacity of 54,000 tons, and the largest marine railway can handle 6,000 tons. The shipyard at Newport News is one of the largest and best equipped in the United States; the principal graving dock has a length of 1,600 feet on the keel blocks. There are many other yards that are especially equipped to handle medium-sized and small vessels. More details on these repair facilities are given with the discussion of the waterway or port in which they are located.

(85) **Small-craft facilities.**—Complete services and repairs are available at Hampton Roads ports. There are marine railways up to 11 tons and mobile hoists up to 60 tons for repairs. (See small-craft facilities tabulations on charts 12205 and 12206 for services and supplies available.)

(86) **Communications.**—Hampton Roads ports are served by a terminal beltline, several large railroads, and by more than 50 motor carriers. In addition, over 90 steamship lines connect Hampton Roads with the principal U.S. and foreign ports; most of the lines have regular sailings, and others maintain frequent but irregular service. Three airlines offer prompt airfreight, express, and passenger service from Norfolk and Newport News to major U.S. cities with connecting service overseas.

(87) **Thimble Shoal Light** (37°00.9'N., 76°14.4'W.), 55 feet above the water, is shown from a red conical tower on a brown cylindrical pier on the eastern edge of the shoal; a fog signal is sounded from the station. The light is 12.3 miles from the Virginia Capes. Thimble Shoal is the southern edge of **Horseshoe,** described in chapter 11.

(88) The entrance to Hampton Roads is between Willoughby Spit and Old Point Comfort, 2 miles to the northward.

(89) **A bridge-tunnel complex** crosses Chesapeake Bay from Willoughby Spit to Hampton.

(90) **Old Point Comfort** is the site of historic **Fort Monroe.** The Chamberlin Hotel is an excellent landmark. **Old Point Comfort Light** (37°00.1'N., 76°18.4'W.), 54 feet above the water, is shown from a white tower. Only Government craft can tie up at the wharf on the south waterfront of Old Point Comfort.

(91) A naval **restricted area** extends eastward and southward of Old Point Comfort, and a **danger zone** of an army firing range extends to seaward from a point 1.5 miles northward of the point. (See **334.350,** and **334.360,** chapter 2, respectively, for limits and regulations.)

(92) **Hampton Bar** begins about 200 yards southwestward of Old Point Comfort and extends 2 miles southwestward; depths on the bar are 1 to 5 feet. The bar is marked by two lights and by buoys along its southern edge. These lights, together with one on Hampton Flats, aid vessels in mooring in the naval and other anchorages northward of the main channel.

(93) A dredged channel, marked by a light and daybeacons, leads along the west side of Old Point Comfort to the fish wharves at **Phoebus.** In September 1980, the channel had a controlling depth of 11 feet. The wharves have depths of 8 to 12 feet at their outer ends, but are in poor condition. Small craft can anchor in depths of 8 to 20 feet along the sides of the channel. The Fort Monroe yacht piers are on the east side of the channel 0.4 mile above Old Point Comfort.

(94) **Hampton River,** 1.5 miles westward of Old Point Comfort, is entered by a marked channel through Hampton Bar and Flats to a point just below the highway bridge at Hampton. Federal project depths are 12 feet. (See Notice to Mariners and latest editions of the charts for controlling depths.) Some small craft also enter west of Hampton Bar. **Hampton,** on the west side of the river 2 miles above the channel entrance, is an important seafood center. Traffic on the river consists of seafood and petroleum products, sand and gravel, and building materials. The residential and commercial areas of Hampton are on the west side of Hampton River; **Hampton Institute** and a Veterans Hospital are on the east side.

(95) **Sunset Creek,** on the west side just above the Hampton River mouth, is entered by a marked dredged channel leading westward from the channel in the river. In December 1980, the controlling depth was 12 feet to the head of the creek.

(96) The principal commercial wharves at Hampton, just below the bridge, have depths of 7 to 12 feet at their faces. The public landing 500 yards below the bridge has depths of 8 feet at the face; small boats anchor between the public landing and the bridge. The wharves along Sunset Creek have depths of 4 to 9 feet at their outer ends.

(97) Supplies and fuel are available at Hampton. A yacht club and several marinas here have berthing space. Repairs can be made; largest marine railway, 120 feet; lift, 35 tons.

(98) **Jones Creek,** on the east side of Hampton River 300 yards above the mouth, has depths of 8 to 11 feet. The bulkheads have depths of 3 to 10 feet alongside and are controlled by the Veterans Hospital on the south and Hampton Institute on the north.

(99) **Salters Creek,** 4 miles west-southwestward of Old Point Comfort, has a narrow unmarked approach channel with depths of 2 feet. The fixed highway bridge over the entrance has a channel width of 24 feet and a clearance of 9 feet. Numerous small craft moor above the bridge in a basin that has depths of about 5 feet.

(100) The 55-foot project channel to Newport News was discussed earlier. Depths along the edges of the dredged section are 19 to 25 feet. The currents do not always set fair with the channel, especially with strong winds, and deep-draft vessels sometimes find it difficult to stay in the channel.

(101) **Newport News Middle Ground Light** (36°56.7'N., 76°23.5'W.), 52 feet above the water, is shown from a red conical tower on a red cylindrical pier in 15 feet of water near the western end of the shoal; a seasonal fog signal is at the light.

(102) **Newport News Point** (36°57.8'N., 76°24.7'W.) on the north side of the entrance to James River, is 21.5 miles from the Virginia Capes. The city of **Newport News** extends several miles along the northeast bank of James River.

(103) **Newport News Creek,** just west of Newport News Point is a city-owned small-boat harbor used by fishing boats, pleasure craft, and petroleum barges. In January 1985, the controlling depth was 12 feet in the dredged channel for about 0.6 mile above the mouth. Fuel, supplies, and slips are available, and repairs can be made. A 75-ton marine railway and a 40-ton mobile hoist are available.

(104) Newport News Shipbuilding and Drydock Company is just below the James River Bridge on the east side of the river. A security zone is along the waterfront of the company property. (See **165.30, 165.33 and 165.504,** chapter 2, for limits and regulations.)

(105) **Wharves.**—The deepwater piers and wharves at Newport News extend from Newport News Point for 2.5 miles up James River. Only the major facilities are described. All

have access to highways and railroads, freshwater connections, and electric shore-power connections. Unless otherwise indicated, these facilities are owned by the Virginia Ports Authority. The alongside depths given for each facility described are reported depths. (For information on the latest depths, contact the operator.) For a complete description of the port facilities at Newport News, refer to Port Series No. 11, published and sold by the U.S. Army Corps of Engineers. (See appendix for address.)

(106)   **Chart 12245:**

(107)   **Newport News Marine Terminal Pier 2** (36°58′24″N., 76°26′00″W.): north and south sides 606 feet long; 32 feet along north side, 35 feet along south side; deck height, 8 feet; receipt and shipment of bulk cargo; operated by Virginia International Terminals.

(108)   **Newport News Marine Terminal Pier B:** about 200 yards southeastward of Newport News Marine Terminal Pier 2; 543-foot face, north and south sides 620 feet long; 35 feet along north side, 40 feet along south side and face; deck height, 15 feet; 268,000 square feet covered storage; 8 acres of open storage; receipt and shipment of general and roll-on/roll-off cargo; operated by Virginia International Terminals.

(109)   **Newport News Marine Terminal Pier C:** about 150 yards southeastward of Newport News Marine Terminal Pier B; 552-foot face, 35 feet alongside; north side, 755 feet long; 35 feet alongside; south side, 935 feet long; 40 feet alongside; 410,000 square feet covered storage; 200-ton-capacity container crane, 50-ton gantry crane; use of equipment from Pier B; receipt and shipment of general, containerized and roll-on/roll-off cargo; operated by Virginia International Terminals.

(110)   **Pier 8 Terminal:** about 700 yards southeastward of Newport News Marine Terminal Pier 2; 213-foot face; north and south sides 818 feet long; 32 feet alongside; deck height, 15 feet; 138,000 square feet covered storage; 20-ton crane available, forklift trucks; receipt of general cargo; operated by Tidewater Stevedoring Corp.

(111)   **Massey Coal Terminal Pier 9** (36°58′05″N., 76°25′44″W.): east and west sides 1,200 feet long; 46 feet alongside; deck height, 11½ feet; tandem in-line rotary car dumper with unloading rate of 5,000 tons per hour; traveling shiploader with loading rate of 8,000 tons per hour; receipt and shipment of coal; owned and operated by Massey Coal Terminal Corp.

(112)   **C. & O. Pier 14:** about 0.75 mile southeastward of Pier 8 Terminal; east and west sides 1,090 feet long; 45 feet alongside; deck height, 11½ feet; two traveling coal-loading towers, 4,500-ton-per-hour capacity each; shipment of coal; owned and operated by the Chessie System.

(113)   **C. & O. Pier 15:** eastward of C. & O. Pier 14: west side 1,000 feet long; 38 feet alongside; deck height, 9½ feet; one fixed coal-loading tower on each side of the pier, ship-positioning winches; shipment of coal; owned and operated by the Chessie System. East side is not used.

(114)   **Koch Fuels, Inc. Tanker Dock:** about 200 yards eastward of C. & O. Pier 15; offshore wharf, 203 feet with platform; 35 feet alongside; deck height, 13 feet; storage tanks, 520,000-barrel capacity; receipt and shipment of petroleum products, bunkering vessels; operated by Koch Fuels, Inc.

(115)   The facilities of the Newport News Shipbuilding and Drydock Co. begin 1.7 miles northwest of Newport News Point and extend 2 miles upriver. The company operates five outfitting piers; four drydocks, the largest being 862 feet long, 118 feet wide, and a depth of 31 feet over the sill; and three graving docks used for ship construction and repair, the largest being 1,600 feet long and 250 feet wide with a

depth over the sill of 33 feet. Gantry cranes of 900 and 310 tons serve the graving docks. The shipyard also has two inclining shipways with lengths to 650 feet. The largest shaft produced by the shipyard is 76 feet by 60 inches. Most of the outfitting piers are equipped with cranes; largest has a capacity of 50 tons. Floating derricks up to 67-ton capacity are available at the yard.

(116)   **Willoughby Spit,** on the south side of the entrance to Hampton Roads, is a narrow barrier beach 1.3 miles long in an east-west direction. About midway between the spit and Old Point Comfort, on the opposite side of the entrance, is **Fort Wool,** which is on the south edge of the main ship channel; a light is shown from a small gray house on the north side of the island.

(117)   The 45-foot-wide small-boat openings in the south approach bridge to Hampton Roads Tunnel have clearances of 10 feet.

(118)   **Willoughby Bank,** with depths of 3 to 7 feet, extends east-northeastward along the edge of the main channel for about 2.5 miles from Fort Wool.

(119)   **Willoughby Bay,** on the inner side of Willoughby Spit, has general depths of 7 to 12 feet. On the south side of the bay are the prominent buildings of the Norfolk Naval Base and the Naval Air Station. A marked channel, 0.4 mile westward of Fort Wool, leads to a small-boat harbor behind the hook of Willoughby Spit. In September 1987, the controlling depth was 5½ feet. Some supplies, fuel, and berthing are available. Repairs can be made; largest marine railway, 40 feet.

(120)   The western and southern part of Willoughby Bay is a **restricted area.** (See **334.300,** chapter 2, for limits and regulations.) The northern part of the bay is a **small-craft anchorage.** (See **110.1** and **110.168 (f)** and **(h)),** chapter 2, for limits and regulations.)

(121)   A fixed highway bridge with a clearance of 25 feet crosses the yacht anchorage in the northern part of Willoughby Bay.

(122)   **Charts 12245, 12253.–Norfolk Harbor** comprises a portion of the southern and eastern shores of Hampton Roads and both shores of **Elizabeth River** and its Eastern, Southern, and Western Branches, on which the cities of Norfolk, Portsmouth, and Chesapeake are located.

(123)   The harbor extends from off Sewells Point south in Elizabeth River to the seventh bridge over Southern Branch, a distance of 15 miles; it extends 1.5 miles up Western Branch to a point 0.5 mile above the West Norfolk highway bridge, and up Eastern Branch for 2.5 miles to the Norfolk and Western Railway Bridge.

(124)   The main part of Norfolk is on the east side of Elizabeth River north of Eastern Branch, with Berkley, a subdivision, to the southward between Eastern and Southern Branches. South of Berkley is the city of Chesapeake. Portsmouth is opposite Norfolk, and its waterfront extends along the west shore of Southern Branch and the south shore of Western Branch. These cities form practically a single community, united by the same commercial interests and served by the same ship channel.

(125)   A **safety zone** is in effect in the Elizabeth River when a naval aircraft carrier transits the river to or from the Norfolk Naval Shipyard. (See **165.505,** chapter 2, for limits and regulations.)

(126)   **Weather.–**Norfolk, with an average elevation of 13 feet above sea level and almost surrounded by water, has a modified marine climate. The city's geographic position with respect to the principal storm tracks is especially favorable, being south of the average path of storms originating in the higher latitudes and north of the usual

track of hurricanes and other tropical storms. These features combine to place Norfolk in one of the favored climatic regions of the world. The winters are mild, while autumn and spring seasons usually are delightful. Summers, though warm and long, frequently are tempered by cool periods, often associated with northeasterly winds off the Atlantic. Temperatures of 100° or higher are very infrequent. Cold waves seldom penetrate to this area. Occasional winters pass without a measurable amount of snowfall. Most of Norfolk's snow generally occurs in light falls, which usually melt and disappear within 24 hours. The average date of the last freezing temperature in the spring is March 23, while the average date of the first in autumn is November 18. The average annual amount of rainfall is about 45 inches, and considerably more than one-half of it falls in well-distributed amounts during April to October, inclusive. (See page T–4 **Norfolk climatological table.**)

(127)   **Chart 12245.–Sewells Point** (36°57.8'N., 76°19.6'W.), on the east side of the entrance to Elizabeth River, is 18 miles from the Virginia Capes. A breakwater, marked by a light on its outer end, extends about 0.3 mile westward from the point. The piers of the **Norfolk Naval Base** and its annex extend southward from the breakwater along the east bank of the river. Depths at the naval piers are 33 to 45 feet. A jettied basin at the naval base, 0.6 mile south of Sewells Point, affords protection for navy service craft in depths of 21 to 29 feet.

(128)   **Sewells Point Spit**, covered 3 to 6 feet, extends north-northeastward from the point for 1.4 miles to the outer end of Willoughby Channel.

(129)   A channel, marked by lights and daybeacons, extends eastward and southward through Sewells Point Spit for about 1.2 miles to an enclosed boat basin used by small navy boats. In May 1974, the channel had a controlling depth of 10 feet; depths of 7 to 10 feet were available in the basin.

(130)   The approach to the naval piers is a **restricted area.** (See **334.300(b)(1),** chapter 2, for limits and regulations.)

(131)   **Wharves.**–Norfolk Harbor has numerous wharves and piers of all types, the majority of which are privately owned and operated; only the major deepwater facilities are described. These facilities are southward of Sewells Point, between the Norfolk Naval Base and Tanner Point; on Lamberts Point; on Pinner Point; and on Eastern Branch and Southern Branch of Elizabeth River. All have freshwater connections and access to highways and railroads, and most have electrical shore-power connections. Cargo is generally handled by ship's tackle; special cargo-handling equipment, if available, is mentioned in the description of the particular facility. The alongside depths given for each facility described are reported depths. (For information on the latest depths, contact the operator.) For a complete description of the wharves and piers in Norfolk Harbor refer to Port Series No. 11, published and sold by the U.S. Army Corps of Engineers. (See appendix for address.)

(132)   **Facilities southward of Sewells Point, between Norfolk Naval Base and Tanner Point (chart 12245):**

(133)   **Continental Grain Co. Wharf** (36°55'57"N., 76°19'41"W.): face 1,035 feet; 40 feet alongside; deck height 9 feet; face of wharf in line and contiguous with Virginia Ports Authority Pier B to the westward; 3¼-million-bushel grain elevator; railroad car and truck dumpers; loading tower, marine leg, and conveyor system, combined loading rate 80,000 bushels per hour; receipt and shipment of grains; owned by Virginia Port Authority and operated by Continental Grain Co.

(134)   **Sewells Point Division, Piers A and B:** immediately westward of Continental Grain Co. Wharf; 498-foot face, 32 feet alongside; Pier B (north side) 1,211 feet long, 32 feet alongside; Pier A (south side) 1,193 feet long, 32 feet alongside; deck height, 9½ feet; 230,000 square feet covered storage; cranes up to 15-ton capacity; receipt and shipment of general cargo and shipment of scrap metal; owned by Virginia Ports Authority and operated by Lamberts Point Docks, Inc. A buoy marks a shoal just northward of Pier B.

(135)   **Lehigh Portland Cement Pier:** 150 yards southward of Virginia Ports Authority Piers; 40-foot face, 205 feet with dolphins; 33 feet alongside; deck height, 11½ feet; 33,000-ton storage capacity; unloading rate 600 tons per hour; receipt of bulk cement; owned and operated by Lehigh Portland Cement Co.

(136)   **Exxon Co., U.S.A. Pier** (36°55'39"N., 76°20'00"W.): about 0.2 mile southward of Sewells Point Division Piers; north and south sides 1,300 feet; north side, 40 feet alongside; south side, 20 to 30 feet alongside; deck height, 9 feet; storage tanks, 2½-million-barrel capacity; receipt and shipment of petroleum products, bunkering vessels; owned and operated by Exxon Co., U.S.A.

(137)   **Norfolk International Terminals:** 900,000 square feet covered storage; 300,000 cubic feet cold storage; 55 acres open storage; deck heights, 9½ feet; receipt and shipment of general and containerized cargo; receipt of logs; passengers; owned by Virginia Ports Authority and operated by Virginia International Terminals.

(138)   **Pier 2** (36°55'02"N., 76°19'56"W.): 334-foot face, north and south sides 1,328 feet long; 35 feet along north side, 42 feet along south side.

(139)   **North Berth:** immediately northward of Pier 2; 950-foot marginal wharf; 32 feet alongside; roll-on/roll-off berth.

(140)   **Pier 1:** about 200 yards southward of Pier 2; 308-foot face, north and south sides 1,320 feet long; 42 feet along north side, 35 feet along south side; fumigation chambers.

(141)   **Container Berths 1, 2, 3, and 4:** immediately southward of Pier 1; 2,688-foot marginal wharf; 35 to 41 feet alongside; one 30-ton and three 40-ton dual hoist cranes, three 40-ton traveling container carriers.

(142)   **Facilities at Lamberts Point (chart 12253):**

(143)   **Norfolk and Western Railway Co. Piers:** owned and operated by Norfolk and Western Railway Co.; shipment of coal.

(144)   **Pier 6** (36°52'45"N., 76°19'54"W.): 88-foot face; 45 feet alongside; north and south sides 1,600 feet, 1,850 feet with dolphins, 50 feet alongside; deck height, 11 feet; two electric shiploaders, loading rate 5,000 tons per hour each.

(145)   **Pier 5:** about 200 yards southward of Pier 6; 74-foot face; north and south sides 1850 feet; 36 feet alongside; deck height, 11 feet; one electric dumper with a loading capacity of 1,000 tons per hour; ship-positioning winches on south side.

(146)   **Virginia Ports Authority Terminal, Piers N, L, and P:** 1.5 million square feet covered storage; 100,000 cubic feet cold storage space; fumigation chambers; storage tanks, 10,000-ton capacity; forklift trucks and other portable mechanized cargo-handling equipment; cranes up to 25-ton capacity; receipt and shipment of general and containerized cargo; receipt of castor oil and shipment of soybean, palm and coconut oils; owned by Virginia Ports Authority and operated by Lamberts Point Docks, Inc.

(147)   **Pier N** (36°52'00"N., 76°19'06"W.): 390-foot face, 24 feet alongside; north and south sides 1,100 feet long, 32 feet alongside; deck height, 11½ feet.

(148)   **Pier L:** about 200 yards southeastward of Pier N; 243-foot face; north side 1,180 feet, south side 1,200 feet long; 32 feet alongside; deck height, 9 feet.

(149) Pier P: about 600 yards southeastward of Pier N; 396-foot face; north and south sides 1,196 feet long; 32 feet alongside; deck height, 11 feet.

(150) **Facilities at Port Norfolk (chart 12253):**

(151) **Portsmouth Marine Terminal** (36°51'27"N., 76°19'27"W.): 2,536-foot face; 60-foot roll-on/roll-off ramp; 36 feet alongside except 31 feet near the west end; deck height, 12 feet; 200,000 square feet covered storage, 215 acres open storage; cranes to 110 tons, container cranes to 30 tons; fumigation chambers; receipt and shipment of general, containerized and roll-on/roll-off cargo; receipt of automobiles; shipment of tobacco; owned by Virginia Ports Authority and operated by Virginia International Terminals.

(152) **Sea-Land Service Terminal** (36°51'28"N., 76°19'04"W.): 600-foot face, 1,000 feet with dolphins; 38 feet alongside; deck height, 12 feet; 30,000 square feet covered storage, open storage for 650 containers; two 30-ton container cranes; receipt and shipment of general and containerized cargo; owned and operated by Sea-Land Service, Inc.

(153) **Facilities in Eastern Branch of Elizabeth River (chart 12253):**

(154) **Norfolk, Baltimore, and Carolina Line Terminal:** 33,000 square feet covered storage area; receipt and shipment of containerized general cargo in the intracoastal trade; owned and operated by the Norfolk, Baltimore, and Carolina Line, Inc.

(155) Pier No. 2 (36°50'33"N., 76°17'07"W.): 68-foot face; 20 feet alongside; deck height, 8 feet.

(156) Pier No. 1: about 50 yards eastward of Pier 2; 46-foot face, 20 feet alongside; deck height, 8 feet.

(157) **Chemphalt Wharf** (36°50'19"N., 76°16'19"W.): 50-foot offshore wharf with 300 feet of berthing space with dolphins; 35 feet alongside; deck height, 9 feet; storage tanks, 300,000-barrel capacity; receipt of asphalt, liquid fertilizer, and styrene monomer; owned and operated by Chemphalt of Carolina Corp.

(158) **Facilities in Southern Branch of Elizabeth River, Berkley, Chesapeake, and Portsmouth (chart 12253):**

(159) **U.S. Gypsum Co. Wharf** (36°49'18"N., 76°17'23"W.): 40-foot offshore wharf, 370 feet with dolphins; 27 feet alongside; deck height, 10 feet; storage shed, 47,000-ton capacity; open storage for 100,000 tons; receipt of gypsum rock; owned and operated by U. S. Gypsum Co.

(160) **Crown Central Petroleum Corp. Wharf** (36°49'14"N., 76°17'24"W.): 40-foot T-head pier, 145 feet with dolphins; 30 feet alongside; deck height, 6 feet; 214,000-barrel storage capacity; receipt and shipment of petroleum products; operated by Crown Central Petroleum Corp.

(161) **Mobil Oil Corp. Tanker Wharf** (36°49'11"N., 76°17'23"W.): 75-foot T-head wharf, 750 feet with dolphins; 36 feet alongside; deck height, 10 feet; receipt and shipment of petroleum products, bunkering vessels; 683,000-barrel storage facility; owned by Mobil Oil Corp., operated by Mobil Oil Corp., and Union Oil Co. of California.

(162) **Gulf Oil Co. Wharf:** 200 yards south of Mobil Oil Wharf; 1,020-foot face, 30 to 32 feet alongside; deck height, 12 feet; receipt and shipment of petroleum products, bunkering vessels; 800,000-barrel storage facility; owned and operated by Gulf Oil Refining and Marketing Co.

(163) **Lone Star Industries, Cement Wharf:** 100 yards south of Gulf Oil Co. Wharf; 27-foot platforms with 267 feet of berthing space; 35 feet alongside; deck height, 10 feet; silos, 37,000-ton capacity; receipt of cement clinker; owned and operated by Lone Star Industries, Inc.

(164) **Royster Co. Wharf** (36°48'46"N., 76°17'24"W.): marginal type wharf, 450 feet with dolphins; 25 feet alongside;

deck height, 9 feet; shipment of fertilizer products; owned and operated by Royster Co.

(165) **Amoco Oil Co. Wharf** (36°48'21"N., 76°17'22"W.): 60-foot T-head pier, 235 feet with dolphins; 27 to 29 feet alongside; deck height, 11 feet; 655,000-barrel storage facility; receipt and shipment of petroleum products; receipt of asphalt; shipment of soybean oil; bunkering vessels; owned and operated by Amoco Oil Co.

(166) **Cargill Grain South Elevator Dock** (36°48'06"N., 76°17'20"W.): 500-foot face 39 feet alongside; deck height, 10 feet; 6¾-million-bushel elevator; elevator loading rate 60,000 bushels per hour; shipment of grain and soybean meal; owned and operated by Cargill Inc.

(167) **Texaco Oil Co. Wharf** (36°47'51"N., 76°17'29"W.): marginal wharf, 565 feet with dolphins; 32 feet alongside; deck height, 12 feet; 1½-million-barrel storage capacity; receipt and shipment of petroleum products; receipt of asphalt; bunkering vessels; owned and operated by Texaco Inc.

(168) **Conoco Wharf** (36°47'44"N., 76°17'32"W.): 145-foot T-head wharf, 650 feet with dolphins; 31 feet alongside; deck height, 10 feet; receipt and shipment of petroleum products; 700,000-barrel storage facility; owned and operated by Conoco.

(169) **Lone Star Industries Ulexite Plant Pier** (36°47'27"N., 76°17'50"W.): north side, 447 feet long; 36 feet alongside; deck height, 12 feet; open storage for 27,000 tons; receipt and shipment of pumice and ulexite, shipment of fertilizer; owned and operated by Lone Star Industries, Inc.

(170) **Tenneco-Cities Service Pier** (36°47'22"N., 76°18'07"W.): 55-foot face, 208 feet with dolphins; 27 feet alongside; deck height, 8 feet; storage tanks, 350,000-barrel capacity; receipt and shipment of petroleum products; receipt of creosote and coal tar; owned and operated by Tenneco-Cities Service.

(171) **Amerada Hess Corp. Tanker Dock** (36°47'06"N., 76°18'10"W.): 68-foot offshore wharf with berthing space for vessels to 700 feet; 35 feet alongside; deck height, 13½ feet; tanks, 500,000-barrel storage capacity; receipt and shipment of petroleum products; owned and operated by Amerada Hess Corp.

(172) **Atlantic Cement Co. Wharf** (36°46'42"N., 76°18'22"W.): 465 feet long with dolphins; 30 to 31 feet alongside; deck height, 10½ feet; 31,000-ton capacity storage silos; receipt of bulk cement; owned and operated by Atlantic Cement Co.

(173) **Elizabeth River Terminals, Piers 1 and 2** (36°46'40"N., 76°18'05"W.): Pier 1, 1200 feet long with dolphins; 35 feet alongside; deck height, 8½ feet; Pier 2, 750 feet long with dolphins; 14 feet alongside; deck height, 11 feet; 225,000 square feet covered storage; 350,000 square feet of open storage; 36,000 tons of tank storage; cranes to 50 tons; receipt and shipment of liquid sulfur; receipt of chemicals, scrap metals, and bulk materials; shipment of fertilizer and animal feed; owned and operated by Elizabeth River Terminals, Inc.

(174) **Chilean Nitrate Wharf** (36°46.6'N., 76°17.7'W.): 350-foot offshore wharf, 395 feet with dolphins; 32 feet alongside; deck height, 11 feet; covered storage for 28,000 tons of fertilizer; receipt of bulk fertilizers; owned and operated by the Chilean Nitrate Sales Corp.

(175) **Smith-Douglass Wharf** (36°46'25"N., 76°17'40"W.): 365-foot face, 500 feet long with dolphins; 30 feet alongside; deck height, 12 feet; covered storage for 65,000 tons of fertilizer; receipt of spent sulphuric acid; owned and operated by Smith-Douglass Division of Borden Chemical Co.

(176) **Hitch Terminal Tanker Wharf** (36°46′21″N., 76°17′51″W.): 30-foot offshore wharf, 200 feet long with dolphins; 30 feet alongside; deck height, 8 feet; tank storage for nitrogen, capacity 146,000 barrels, petroleum tank storage, capacity 323,000 barrels; receipt of liquid nitrogen; owned by Arthur Hitch, Jr.; operated by Hitch Terminal Corp. and Swift Nitrogen Terminal.

(177) **American Hoechst Corp. Wharf** (36°45′28″N., 76°17′37″W.): offshore wharf, 190 feet long with dolphins; 22 feet alongside; deck height, 10 feet; storage tanks for 120,000 barrels; receipt of styrene monomer; owned and operated by American Hoechst Corp.

(178) **Portsmouth Power Station Wharf** (36°46′11″N., 76°17′55″W.): 75-foot face, berthing space for vessels to 800 feet; 36 feet alongside; deck height, 10 feet; storage tanks for 475,000 barrels; receipt of fuel oils for plant consumption; owned and operated by Virginia Electric and Power Co.

(179) **Swann Oil Co. Wharf** (36°46′36″N., 76°18′25″W.): 50-foot T-head pier, 280 feet with dolphins; 35 feet alongside; deck height, 12 feet; 850,000-barrel storage facility; receipt of petroleum products; owned and operated by Swann Oil Co.

(180) **Atlantic Energy, Inc. Wharf** (36°46′43″N., 76°18′41″W.): 30-foot offshore wharf, 700 feet of berthing with dolphins; 32 feet alongside; storage tanks, 480,000-barrel capacity; receipt of liquified petroleum gases; owned and operated by Atlantic Energy, Inc.

(181) **Alcoa Transfer Station Pier** (39°47′54″N., 76°17′42″W.): 750 feet long; 42 feet alongside; deck height, 15 feet; 55,000-ton storage tank; unloading tower with unloading rate of 1,100 tons per hour; and conveyor system to storage tank; receipt of alumina; owned and operated by Aluminum Co. of America.

(182) **BP Oil Co. Wharf** (36°47′57″N., 76°17′45″W.): 317-foot offshore wharf, 360 feet of berthing with dolphins; 30 feet alongside; deck height, 12 feet; storage tanks, 410,000-barrel capacity; shipment of petroleum products; owned and operated by the BP Oil Co., Inc.

(183) **Allied Mills Wharf** (36°48′00″N., 76°17′45″W.): 81-foot face, 275 feet of berthing with dolphins; 25 feet alongside; deck height, 12 feet; receipt of bulk molasses; 2-million-gallon molasses storage tank; grain elevator, 375,000-bushel capacity; owned by Allied Mills Inc.; operated by Southgate Molasses Co. Inc.

(184) A disposal area, enclosed by levees, is in Hampton Roads on the north side of Craney Island. A smaller levee extends eastward from the lower east side of the disposal area to a dolphin 0.2 mile west of the ship channel; the section of the levee east of about 36°54.0′N., 76°20.8′W. covers at high water.

(185) **Lafayette River** empties into the east side of Elizabeth River 4 miles south of Sewells Point and 22 miles from the Virginia Capes. The river, used exclusively by pleasure and recreational craft, is entered by a marked dredged channel between **Tanner Point** and Lamberts Point, 1.5 miles to the southward. A light, 0.6 mile south of Tanner Point, marks the channel entrance. The dredged channel leads for 1.1 miles to a point about 0.3 mile westward of the Hampton Boulevard Bridge. From this point, a marked natural channel leads for about 2.4 miles to where the river divides into two forks. In August 1984, the controlling depth was 8 feet in the dredged section; thence depths of about 6 feet to the forks, and 2 to 4 feet up each fork; the chart is the best guide. The dredged channel turns sharply at the light off **Lawless Point,** a mile above the entrance, and vessels must be on the alert to avoid grounding. **General and small-craft anchorages** extend up Lafayette River to the first bridge.

(See **110.168 (c) and (h)**, chapter 2, for limits and regulations.)

(186) **Hampton Boulevard Bridge,** 1.5 miles above the entrance to Lafayette River, has a fixed channel span with a clearance of 26 feet. A yacht club is just below the north end of the bridge.

(187) **Knitting Mill Creek,** is on the south side of Lafayette River about 3 miles above the mouth. In May 1985, the creek had a midchannel controlling depth of 4 feet to the head. Some supplies, gasoline, and berths are available within the creek. Repairs can be made; largest marine railway, 40 feet; lift, 10 tons.

(188) **East Haven,** on the south side of Lafayette River about 3.5 miles above the mouth, has a dredged channel that leads to a settling basin and boat ramp at the head. In January 1981, a controlling depth of 6 feet was in the channel and 8 feet in the basin.

(189) **Granby Street Bridge,** 3.5 miles above the entrance to Lafayette River, has a 40-foot fixed span with a clearance of 22 feet.

(190) Just above Granby Street Bridge (chart 12253), Lafayette River divides into two forks, both unmarked. A fixed highway bridge over the mouth of the north fork has a channel width of 30 feet and a clearance of 10 feet. In 1986, a replacement fixed bridge with a design clearance of 18 feet was under construction adjacent to the existing bridge. A fixed highway bridge over the south fork, a mile from Granby Street Bridge, has a channel width of 27 feet and a clearance of 9 feet; another fixed highway bridge 0.3 mile farther up the south fork has a channel width of 23 feet and a clearance of 4 feet.

(191) **Chart 12253.**–**Craney Island,** now a part of the mainland, is on the west side of Elizabeth River 4.5 miles south of Sewells Point. The low and thinly wooded area is the site of a navy fuel depot, and the offshore wharf and piers, all on the eastern side, are used only by Government vessels. Two daybeacons close off the northeast end of Craney Island mark submerged rocks. The offshore wharf and piers have depths of 22 to 47 feet alongside. A submerged water main crosses from Craney Island to the north side of Lamberts Point; vessels are cautioned not to anchor in the vicinity of the lighted range that marks the crossing. **Portsmouth Coast Guard Station** is on the west side of the entrance to Craney Island Creek.

(192) **Lamberts Point,** on the east side of Elizabeth River 5.3 miles south of Sewells Point, is the site of several deepwater piers. These facilities were described earlier in this chapter under Wharves, Norfolk Harbor.

(193) **Western Branch** (36°52.0′N., 76°19.7′W.) empties into the southwest side of Elizabeth River 5.8 miles south of Sewells Point and 23.8 miles from the capes. A marked channel leads from the main channel in Elizabeth River for 4.5 miles upstream. In June-July 1987, the midchannel controlling depth was 18 feet in the dredged channel to about 0.25 mile above the first bridge; then in 1980, about 7 feet could be carried to **Drum Point,** 0.5 mile above the third bridge.

(194) A 540-foot lighted pier about 1 mile above the entrance to Western Branch extends to the northern edge of the marked channel; mariners are advised to use caution in the area. A fixed highway bridge, about 1.2 miles above the entrance, has a clearance of 45 feet.

(195) **West Norfolk,** northward of the fixed bridge, has a shipyard and small-craft facilities. Supplies, fuel, and slips are available. Repairs can be made; largest marine railway, 220 feet.

(196) **Churchland** twin fixed highway bridges, 2.3 miles above the entrance to Western Branch, have clearances of 38 feet. The overhead power cable on the upper side of the bridge has a clearance of 45 feet; the transmission towers are marked by lights.

(197) A 280-foot fishing pier extends from the southeast shore about 1.4 miles above the Churchland bridges. An overhead power cable close upstream of the pier has a clearance of 47 feet. **Hodges Ferry** fixed highway bridge, 4.7 miles above the entrance, has a clearance of 18 feet. The overhead power cable on the upstream side of the Hodges Ferry bridge has a clearance of 37 feet.

(198) **Pinner Point** (36°51.3′N., 76°19.1′W.) is on the southwest side of Elizabeth River, 6.8 miles from Sewells Point. Most of the piers at the point have been destroyed by fire or are in poor condition; they are being razed or renovated. The Portsmouth Marine Terminals, Inc. operates the facilities at the Portsmouth Marine Terminal about 0.3 mile northwestward of Pinner Point. A marked dredged channel leads from Elizabeth River to a docking area at the terminal. In July 1979, the controlling depth to and in the docking area was 35 feet. The facilities of the Portsmouth Marine Terminal and those at Pinner Point were described earlier in this chapter under Wharves, Norfolk Harbor.

(199) **Scott Creek** (36°51.1′N., 76°18.5′W.), on the southwest side of Elizabeth River 7.3 miles from Sewells Point, is entered through a channel, marked by daybeacons, which had a controlling depth of 4½ feet in March 1971. The channel leads to old fishing wharves now used by pleasure craft. A marina with a 60-ton lift is on the S side of the creek about 0.4 mile above channel entrance. A marina is on the point on the south side of the creek, about 0.9 mile above the channel entrance. Berths, water, a 60-foot marine railway, and a 3½-ton fixed lift are available; hull repairs can be made.

(200) **Hospital Point**, on the southwest side of Elizabeth River 7.5 miles from Sewells Point, is the site of a U.S. Naval Hospital. The main hospital building, the largest structure along the southwest side of Elizabeth River, is visible for many miles. The hospital landing has depths of about 18 feet at the face.

(201) **Norfolk**, or parts of it, has been described at some length in the preceding text. The midpoint of the downtown section can be taken as the **City Wharf** (36°50.9′N., 76°17.8′W.) at the foot of West Main Street, which is on the northwest side of Elizabeth River 7.7 miles from Sewells Point and 25.7 miles from the Virginia Capes. City Wharf has depths of 15 feet at the face, but is in poor condition. The wharves northwest and southwest of West Main Street have depths of 14 to 20 feet alongside.

(202) (See page T–7 for **Norfolk climatological table.**) A **weather** summary for Norfolk is given in the preceding text under Norfolk Harbor.

(203) **Smith Creek**, opposite Hospital Point 7.5 miles from Sewells Point, has entrance depths of about 3 feet with deeper water inside, but the entrance is restricted by a 48-foot-wide fixed highway bridge with a clearance of 13 feet. **Small-craft anchorages** are in Smith Creek. (See **110.1 and 110.168 (d)(4) and (h)**, chapter 2, for limits and regulations.)

(204) The **Atlantic Marine Center**, the Atlantic shipbase of the National Ocean Service, is on the east side of the entrance to Smith Creek. There are 243-, 251-, and 312-foot berths along the bulkhead wharf, which has depths of 20 feet alongside.

(205) **Waterside** is in the downtown area of **Town Point**, on Norfolk, the north side of the intersection between Elizabeth River and Eastern Branch. A municipal marina at this popular tourist stop has reported depths of about 16 feet at the entrance, inside the marina, and alongside the berths. Transient berths are available year-round. A sewage pump-out station is at the marina. Electricity is at the berths; ice and provisions are available nearby. The marina staff monitors VHF-FM channels 16 and 68.

(206) **Eastern Branch** (36°50.5′N., 76°17.6′W.) empties into the east side of Elizabeth River 8 miles from Sewells Point and 26 miles from the Virginia Capes.

(207) A Federal project provides for a channel 25 feet deep to the Norfolk and Western Railway Bridge, 2.5 miles above the entrance. (See Notice to Mariners and latest edition of the charts for controlling depths.)

(208) Above the Norfolk and Western Railway Bridge, the natural channel has depths of 10 to 18 feet to the forks 3.3 miles from the entrance, and usually is marked by bush stakes.

(209) **General anchorages** are in Eastern Branch. (See **110.168 (e) and (h)**, chapter 2, for limits and regulations.)

(210) Downtown Norfolk is on the north side of Eastern Branch, and **Berkley**, a subdivision, is on the south side. Traffic is fairly heavy as far as Campostella Bridge. Depths at most of the piers on both sides of the branch range from 14 to 25 feet.

(211) The highway bridge, 0.4 mile above the entrance to Eastern Branch, has a bascule span with a clearance of 48 feet. The Norfolk and Western Railway Bridge, 1 mile above the entrance, has a bascule span with a clearance of 4 feet. (See **117.1 through 117.49**, chapter 2, for drawbridge regulations.) An overhead power cable 200 yards east of this bridge has a clearance of 150 feet.

(212) **Campostella Bridge**, 1.4 miles above the entrance to Eastern Branch, has a fixed span with a clearance of 65 feet. The Norfolk and Western Railway Bridge, 2.5 miles above the entrance, has a swing span with a clearance of 6 feet. (See **117.1 through 117.59 and 117.1007(a)**, chapter 2, for drawbridge regulations.)

(213) There are several shipyards along Eastern Branch: the largest floating drydock has a 3,200-ton capacity and handles vessels up to 316 feet; the largest marine railway has a 5,500-ton capacity and can handle vessels to 380 feet.

(214) **Southern Branch**, the continuation of Elizabeth River south of the junction with Eastern Branch, is a part of the **Intracoastal Waterway** route southward to Albemarle Sound. The waterway is described at length in **United States Coast Pilot 4, Atlantic Coast, Cape Henry to Key West.**

(215) The Federal project for Southern Branch provides for a channel 40 feet deep to the third bridge, thence 35 feet deep to the seventh bridge. The channel is maintained at or near project dimensions, and is well marked. (See Notice to Mariners and latest edition of the charts for controlling depths.)

(216) A **speed limit** of 6 knots is prescribed by **162.55**, chapter 2, for that part of Southern Branch between Eastern Branch and the first bridge.

(217) The Norfolk and Portsmouth Belt Line Railroad Bridge, 1.9 miles south of the junction with Eastern Branch and 9.9 miles from Sewells Point, has a vertical-lift span with a clearance of 6 feet down and 142 feet up. (See **117.1 through 117.49**, chapter 2, for drawbridge regulations.) State Route 337 highway bridge, 0.2 mile southward of the Norfolk and Portsmouth Belt Line Railroad Bridge, has a vertical lift span with a clearance of 15 feet down and 145 feet up. The Norfolk and Western Railway Bridge, 10.9 miles from Sewells Point, has a vertical lift span with a clearance of 10 feet down and 135 feet up. (See **117.1 through 117.59 and 117.997**, chapter 2, for drawbridge regulations.)

(218) U.S. Routes 13 and 460 highway bridge and the Norfolk and Western Railway Bridge, immediately to the southward, 13.1 miles from Sewells Point, have bascule spans with a least clearance of 7 feet. (See **117.1 through 117.49,** chapter 2, for drawbridge regulations.) Large vessels must exercise caution when making the turns to these bridges because of the current.

(219) The facilities on the east side of Southern Branch are mostly shipyards, oil terminals, and bulk-cargo piers, while Government installations front most of the west side.

(220) The port facilities on the Berkley side of Southern Branch were described earlier in this chapter under Wharves, Norfolk Harbor.

(221) The shipyard at Berkley has six piers that can accommodate vessels up to 1,200 feet. The largest floating drydock at the yard is 850 feet long over the keel blocks, 192 feet wide, 36 feet deep over the keel blocks, and has a lifting capacity of 54,250 tons. A marine railway with a capacity of 1,000 tons is available at the shipyard; cranes up to 67 tons are also available. The largest shaft the shipyard is able to produce is 100 feet by 30 inches.

(222) The **Norfolk Naval Shipyard** is on the **Portsmouth** side of Southern Branch, 3.5 miles from Lamberts Point, and occupies about 2 miles of waterfront. There are naval **restricted** areas along this reach. (See **334.290,** chapter 2, for limits and regulations.)

(223) Most of the oil terminals are at **Chesapeake,** on the east side of Southern Branch, 10 miles from Sewells Point and 28 miles from the Capes. These facilities, as well as the deep-draft bulk cargo, grain, chemical, and fertilizer piers and wharves, were described earlier in this chapter under Wharves, Norfolk Harbor.

11. CHESAPEAKE BAY, YORK AND RAPPAHANNOCK RIVERS

(1) This chapter describes the western shore of Chesapeake Bay from Old Point Comfort to the Potomac River including its principal tributaries Back, Poquoson, York, Piankatank, Rappahannock, and Great Wicomico Rivers, and Mobjack Bay. Also discussed are the ports of Yorktown, Fredericksburg, West Point, Tappahannock, Kilmarnock, and Reedville, as well as several of the smaller ports and landings on these waterways.

(2) **COLREGS Demarcation Lines.**–The lines established for Chesapeake Bay are described in **80.510**, chapter 2.

(3) **Charts 12221, 12225.**–The western shore of Chesapeake Bay from Old Point Comfort to the Potomac River is mostly low. York and Rappahannock Rivers are broad and deep at their entrances and are navigable for long distances.

(4) **Fishtraps** are thicker in this area than in any other part of the bay. **Ice** is seldom encountered this far south in the bay, but may be found in the upper parts of some of the tributaries.

(5) **Channels.**–The Federal project for Chesapeake Bay provides for depths of 50 feet in the main channel between the Virginia Capes and Fort McHenry, Baltimore. There are three dredged sections in the lower Chesapeake Bay: the first off Cape Henry, just above the Virginia Capes; the second off York Spit, 11 to 22 miles above the Capes; and the third off Rappahannock Spit, 40 to 46 miles above the Capes; they are well marked. (See Notice to Mariners and latest editions of the charts for controlling depths.)

(6) **York Spit Channel** begins 11 miles above the Capes and extends northward another 11 miles. The current velocity is about 1.0 knot in the channel.

(7) **Chart 12222.**–Horseshoe is a shoal that extends several miles out from the shore between Old Point Comfort and Back River, 6.5 miles to the northward. The southern edge of the shoal lies along the north side of the main channel into Hampton Roads; the eastern half has depths of 13 to 18 feet, and the western half, 6 to 11 feet. Local vessels drawing 7 feet or less use the lanes through the fishtraps on the Horseshoe when navigating between Hampton Roads and York River or Mobjack Bay. The tidal current velocity is 0.5 knot over the Horseshoe and is rotary, turning clockwise.

(8) A naval **restricted area** extends eastward and southward of Old Point Comfort, and a **danger zone** of the **Fort Monroe** firing range extends to seaward from a point 1.5 miles northward of the point. (See **334.350 and 334.360**, chapter 2, for limits and regulations, respectively.)

(9) **Salt Ponds** is entered through a privately dredged inlet on the west side of Chesapeake Bay about 4 miles north of Old Point Comfort. The entrance is marked by private aids. In 1980, the controlling depth just inside the inlet was 6½ feet. Sand dunes protect Salt Ponds from the open waters of the bay. A marina is on the east and west sides of Salt Ponds.

(10) **Back River** empties into the west side of Chesapeake Bay 7 miles northward of Old Point Comfort between **Northend Point** and **Plumtree Island**, 1 mile to the northward. A firing and bombing **danger zone** is north of the entrance to Back River. (See **334.340**, chapter 2, for limits and

regulations.) The approach to Back River, from southeastward through a lane in the fishtraps, is well marked. The mean range of tide is 2.3 feet at the entrance.

(11) About 2 miles above the mouth, Back River divides into **Northwest Branch** and **Southwest Branch**, which have general depths of 2 to 5 feet. The **Langley Field** hangars, water tanks, and wind tunnel back of Willoughby Point, between the branches, can be seen for many miles. In 1979, the marked channel that extends 3 miles from the mouth of the river to the Langley Field fuel pier on the west side of Southwest Branch had a controlling depth of about 12 feet. In August 1982, shoaling to 3 feet was reported on the south side of the channel about 150 yards east-northeastward of Light 9. In December 1985, a bare shoal was reported to extend about 60 feet north of Light 9. The Langley Yacht Club, just south of the fuel pier, has gasoline and supplies; the depth in the basin is about 4 feet. A marked side channel to the Langley Field boathouse, on the south side of Northwest Branch 3 miles above the river mouth, has a controlling depth of about 7 feet.

(12) A marina on the south side of Back River, just east of **Windmill Point** 1 mile above the mouth, has gasoline, diesel fuel, and supplies; marine railways can handle boats up to 40 feet. The reported depth to the marina is about 6½ feet.

(13) **Harris River,** on the south side of Back River west of **Windmill Point**, has depths of 6 feet in a marked channel that leads to a marina inside **Stony Point**. Some supplies, gasoline, diesel fuel, and berths are available. Repairs can be made; mobile lift, 20 tons.

(14) **Messick Point** is on the north side of Back River, 1.5 miles above the mouth.

(15) The side-by-side highway and rail bridges over Southwest Branch, 1.5 miles above Willoughby Point, have fixed spans with a minimum width of 18 feet and a clearance of 6 feet.

(16) Between Back River and Poquoson River are shoals that extend 1 to 3 miles from shore; on the shoals are scattered oyster rocks that bare, or nearly bare, at low water. Strangers should stay outside the 6-foot curve. A buoyed lane, about 0.6 mile outside the 6-foot curve, extends northwestward through a fishtrap area from about 2.4 miles east-southeast of Northend Point to about 1.6 miles west-southwest of York Spit Light. In September 1980, poles were reported in the lane in about 37°09′54″N., 76°16′21″W., 37°10′45″N., 76°16′42″W., and 37°10′51″N., 76°16′48″W.

(17) **Chart 12238.**–Poquoson River, which empties into Chesapeake Bay 5 miles northwest of Back River, has depths of 7 feet to the village of **Yorkville**, on the west side 2.5 miles above the mouth. The marked approach to the river is from northeastward and is clear of fishtraps for a width of 400 yards. There is a light on either side of the entrance. The mean range of tide is 2.4 feet.

(18) **Bennett Creek,** on the southeast side of the Poquoson River mouth, has depths of 6 feet or more for 1.3 miles to **Easton Cove**, which makes off to the eastward. The channel is marked as far as White House Cove, on the west side of Bennett Creek 0.8 mile above the mouth; the channel in White House Cove is marked by daybeacons and has depths of 8 to 2 feet for 0.7 mile above the mouth. A 50-ton mobile hoist at the basin on the north side of the cove entrance can handle boats for hull repairs. Gasoline and diesel fuel are

available at a marina near the south end of the cove. A "no wake" **speed limit** is in effect in White House Cove.

(19)   **Chisman Creek,** on the north side of the Poquoson River mouth, has depths of 9 feet or more in a narrow channel for 1.3 miles above its entrance. There are boatyards on the south side, 1 mile above the entrance; gasoline is available; the largest marine railway can handle boats up to 100 feet for hull repairs. The creek is marked by daybeacons and a light.

(20)   **Back Creek,** 1.5 miles south of York River, has depths of 7 feet for 2 miles. The entrance is marked by lights and daybeacons. The creek is used by oystering and fishing boats. A State-owned wharf on the south side, 1.4 miles above the mouth, has a depth of about 9 feet at the face. Gasoline, diesel fuel, limited berthing, and some supplies are available at a marina on the south side, 1.8 miles above the mouth; repairs can be made.

(21)   Passage northward from Back Creek to York River can be made through the **Thorofare,** about 0.8 mile from the mouth of Back Creek. In January-February 1980, the dredged channel, marked by lights and daybeacons, had a midchannel controlling depth of 3½ feet.

(22)   **Charts 12238, 12241, 12243.–York River** formed by the junction of Mattaponi and Pamunkey Rivers 29 miles about the mouth, is 15 miles northward of Old Point Comfort and 26 miles by the main channel from Cape Henry. Traffic on York River consists chiefly of pulpwood, petroleum products, military supplies, and shellfish. Drafts of vessels using the river are mostly 18 feet or less, but deep-draft vessels navigate the lower reaches.

(23)   York River has a broad and fairly straight channel, is well marked and easily followed. Depths are as much as 80 feet off Yorktown. In 1982, the controlling depth in the dredged sections of the river was 18 feet to West Point. Vessels can anchor in the wider parts of York River channel aside from the naval areas described later.

(24)   The mean range of tide is 2.2 feet at the entrance to York River, 2.4 feet at Yorktown, and 2.8 feet at West Point. The currents in York River follow the general direction of the channel except in the narrowest parts where there is a tendency to set a vessel onto the shoals. The velocity varies throughout the river; the times of slack water and strengths of current become later going up the river. The normal conditions are subject to change by winds and freshets.

(25)   **Ice** sometimes interferes with navigation of York River for short periods during severe winters, but in ordinary winters there is no interruption below West Point.

(26)   **Caution.–**Ships and craft underway in York River are to proceed at reduced speed and exercise extreme caution in order to reduce generated water motion and to prevent damage to the Virginia Fisheries Laboratory equipment and facilities located downstream from the Coleman Memorial Bridge, in the vicinity of Gloucester Point, ships and craft loading volatile fuels at the American Oil Co. refinery pier, and other craft and property close to the shores of the river. In no instance should the **speed** of ships underway upriver from the Tue Marshes Light exceed 12 knots.

(27)   **Pilotage** on the York River is compulsory for all foreign vessels and for U.S. vessels under register in the foreign trade. Pilotage is optional for U.S. vessels in the coastwise trade which have on board a pilot licensed by the Federal Government to operate in these waters.

(28)   The Chesapeake and Interstate Pilots Association offers pilot services to U.S. vessels, engaged in the coastwise trade, and public vessels to any port or place on the York River. Arrangements for pilots may be made through ships'

agents or the pilot office in Norfolk (telephone, 804-855-2733; cable, CINPILOT). Pilots will meet vessels entering from sea at Cape Henry (discussed in chapter 9), and will meet a vessel at its port if it is on the Chesapeake Bay and its tributaries or Delaware Bay and River and provide pilot services directly to the York River. The Virginia Pilots Association offers pilotage to all vessels. Pilot service above Cheatham Annex is available only during daylight. (See Pilotage, chapters 3 and 9.)

(29)   **Supplies** are available at Yorktown, West Point, and at other places described in this chapter. **Repairs** can be made to small vessels in Perrin River, Sarah Creek, and at other places.

(30)   **Chart 12238.–York Spit** extends outward along the northeast side of the York River approach channel for 7 miles from Guinea Marshes; the inner half of the spit has depths of 1 to 6 feet, and the outer half 10 to 20 feet.

(31)   **York Spit Light** (37°12.6'N., 76°15.3' W.), 30 feet above the water, is shown from a pile with a red and white diamond-shaped daymark, in depths of 12 feet near the outer end of the spit. The light is 19.8 miles above Cape Charles.

(32)   The York River approach channel, extending from about 7 miles southeast of York Spit Light to about 3 miles northwest of the light, has a controlling depth of about 37 feet and is well marked. There are natural depths in excess of 37 feet from the north end of the dredged section to the naval installation 5 miles above Yorktown bridge.

(33)   About 1.5 miles northwest of York Spit Light, a buoyed lane extends northeastward through the fishtraps. The lane has depths of 15 feet or more and can be used by medium-draft vessels approaching York River from northward.

(34)   The swash channel through York Spit about 5 miles northwest of York Spit Light has a controlling depth of about 7 feet; it is marked by a light and daybeacons. The channel shows up well on a bright day.

(35)   **Chart 12241.–**The entrance to York River is between **Tue Point** and **Guinea Marshes,** 25.9 miles above the Virginia Capes.

(36)   **Tue Marshes Light** (37°14.1'N., 76°23.2'W.), 41 feet above the water, is shown from a pile with a green and white diamond-shaped daymark, in depths of 4 feet 0.3 mile north of Tue Point.

(37)   **Perrin River,** on the north side of York River 2 miles above the mouth, has depths of 6 feet or more in the approach and through a narrow marked channel to the wharf at **Perrin,** on the north side 0.3 mile above the entrance. A marina on the east side has gasoline, diesel fuel, some supplies, and a 20-ton mobile hoist; hull and engine repairs can be made. Gasoline and diesel fuel can be obtained at several of the oysterhouse wharves, on the east side of the river entrance; depths of 4 to 7 feet are alongside the wharves.

(38)   The Amoco offshore pier, on the south side of York River 3.3 miles above the mouth, has reported depths of 40 feet along the 1,240-foot outer face. The pier, connected to shore by a 0.5 mile long catwalk, is marked at its easterly end by a private light.

(39)   The intake for an electric powerplant, on the south side of the river 4.2 miles above the mouth, is marked by two lights.

(40)   **Wormley Creek** and **West Branch** have a common entrance on the south side of York River, 4.5 miles above the mouth; a light marks the entrance. A privately dredged channel leads through the entrance to the Coast Guard Reserve Training Center basin and pier on the north side of

West Branch 0.8 mile above the entrance light. In October 1984, the channel, marked by a light, buoys, and daybeacons, had a centerline controlling depth of 5 feet to the Coast Guard basin. Local knowledge is advised. Gasoline diesel fuel, berths, water, electricity, a 37-ton mobile lift, and marine supplies can be obtained at a marina on the east side of Wormley Creek just above the entrance; hull and engine repairs can be made.

(41)   The Coast Guard T-pier (37°13.6'N., 76°28.7'W.), on the south side of York River 5 miles above the mouth, has depths of 30 feet reported at the outer end.

(42)   A naval explosives handling berth is northward of the Coast Guard pier. (See 334.260, chapter 2, for limits and regulations.)

(43)   Sarah Creek, on the north side of York River 6 miles above the mouth, has depths of 7 feet through the marked entrance channel and for about 0.8 mile up both its branches. A large yacht haven, on the west side 0.3 mile above the entrance, has supplies, gasoline, diesel fuel, a 35-ton lift, a pumpout station and numerous berths. Repairs can be made at a boatyard 0.3 mile up Northwest Branch; marine railway, 76 feet; largest lift, 60 tons.

(44)   A fixed highway bridge with a clearance of 6 feet and channel width of 47 feet crosses Northwest Branch about 0.8 mile above its mouth.

(45)   Yorktown, the historic Revolutionary War town, is on the southwest side of York River 6.7 miles above the mouth. High on the bluff in the southerly part is the Yorktown Monument, and a group of buildings is prominent on the shore back of the wharves. The main part of the town is not visible from the river. George P. Coleman Memorial Bridge, from Yorktown to Gloucester Point, has twin spans with clearance of 60 feet; the two spans open clockwise simultaneously. The bridgetender monitors VHF-FM channel 13; call sign KQ-7166. (See 117.1 through 117.49, chapter 2, for drawbridge regulations.)

(46)   The public wharf at the Yorktown end of the bridge has depths of 6 feet at its face, but depths of 20 feet or more are only 5 feet off of it. The post office is at the wharf. Supplies are available nearby.

(47)   Permission to use the wharf facilities may be obtained from the Board of Trustees, P.O. Box 512, Yorktown, Va. 23690.

(48)   Gloucester Point is a village at the northeast end of Coleman Bridge. There are several piers and buildings on the low point, and the red brick building of the Virginia Institute of Marine Science is about 500 yards northeastward. The long T-head pier (37°14'46"N., 76°30'02"W.), owned by the Institute, has reported depths of 8 feet at the face. A shorter pier of the Institute is about 150 yards to the northward; depths of 6 feet are reported at the face.

(49)   The Yorktown Naval Weapons Station piers on the southwest side of York River, 8 miles above the mouth, have depths of about 39 feet at their outer ends. A prohibited area and a restricted area for mine service testing are off the piers. (See 334.260, chapter 2, for limits and regulations.) A naval anchorage begins off the Naval Weapons Station piers and extends upriver about 4 miles. (See 110.166, chapter 2, for limits and regulations.)

(50)   The Naval Supply Center piers at Cheatham Annex Depot, on the southwest side of York River 11.5 miles above the mouth, have reported depths of 22 feet at the southeasterly T-pier and 14 feet at the northwesterly L-pier; greater depths were reported close off the pier faces. The piers are within a naval restricted area. (See 334.270, chapter 2, for limits and regulations.)

(51)   Chart 12243.—Queen Creek (37°18.1'N., 76°36.9'W.), on the southwest side of York River 13 miles above the mouth, has depths of about 5 feet with local knowledge through a marked channel across the flats at the entrance and deeper water through a narrow channel inside for 2.7 miles to Hawtree Landing. The channel inside is marked by daybeacons to a point about 0.6 mile below Hawtree Landing. Stakes on either side of the entrance mark the limits of the State's experimental oyster beds.

(52)   Aberdeen Creek, on the northeast side of York River 14 miles above the mouth, has a marked dredged channel leading to a turning basin and public landing 0.4 mile above the entrance. In 1982-March 1983, the controlling depth was 2 feet at midchannel to the basin, thence 3 feet in the basin. Gasoline and diesel fuel are available at a seafood company wharf just north of the public landing.

(53)   The ruins of a long T-head pier are at Clay Bank, on the northeast side of York River 15 miles above the mouth.

(54)   Poropotank Bay, on the northeast side of York River 22 miles above the mouth, has depths of 5 feet at the entrance; the best water favors the eastern side which is marked by bush stakes. From the entrance, depths of about 5 feet can be carried 4 miles through Morris Bay and Poropotank River to Miller Landing. There are several other landings along the river. The channel is usually marked by bush stakes, but is crooked and narrow in places and difficult to navigate without local knowledge.

(55)   West Point, at the junction of Mattaponi and Pamunkey Rivers 29 miles above the mouth of York River, has waterborne commerce in pulpwood, paper products, and petroleum. The town is the terminus of a Southern Railway branch line. The pulp, paper, and paperboard wharves just above the Eltham Bridge have reported depths of 16 feet alongside.

(56)   At West Point, the maximum current velocity is 0.8 knots on the flood in Mattaponi River, and 0.9 knots on the ebb in Pamunkey River. Broken-off piling extends off the south side of West Point.

(57)   A public pier is at the southeast end of West Point, at the mouth of Mattaponi River. Gasoline is available at an oil wharf with depths of 5 to 15 feet alongside 0.4 mile south of the Lord Delaware Bridge; diesel fuel can be delivered by truck. An oil pier 0.2 mile above the bridge has depths of 18 feet alongside. Supplies can be obtained in town.

(58)   Chart 12243.—Mattaponi River, which empties into York River eastward of West Point (37°31.7'N., 76°47.7'W.), is one of two tributaries that combine to form York River. Traffic on Mattaponi River consists chiefly of pulpwood. Drafts of vessels using the river above West Point usually do not exceed 10 feet.

(59)   Controlling depths in Mattaponi River are as follows: 12 feet to Courthouse Landing, 13 miles above the mouth; thence 9 feet for 10 miles to Locust Grove; and thence 2 feet to Aylett, 32 miles above the mouth.

(60)   The channel in Mattaponi River is unmarked and is difficult to navigate without local knowledge. The mean range of tide is 2.8 feet at West Point and 3.9 feet at Walkerton. Freshets occur at irregular intervals, being more severe in March and April, and have reached a height of 17 feet above low water at Aylett, though this is exceptional; the freshet rise is negligible at and below West Point.

(61)   The Lord Delaware Bridge over Mattaponi River at West Point has a swing span with a clearance of 12 feet; the eastern opening is used as there are no fenders on the western opening. (See 117.1 through 117.59 and 117.1015, chapter 2, for drawbridge regulations.) Overhead power cables

about 1.8 and 13 miles above the mouth have clearances of 62 feet and 90 feet, respectively.

(62) The **Walkerton** highway bridge, 24.5 miles above the mouth of Mattaponi River, has a swing span with a clearance of 6 feet through the southerly opening which has fenders. (See **117.1 through 117.59 and 117.1015,** chapter 2, for drawbridge regulations.) Two fixed bridges cross the river at Aylett, 32 miles above the mouth; minimum clearance is 20 feet. The minimum clearance of the overhead power cables between the bridges at Walkerton and Aylett is 42 feet.

(63) **Pamunkey River,** the westerly of the two tributaries that form York River, has many landings along its banks. Traffic on the river consists chiefly of pulpwood; there is a grain elevator platform at **Port Richmond,** 2 miles above the mouth. Vessels with drafts up to 12 feet navigate the river to Port Richmond.

(64) Controlling depths in Pamunkey River are about 12 feet from the mouth to **Cumberland Landing,** 20 miles above the mouth, thence 8 feet to **White House,** 28 miles above the mouth, and 4 feet to the Newcastle Bridges 46 miles above the mouth. The mean range of tide is 2.7 feet at **Sweet Hall Landing,** 15 miles above the mouth, and 3.3 feet at **Northbury,** 35 miles above the mouth. Freshets occur at irregular intervals, being more severe in March and April.

(65) Pamunkey River is easy to navigate as far as **Brickhouse Landing,** 16 miles above the mouth; farther up, navigation is difficult without local knowledge. Freshwater is available at some of the landings, and the river water is fresh above Cumberland Landing. Several narrow cutoffs have depths enough for small boats, but their use requires local knowledge. Above **Retreat,** 36 miles above the mouth, the river is covered with floating debris and snags.

(66) The Eltham Bridge over Pamunkey River at West Point has a swing span with a clearance of 10 feet; the southwest opening is preferred, as there are no fenders along the northeast opening. The bridgetender monitors VHF-FM channel 13; call sign KQ-7168. Power cables crossing the river about 2 and 14.6 miles above the mouth have clearances of 60 and 90 feet, respectively. The railroad bridge at White House has a swing span with a clearance of 4 feet; the easterly opening is used. (See **117.1 through 117.49,** chapter 2, for drawbridge regulations.)

(67) **Chart 12238.**–**Mobjack Bay,** which is entered between Guinea Marshes at the shore end of York Spit, and New Point Comfort, 4 miles east-northeastward, includes several tributaries, the most important being East, North, Ware, and Severn Rivers. The bay is obstructed by extensive shoals, but has depths of 22 feet in the entrance and 15 feet for considerable distances into the tributaries. Many of the shoals are marked by lights and buoys.

(68) The only prominent marks in the approach to Mobjack Bay are York Spit Light on the south and the white tower of the abandoned lighthouse on New Point Comfort on the north. The approach channel extends between fishtrap buoys; numerous crab pots exist shoreward of these buoys. Good anchorage, sheltered from all but southerly and southeasterly winds, can be found in the bay. Small craft find safe anchorage in the bight westward of New Point Comfort and in the rivers and creeks. The mean range of tide is 2.3 feet at the entrance.

(69) **New Point Comfort** is the south end of a low, partly wooded island which is separated from the mainland by **Deep Creek,** a crooked and unmarked natural channel. The pile remains of **Bayside Wharf,** visible at high water 1.5 miles northwest of New Point Comfort, extend about 0.4 mile channelward.

(70) **Davis Creek,** 1.6 miles northwest of New Point Comfort, has a marked dredged channel leading to a public landing in the western arm about 0.8 mile above the entrance. In October 1986, the controlling depth was 7 feet in the east half of the channel from Light 1 to Light 8, thence 9 feet to the turning basin with 10 feet in the basin. Depths of 8½ to 10 feet are alongside the face of the public landing. Several wharves are on the shore in the upper part of the creek; gasoline and diesel fuel are available.

(71) **Pepper Creek,** 3 miles northwest of New Point Comfort, has depths of 4 feet for about 0.7 mile above the entrance. The approach is marked by daybeacons.

(72) **East River,** 5 miles northwest of New Point Comfort, has a marked narrow channel with depths of 10 feet for 3.5 miles above the entrance, and thence 4 feet for another 2 miles to the head. Shoals, sometimes marked by bush stakes, extend for some distance off many of the points above the entrance, but the midchannel is clear.

(73) **Diggs Wharf,** on the east side of East River just inside the entrance, is in ruins. There are no commercial facilities at **Mobjack** opposite Diggs Wharf.

(74) **Williams Wharf,** on the northeast side of East River about 2.5 miles above the entrance, has reported depths of 6 to 8 feet alongside the abandoned oysterhouse bulkhead. A boatyard on the western shore opposite Williams Wharf has a 50-foot marine railway; repairs can be made.

(75) **North River,** which empties into the head of Mobjack Bay from northward, is wide, but has long shoals making off from many of the points. The channel has depths of 12 feet for 4 miles and is well marked; depths of 7 feet can be carried 2 miles farther. **Blackwater Creek** empties into North River 3 miles above the mouth. The entrance is marked by a light and depths of 7 feet can be carried for 0.5 mile to a boatyard and a marina just inside the entrance of **Greenmansion Cove;** gasoline, diesel fuel, and some supplies are available. The depth at the face of the dock is 5 feet. Hull and engine repairs can be made; marine railway, 50 feet; mobile hoist, 6 tons.

(76) **Ware River,** which flows into the head of Mobjack Bay from northwestward, has depths of 15 feet to the mouth of **Wilson Creek,** on the west side 3 miles above the entrance, and 7 feet for another 2 miles. Long shoals, some of which are marked by lights and daybeacons, extend off many of the points. The only commercial landing on Ware River is the J. C. Brown Co. wharf, on the east side about 4 miles above the entrance, which has a depth of about 5 feet off the end; gasoline is available. **Schley,** 0.5 mile inland from the wharf, has a store.

(77) **Severn River,** on the west side of Mobjack Bay, has depths of 18 feet to the junction with **Northwest Branch** and **Southwest Branch,** 8 feet for 1.3 miles in Southwest Branch, and 8 feet for 1.8 miles in Northwest Branch. The most prominent shoals are marked by lights or daybeacons.

(78) A wharf at **Glass,** on the north side of Southwest Branch 1.1 miles above the fork, has depths of about 7 feet to the outer end. Mariners are advised to stay within the marked channel to avoid the 1-foot shoal extending from the point 0.4 mile eastward of the wharf. Gasoline, diesel fuel, and marine supplies are available. Hull and engine repairs can be made; marine railway, 60 feet. A marina on the west side of **Rowes Creek,** 0.5 mile southeast of the Glass Wharf, has gasoline, diesel fuel, marine supplies, and a 10-ton mobile hoist.

(79) **Browns Bay,** 1 mile south of Severn River, is marked by lights at the entrance and by bush stakes inside. Gasoline and diesel fuel are available at a wharf, with a depth of 4 feet at the end, at the head of the bay. A store is at **Severn,** about 1 mile westward of the wharf.

(80) **Dyer Creek,** which empties into Chesapeake Bay 2 miles north of New Point Comfort, has depths of 3 feet in the entrance and 4 to 5 feet inside. The creek is bush-staked, but local knowledge is essential. Overhead power cables across the creek have a least clearance of 17 feet.

(81) **Horn Harbor** is entered through a dredged channel marked by lights 2.4 miles northward of New Point Comfort; lights and daybeacons mark the channel in the upper part of the harbor. In January-February 1990, the controlling depth was 7 feet in the dredged channel, thence in 1977, about 5 feet to a point 3.5 miles above the entrance. In April 1982, a 3-foot shoal was reported on the northeast edge of the channel at the bend opposite Horn Harbor Light 3. A cluster of submerged piling of a former fishhouse is on the east side of the channel about 1 mile above the entrance. Traffic consists chiefly of fish, shellfish, and pleasure craft.

(82) The ruins of a fish wharf are at **New Point,** 0.7 mile above the Horn Harbor entrance. A marina, 3.5 miles above the entrance, has gasoline, diesel fuel, and some supplies. An 80-foot marine railway can haul out boats for repairs.

(83) **Winter Harbor** is entered through a dredged channel marked by lights and daybeacons 4.3 miles north-northeast of New Point Comfort. The channel leads to a turning basin and public landing 1.5 miles above the entrance. In December 1990-January 1991, the controlling depth was less than 1 foot to the turning basin with 1 to 3 feet available in the basin, except for shoaling to bare along the north edge. Commerce in the harbor consists chiefly of fish and shellfish.

(84) **Wolf Trap,** the area of broken ground 6 miles northward of New Point Comfort, has numerous shoal spots 5 to 10 feet deep which extend as much as 3 miles from the western shore of Chesapeake Bay. All the shoal area lies in the fishtrap limits. **Wolf Trap Light** (37°23.4'N., 76°11.4' W.), 52 feet above the water, is shown from an octagonal red-brick dwelling with a square tower on a brown cylinder, in depths of 16 feet near the outer end of the shoal area. The light is 5 miles due west of a point in the main channel 28.8 miles above the Capes.

(85) **Chart 12225.**–The **danger zone** of a naval firing range begins about 4 miles north-northeastward of Wolf Trap Light and extends northward to Tangier Sound Light, just south of **Tangier Island.** (See **334.220,** chapter 2, for limits and regulations.) The danger zone also contains a designated hurricane anchorage for shallow and deep-draft naval vessels. During hurricane warnings, naval ships may be anchored in the fairway; caution is advised.

(86) The ruins of a former degaussing range control tower, 6.2 miles eastward of Wolf Trap Light, are covered 3½ feet. A lighted bell buoy, 150 yards to westward, marks the obstruction.

(87) **Chart 12235.**–**Piankatank River** is 11 miles northward of Wolf Trap Light. The entrance is between **Cherry Point** (37°31.0'N., 76°17.8'W.), at the north end of **Gwynn Island,** and Stingray Point, 2.5 miles to the northward. The entrance point is 45.3 miles above the Virginia Capes. **Stingray Point Light** (37°33.7'N., 76°16.2'W.), 34 feet above the water, is shown from a pile with a green and white diamond-shaped daymark on piles in depths of 6 feet 1.3 miles east of the point.

(88) Traffic on Piankatank River consists of fish, shellfish, and shells. Drafts of vessels using the river are mostly 6 feet, but drafts up to 11 feet are on record. The river has depths of about 18 feet in the approach from northeastward through a buoyed lane in the fishtraps, 16 feet or more to

the fixed bridge 9 miles above the mouth, and 7 feet to Freeport, 13.5 miles above the mouth. Lights and buoys mark the lower 6 miles of the river channel.

(89) The mean range of tide is 1.2 feet in the lower part of Piankatank River. During severe winters, the river is sometimes closed by ice for short periods. Hull repairs can be made to medium-size vessels in Fishing Bay; gasoline and diesel fuel are available.

(90) **Jackson Creek,** on the north side of Piankatank River 1 mile above the mouth, has a dredged entrance channel marked by a light and daybeacons. The controlling depth in August 1987 was 8 feet in the entrance, with natural depths of 8 to 10 feet inside. In August 1987, a shoal spot less than 1 foot was reported to be in the channel about 20 yards downstream from Daybeacon 5. Stakes usually define the channel edges. **Deltaville** is at the head of the north arm.

(91) There is a marina along Jackson Creek where fuel, supplies, and berths can be obtained. The largest lift can handle boats to 35 tons feet for hull and engine repairs.

(92) **Hills Bay,** on the south side of Piankatank River 2 miles above the mouth, has general depths of 14 to 20 feet, and is the approach to Queens Creek and Milford Haven.

(93) **Queens Creek,** at the head of Hills Bay, is entered by a dredged channel that leads across the bar at the entrance and thence to a turning basin about 0.6 mile above the entrance. In February-March 1989, the controlling depth was 1 foot in the entrance channel to Light 5, thence 3½ feet at midchannel to the turning basin, and 5½ feet in the basin. The channel across the bar and to the turning basin is marked by lights and daybeacons. A few broken piles that remain of the wooden jetty on the north side of the entrance are marked at the outer end by a daybeacon.

(94) **Milford Haven,** the strait between Gwynn Island and the mainland to the southwestward, is entered from the head of Hills Bay. Traffic on the waterway consists chiefly of fish and shellfish carried in vessels drawing up to 7 feet. A marked channel with a controlling depth of 7½ feet (9½ feet at midchannel) in August 1987 leads from Hills Bay to natural depths of 15 to 8 feet in Milford Haven.

(95) The jetty on **Narrows Point,** at the north side of the Hills Bay entrance to Milford Haven, is marked by a light. The highway bridge from the mainland to Gwynn Island has a swing span with a clearance of 12 feet in the north opening. (See **117.1 through 117.49,** chapter 2, for drawbridge regulations.)

(96) A marina on Gwynn Island just west of the bridge has gasoline, diesel fuel, supplies, and berths; Hull and Engine repairs can be made; lift, 40 tons, railway, 60-foot long. A public landing pier is on Gwynn Island just east of the bridge. **Milford Haven Coast Guard Station** is 0.2 mile east of the south end of the bridge.

(97) **Callis Wharf** at **Grimstead,** on the Gwynn Island side of Milford Haven 0.7 mile from the jetty, has depths of 9 feet at the face. Gasoline, diesel fuel, and some other supplies are available. A marine railway on the southeast side of the entrance to **Edwards Creek,** 0.5 mile eastward of Callis Wharf, can handle boats up to 35 feet for hull repairs.

(98) A wharf at **Cricket Hill,** on the west side of **Lanes Creek,** opposite Edwards Creek, has gasoline, diesel fuel, and ice; depths of 8 feet are reported at the face.

(99) Milford Haven can also be entered from Chesapeake Bay at the south end of Gwynn Island. This passage, known as **The Hole in the Wall** has a reported controlling depth of about 4 feet and is used by small local boats, but is exposed to heavy seas. The passage is marked by lights, daybeacons, and a buoy. Local knowledge is recommended when transiting the passage.

(THIS PAGE INTENTIONALLY LEFT BLANK)

14. CHESAPEAKE BAY, EASTERN SHORE

(1) This chapter describes the Eastern Shore of Chesapeake Bay from Cape Charles to Swan Point, about 6 miles northward of the entrance to Chester River, and several bodies of water and their tributaries that empty into this part of the bay. Included are Pocomoke Sound, Pocomoke River, Tangier Sound, Wicomico River, Nanticoke River, Little Choptank River, Choptank River, Eastern Bay, and Chester River, and the off-lying islands of Tangier, Smith, Hooper, and Tilghman.

(2) Also described are the ports of Cape Charles, Pocomoke City, Tangier, Crisfield, Salisbury, Easton, Cambridge, St. Michaels, and several smaller ports and landings.

(3) **COLREGS Demarcation Lines.**–The lines established for Chesapeake Bay are described in **80.510**, chapter 2.

(4) During the ice navigation season, the Maryland waters of Chesapeake Bay described in this chapter are a **regulated navigation area.** (See **165.503**, chapter 2, for limits and regulations.)

(5) **Charts 12221, 12225, 12230, 12263, 12273.**– The Eastern Shore of Chesapeake Bay, from Cape Charles to Chester River, is mostly low and has few prominent natural features. The mainland and the islands are subject to erosion, and many of the islands and points have completely washed away. **Fishtrap** limits are shown on the charts and usually are marked by black and white horizontal-banded buoys. In the tributaries of Pocomoke Sound, **ice** sufficient to interfere with the navigation of small vessels may be encountered at any time from January through March. The ice from Pocomoke Sound does not interfere with the larger vessels in the bay, but the smaller oyster and fishing boats frequently are held up and sometimes require assistance, especially in Kedges and Hooper Straits.

(6) **Charts 12224.**–**Wise Point** (37°07.0'N., 75°58.3'W.), the mainland tip of Cape Charles, is included in chapter 9, which also describes Fishermans Island, Cape Charles Light on Smith Island, and the Atlantic entrance to Chesapeake Bay.

(7) **Kiptopeke Beach**, 3.2 miles northward of Wise Point, is the site of a former ferry terminal. The offshore breakwaters are obsolete ships filled with sand and sunk end-to-end. Just northward of the abandoned terminal is **Butlers Bluff**, which has steep bare faces conspicuous from the bay.

(8) **Old Plantation Creek**, 7 miles northward of Wise Point, has depths of about a foot. Many of the bars and middle grounds are marked by discolored water, and the channel usually is marked by bush stakes, but it is narrow and difficult to navigate without local knowledge. The opening in the thick woods at the mouth is visible from outside. No supplies are available along the creek.

(9) **Old Plantation Flats Light** (37°13.7'N., 76°02.8'W.), 39 feet above the water, is shown from a pile with a black and white diamond-shaped daymark in 11 feet on the north end of the flats about 1.5 miles from shore. The current velocity is about 1.3 knots 0.5 mile west of the light.

(10) **Cape Charles Harbor**, 9 miles northward of Wise Point, is a dredged basin on the south side of the town of **Cape Charles.** A well-marked dredged channel just north of Old Plantation Flats Light leads to the harbor between sand flats on the south and a stone jetty on the north. Two small dredged basins are eastward of the main harbor basin. The northerly basin is known as the Harbor of Refuge, and the southerly basin as Mud Creek Basin. In December 1987-February 1988, the dredged channel to Cape Charles Harbor had a controlling depth of 17 feet at midchannel with 18 feet available in the harbor basin; thence in December 1988, depths of 4 to 6½ feet were available in the Harbor of Refuge Basin. In May 1987-January 1988, depths of 6½ to 10 feet were available in Mud Creek Basin except for shoaling to bare at the NE corner.

(11) **Cape Charles Coast Guard Station** is on the spit between Mud Creek and the Harbor of Refuge.

(12) The mean range of tide is 2.4 feet at Cape Charles. The tidal currents set across the entrance to and across the southwest section of the dredged channel, but farther north they follow the general direction of the axis. The channel is exposed to westerly winds, but is partially protected by the flats to the westward, and seldom is too rough for motorboats. However, during severe W weather heavy surges may occur in the harbor. Ice may hinder navigation in the harbor during severe winters. Because of the limited space in the channel and harbor, the larger vessels and tows occasionally are somewhat of a hazard to small boats.

(13) Cape Charles is a **customs port of entry.**

(14) Cape Charles Harbor is a terminus of the Eastern Shore Railroad. The railroad operates floats to Little Creek. Floats are usually brought into the harbor in the late afternoon, although there are also occasional early morning arrivals. Due to the limited maneuvering room in the channel and the harbor, larger vessels and tows are sometimes a hazard to small craft. The tugs that handle the floats monitor VHF-FM channels 13 and 16.

(15) There is public access to the bulkheads and slips at the eastern end of the harbor. Anchoring is forbidden in any part of the harbor or the basins. A "no-wake" **speed limit** is enforced. A **harbormaster** enforces harbor regulations, and a **dockmaster** supervises docking at the municipal facilities. Gasoline, diesel fuel, and water are available. Some marine supplies may be obtained in town.

(16) **Cherrystone Channel** is a passage inside Old Plantation Flats that leads from deep water 2 miles south-southeastward of Old Plantation Flats Light northward to Kings Creek and Cherrystone Inlet. The route follows part of the dredged channel to Cape Charles Harbor for about 1 mile. That part of Cherrystone Channel southward of the dredged channel to Cape Charles Harbor is unmarked and little used. Cherrystone Channel above Cape Charles Harbor is marked by lights and daybeacons to the vicinity of **Sandy Island.** This part of the channel has depths of about 10 feet, but is narrow in places, and local knowledge is required to carry the best water. The recommended southerly approach to Kings Creek and Cherrystone Inlet is via the marked dredged channel to Cape Charles Harbor, which was discussed earlier in this chapter.

(17) **Kings Creek**, about 1 mile northward of Cape Charles Harbor and eastward of Sandy Island, has depths of 3½ feet for 1 mile upstream. The shoal that extends out from the north side of the entrance bares at low water; lights and daybeacons mark the entrance. The creek is used extensively by fishermen and pleasure craft. Gasoline, berths, and some marine supplies are available at a marina just inside the entrance; a marine railway can haul out boats up to 60 feet for minor repairs.

ATLANTIC OCEAN DISTANCES
MONTREAL, CANADA, TO PANAMA CANAL ZONE
(Nautical Miles)

Figure at intersection of columns opposite ports in question is the nautical mileage between the two. Example: New York, N.Y., is 1399 nautical miles from San Juan, P. R.

Ports (diagonal headers), with coordinates:

Port	Latitude / Longitude
MONTREAL, CANADA* (St. Lambert Lock)	—
Cabot Strait	47°07.0'N., 60°17.0'W.
Gut of Canso (Lock)	45°39.0'N., 61°25.0'W.
Portland, Maine	43°39.4'N., 70°14.7'W.
Boston, Mass.	42°22.0'N., 71°03.0'W.
NANTUCKET SHOALS	40°30.0'N., 69°25.0'W.
NEW YORK, N.Y.	40°42.0'N., 74°01.0'W.
Philadelphia, Pa.	39°56.8'N., 75°08.3'W.
Baltimore, Md.	39°16.0'N., 76°34.5'W.
CHESAPEAKE BAY ENT.	36°56.3'N., 75°58.8'W.
Norfolk, Va.	36°50.9'N., 76°17.9'W.
DIAMOND SHOALS	35°08.0'N., 75°15.0'W.
Wilmington, N.C.	34°14.0'N., 77°57.0'W.
Charleston, S.C.	32°47.2'N., 79°55.2'W.
Savannah, Ga.	32°05.0'N., 81°05.7'W.
Jacksonville, Fla	30°19.2'N., 81°39.0'W.
Key West, Fla	24°33.7'N., 81°48.5'W.
STRAITS OF FLORIDA	24°25.0'N., 83°00.0'W.
Tampa, Fla.	27°55.5'N., 82°26.7'W.
Pensacola, Fla	30°24.0'N., 87°13.0'W.
Mobile, Ala.	30°42.4'N., 88°02.5'W.
NEW ORLEANS, La (via SW Pass)	29°57.0'N., 90°03.7'W.
Port Arthur, Tex.	29°49.5'N., 93°57.6'W.
Galveston, Tex.	29°19.0'N., 94°47.0'W.
Corpus Christi, Tex.	27°48.5'N., 97°24.0'W.
San Juan, P. R.	18°27.8'N., 66°06.7'W.
YUCATAN CHANNEL	21°50.0'N., 85°03.0'W.
Panama Canal (Atlantic Ent.)	9°23.5'N., 79°55.3'W.
PANAMA CANAL (Pacific Ent.)	8°53.0'N., 79°31.0'W.

Distance matrix (nautical miles), distance from origin (row) to each subsequent port:

From MONTREAL → Cabot Strait 681, Gut of Canso 717, Portland 1276, Boston 1318, Nantucket Shoals 1311, New York 1534, Philadelphia 1682, Baltimore 1630, Chesapeake Bay Ent 1669, Norfolk 1716, Diamond Shoals 1729, Wilmington 1940, Charleston 2014, Savannah 2089, Jacksonville 2172, Key West 2479, Straits of Florida 2540, Tampa 2772, Pensacola 2977, Mobile 3011, New Orleans 3080, Port Arthur 3240, Galveston 3242, Corpus Christi 3347, San Juan 2445, Yucatan Channel 2730, Panama (Atl) 3203, Panama (Pac) 3249

From Cabot Strait → Gut of Canso 120, Portland 595, Boston 637, Nantucket 630, New York 853, Philadelphia 1001, Baltimore 1157, Chesapeake 1006, Norfolk 1035, Diamond 1046, Wilmington 1267, Charleston 1333, Savannah 1407, Jacksonville 1491, Key West 1796, Straits 1859, Tampa 2091, Pensacola 2296, Mobile 2330, New Orleans 2399, Port Arthur 2559, Galveston 2561, Corpus Christi 2666, San Juan 1764, Yucatan 2049, Panama (Atl) 2522, Panama (Pac) 2568

From Gut of Canso → Portland 484, Boston 526, Nantucket 519, New York 742, Philadelphia 890, Baltimore 1046, Chesapeake 896, Norfolk 923, Diamond 936, Wilmington 1155, Charleston 1221, Savannah 1295, Jacksonville 1379

From Portland → Boston 100, Nantucket 203, New York 426, Philadelphia 575, Baltimore 734, Chesapeake 584, Norfolk 611, Diamond 626, Wilmington 847, Charleston 913, Savannah 987, Jacksonville 1071

From Boston → Nantucket 163, New York 386, Philadelphia 535, Baltimore 694, Chesapeake 544, Norfolk 571, Diamond 588, Wilmington 807, Charleston 873, Savannah 947, Jacksonville 1031

From Nantucket Shoals → New York 223, Philadelphia 372, Baltimore 531, Chesapeake 381, Norfolk 406, Diamond 425, Wilmington 644, Charleston 710, Savannah 784, Jacksonville 868

From New York → Philadelphia 240, Baltimore 417, Chesapeake 267, Norfolk 294, Diamond 322, Wilmington 541, Charleston 607, Savannah 681, Jacksonville 765

From Philadelphia → Baltimore 392, Chesapeake 242, Norfolk 269, Diamond 294, Wilmington 564, Charleston 630, Savannah 704, Jacksonville 788

From Baltimore → Chesapeake 150, Norfolk 173, Diamond 267, Wilmington 466, Charleston 552, Savannah 626, Jacksonville 710

From Chesapeake Bay Ent → Norfolk 27, Diamond 117, Wilmington 336, Charleston 402, Savannah 476, Jacksonville 560

From Norfolk → Diamond 144, Wilmington 363, Charleston 429, Savannah 503, Jacksonville 587

From Diamond Shoals → Wilmington 219, Charleston 285, Savannah 359, Jacksonville 443

From Wilmington → Charleston 151, Savannah 227, Jacksonville 315

From Charleston → Savannah 102, Jacksonville 197

From Savannah → Jacksonville 145

Panama Canal (Atlantic Ent.) → Panama Canal (Pacific Ent.) 46

*Quebec, Canada - SUBTRACT 139 miles

All tabular distances are by outside routes which can be used by the deepest-draft vessel that the listed ports can accommodate. Lighter-draft vessels can save considerable mileage by transiting Canso Lock (Canada), the Cape Cod Canal (Massachusetts), and the Chesapeake and Delaware Canal (Delaware-Maryland); see the detailed tables. Gulf of Mexico distances are through the Shipping Safety Fairways.

COASTWISE DISTANCES
NEW YORK, N.Y., TO CHESAPEAKE BAY ENTRANCE, VA.
(Nautical Miles)

Figure at intersection of columns opposite ports in question is the nautical mileage between the two. Example: New York, N.Y., is 240 nautical miles from Philadelphia, Pa.

No.	Location	Position
1	NANTUCKET SHOALS	40°30.0'N, 69°25.0'W
2	MONTAUK POINT, N.Y.	41°01.7'N, 71°47.3'W
3	NEW YORK, N.Y.	40°42.0'N, 74°01.0'W
4	Manasquan Inlet, N.J.	40°06.1'N, 74°01.9'W
5	Barnegat Inlet, N.J.	39°46.0'N, 74°06.3'W
6	Atlantic City, N.J.	39°22.6'N, 74°24.9'W
7	Cape May Harbor, N.J.	38°57.1'N, 74°52.6'W
8	DELAWARE BAY ENTRANCE	38°50.5'N, 75°03.3'W
9	Harbor of Refuge, Del.	38°49.0'N, 75°05.2'W
10	CHES. & DEL. CANAL E. ENT.	39°33.8'N, 75°32.8'W
11	Wilmington, Del.	39°43.2'N, 75°31.5'W
12	Marcus Hook, Pa.	39°48.2'N, 75°25.2'W
13	Chester, Pa.	39°50.0'N, 75°22.0'W
14	Philadelphia, Pa.	39°56.8'N, 75°08.3'W
15	U.S. Steel Basin, Pa.	40°08.2'N, 74°45.3'W
16	Trenton, N.J.	40°11.4'N, 74°45.4'W
17	Indian River Inlet, Del.	38°36.5'N, 75°03.6'W
18	Ocean City, Md.	38°19.6'N, 75°05.6'W
19	Chincoteague, Va.	37°56.1'N, 75°22.8'W
20	CHESAPEAKE BAY ENT	36°56.3'N, 75°58.6'W

Distance matrix (nautical miles):

To \ From	1	2	3	4	5	6	7	8	9	10	11	12	13	14	15	16	17	18	19
2	113																		
3	223	122																	
4	212	117	40																
5	221	131	63	22															
6	242	159	94	52	32														
7	271	192	128	85	65	37													
8	285	212	153	97	78	49	16												
9	285	212	153	98	79	50	17	2											
10	336	263	204	148	129	100	67	51	52										
11	347	274	215	159	140	111	78	62	63	11									
12	353	280	221	165	146	117	84	68	69	17	8								
13	356	283	224	169	150	121	88	72	73	21	11	3							
14	372	299	240	184	165	136	103	87	88	36	26	18	15						
15	395	322	263	207	188	159	126	110	111	59	49	41	38	23					
16	400	327	268	212	193	164	131	115	116	64	54	46	43	28	5				
17	285	209	145	105	86	57	24	15	14	66	77	83	86	101	124	129			
18	295	227	161	121	101	73	40	32	31	83	95	101	104	119	142	147	20		
19	328	262	201	161	141	113	80	72	71	123	134	140	144	159	182	187	60	41	
20	381	322	267	219	199	171	141	155	155	206	218	224	227	242	265	270	118	100	69

Ambrose Light (40°27.6'N., 73°49.9'W.) to New York, 20.7 miles.
Five Fathom Bank Lighted Horn Buoy F(LNB) (38°47.3'N., 74°34.6'W.) to Philadelphia, 111 miles.
Delaware Lighted Horn Buoy D (38°27.3'N., 74°41.8'W.) to Philadelphia, 116 miles.
Chesapeake Light (36°54.3'N., 75°42.8'W.) to Norfolk, 42 miles; Baltimore, 165 miles.

DISTANCES BY INTRACOASTAL WATERWAY
MANASQUAN INLET, N.J., TO CAPE MAY CANAL, N.J.
(Nautical Miles)

Figure at intersection of columns opposite ports in question is the nautical mileage between the two. Example: Atlantic City N.J., is 13 nautical miles from Ocean City, N.J.

* Outside distances between New York and Manasquan Inlet.

Ports (with coordinates):

- CHES. & DEL CANAL E. ENT. — 39°33.8'N., 75°32.8'W.
- CAPE MAY CANAL W. ENT. — 38°58.0'N., 74°58.0'W.
- Cape May Harbor — 38°57.1'N., 74°52.6'W.
- Wildwood — 39°00.5'N., 74°49.8'W.
- Stone Harbor — 39°03.4'N., 74°46.0'W.
- Avalon — 39°06.6'N., 74°44.0'W.
- Sea Isle City — 39°09.4'N., 74°42.0'W.
- Ocean City — 39°17.3'N., 74°34.4'W.
- Meys Landing — 39°26.9'N., 74°43.4'W.
- Atlantic City — 39°22.6'N., 74°24.9'W.
- Beach Haven — 39°34.0'N., 74°14.8'W.
- Barnegat Inlet — 39°46.0'N., 74°06.3'W.
- Forked River (town) — 39°50.1'N., 74°11.7'W.
- Seaside Park — 39°55.3'N., 74°05.0'W.
- Toms River (town) — 39°56.9'N., 74°11.8'W.
- Mantoloking — 40°02.2'N., 74°03.4'W.
- Bay Head — 40°03.8'N., 74°03.1'W.
- Manasquan Inlet* — 40°06.1'N., 74°01.9'W.
- Shark River Inlet* — 40°11.2'N., 74°00.5'W.
- NEW YORK N.Y. (The Battery)* — 40°42.0'N., 74°01.0'W.

Distance matrix (nautical miles). Read the value at the intersection of the "From" row and the destination column.

From \ To	Shark River Inlet	Manasquan Inlet	Bay Head	Mantoloking	Toms River	Seaside Park	Forked River	Barnegat Inlet	Beach Haven	Atlantic City	Meys Landing	Ocean City	Sea Isle City	Avalon	Stone Harbor	Wildwood	Cape May Harbor	Cape May Canal W. Ent.	Ches. & Del. Canal E. Ent.
Cape May Canal W. Ent.																			48
Cape May Harbor																		4	52
Wildwood																	5	9	57
Stone Harbor																5	9	14	62
Avalon															5	10	15	19	67
Sea Isle City														4	9	14	18	23	71
Ocean City													11	15	20	25	30	34	82
Meys Landing												18	29	33	38	43	47	52	100
Atlantic City											30	13	25	28	34	39	43	47	95
Beach Haven										18	45	29	40	44	49	54	59	63	111
Barnegat Inlet									20	38	65	49	60	64	69	74	79	83	131
Forked River (town)								8	21	39	66	50	61	65	70	75	80	84	132
Seaside Park							10	13	26	44	71	55	66	70	75	80	85	89	137
Toms River (town)						7	15	18	31	49	77	60	72	75	81	86	90	94	142
Mantoloking					12	9	17	20	33	51	79	63	74	77	83	88	92	96	144
Bay Head				2	14	10	19	22	35	53	80	64	76	79	85	89	94	98	146
Manasquan Inlet			4	6	18	14	23	26	39	57	84	68	79	83	88	93	98	102	150
Shark River Inlet		6	9	11	23	20	29	32	45	62	90	74	85	89	94	99	103		156
NEW YORK N.Y. (The Battery)	34	40	44	46	58	54	63	66	79	97	124	108	119	123	128	133	138	142	190

DISTANCES ON DELAWARE BAY AND RIVER
(Nautical Miles)

Figure at intersection of columns opposite ports in question is the nautical mileage between the two. Example: Salem, N.J., is 41 nautical miles from Philadelphia, Pa.

Ports (with positions):

#	Port
1	Trenton, N.J. 40°11.4'N., 74°45.4'W.
2	Bordentown, N.J. 40°09.1'N., 74°43.0'W.
3	U.S. Steel Basin, Pa. 40°08.2'N., 74°45.3'W.
4	Burlington, N.J. 40°04.9'N., 74°51.8'W.
5	Philadelphia, Pa. 39°56.8'N., 75°08.3'W.
6	Schuylkill River Mouth, Pa. 39°52.8'N., 75°11.9'W.
7	Chester, Pa. 39°50.0'N., 75°22.0'W.
8	Bridgeport, N.J. 39°48.0'N., 75°21.3'W.
9	Marcus Hook, Pa. 39°48.2'N., 75°25.2'W.
10	Wilmington, Del. 39°43.2'N., 75°31.3'W.
11	New Castle, Del. 39°39.4'N., 75°33.6'W.
12	CHES. & DEL. CANAL E. ENT. 39°33.8'N., 75°32.6'W.
13	Salem, N.J. 39°34.6'N., 75°28.7'W.
14	Smyrna River Mouth, Del. 39°22.2'N., 75°30.2'W.
15	Bridgeton, N.J. 39°25.5'N., 75°14.2'W.
16	Mauricetown, N.J. 39°17.1'N., 74°59.5'W.
17	St. Jones River Mouth, Del. 39°04.0'N., 75°22.5'W.
18	Cape May Canal W. Ent., N.J. 38°58.0'N., 74°58.0'W.
19	Roosevelt Inlet, Del. 38°47.7'N., 75°09.4'W.
20	DELAWARE BAY ENT. 38°50.5'N., 75°03.3'W.

Triangular distance chart (each row lists the distance from that port to ports 1, 2, 3, … in order):

Port	Distances to preceding ports
2 Bordentown	4
3 U.S. Steel Basin	2, 5
4 Burlington	7, 9, 12
5 Philadelphia	16, 23, 25, 28
6 Schuylkill River Mouth	7, 23, 29, 31, 34
7 Chester	9, 15, 31, 38, 40, 43
8 Bridgeport	6, 14, 22, 37, 44, 46, 49
9 Marcus Hook	4, 3, 12, 18, 34, 41, 43, 46
10 Wilmington	8, 11, 11, 19, 26, 42, 49, 51, 54
11 New Castle	5, 12, 15, 15, 23, 30, 46, 53, 55, 58
12 CHES. & DEL. CANAL E. ENT.	7, 11, 17, 21, 21, 29, 36, 52, 59, 61, 64
13 Salem	5, 12, 16, 22, 26, 26, 34, 41, 57, 64, 66, 69
14 Smyrna River Mouth	16, 13, 20, 24, 30, 34, 34, 42, 49, 65, 72, 74, 77
15 Bridgeton	25, 39, 36, 43, 47, 53, 57, 57, 65, 72, 88, 95, 97, 100
16 Mauricetown	51, 39, 54, 51, 58, 62, 68, 72, 72, 80, 87, 103, 110, 112, 115
17 St. Jones River Mouth	30, 35, 21, 36, 34, 40, 45, 51, 55, 55, 63, 69, 85, 92, 94, 97
18 Cape May Canal W. Ent.	21, 26, 47, 36, 51, 48, 55, 59, 65, 69, 69, 77, 84, 100, 107, 109, 112
19 Roosevelt Inlet	14, 20, 37, 52, 40, 55, 52, 59, 63, 69, 73, 73, 81, 88, 104, 111, 113, 116
20 DELAWARE BAY ENT.	6, 9, 20, 33, 51, 39, 54, 51, 58, 62, 68, 72, 72, 80, 87, 103, 110, 112, 115

CHESAPEAKE BAY DISTANCES
(Nautical Miles)

Figure at intersection of columns opposite ports in question is the nautical mileage between the two. Example: Washington, D.C., is 155 nautical miles from Annapolis, Md.

Ports (with coordinates):

1. CHESAPEAKE BAY ENT. — 36°56.3'N, 75°58.6'W
2. Norfolk, Va — 36°50.9'N, 76°17.9'W
3. Richmond, Va — 37°31.4'N, 77°25.2'W
4. Petersburg, Va — 37°14.1'N, 77°24.0'W
5. Hopewell, Va — 37°19.0'N, 77°16.4'W
6. Suffolk, Va — 36°44.3'N, 76°35.0'W
7. Newport News, Va — 36°58.0'N, 76°26.0'W
8. West Point, Va — 37°31.6'N, 76°48.1'W
9. Yorktown, Va — 37°14.4'N, 76°30.5'W
10. Cape Charles, Va — 37°15.9'N, 76°01.4'W
11. Fredericksburg, Va — 38°17.8'N, 77°27.2'W
12. Crisfield, Md — 37°58.6'N, 75°51.9'W
13. Washington, D.C. — 38°52.4'N, 77°01.4'W
14. Potomac River Mouth — 37°57.7'N, 76°16.7'W
15. Salisbury, Md — 38°21.9'N, 75°36.3'W
16. Solomons, Md — 38°19.2'N, 76°27.4'W
17. Cambridge, Md — 38°34.4'N, 76°04.3'W
18. St. Michaels, Md. — 38°47.2'N, 76°13.2'W
19. Annapolis, Md. — 38°59.0'N, 76°28.6'W
20. Chestertown, Md. — 39°12.4'N, 76°03.8'W
21. Baltimore, Md — 39°16.0'N, 76°34.5'W
22. Havre de Grace, Md — 39°32.7'N, 76°05.0'W
23. Chesapeake City, Md — 39°31.8'N, 75°48.9'W
24. CHES. & DEL. CANAL E. ENT. — 39°33.6'N, 75°32.6'W

Distance table (columns = "to" port numbered 1–23 above; rows = "from" port):

From \ To	1	2	3	4	5	6	7	8	9	10	11	12	13	14	15	16	17	18	19	20	21	22	23
2 Norfolk	27																						
3 Richmond	101	90																					
4 Petersburg	92	80	28																				
5 Hopewell	82	70	19	10																			
6 Suffolk	42	29	98	89	79																		
7 Newport News	24	12	77	68	58	21																	
8 West Point	56	66	140	123	122	78	63																
9 Yorktown	34	58	132	101	114	55	55	22															
10 Cape Charles	21	32	106	97	88	48	29	50	28														
11 Fredericksburg	136	146	220	211	201	161	143	154	132	122													
12 Crisfield	67	77	151	142	132	92	74	86	64	51	129												
13 Washington	163	185	259	233	240	185	182	186	164	146	221	121											
14 Potomac River Mouth	67	89	163	137	144	89	86	90	68	50	125	27	96										
15 Salisbury	103	113	187	178	168	128	110	122	100	87	165	43	141	49									
16 Solomons	92	100	174	165	155	115	97	109	87	76	150	42	118	27	51								
17 Cambridge	123	132	206	197	187	147	129	140	117	107	102	72	149	58	81	39							
18 St. Michaels	132	141	215	206	196	156	138	149	126	190	80	156	65	89	48	36							
19 Annapolis	129	140	213	204	194	152	136	152	130	112	77	155	64	86	45	39	25						
20 Chestertown	162	170	244	235	225	185	167	178	156	146	219	110	187	96	119	78	72	59	40				
21 Baltimore	150	173	247	222	228	172	170	174	155	98	175	84	107	66	60	45	28	45					
22 Havre de Grace	166	175	249	240	230	190	172	185	163	149	224	115	192	101	124	84	78	62	45	61	41		
23 Chesapeake City	174	196	271	246	252	196	194	201	179	156	230	121	200	109	130	90	85	70	52	65	49	20	
24 Ches. & Del. Canal E. Ent.	187	209	284	259	265	209	207	214	192	169	243	134	213	122	143	103	98	83	65	78	62	33	13

DISTANCES ON POTOMAC RIVER
(Nautical Miles)

Figure at intersection of columns opposite ports in question is the nautical mileage between the two. Example: Colonial Beach, Va., is 63 nautical miles from Washington, D.C.

The reference ports (listed from the head of navigation to the river mouth), with coordinates:

- Chain Bridge — 38°55.7'N., 77°07.0'W.
- Key Bridge — 38°54.1'N., 77°04.2'W.
- Washington, D.C. — 38°52.4'N., 77°01.4'W.
- Bladensburg, Md. — 38°56.1'N., 76°56.4'W.
- Alexandria, Va. — 38°48.2'N., 77°02.3'W.
- Mount Vernon, Va. — 38°42.3'N., 77°05.3'W.
- Marshall Hall, Md. — 38°41.2'N., 77°06.2'W.
- Indian Head, Md. — 38°36.4'N., 77°10.1'W.
- Occoquan, Va. — 38°41.0'N., 77°15.4'W.
- Quantico, Va. — 38°31.2'N., 76°17.2'W.
- Potomac River (U.S. 301) Bridge — 38°21.7'N., 76°59.4'W.
- Dahlgren, Va. — 38°19.1'N., 77°02.1'W.
- Colonial Beach, Va. — 38°14.4'N., 76°57.9'W.
- Wicomico River mouth, Md. — 38°14.5'N., 76°49.1'W.
- Breton Bay Entrance, Md. — 38°14.0'N., 76°41.8'W.
- Nomini Bay, Va. — 38°08.6'N., 76°43.4'W.
- Lower Machodoc Creek, Va. — 38°08.5'N., 76°39.1'W.
- Piney Point, Md. — 38°08.0'N., 76°32.0'W.
- Yeocomico River Mouth, Va. — 38°02.1'N., 76°31.0'W.
- St. Marys River Mouth, Md. — 38°06.2'N., 76°26.3'W.
- Smith Creek Mouth, Md. — 38°05.8'N., 76°24.0'W.
- Coan River Mouth, Va. — 37°58.7'N., 76°27.1'W.
- Potomac River Mouth — 37°57.7'N., 76°16.7'W.

Distance chart (each row lists the mileage from that port to the ports upriver of it, ending at Chain Bridge):

Port (row)	Distances to upriver ports (nautical miles)
Key Bridge	3
Washington, D.C.	5, 8
Bladensburg, Md.	8, 11, 14
Alexandria, Va.	10, 4, 7, 10
Mount Vernon, Va.	9, 19, 13, 16, 19
Marshall Hall, Md.	2, 9, 19, 13, 16, 19
Indian Head, Md.	7, 8, 16, 26, 20, 23, 26
Occoquan, Va.	7, 8, 15, 23, 33, 27, 30, 33
Quantico, Va.	12, 6, 15, 16, 24, 34, 28, 30, 33
Potomac River (U.S. 301) Bridge	24, 36, 32, 39, 40, 48, 58, 52, 55, 58
Dahlgren, Va.	6, 30, 42, 38, 45, 46, 53, 63, 58, 60, 63
Colonial Beach, Va.	10, 11, 35, 47, 43, 50, 51, 58, 68, 63, 65, 68
Wicomico River mouth, Md.	9, 12, 13, 38, 50, 45, 52, 53, 61, 71, 65, 68, 71
Breton Bay Entrance, Md.	9, 16, 20, 21, 46, 58, 54, 61, 62, 69, 79, 74, 76, 79
Nomini Bay, Va.	6, 8, 15, 19, 20, 45, 57, 52, 59, 60, 68, 78, 72, 75, 78
Lower Machodoc Creek, Va.	5, 6, 10, 17, 21, 22, 47, 59, 55, 62, 63, 70, 80, 75, 77, 80
Piney Point, Md.	7, 11, 11, 15, 22, 27, 28, 52, 64, 60, 67, 68, 75, 85, 80, 82, 85
Yeocomico River Mouth, Va.	9, 16, 20, 19, 24, 31, 35, 36, 61, 72, 68, 75, 76, 84, 94, 88, 91, 94
St. Marys River Mouth, Md.	7, 8, 15, 19, 19, 23, 30, 34, 35, 60, 72, 68, 74, 76, 83, 93, 87, 90, 93
Smith Creek Mouth, Md.	3, 8, 10, 17, 21, 21, 25, 32, 36, 37, 62, 74, 69, 76, 76, 85, 89, 92, 95
Coan River Mouth, Va.	17, 8, 11, 18, 22, 22, 26, 33, 37, 38, 63, 75, 70, 77, 79, 86, 96, 90, 93, 96
Potomac River Mouth	11, 11, 12, 13, 16, 23, 27, 26, 31, 38, 43, 44, 68, 60, 76, 83, 84, 91, 101, 96, 98, 101

INDEX

The numbers of the largest scale charts on which the names appear follow the indexed items. Some geographic names are indexed more than once when more than one place has the same geographic name. Charts published by the Defense Mapping Agency Hydrographic/Topographic Service are indicated by an asterisk.

* U.S. GOVERNMENT PRINTING OFFICE : 1993 O – 362-144

ISBN 0-16-041958-1

90000

9 780160 419584

CPSIA information can be obtained
at www.ICGtesting.com
Printed in the USA
LVOW02s2151211216
518241LV00003B/3/P